Principles of
Avionics

Fourth Edition

Albert Helfrick

Avionics Communications Inc.
Leesburg, VA, USA

Library of Congress Cataloging-in-Publication Data

Helfrick, Albert D.
  Principles of avionics / Albert Helfrick. — 4th ed.
    p. cm.
Includes bibliographical references and index.
ISBN 978-1-885544-26-1
1. Avionics. I. Title.

TL695.H442 2007
629.135—dc22

                                          2007011815

Printed in the United States of America

Avionics Communications Inc.
Leesburg, VA 20175 USA

Tel: 703/777-9559
Fax: 703/777-9568
E-mail: publisher@avionics.com

www.avionics.com

Acknowledgements

Preparing any text book is a time consuming and often hectic process. The job always goes easier if an author has help. I would like to recognize those who contributed to this effort.

Jennie Gibbs, our overworked department secretary for her typing and e-mailing and U.S. mailing and checking.

Daniela Kratchounova, my graduate teaching assistant, now graduated teaching assistant, for doing much of the work on the figures and other assistance.

Kal Ivanov, Daniela's son, my volunteer laboratory assistant, for helping with the figures and running all sorts of errands.

My wife, Toni Helfrick, who puts up with a husband who, at times, seems to be permanently connected to his computer. And then seems to disconnect only to go away on a trip.

Finally, Len Buckwalter, my publisher, who spent untold hours putting this text together.

Cover: Starburst Galaxy, NASA photo/Hubble Space Telescope.

Contents

Preface

This book covers major phases of avionics, from navigation, communications and surveillance to sophisticated systems using state of the art sensors and computation. Procedures and practices are also presented. The intent is to give the student, technician or engineer an overview of the entire avionics field, not just a single airborne or ground system.

This book is arranged to be used as a text for avionics courses at community colleges and universities, as well as for self-study. Each chapter begins by covering the subject with a simple overview that can be grasped by readers with a limited understanding of engineering and mathematics. This is followed by more detail which requires some knowledge of calculus and college-level physics. For the four-year degree student, exercises are provided that require calculation and application of important engineering fundamentals.

This book includes a number of learning aids, such as end-of-chapter review questions. Numerous examples are given, including the use of computer software such as MatLab and circuit analysis programs. The text is provided with generous figures, diagrams and photographs to illustrate principles and show actual hardware.

Abbreviations and acronyms---GNSS, RAIM, ATCRBS, GDOP, etc.---are an important part of the aviation industry. After they are introduced in the text they are spelled out for several occurrences to help the reader gain familiarity. A glossary at the end is also available for ready reference. Some terms are spoken by pronouncing each letter, such as "F-A-A." Others are said as whole words, for example; "ATCRBS" is pronounced as "Atcrabs." Because there is no rule, the text spells out the way the term is said by people in the avionics industry.

Writing a text for avionics is challenging. FAA plans extensive changes in the National Airspace System, NAS, and this is particularly true for radio navigation, as outlined in the Federal Radio Navigation Plan, RNP. In this document the U.S. Federal Government's plan for increasing or decreasing radio navigation aids is outlined. The document at the time of this writing calls for the elimination of many, if not all, of the old radio navigation systems in favor of a space-based system. Not everyone in government and industry would agree the plan is a good one, and the Federal Government has responded by modifying it several times. One point remains; although existing navigation aids may not be totally phased out, they will be phased down to fewer installations.

Since the birth of avionics in the 1920s, changes are always being discussed by international agencies and standardizing organizations. To prevent this text from becoming obsolete the day it is printed, every effort was taken to discuss the latest practices. This is problematic in that the latest technology may not yet be in common use. The long life of avionics systems insures that a wide range of technologies will be operating in aircraft.

In some areas it is necessary to discuss possibilities for the future. This is when a system is slated to be changed but the new form is not yet known. It is necessary in these cases to outline the most likely possibilities.

In some instances, phase-outs have begun and, in one example, is already complete. In September, 1997, the long range navigation system, Omega, was turned off. Many in the industry did not believe the radio navigation plan, RNP, would actually happen but when Omega disappeared, credibility increased.

At the time of this writing, navigation aids to be silenced are the backbone of the National Airspace System, NAS. Hundreds of thousands of airborne units fly every day. Thousands of ground stations, some with old equipment, are still on the job. There is the special case of the microwave landing system, MLS, that is obsolete in the U.S. but operating in Europe and the U.S. military. Some in the avionics industry believe that MLS should come back and, unlike Omega, could be reinstated.

Many technological changes are reflected in this edition. The reader will notice there is much more emphasis on computer communications. This includes data communications, error detection, modulation techniques and networking. In the information age, methods are being formulated and built to provide all the information needed for safe flight to a computer terminal on board an aircraft.

Also included in this edition are revised listings of important documents and other references. RTCA DO-documents and ARINC 700 series characteristics are included in the appendices.

Since the publication of the third edition some of the legacy systems have been given several more years before scheduled phase-out. However, the RNP still calls for decommissioning of many navigation aids.

Albert Helfrick
Embry-Riddle Aeronautical University
Daytona Beach, Florida, U.S.A.

Introduction

There is no doubt from our vantage point in the 21st century that electronics plays an important role in aviation. There were times, however, when it was debated just how much of a role electronics should play. Throughout the evolution of the aircraft industry and into the space age it became abundantly clear that the capability and utility of an aircraft or space vehicle had more to do with its electronics than any other component.

On a cold and blustery day in 1903 on the shore of the Atlantic Ocean, two brothers carefully moved a strange-looking contraption into position. It was their intention that one of them would climb aboard and, under power from a crude gasoline engine, rise from the earth and fly as free as a bird.

Both brothers were eager to be the first man to take off and land on a powered, heavier-than-air craft. A coin toss decided it would be Orville, while his brother Wilbur Wright would watch history being made.

The first flight lasted 12 seconds and traveled a distance of 37 meters, or 120 feet. Before the day was over brother Wilbur flew for 50 seconds over a distance of 260 meters, or 852 feet.

Two years and five days earlier, on the shore of the same Atlantic Ocean, 900 miles north of Kitty Hawk, North Carolina, another pair of young men had also achieved an important "first". The place was St. Johns, Newfoundland and the men were Guglielmo Marconi and his assistant, "Mr. Kemp". It was Marconi's dream to take to the air in a different way by sending signals over the "airwaves" from the eastern to the western shore of the vast Atlantic Ocean.

Like the Wrights, who first experimented with gliders before attempting powered flight, Marconi had successfully transmitted his wireless signals various distances. But Marconi had never attempted a distance as wide as the North Atlantic.

Marconi had constructed a powerful transmitting station in Poldhu, Cornwall, England and traveled to across the ocean to Newfoundland with two of his assistants. After several aborted attempts at an antenna, Marconi successfully raised a long receiving antenna attached to a kite. Those same blustery sea breezes that attracted the Wrights served an important role in Marconi's achievement.

Weary from the trials and tribulations of raising the antenna, assembling the receiving station and hours of straining to hear a weak signal, Marconi handed the headphones to his assistant.

"See what you can hear, Mr. Kemp". Only the two, Marconi and Mr. Kemp, alone in a cold and damp abandoned barracks, shared a moment in history.

"I hear it" Mr. Kemp related; three dots sounded the Morse code letter S.

Both events were not "absolute" firsts but "relative" firsts. Marconi was not the first to communicate with wireless and the Wrights were not the first to fly. The achievements of the Wrights and Marconi were significant milestones in the beginning of two very important industries. The Wrights made aircraft based on their designs, which opened the skies for many to follow. Marconi amassed a fortune building and installing wireless systems for land and ship and showed the way for other companies to do the same.

Wireless and Aircraft

The idea to install wireless in aircraft dates back to World War I. The airplane was recognized as a valuable tool for battlefield observation. Aircraft were fitted with machine guns, which were more of a defensive, rather than offensive, tool. The first military application of aircraft was forward observation and machine guns were for protection. Pre-WWI aircraft did not have the capacity to carry meaningful bomb loads. The aircraft's ability to have a significant effect on the outcome of a war would have to wait until the next war. Thus the concept of aircraft with machine guns as an offensive weapon or fighter aircraft protecting bombers was to occur later.

Unfortunately, pre-WWI aircraft did not have the capacity to carry significant *wireless* equipment either! This severely limited the aircraft as an observation platform. In order to perform reconnaissance, the pilot had to return to base and verbally make a report. Artillery observation was ideally suited for aircraft but requires instant communications. The United States Army fully recognized this need and organized a wireless communications laboratory in France as a part of the American Expeditionary Forces, AEF, during WWI.

As luck would have it, Edwin Howard Armstrong, inventor of the regenerative receiver, the superheterodyne receiver and frequency modulation, was assigned to the lab in Paris to investigate wireless equipment in aircraft. A number of manufacturers in the United States and Europe had submitted communications "sets" to be evaluated in aircraft. Armstrong found several wireless installations to be quite acceptable. One in particular weighed only 60 pounds and was capable of communicating "several miles"! In our technologically advanced world the common cell phone fits into the smallest pocket, weighs but ounces and can communicate "several miles" to the nearest cell tower where it can connect to the world!

To WWI aircraft, the ability to communicate several miles was sufficient to make aircraft useful for observation behind enemy lines, at least by "several miles", which is several miles more than it was capable of without wireless. It is debatable whether wireless had a significant role in WWI but one thing was certain; aircraft would have an effect on future wars.

The war ended in 1919 and the first broadcast station, KDKA, went on the air in Pittsburgh in 1920. The arrival of broadcasting had a profound effect on the development of electronics. Wireless was now "radio" and the tremendous success of broadcasting brought large revenues to the radio industry. While most of the profits from broadcasting were plowed back into research for home entertainment radio, there were spin-off benefits in other areas. One was military and civilian aircraft radio.

After WWI it was very clear the airplane would play an important role in air transport and warfare only if certain deficiencies were corrected. As crude as it was, the airplane had shown its value as an observer. The next step was to drop munitions behind enemy lines from above. It was also clear that bombers would have to be protected from hostile fire by smaller, more agile aircraft, to become known as fighter aircraft. Future wars would be fought not only on land and sea but also in the air. Command and control of aircraft was essential.

During the 1920s a fledgling airline industry was forming. Key to the success of the air transport industry was the ability to fly a schedule. Most aircraft of the 1920s had no radio equipment of any sort and were forced to fly only during the day. Because aircraft were not pressurized they were limited to altitudes of less than 10,000 feet and incapable of flying above the weather.

For nighttime flying the United States Department of Commerce, Aeronautics Branch, provided light beacons at strategic locations along what became airways. By the late 1920s a network of airways was established from coast-to-coast. Flying was still a clear-weather event as light beacons were not visible in bad weather. A method of navigation that would work in any visibility was needed.

Radio was the solution for penetrating clouds and fog and a number of radio navigation systems were developed. One of the first was radio direction finding using ground-based non-directional beacons. The aircraft used a directional antenna and a radio receiver to find the heading to the beacon and "home" or fly to the beacon. This was a major navigation system for many years and is still being used today.

Homing allows an aircraft to fly to a specific location but does not insure that the aircraft will remain on an airway. For safe separation, aircraft should remain on an airway or a specific course. Radio direction finding provided heading information but a system that provided course information was needed.

A radionavigation system called the A-N range was invented that provided up to four courses. Course information started at the radio station and extended out about 100 to 150 nautical miles. A network of A-N range stations was installed along the airways that were created earlier by light beacons.

Although A-N range stations improved long-distance flying immensely there was no provision for landing in bad weather. A successful airline industry would remain out of reach as long as there was no way to insure take off and landing under most weather conditions.

There had been a number of attempts at permitting bad weather takeoffs and landings. These ranged from giant fans to blow the vapor away, to heaters using radio frequency energy to condense the water. These attempts were early in the century, when making giant fans and radio frequency energy was, in itself, a challenge! In fact, some early attempts at dispersing fog were for railroad use, not aircraft! The military was acutely aware of the need for all-weather operation and set up a program whimsically called, "Fog, Intense, Dispersal Of", or FIDO.

There was one common outcome for all fog dispersal programs: it is not practical to disperse fog.

Daniel Guggenheim, a wealthy American industrialist, in 1926, created a fund for the promotion of aeronautics. The fund established the "Full Flight Laboratory", which was charged with finding methods of all-weather flying. As a first order of business, the Laboratory declared all fog dispersal programs failures and set its sights on a radio-based landing system.

The goal of the Guggenheim Foundation was to demonstrate what was called "blind flight" by taking off, flying a closed course and landing with no reference to the external world.

For the radio receiver to operate with a landing system, the Guggenheim Foundation contacted Radio Frequency Laboratories in Boonton, N.J., some 35 miles west of New York City. Radio Frequency Laboratories had an Aircraft Radio Division, which was solely dedicated to the development of airborne receivers. Radio Frequency Laboratories owned a number of key patents used in many receivers manufactured in the 1920s. They also had a very extensive facility where practically any component could be fabricated. Special parts required for the harsh aviation environment could be custom-fabricated.

On September 29, 1929, test pilot Lt. James "Jimmy" Doolittle and check pilot Lt. Benjamin Kelsey, took off, flew a closed course and landed successfully while Doolittle was covered with a canvas canopy. In spite of the demonstration, it would be decades before aircraft were taking off and landing in bad weather using a radio-based landing system.

The depression years were a time of unprecedented growth for what is now called "radio". The same could be said of the air transport industry. In 1931, Aviation Magazine observed; "Air transport has won fame as a depression-proof industry. Of how many other industries can that be said?". The answer was not in the article but in "radio". The "golden years of radio" were in the depths of the depression.

In the decade of the 1930s tremendous advances were made in navigation, excluding a landing system and air traffic control. The first radio-equipped control tower was constructed in Cleveland in 1930. Aeronautical Radio, Inc. was formed to consolidate radio communications for the scheduled airlines. Passenger revenue increased. Airframe manufacturers were building civilian and military aircraft, with much of the military aircraft going to Europe for the war. All of this came to an end on December 7, 1941 and the entry of the U.S. into World War II. After this date, no civilian aircraft were made and those on the production line or in service diverted to the war effort.

World War II was a time of tremendous advancement in aviation electronics. As suspected, at the end of the war the airplane was playing an important role. Predictions made in the earlier world war came true in a magnitude never imagined.

The airplane was making itself known as a serious war machine in 1940 during devastating bombing raids on London. The British had developed a radio-based warning system, called "Chain Home", that was capable of detecting incoming aircraft. The system, however, did not have sufficient resolution to accurately locate incoming aircraft, where a fighter aircraft could be dispatched to engage the bomber. The main reason Chain Home did not have the resolution was its long wavelengths, between one and ten meters. Shorter wavelengths measured in centimeters would be ideal for detecting aircraft.

Electronics available at the outbreak of war in Europe had no hope of generating energy at frequencies of 3 GHz and higher (10 cm and shorter wavelengths). This was particularly true if high power was required.

The bombing raids over London were so devastating that without a truly effective radio direction finder, or RDF, what the British called their Chain Home, the outcome of the war looked bleak. A concerted effort was launched to develop a source of short wavelength, high-powered radio energy that could improve the RDF system. The device developed by the British was called the magnetron.

In 1941, the magnetron had been brought to a point where it could be produced and designed into RDF equipment. The British industrial base, however, was overwhelmed with war material orders and vulnerable to attack. It was decided to take the magnetron to the United States.

The magnetron arrived with full documentation at Bell Telephone Laboratories in Whippany, N.J., in October 1941. The device met a lukewarm reception until people present at the meeting learned the device sitting before them in its wooden box could produce 10 thousand watts of 3 cm radio energy! Never before in America had this much power been generated at such a short wavelength.

The decision was made. The magnetron would be reverse-engineered and made ready for production. However, no RDF---called RADAR in the United States---existed that could use the new magnetron.

Bell Telephone Laboratories was assigned the task to reverse-engineer the magnetron, while a new facility, The Radiation Laboratory, was established at the Massachusetts Institute of Technology. Also known as Rad Lab, it was to develop radar systems employing the magnetron. More than just radar systems were required. Since virtually no work was ever done at these short "micro" waves, there was no test equipment, no test methods and no nomenclature. An entire science had to be created.

The Rad Lab developed scores of radar sets, some for detecting aircraft and others for use aboard aircraft. There was shipboard radar for detecting both aircraft and other ships. There were radars for directing anti-aircraft artillery. The Lab also produced test equipment, test procedures and an entire base of knowledge that would play an important role in the development of radar systems for decades to come.

Radar was one of the first electronic warfare, EW, systems. Radar detectors and jammers, or electronic countermeasures, soon followed. The development of radar during WWII completely changed the makeup of aircraft. In the two decades preceding the war, military aircraft went from having virtually no electronics, to a war machine bristling with antennas. The fully equipped WWII aircraft had VHF and HF communications, on-board radar, possibly radar countermeasures, a secondary radar system, electronic navigation and an electromechanical bombsight.

A New Threat

England enjoyed several years of relative safety from aerial attack, but May 1944 a new threat appeared, the V1 flying bomb. This unmanned aircraft, powered by a pulse jet, was simply aimed in the direction of the intended target, the flight distance programmed in, and the bomb launched. After flying the prescribed distance, the engine was stopped and the bomb simply fell to earth. Other than a simple gyroscope, the V1 had no guidance system and was not very accurate. The V1 was cheap, however, and involved no loss of German life. V1s could be launched by the hundreds in a hit or miss fashion and enough would hit to make the bomb a serious threat. Fortunately, the latest radar from the Rad Lab could detect the V1 lifting off, which gave sufficient time to dispatch fighter aircraft to shoot it down.

In 1945, first in Europe and then in the Pacific, the war ended. Much technology developed during the war was put to peaceful use and nowhere was it more true than in aviation. Wartime radar began to track aircraft in the National Airspace System. Navigation systems appeared in civilian aircraft. Bad weather was detected by radar. Finally, some twenty years since Doolittle demonstrated blind flight, a landing system was available.

New air transport aircraft were designed and produced. They were pressurized and able to fly higher and farther than ever before. They were fitted with the latest avionics; VHF Omni Range, VHF communications, instrument landing systems and radar transponders. Much of what was learned from the design of WWII bombers was carried over to peacetime aircraft.

Air traffic control was now radar-based. Before the American air transport industry closed down in 1941, when the United States entered the war, air traffic control was accomplished by ground observers and radio communications. Information was forwarded to the landing airport via telephone and teletype. Actual positions of aircraft in flight were determined by the crew or ground observers. The reliability of position fixes was determined by the capability of the crew. This was at a time when navigation was not precise. To insure safe operation, aircraft had to be separated by many miles. After the war, the increase of commercial air traffic severely limited the number of aircraft that could be handled by the air traffic control system.

To solve the problem, war-time radar systems were installed along the airways in the United States. This allowed air traffic controllers to see the position of aircraft without waiting for position reports. This permitted much closer separation and greatly increased the capacity of the air traffic control system. The IFF (Interrogation, Friend or Foe) transponder system was modified for civilian use to further increase the capacity of air traffic.

One WWII development took 5 to 7 years to achieve peacetime status but when it did it changed forever the way we fly. In 1952 the British Aerospace Corporation flew the first turbojet-powered passenger aircraft, the BAE Comet. Unfortunately, early models broke apart in flight, a problem traced to metal fatigue. Never before had aircraft flown at such high altitudes and the repeated pressurizing of the aircraft caused premature metal failure.

Another early passenger jet was the Boeing 707, which was an immediate success. The 707 was capable of economical transatlantic flight and responsible for the rapid demise of the transatlantic steam ship.

The 707 was full of the latest avionics, including distance measuring equipment, autopilot and airborne weather radar.The 707 was one of the first air transport aircraft to see the installation of transistorized equipment. Loading up an aircraft with vacuum tube electronics meant racks and racks, even small rooms, full of power-hungry equipment. Transistorized equipment promised smaller, lighter, more power-efficient equipment and higher reliability. The 707 flight deck was fitted with the latest in display devices and automatic control.

In the 1950s, flight took on a meaning beyond aircraft. In 1957 a small package was placed into orbit around the earth and transmitted back warbling tones containing telemetry information. This was the first of many Sputniks, marking the beginning of the space race and, later, the cold war. World War II was called the "Wizard War" because much of the outcome was determined by technology, but the real wizard war would be the cold war. During three decades the cold war went from the warbling Sputnik to the moon. There were spy satellites, intercontinental ballistic missiles, high-flying spy planes---and every one of their payloads was electronic equipment. Even conventional aircraft had more electronic systems than any other. The capability of an aircraft was no longer how high, how fast, how far, but by the electronics on board.

Not all the sophisticated electronics were intended to cause death and destruction. More and more systems were being installed in civilian aircraft. The early airline crew of three was reduced to two; the flight engineer being replaced by electronic systems. The integrated circuit permitted extremely sophisticated electronics to be stuffed into the smallest of containers. The microcomputer, having reached a level of maturity, was controlling many tasks required for long distance flights. The workload of the flight crew was being reduced, thus lessening fatigue and increasing performance. The glass cockpit permitted graphic displays of flight data that is more intuitive and easy to understand.

In the 1980s an electronic collision avoidance system was installed in aircraft after years of false starts. An improved air traffic radar transponder complemented the collision avoidance system for improved safety. In the mid 1990s the global positioning system, GPS, reached full operational capability and permitted pin-point accuracy anywhere in the world at any time. Aircraft can communicate to any place in the world using satellites.

The aircraft of 2003 was a hundred years in the making; its sophistication has more to do with electronics than aerodynamics. No one who was alive when the Wright brothers made history would have ever predicted the future for aviation 100 years hence; not even the prophet Nostradamus.

Further Reading

Augustine, Norman R., <u>America's Space Program: wishing upon a star or going to the stars?</u> Washington, D.C.: Smithsonian Institution Press, 1992.

Bilstein, Roger E., <u>The American Aerospace Industry: from workshop to global enterprise</u>. New York: Twayne Publishers, 1996.

Brown, Louis, <u>A RADAR History of World War II: Technical and Military Imperatives</u>. (Philadelphia: Institute of Physics Publishing, 1999.

Buderi, Robert, <u>The Invention that Changed the World: how a small group of radar pioneers won the Second World War and launched a technological revolution</u>. New York: Simon and Schuster, 1996.

Bush, Vanevar, <u>Modern Arms and Free Men: a discussion of the role of science in preserving democracy</u>. New York: Simon and Schuster, 1949.

Doolittle, James, <u>I Could Never be so Lucky Again;</u> an autobiography. New York: Bantam Books, 1991.

Fisk, Fred C., Todd, Marlin W., <u>The Wright Brothers from Bicycle to Biplane: An Illustrated History of the Wright Brothers. Dayton</u> Ohio: Toddfisk, 1990.

Helfrick, Albert, <u>Electronics in the Evolution of Flight,</u> College Station, Texas, The Texas A&M Press, 2004.

Giancarlo Masini et. al., <u>Marconi</u>. New York: Marsilio Publications 1999.

Jablonski, Edward, <u>Doolittle: a biography</u>. Garden City, N.Y.: Doubleday, 1976.

Kirk, Stephen, <u>First in Flight: The Wright Brothers in North Carolina.</u> Winston-Salem N.C.: J. F. Blair, 1995.

Komons, Nick A<u>., Bonfires to Beacons: Federal Civil Aviation Policy Under the Air Commerce Act, 1926-1938</u>. Washington D.C., Smithsonian Institution Press, 1989.

McCurdy, Howard E., <u>Space and the American Imagination</u>. Washington, D.C.:

Smithsonian Press, 1997.

Parramore, Thomas C., <u>Triumph at Kitty Hawk: The Wright Brothers and Powered Flight</u>. Raleigh, N.C.: Division of Archives and History, North Carolina Department of Cultural Resources, 1993.

The Radio Club of America, ed., <u>The Legacies of Edwin Howard Armstrong</u>. New York: the Radio Club of America, 1990.

Reynolds, Quentin, <u>The Amazing Mr. Doolittle; a biography of Lt. Gen. James H. Doolittle</u>. New York: Arno Press, 1953, 1972.

Schiffer Publishing, Ltd. Ed., <u>Pilot's Information File, 1944: The authentic WWII guidebook for pilots and flight engineers</u>. Atglen, Pa.: Schiffer Publishing, 1995.

Stewart, Irvin, <u>Organizing Scientific Research for War: the administrative history of the Office of Scientific Research and Development</u>. Boston: Little Brown, 1948.

Streetly, Martin, <u>Airborne Electronic Warfare: history, techniques and tactics</u>. London: Janes, 1988)

Wright, Orville, <u>How We Invented the Airplane: an illustrated history</u>. New York: Dover publications, 1988, reprint of original 1920 and 1953 editions.

Chapter 1

Introduction to Avionics

1.1 History

Avionics, which is "aviation electronics," combines two large and exciting fields that reached maturity during the 20th century. Major developments in aviation date back to the 18th century with experiments in lighter-than-air craft, followed by flights in non-powered gliders. There was also much theorizing and experimentation in electricity during the 18th and 19th centuries. Marconi's 1901 milestone, spanning the Atlantic with radio waves, was the most advanced application of electricity for that time. It marked an important event in the birth of an industry that became radio engineering, precursor of electronics.

A few years after Marconi's achievement, on December 17, 1903, Wilbur and Orville Wright also performed a feat never before accomplished; taking off, flying and landing in a manned, powered, heavier-than-air craft.

Marconi's transatlantic signals were not the first time messages were transmitted by radio. Nor was the Wrights' flight the first time man ever flew. What they did differently was to thoroughly understand and solve their problems. These accomplishments were not by chance. Marconi performed numerous experiments with radio and knew what it would take to span the Atlantic. The Wrights were the first to use a wind tunnel to prove airfoil designs, rather than risking their lives to trial and error.

1.2 Flying Blind

Weather profoundly affected airline travel in the 1920s. A clear day was required not only for take off, but along the route and at the destination. Over long distances, consistently good flying weather was unlikely. Without the ability to fly at any time, practical application of aircraft was severely limited. The US Army was so concerned about its military operations, it began an investigation in 1925 into what it called "blind flight".

Based on the 24 years since the Wrights' first flight in 1903, the researchers determined a need for three systems to make blind flight possible. First would be an altimeter of sufficient accuracy to enable the pilot to avoid unseen mountains and other obstructions. The instrument would require sufficient accuracy for landing at a fog-bound airport. Altimeters based on barometric pressure were already aboard aircraft, but accuracy was only on the order of 1000 feet, hardly precise enough for flight in low visibility.

The second item was a reference to the natural horizon. When fog, clouds or other precipitation obscure the earth's horizon, a pilot cannot depend on his senses to determine up from down. If you stand on the earth you can easily tell which way is "up", even with eyes closed because you feel the force of gravity on your body. In an aircraft, however, there are several forces acting on the body; gravity acceleration plus acceleration due to turning (centrifugal force). Only if the pilot sees the natural horizon can he avoid being fooled by the force developed as the airplane turns. So the second requirement was an artificial horizon to provide visual references to control the airplane.

The final requirement was navigation to guide the pilot to a destination without seeing landmarks, stars or other features outside the cockpit. This was particularly critical during the arrival and landing phase, where the runway may not be visible until just before touchdown. In some instances, the pilot must land without ever seeing the runway.

Optical systems for guidance were out of the question because light cannot penetrate clouds and the inability of optical or light signals to move through clouds created the problem in the first place. The researchers found the answer in radio.

The nature of radio was well understood in 1925. It was known that waves travel in straight lines as does light, but radio's longer wavelengths are not distorted or reflected by clouds. The third ingredient, therefore, would be a radio beam to lead the aircraft to the runway.

On September 24, 1929, an aircraft rolled out of a hangar at Mitchell Field, New York. Two young army lieutenants, experienced fliers in spite of their youth, climbed aboard. The rear seat in their two-place airplane was equipped with a canopy to block any view of the outside world. The pilot in the forward cockpit was able to look out and acted as safety pilot. The aircraft would be flown entirely by the rear pilot under a canvas canopy. The safety pilot was Benjamin Kelsey and the pilot making the epic blind flight was James "Jimmy" Doolittle.

In a remarkable demonstration, the aircraft took off, flew a 15-mile closed course and landed ----all without Doolittle seeing outside. To the crowd of press and government observers, it was positive proof that an aircraft could be flown in all types of weather, and be viable for passenger transportation and military operations. Aviation electronics, however, had a long way to go before the dream of blind flight could be realized.

1.3 Radio Comes of Age

Nine years before the Doolittle flight, on August 20, 1920, commercial broadcasting commenced in Pittsburgh, PA, with the signing on of KDKA. Although the station had no audience to broadcast to, KDKA's owner, Westinghouse Electric and Manufacturing Company, knew exactly what it was doing. The company made radio receivers. Westinghouse couldn't sell them until there

Jimmy Doolittle flew the first blind flight in September, 1929, with instruments that included an artificial horizon, directional gyro and radio receiver with two vibrating reeds that indicated the radio "beam". He used two biplanes as flying laboratories. The airplane shown here, a fast Vought Corsair Navy fighter, was flown in early cross-country instrument flight tests.

were stations---and stations couldn't make a penny until there were receivers. When Westinghouse got production rolling, advancements in the 9 years since the Doolittle flight were phenomenal. The technology for rugged, light weight equipment for blind flight, however, was not yet available.

During the 1929 attempt to install electronics in aircraft, automobile radios were virtually nonexistent. This made the challenge even more daunting. Electronics of the period were large and heavy, and the cost for every gram of mass in an aircraft is high. Heavy aircraft require larger wing area and more powerful engines to provide sufficient lift. This implies more fuel and higher rates of consumption. Electrical power requirements rise, calling for a larger generator and battery, hence more weight and larger engine.

The environment was harsh, especially wide temperature ranges. An aircraft on the ramp in an Arizona desert could reach 43 degrees C. After cruising at 10,000 feet during a day's travel to the north, temperature might drop to -40 degrees C, a variation of 83 degrees in a few hours.

Large engines turning propellers in a light vehicle create enormous vibration. There is shock and low frequency shake while landing on concrete or grass. Never before were electronic systems put to such tests. It was clear that new and specific equipment was needed.

Providing communications was even more challenging than navigation. There were problems of installing a transmitter in an aircraft, satisfying high power consumption and mounting a long antenna. Edwin Armstrong encountered these problems during tests in France during WWI. Using short radio wavelengths could solve the antenna problem but there was no practical technology for VHF transmitters or receivers. Because the first equipment was for navigation and one-way radio reception, only receivers, with no transmitters, were needed. It was common for an aircraft to blink a landing light or wiggle its wings in response to a transmission from a controller on the ground.

The ground environment wasn't much better. Countries like the United States have wide-open spaces and high peaks, areas where navigation is most important. Over the great plains and mountains there were virtually no landmarks at night. In fact, one of the first navigation aids for night flying were bonfires maintained by farmers paid to perform the task.

In the 1920s many places had no electrical power, including areas where navigation aids were most needed. The first light beacons were placed on mountain tops to cover the greatest range and warn aviators of obstructions. Some beacons were assembled by hauling components to the top with mules. It was ironic that the latest in transportation, the airplane, depended on one of the earliest forms of transportation, the pack animal! The lights were powered by diesel generators that worked for weeks without maintenance or refilling. Temperatures below –30 C in winter and snow often made access roads impassable. When radio navigation and communications became a reality, many light beacons became sites for radio equipment. Operators manned the sites a week at a time and, if snowed in, for longer periods.

The first navigation aid, the non-directional beacon, or NDB, was a homing beacon because aircraft homed in on its signal with a directional antenna. Like a light in the night, it provided a heading to fly If there were no crosswinds or other perturbations in the flight path, the course is a straight line. If the aircraft deviates, however, the path to the beacon is an arc. As a method of long distance navigation, homing beacons were lacking because the only courses are straight line segments connecting one beacon to another. If the wind angle is not known, it is not easy to fly and maintain the course. A navigation system was needed to provide more graphic guidance on how to return to a selected course.

The first navigation system with course information was the A-N range. It derived its name from the method of operation; the pilot listened to Morse code signals (the letters "A" and "N") from the ground transmitter. If the aircraft was exactly on one of four courses emanating from the station, the pilot heard a steady tone as the two signals overlapped. If the aircraft deviated, the letter A (*dit-dah*) or N (*dah-dit*) would be heard. No special indicating instruments were required; just a radio receiver and pair of headphones. The radio could also receive voice messages and updates on weather. The electronics to provide an indicator or dedicated navigation receiver in this era of the vacuum tube would add excessive weight to the aircraft. The simplicity of the A-N range system ---just listen to audio tones--- was an important reason for its success.

1.4 Beginning of the National Airspace System

By the late 1930's, just before World War II, a network of ground stations had been completed. A-N ranges were mainly for en route navigation and homing beacons helped find the airport. The most modern aircraft of the day was the Douglas DC-3, an unpressurized twin-engine transport equipped with a direction finding receiver for homing beacons and a low frequency receiver for the A-N range and communications. Some DC-3s had high frequency (HF) radio transmitters to communicate with airway ground stations that would reply on low frequency (LF).

If a traveler was fortunate, New York to Los Angeles could be flown in two days with a stopover in Kansas City. Since the DC-3 was not pressurized, it would not fly higher than about 10,000 feet, preventing it from topping the weather or the Rocky Mountains. It had to fly through clouds and inside the mountain passes. Since A-N ranges provided only four courses per station, there were not many alternate routes for avoiding weather. When conditions turned bad, the 2-day trip could run 3 or more days. New Yorkers serious about arriving in Los Angeles took the train.

There were other problems with the A-N range and homing beacon. One was the frequency spectrum between 100-500 kHz. These frequencies are affected by a variety of atmospheric conditions; electrical noise from lightning strokes and precipitation static (P-static) caused by ice crystals commonly found in clouds. In the summer over most of continental United States, thunderstorms are frequent. During bad weather, when a navigation aid is needed most, the early systems were most likely to be corrupted by interference.

Low frequency signals are also degraded by atmospheric propagation. These frequencies not only travel in straight lines along the surface of the earth but "bounce" off the ionosphere. This upper layer in the atmosphere has highly ionized, conductive molecules. The reflected signals, called *sky waves*, interfere with ground waves (from the same station). Sky waves distort signals and cause inaccuracies in navigation.

When World War II began, there was a much-enhanced network of radio beacons for air navigation. As useful as beacons were, however, they lacked the precision and versatility for military operations. During this period, radar was developed to detect targets. This was followed by *secondary radar* for determining target identity. Called *identification friend or foe*, IFF, it is still used today. Aircraft appear as blips on a radar screen and IFF provides a positive identification of a target as friendly or hostile. For civil use, this system was modified to display aircraft altitude, enabling radar to depict an aircraft position in three dimensions. The civil system is known as the Air Traffic Control Radar Beacon System or ATCRBS, (pronounced *at-crabs*), which is in operation today,

A deficiency at the beginning of World War II was the lack of a landing navigation aid. It led to the use of very high frequencies, VHF, and a system capable of providing a large number of courses. Called VHF Omni Range, or VOR, its frequency region is not significantly affected by precipitation static and other interference. Secondly, it is "omni," or "all" range, which means it can provide any desired course.

To further guide landing aircraft, another VHF-based system called the *localizer* was developed to provide the pilot with horizontal (left-right) guidance. For vertical guidance, it was matched with a companion system called the *glide slope,* which operates in the UHF frequency range. Localizer and glide slope, with ancillary equipment are called the *ILS*, or Instrument Landing System.

Most ILS development took place during the war but the system did not become available for civil use until later. In 1947, the International Civil Aviation Organization (ICAO, pronounced *eye-kay-oh)*, was formed and adopted ILS and VOR as the en route, approach and landing system for world-wide use. They are the backbone of electronic navigation used by all countries today.

Communications systems also emerged during the war years. High frequency (HF) gave way to VHF with the arrival of new components capable of producing power at VHF frequencies.

Another navigation system developed during the war provided the position of a vessel in latitude and longitude. Called Long Range Navigation or LORAN, the early system was slow and cumbersome and intended for ships, but did find some application in aircraft. A later version, LORAN-C, is used extensively on aircraft.

Many current navigation techniques started as military systems. This is also true of aircraft. As more were built during the war than in all of history, airframes were improved and production techniques refined. Advances in electronics were amazing and every system was improved by smaller, more effective components. Electronics were also developing in the civil sector; such as television, which was approaching practicality just before the war but delayed until the late 1940's with the return of peace.

The next period, from 1950 to 1970, was also time of technology improvement. Two new systems appeared: OMEGA for world-wide navigation, and LORAN-C for coastal United States and other maritime areas in the world. OMEGA is now off the air, having lasted for about 35 years, while LORAN-C was extended over continental US and is still in service.

The 1950s to the late 80s saw tremendous advances in electronics, beginning with the transistor, followed by the integrated circuit. These inventions are of extreme importance to aviation electronics as keys to miniaturization. One integrated circuit, the microprocessor, could perform tasks never dreamed possible.

A revolution took place in the aviation world in the early 1990s when the Global Positioning System, GPS, became operational. More than any other electronic navigation system, GPS has changed the way aircraft navigate, from take-off to landing. Based on satellites, it provides navigation everywhere at any time with reliability and precision.

The venerable VOR and ILS systems have also been improved, mostly with better antennas for ground stations. Performance of these systems depends heavily on antenna design, and they have been refined about as much as the laws of physics allow.

1.5 Navigation Principles

The earliest navigation was "dead reckoning". There are several theories of how the name evolved but it is a method of determining where you are by knowing where you have been, how fast you are traveling and the direction you followed. With a clock and simple arithmetic, your position may be calculated. This system works only if the clock and speed are accurate and you really know from where you started.

In aircraft navigation, winds affect speed of the aircraft and it is sometimes difficult to determine a reference position when the weather is hazy, cloudy or dark. The longer one travels with dead reckoning, the less precise navigation becomes. This is not unique to dead reckoning; there are other systems, such as inertial navigation, where this phenomenon also occurs. To restore accuracy a known fix is required. It can be a reference point on the ground or a radio beacon signal. Dead reckoning, however, is useful in aircraft only for short distance, short time navigation.

1.5.1 Charts and Maps

A requirement of navigation is to locate a position on the earth with a coordinate system. The earth, which is nearly spherical in shape, requires spherical geometry to describe points on its surface. Because the earth spins around an axis, the north and south poles of rotation were chosen as reference points for the coordinate system. Circles are drawn around the earth which pass through the geographic poles. The term "geographic" applies because the poles are different from the earth's magnetic poles that attract the compass. These lines (which run vertically on an aeronautical map) are called longitude and named in angular measurement of degrees. The reference circle was defined by England, at the time a world leader in navigation. Longitude is an indication, therefore, of how far east or west we are of the "zero meridian," which passes through the Royal Observatory in Greenwich, England.

To identify north and south on the globe, there are concentric circles with a common center on the earth's axis of rotation. Called latitude (the horizontal lines on an aeronautical chart), they are also designated in degrees. The reference latitude encircles the earth at the equator and is zero degrees. (This produces a circle with the largest radius.) As latitude circles proceed north or south, the radii decrease, until they end at the north and south poles. The angle at the poles is 90 degrees, where latitude circles have no radius.

Latitude and longitude locate points anywhere on earth. Daytona Beach International Airport (Florida) is 29 degrees, 11 minutes north (latitude) and 81 degrees and 3 minutes west (longitude). The terms north, south, east and west are included because longitude angles only go from 0 to 180 degrees, and latitude runs from 0 degrees to 90 degrees. For example; both New York and Calcutta, India are at 75 degrees longitude. But New York is west and Calcutta is east of the zero reference line at Greenwich, England. The greatest longitude angle is 180 degrees, approximately at the International Date Line running through the middle of the Pacific Ocean. The date line does not exactly follow the 180 line of longitude to avoid splitting countries or islands in a group into two different days! Sometimes locations are given in degrees, minutes and fractions of minutes for greater accuracy.

Since aeronautical charts are flat, longitude does not form parallel lines. This is apparent far north or south and is most visible at the poles. Latitude lines, however, are always parallel, being concentric circles. In fact, lines of latitude are sometimes called "parallels" such as the well-known 38th parallel meaning the line of latitude at 38 degrees north separating North and South Korea. A map is a plot of the earth showing geographical features such as rivers, mountains and oceans, as well as boundaries of countries, states and highways or rail lines. A chart is a specialized map showing more than geographical features. Charts in aviation show navigation aids and airways, which are highways in the air. This is a good example of how map and chart differ. A roadway is a physical feature that can be seen, even if there are no vehicles. The airway is invisible; look skyward and there is no evidence of an airway except when an aircraft flies overhead. It could be noticed that many aircraft are flying that same path.

Geographical features are shown on a chart, such as large rivers and lakes. Political boundaries, particularly national borders, appear because specific rules cover international flights. On the other hand, there are uniform aviation rules for the United States and state boundaries are not always shown. Some charts have virtually no geographical features. One is a high altitude chart where aircraft are at such high flight levels that geographic features are not easily seen, or the aircraft is above the weather. These charts contain only detailed data on navigation aids and airways.

1.5.2 Heading and Course

Heading is the direction the aircraft nose is pointed. If there are no winds, the aircraft goes where it is headed. The desired path over the ground, which for this discussion is a straight line, is called the course

Heading is relative to one of two references, true north and magnetic north. We are fortunate that earth has a magnetic field, created when a molten nickel-iron core solidified while the earth rotated on its axis. This field is a valuable aid in navigation because a freely rotating magnet aligns with the direction of the earth's magnetic field. Historically, ships and aircraft use a magnetic compass to take up a heading. However, a map or chart is drawn with lines of longitude aligned with *geographical* north. To compound matters, magnetic and geographical north differ between the northerly directions and with location. The angle between true and magnetic north also changes with time.

The angle between true north and magnetic north is called magnetic variation and is shown on all aeronautical charts. These values are updated regularly to account for time changes.

Since a total lack of wind seldom occurs, crosswinds tend to blow an aircraft off course. This is counteracted by turning the aircraft into the wind to offset the drift. The angle between course and heading is the "crab" angle, or angle at which the aircraft must be turned into the wind to remain on course. The stronger the crosswind, the greater the crab angle.

Distances in aviation are measured in nautical miles. The original intent, as the name implies, was to simplify navigation at sea. A nautical mile is roughly the distance between one minute of arc of longitude at the equator. "Roughly," because the nautical mile was invented before dimensions of the earth were well known. As it turns out, the nautical mile is not exactly one minute of arc at the equator.

For measuring distance at elevations of latitude other than the equator, a correction is applied. The distance between one minute of arc is:

$$D = \theta \cos \phi \qquad\qquad (1.1)$$

where D is the distance in nautical miles, θ is the distance in minutes of longitude and ϕ is the latitude.

Exercise:
The location of Daytona Beach airport was given within 1 minute of arc. How precise is this location?

Solution:
First, determine the distance represented by 1 minute of arc of both longitude and latitude. In the case of latitude, one minute of arc is approximately 1 NM. The longitude one minute of arc is

$$D = \theta \cos \phi = \cos (29.183 \ degrees) = 0.873 \ NM$$

A nautical mile has had different lengths over history as dimensions of the earth were corrected. At this time a nautical mile is defined as exactly 1852 meters, (6076 feet), and should never be changed again.

Engineers and scientists need to be aware of differences between navigation and scientific measurements. Notice that angles are measured from north, which is shown on charts as up. Scientific angles are usually measured from the horizontal. Notice, too, that angles increase with clockwise rotation. For example, east is 90 degrees. Scientific angles increase with counterclockwise rotation; 90 degrees is usually up. Third, angles are in degrees and minutes and sometimes seconds, never radians. In later chapters we will discuss altitude in feet and pressures in inches of mercury, instead of meters and pascals.

Most engineers use international standard units; meters, kilograms and seconds, MKS or SI, which is an abbreviation for "international standard" in French. Non-SI units in aviation are a hold-over from when the U.S. dominated aviation and English units were accepted as a worldwide standard. Notice that the nautical mile is defined as exactly 1852 meters and, thus, is a "metric" or SI measure.

Standards, and the organizations that maintain them, are important to the aviation industry. The National Bureau of Standards (now the National Institute of Standards and Technology, or NIST) was created after a tragic incident more than 100 years ago. During the great Chicago Fire of 1871 when apparatus from neighboring towns arrived in Chicago to aid in fire fighting, hoses could not connect to Chicago fire hydrants. Different threads were used in neighboring towns. Imagine the potential problems for airports separated by thousands of miles, or located in different countries. Worldwide aviation standards assure global uniformity.

1.6 Regulatory and Advisory Agencies
Standardization of aviation is divided into two types of organizations, regulatory and advisory. Only governments can maintain regulatory organizations to mandate aviation standards. Since there is no world government, there are only advisory agencies for international standardization and control.

International Civil Aviation Organization (ICAO). This organization is a branch of the United Nations and headquartered in Montreal, Canada. It grew out of a conference conducted on December 7, 1944 in Chicago, which realized there would be significant growth in international aviation. Most of the world's countries are members of ICAO and they agree to implement recommendations put forth by the organization. In rare cases where a "state," as members are called, cannot follow the recommendation, that country must publish the deviation from the accepted practice. Nations that do not join ICAO will find it difficult convincing airlines to service their country---so it is in the best interest of any nation to be a member.

ICAO covers all phases of aviation. For example, ICAO Annex 14 describes airport characteristics, specifying the size and shape of runways. It is no coincidence that every runway engaged in airline transport in the world looks much the same. Numbers are the same size and designate the runway heading. Approach lights are the same, as are taxi lights. ICAO Annex 10 regulates radio navigation aids and communications, insuring that signals from ground stations or satellites are compatible in every part of the world.

ICAO can only make recommendations, which are known as SARPS, for "Standards and Recommended Practices"; it is up to member nations to turn them into law. If a member does not follow an ICAO recommendation, the non-standard practice appears in ICAO publications.

FAA: Federal Aviation Administration. The agency responsible for regulating aviation safety in the United States is the Federal Aviation Administration. This organization is a part of the Department of Transportation, DOT, which is headed by the Secretary of Transportation, a cabinet post and part of the executive branch of government. The FAA top official is the Administrator, who reports to the Secretary of Transportation. Every member of ICAO has an organization similar to the FAA. Smaller nations often model their regulatory agencies after the FAA and other larger nation's equivalents.

The history of the FAA dates back to the earliest days of flying. It was recognized in the early to mid-1920s that some form of government regulation was required if flying was going to be safe, practical and profitable. In May of 1926 the "Air Commerce Act" was passed by the United States Congress. This legislation placed the responsibility of regulating air commerce under a new Aeronautics Branch of the Department of Commerce. This branch tested and licensed pilots, certified aircraft designs, and provided for radio communications and navigation. The Aeronautics Branch assumed operation of lighted airways, which had been operated by the Lighthouse Service! What is most fascinating about the introduction of licensing and certification is to realize that before the Air Commerce Act of 1926, there was virtually no licensing or certification at all!

In 1934 the Aeronautics Branch was renamed the Bureau of Air Commerce to recognize the increased authority and operations of the branch. In 1938 the Bureau of Air Commerce had grown to a point that it was too important and big to be a part of the Department of Commerce. The Civil Aeronautics Act of 1938 established a new independent agency, the Civil Aeronautics Authority, CAA. The new authority had expanded powers including the ability to regulate airline routes and fares.

In 1940 the CAA was divided into two agencies, the Civil Aeronautics Administration and the Civil Aeronautics Board, CAB. The CAB controlled airline routes and fares as well as flight safety. The CAA was responsible for licensing and certification, navigation systems and air traffic control.

With the rapid growth of air transport at the introduction of jet aircraft, safety problems appeared. The Federal Aviation Act of 1958 created the Federal Aviation Adminstration FAA, which placed the responsibility of aviation safety on one agency. Entrusting aviation safety to two organizations had resulted in gaps which were responsible for some accidents.

In 1966 Congress authorized the establishment of a cabinet-level Department of Transportation, DOT. The FAA, now with a new name, the Federal Aviation Administration, was one of the first organizations to operate under the new DOT.

The FAA writes and enforces regulations for many phases of private and commercial aviation. Contained in Title 14 of the Code of Federal Regulations, or CFR, they cover the design and manufacture of aircraft, testing and licensing of pilots, mechanics and air traffic controllers, and testing and certification of aircraft. The agency owns and operates navigation systems and air traffic control facilities, investigates accidents and conducts research to improve aviation safety and effectiveness.

FAA headquarters are in Washington DC, with branch offices through the U.S. and overseas. One is the Flight Safety District Office or FSDO (often pronounced "fizz-doe"). It's responsible for activities affecting safety of flight within its area. There are also regional engineering offices which oversee the certification of new systems.

NTSB: National Transportation Safety Board. This is an independent agency that is charged with investigating transportation accidents and reports directly to congress. Originally the NTSB was funded by the DOT but in 1975 all ties with DOT were severed . Since its creation, the NTSB has investigated more than 120,000 aviation accidents and a smaller number of surface vehicle accidents. The NTSB's reputation for thorough accident investigation has resulted in the NTSB investigating accidents throughout the world, even when U.S. aircraft or airspace are not involved.

The concept of the NTSB is an unbiased organization that immediately investigates accidents and reports its findings to the people of the United States through their elected representatives in the House and Senate. An investigation by the NTSB does not preclude other agencies from performing independent investigations. Most aviation accidents are investigated by the NTSB and FAA and often local and state investigators.

FCC: Federal Communications Commission. This agency is a part of the Department of Commerce. A Commissioner who heads it reports directly to the Secretary of Commerce and, like the FAA, is a part of the executive branch of government. As with the FAA, most countries have an equivalent to the FCC, which is often under the post office department.

Another similarity of the FCC to the FAA is the FCC's involvement with international advisory organizations for telecommunications. Like airspace, the radio frequency spectrum is a worldwide venue. One advisory group is the International Telecommunications Union, ITU, with headquarters in Geneva, Switzerland.

The FCC is responsible for the orderly operation of communications within the U.S. This covers wired communications, such as telephone and cable television, as well as radio transmissions. The agency is responsible for licensing equipment that can transmit a radio signal. The FCC also helps prevent undesired radiation that might emanate from a consumer electronic device, such as a computer. The FCC is important to aviation because so many avionics systems emit radio transmissions. FCC licenses must be obtained for radio transmitting equipment in aircraft and ground-based navigation and communications systems.

RTCA. Another advisory group with a major role in avionics is RTCA. This organization started out in 1935 as the Radio Technical Committee for Aeronautics. The name was changed to Radio Technical Commission for Aeronautics in 1941 after a reorganization and was changed again to RTCA Inc. in 1991. RTCA now stands for "Requirements and Technical Concepts for Aviation".

RTCA is an advisory committee to the FAA. Privately-owned, it is a not-for-profit corporation supported by dues of members, which include avionics manufacturers, airlines, military, universities and interested individuals.

Most RTCA activity occurs in Special Committees. If a problem needs study, the FAA requests that RTCA form a special committee to investigate and propose a solution. Members attend committee functions at no cost to RTCA because those attending need to be a part of the investigation and solution. As an example, in 1992 the FAA became concerned about incidents of interference from portable electronic devices carried aboard aircraft. RTCA was requested to form a Special Committee which received the designation "SC-177". The goal was established and those interested were invited to attend committee meetings.

Many who attended were portable electronic device manufacturers, a consumer electronics trade organization, airlines, avionics manufacturers, organizations that measure radiation from electronic equipment and the U S Government. It is clear that these attendees had an interest in resolving the problem.

After a series of meetings, the committee writes a final report and submits it to the FAA, also making it available to members and the public. RTCA reports do not receive the same designation as the committee because some committees produce more than one document. Numbers begin with "DO-", such as DO-233, the document produced by SC-177 on interference due to portable electronic devices.

MOPS and TSO. One area where RTCA provides important information to the FAA is "minimum operational performance standards" (MOPS). Special committees discuss operational characteristics of various avionics systems, leading to documents containing technical characteristics and test procedures for their evaluation. These documents become the basis for a "TSO," or Technical Standard Order, issued by the FAA. TSOs cover all types of equipment for an aircraft; engines, propellers, tires, wheels, etc. They insure that equipment meets a minimum standard.

Equipment intended to receive TSO approval from the FAA is designed and thoroughly tested to meet requirements of the document. Testing is exhaustive and involves environmental conditions which include ambient temperature, relative humidity, altitude and electric and magnetic fields. The standard that outlines environmental conditions is a generic document applied to all avionics and, at the time of this writing, is RTCA DO-160D.

DO- documents are updated if conditions warrant it. In the case of environmental conditions, new sections were added due to changes in aircraft design and vulnerability.

Once a piece of equipment complies with the TSO document, test and design data are submitted by the manufacturer to the FAA. If the agency is satisfied, a TSO is issued, which is stated on the equipment nameplate. If avionics equipment is granted a TSO it is said to be TSO'd.

The TSO number issued by the FAA is not the same as the RTCA DO- document. As an example, TSO C-119A is based on RTCA document DO-185. If a TSO document is obtained, it would most likely be a single sheet of paper that says the equipment must meet requirements of DO-185 under conditions outlined in DO-160-C. Notice that the environmental document is not the same as the current document. If the original testing was done to DO-160-C, the TSO remains in force even though the environmental document could change several times since testing was performed. A new TSO would require the updated document.

To continue to market a piece of TSO'd equipment, the manufacturer must build it to the specification of the original tested item. The manufacturing process must be monitored so any changes in design or manufacturing process will not jeopardize the ability to meet the TSO standard.

Not all equipment in an aircraft is must be TSO'd. The TSO mostly relates to the aircraft's type of service. A private aircraft for pleasure flying requires the least amount of TSO'd equipment; air transport category aircraft in scheduled passenger service require the most.

Although a TSO is not always a requirement, much avionics in service is TSO'd. It certifies that equipment meets a certain standard of performance and is, therefore, a strong selling feature used by manufacturers. Many aircraft owners purchase TSO'd equipment, even though it is not mandatory and are suspicious of equipment that does not carry that certification.

ARINC. Pronounced "air-ink," ARINC is an acronym for Aeronautical Radio Incorporated, a not-for-profit organization owned by U.S. air carriers. It provides services to airlines, mainly the operation of a private air-ground communications system called the Aeronautical Telecommunications Network (ATN). It provides what is usually called "company communications" --- messages which are not handled by FAA air traffic control facilities This concerns departure and arrival times, maintenance information, crew and passenger data, provisions, gate assignments and so on. Airlines obtain this service as a telephone subscriber would pay for private telephone service.

A second function of ARINC is generating avionics standards and research. ARINC standards are similar to TSOs, except they specify more than basic operating parameters. Covered are physical dimensions, connector descriptions, pin numbers and signal definitions. These standards, known as "ARINC Characteristics," describe the "form, fit, and function" for airline avionics. Sufficient detail is provided in the document so an avionics unit made by one manufacturer can plug in and replace a unit of another brand. This does not mean the inner circuits of the box are the same; manufacturers may meet the same performance standards in different ways. They need only comply with the form, fit and function described in the ARINC characteristic---which frees the airline to buy replacements from any supplier. A simple example is the common light bulb. A replacement from any manufacturer can be installed in the standard socket, operate at the same voltage and provide the same amount of light. Equipment meeting ARINC Characteristics are primarily LRUs, or line replaceable units. An LRU can be easily removed and replaced with another unit with no adjustments. This means LRUs can be changed on an aircraft while "on line," that is, actively carrying passengers.

European Aviation Safety Agency, EASA. This organization represents member nations of the European Union for the purpose of establishing common requirements. The agency develops standards covering aircraft, from design and manufacture through certification and operation. EASA coordinates its work with other regulatory agencies, particularly the United States (FAA), RTCA and ICAO. The work of EASA was formerly accomplished by the Joint Aviation Authorities, JAA. All functions and activities of JAA, however, are being absorbed by EASA.

European Organization for Aviation Equipment, EUROCAE; This organization is the European counterpart to the RTCA. EUROCAE was formed in 1963 to provide a forum for European airlines, governments and manufacturers to discuss technical problems. EUROCAE produces minimum performance standards, which become the basis for JTSOs used by member states of JAA (now EASA). This is analogous to the RTCA providing technical standards for the issuance of TSOs by the FAA in the United States.

EUROCONTROL; The European Organization for the Safety of Air Navigation has as its main objective the development and maintenance of a seamless European air traffic management, ATM, system. EUROCONTROL trains air traffic control personnel and provides air traffic control services. EUROCONTROL is funded by charging fees for services provided.

1.7 National Airspace System

In the United States, the National Airspace System, NAS, consists of navigation aids, air traffic control, surveillance radar, pilot advisories and a variety of other services. With few exceptions, components of the NAS are provided by the FAA. There are two types of radar services: terminal (in the vicinity of the airport) and en route. Aircraft en route are controlled by "Air Route Traffic Control Centers" or ARTCC. In the terminal area, aircraft are directed by "terminal radar control centers" or TRACONs. ARTCCs and TRACONs connect through communications links and aircraft are "handed off" from one facility to another during controlled flight. A concept called "free flight" is changing how this works but has not been implemented at the time of this writing. Free flight will change the role of controllers from that of air traffic control (ATC) to air traffic management (ATM).

One rather interesting document which has extreme influence on aviation and the NAS is the Federal Radionavigation Plan, called the FRP or sometimes the RNP when it is preferable to write radionavigation as two words. This document is created by both the Department of Defense and the Department of Transportation. The document is kept by the U.S. Coast Guard and updated every two years, on even years but usually a year late. Thus the 2000 version of the plan became available in 2001.

Chapter 1 Review Questions

1.1   What was the major achievement of the Wright brothers on 17th December 1903?
1.2   What was Marconi's achievement two years before the Wrights?
1.3   What were the three new systems required to achieve "blind flight" in 1929?
1.4   Who was the test pilot for the first blind flight?
1.5   What was the state of the field of "electronics" in 1929, when the first blind flight was performed ?
1.6   What were some of the problems encountered when installing radio equipment aboard an aircraft in 1929?
1.7   How did a pilot fly an A-N range?
1.8   When was RADAR invented?
1.9   What distance is represented by a nautical mile?
1.10   What is "nautical" about a nautical mile?
1.11   What distance would be traveled if an aircraft flew along the 45 degree latitude line for one degree of longitude?
1.12   If a navigation aid is to be installed at an airport, what organization(s) would produce documents with information on the proper installation?
1.13   What role in aviation electronics does the FCC play?
1.14   What does RTCA stand for? What did it originally stand for?
1.15   What is a TSO?
1.16   What is included in the National Airspace System?

Further Reading

Doolittle, James H., <u>Early Experiments in Instrument Flight</u>, (Washington D.C.: The Smithsonian Report for 1961)

Komons, Nick A<u>., Bonfires to Beacons: Federal Civil Aviation Policy Under the Air Commerce Act, 1926-1938</u>, (Washington D.C., Smithsonian Institution Press, 1989)

Osmun, William G, <u>The Authority of Agreement; A history of RTCA</u>, (Washington D.C., RTCA)

The Radio Club of America, <u>Seventy-Fifth Anniversary Diamond Jubilee Yearbook</u>, (New York: The Radio Club of America, 1984)

The Radio Club of America, ed., <u>The Legacies of Edwin Howard Armstrong</u>, (New York: The Radio Club of America, 1990)

Chapter 2

Terrestrial Radio Navigation

2.1 Non Directional Beacons and Direction Finding

The first form of electronic navigation was terrestrial, or earth-based. Interestingly, the earliest navigation was not terrestrial, but celestial. For centuries it was known that certain stars could be used for guidance. The pole, or North, star was seen to remain stationary in the night sky and could be followed as a reference---long before the geometry of earth motion was understood. Today, the term "terrestrial" separates earth-based from satellite-based navigation.

The first terrestrial radio navigation in widespread use was the non-directional beacon (NDB), still found in many parts of the world. The beacon transmits an unmodulated CW (continuous wave) carrier in the low and medium frequency bands: LF, 30 kHz – 300 kHz; and MF, 300 kHz – 3 MHz. A directional antenna on the aircraft points to the beacon, enabling the pilot to "home in" on the station.

The non-directional beacon operates in the LF-MF bands for several reasons. The first is a matter of history. When early beacons were installed, the state of the art had not yet extended to higher-frequency transmitters. Secondly, radio waves must take a predictable path to remain stable enough for homing. Frequencies higher than LF or MF also travel via the ionosphere, which varies greatly according to day and night, season of the year and the 11-year sunspot cycle. Transmission through the ionosphere can change the wave's polarization (which can be horizontal or vertical, depending on the transmitting antenna). One component that does not rotate during transmission is the "ground wave"---and it's most effective in the LF-MF band. Third, a directional antenna can have small dimensions if a magnetic, or H-field, antenna is employed. H-field antennas are easily made for LF and MF. Ground waves are always vertically polarized. The polarization of a wave refers to the orientation of the electric field.

The conductive earth makes ground wave propagation possible. Wet earth is a good conductor, water is better and salt water the best. Even dry earth supports some ground wave propagation. During ground wave transmission, currents are induced in the earth which set up magnetic fields. These fields link to and bind with the propagating field. The higher the frequency and shorter the wavelength, the less the wave penetrates the earth and induces currents. Higher frequencies, therefore, do not produce much ground wave, but reach the ionosphere which, in this situation, is what we are trying to avoid.

It is important to be aware that the earth is spherical and waves that apparently move in straight lines are encouraged to follow the curvature. Sudden changes in earth conductivity affect propagation of ground waves. The most common is from land to water. It can bend the signal from a straight path and produce a phenomenon called "shore effect".

Magnetic and electric fields, the two principle components of radio waves, are orthogonal, meaning they're oriented 90 degrees to each other. For a vertically propagating electric field, the magnetic field travels away from the transmitting tower in increasing circles as shown in Fig.2.1.

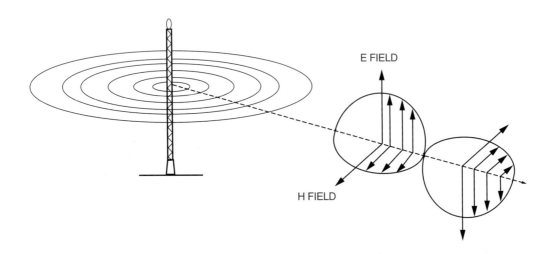

Figure 2.1 Ground wave signals, at left, emitted radially from a vertical tower. At right are E- and H- field components of the radio wave.

A directional magnetic field antenna is used which is, essentially, a loop of wire. An electric field antenna such as dipole is impractical because of limited space on an aircraft. When the antenna is arranged such that the maximum of magnetic field lines passes through the loop the output voltage is at a maximum. When the loop is oriented so that the magnetic field lines do not pass through the coil or the lines are parallel to the plane of the loop, very little or no output voltage is obtained from the coil, this is called a null.

Assume the loop is mounted on the aircraft so it picks up the electromagnetic field without being attenuated by the metal fuselage. Inside the aircraft an indicator shows the orientation of the outside loop. Assume the loop is turned so the received signal is at a null. The indicator now points to the NDB transmitting tower. To home in on the beacon, the pilot changes heading until the airplane points in the direction of the null. The aircraft should proceed to the beacon station.

There is a problem because *two* positions of the rotating loop produce a peak and two positions produce a null. These ambiguities must be resolved or the pilot will not know whether the station is forward or aft of the aircraft. The ambiguity can be removed if we have a phase reference.

Fortunately, there is a reference in the form of the electric field that accompanies the magnetic field. All that is required to make an electric field antenna is to mount a conductor on the aircraft fuselage. (The AM antenna for an automobile is an example of an electric field antenna.) On the aircraft, it is called the "sense" antenna, so named because the electric field can sense the polarity of the loop antenna output.

Let us take the output of an electric field antenna (a short length of wire), and shift phase 90 degrees to account for a 90 degree phase angle between electric and magnetic fields. We adjust the output of loop and sense antennas so a maximum is exactly the same for both. Sense antenna and loop voltages are now added together. When the loop is at a maximum, output is twice that from the loop alone since the sense antenna voltage is the same. When the loop is rotated 180 degrees, loop voltage is the same as the sense antenna voltage, except that loop voltage is now out of phase with the sense antenna and the two cancel each other. This combination of loop and sense voltage produces an antenna pattern with one peak and one null.

A disadvantage of working with the null of the magnetic field antenna is that the signal is at its minimum, causing a low signal to noise ratio. A receiver connected to the loop will operate at full gain and maximum noise. When summing sense and loop antennas, the loop antenna is actually receiving a maximum signal, which is subtracted from the sense antenna. A number of direction finding receivers control the gain of the receiver from the sense antenna signal so a sharp null can be obtained without excessive noise.

2.2 Direction Finding Receivers

The signal from loop and sense antennas is very small; in the region of microvolts. To be useful, it must be greatly amplified. This is a common requirement in the receiver because radio signals are weak compared to the level required to drive a headphone. If we take the signal due to summing of loop and sense antennas and apply it to a receiver with a signal strength meter, we could simply turn the antenna to a null or peak to find the NDB station. The antenna is mechanically connected to a rotating system, which could be driven with an electric motor or cranked by hand. Also, there is a direction indicator to show where the antenna points relative to the longitudinal axis of the aircraft. This arrangement, called a direction finder or DF, was commonly found on early aircraft, such as the DC-3.

In the DF receiver, the loop antenna was physically rotated. This could be done by hand or pushing a switch to control a motor. Either way, motion was initiated by the pilot. If a straight route is flown, such as homing to a beacon, little manipulation of the antenna is necessary. If the maneuver involves several beacons with changes of course or using an NDB for landing, pilot workload becomes excessive. An enhancement of the DF receiver completely automates the antenna, which will be discussed further.

2.2.1 Loop Antenna

The first direction finders used a coil of wire on the order of 20 cm in diameter (Fig. 2.2). Turns of wire are enclosed in a conductive pipe to shield the loop from electric field pickup. The shield must not form a closed loop because that would couple a shorted turn to the coil and cause a large signal loss.

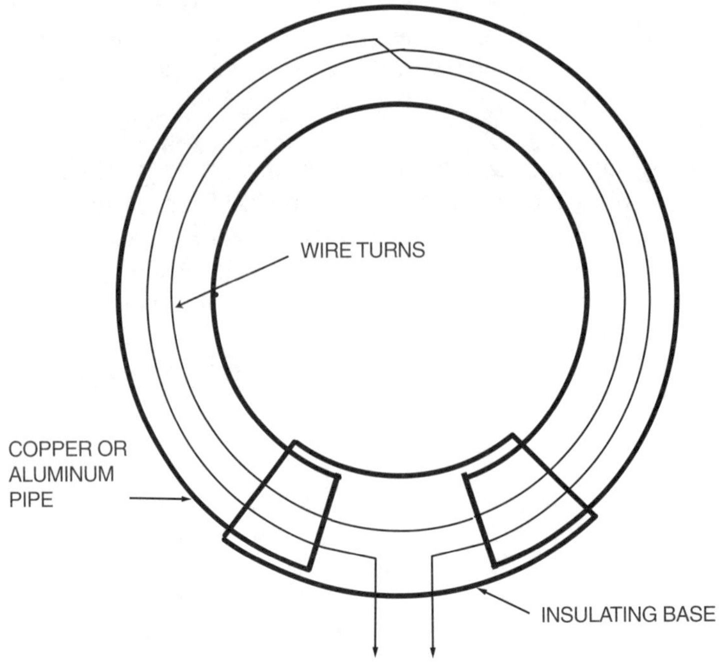

LOOP ANTENNA

WIRE TURNS

COPPER OR
ALUMINUM
PIPE

INSULATING BASE

TO RECEIVER

Figure 2.2 Loop antenna is enclosed in conducting pipe to prevent pickup of electric fields.

A 20 cm loop on the outside of an aircraft creates significant aerodynamic drag. There are also a motor and other devices to relay antenna position to an indicator in the aircraft. All these external components on an aircraft are very undesirable. It is more efficient to contain them inside the airframe where they not only reduce drag, but are protected from wind and weather.

First, a loop antenna is mounted on the exterior to receive the signal. Antenna size is reduced significantly with ferromagnetic material to concentrate the field. Magnetic field lines are attracted to ferromagnetic material, enabling a loop with a smaller area to pass the same number of lines as a larger one with a non-magnetic center. What makes a ferrite valuable is high permeability, an ability to concentrate flux while having low conductivity. Material in the center of the loop must not conduct or it becomes a shorted turn, as would closing the conductive pipe which shields the loop. As an example, common iron is ferromagnetic, but also a good conductor so it would not make a good loop antenna.

Ferromagnetic material reduces the size of the loop, but the antenna still needs to be rotated outside of the fuselage. A better idea is to bring the radio signal inside the aircraft where we can create the effect of a rotating antenna. The external antenna is connected to another loop inside the aircraft. The field received by the external antenna now induces a current in a small, inside loop.

Next, a second outside loop is added to the first one, placing it at an angle of 90 degrees. The same addition is made for the internal loop. The two loops on the outside of the fuselage pick up current proportional to the X and Y components of the magnetic field vector relative to the direction of the aircraft. Since these currents move to the internal coils, a magnetic field is created between the interior coils. These coils are connected to orthogonal (right angle) coils inside the aircraft, generating a magnetic field inside the aircraft with exactly the same direction as the external field. Thus the angle, not necessarily the magnitude, of the external magnetic field vector is recreated---and rotating parts outside the aircraft is eliminated. The receiver only needs to determine the angle of the vector, not the magnitude.

18

A small rotating coil is positioned in the area of the recreated magnetic field vector. Because the vector's angle is the same as outside, the internal rotating coil has the same nulls and peaks as if it were outside the fuselage. The internal device, known as a goniometer, is often placed inside the ADF indicator in General Aviation aircraft.

The construction of the antenna is a solid block of ferrite with two sets of wire windings oriented at 90 degrees. As in the large wire loop, the ferrite block is prevented from picking up electric fields with a copper shield. Similarly, the shield must not be continuous or it will produce a shorted turn.

The electric field picked up by the sense antenna on early systems was a length of wire. Stretched between parts of an aircraft (often from the rudder fin to the top of the cabin) it generates considerable drag. Secondly, if a wire breaks it can tangle in a control surface or other sensitive part of the aircraft. Modern direction finders uses a small sense antenna, usually in the form of a flat plate mounted in the same housing as the ferrite loops. ADF signals are usually strong compared to those of other navigation stations and even a small plate is effective. Atmospheric noise in the MF range is great, and strong signals are required Direction finder antennas may be mounted on the top or bottom of the fuselage because the long wavelengths are not shadowed by aircraft structure.

One point to observe in installing the antenna; it is configured differently for top and bottom mounting. This is because the direction of antenna rotation is reversed from top to bottom. Antennas are configured by changing jumper wires or, in some cases, electronically within the receiver.

2.3 Automatic Direction Finding

To make the direction finder much easier to operate, the *automatic direction finder* (ADF) was developed. It requires no manual operation to find a bearing; the ADF indicator continually points to the NDB station. For an automatic system to turn the antenna to a heading, it needs a signal proportional to the error, as well as its *sign*. If a motor drives the antenna, and the antenna is not at a peak or null, the deviation from the desired heading must be known, including the sign, or polarity. The error tells the motor to turn in the correct direction. If the antenna rotates to a null, signal strength increases on both sides as it moves off the null. There is no way of knowing which side of the null the antenna had deviated from.

Panel-mounted ADF receiver with built-in indicator (Bendix-King)

If we go back to the received magnetic field and consider the goniometer, we have two components of a vector. These components are complete, including a sign. By using the electric field as a reference, the polarities of the vector components are known. The reason that simply feeding the output of the loop and sense antennas summed together to a receiver cannot produce an error output is that we have lost the phase relationship between electric and magnetic fields. Another way of looking at it, we have lost the sign of the component vectors.

If electric and magnetic fields are processed so the phase relationship is not lost, an error signal is produced with a sign. The error signal is amplified to drive a motor and turn the loop antenna or goniometer. One method is to process loop and sense signals with two receivers. Unless the receivers are identical, however, there is a high probability they will introduce two different phase shifts. To prevent this, loop and sense signals are processed through the same receiver.

This is done by "tagging" the two antenna signals so they may be combined, fed to the receiver and retrieved without mutually interfering. This is the same requirement for multiplexing, which is applying more than one information signal in the same range of frequencies.

One method is quadrature multiplexing, where two signals occupy the same spectrum. This is important for identical phase shift from loop and sense antennas. It's done by modulating two carriers in "quadrature." At the input of the receiver there are three signals; two loop and one sense antenna output. Let us modulate the X and Y loops by a low frequency sine and cosine wave. A suitable frequency lies below the audio range, say 45 Hz. Modulation will be multiplexing using a balanced modulator, which produces a double sideband suppressed carrier (DSBSC) output.

If the two outputs are fed to a radio receiver, by virtue of their quadrature modulation, they can be demodulated independently. This requires that signals be demodulated and multiplied by the sine and cosine functions which generated the DSBSC signal. One problem in suppressed carrier is that the carrier must be reinserted to demodulate the signal. We cannot use the carrier from either loop because one could be in a null, meaning there is no carrier. Further, the polarity of the loop depends on its orientation. The source of a constant carrier is the sense antenna, whose voltage without modulation is summed with the modulated loop signals and fed to the receiver

To the receiver, the signal appears as a carrier and sidebands at plus or minus 45 Hz from the carrier frequency. There are two sets of sidebands, in quadrature, that occupy the same spectrum or multiplexed on the same carrier. Referring to Fig. 2.3, loop signals are multiplied by a sine and cosine function, I and Q signals, with a carrier frequency of 45 Hz. The loop signal is double side-band, suppressed carrier modulated, while the sense antenna signal is summed without modulation.

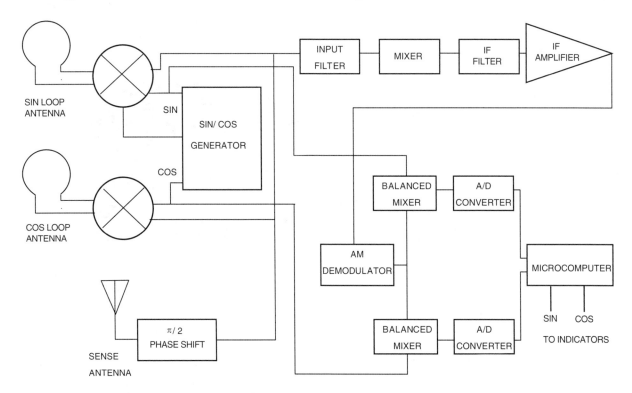

Figure 2.3 All-electronic Automatic Direction Finder (ADF)

Because a constant amplitude carrier is present from the sense antenna, when the signal from the sense antenna is added to the two double sideband signals, the result is an amplitude modulated signal. Information from the two loops is present in the sidebands, including the sign of the amplitude. A conventional AM detector in the receiver demodulates both sidebands. After detection, the result is the sum of a sine and cosine function. The frequency of the sine and cosine function is 45 Hz, and they are phase coherent with the original modulating signals. The amplitudes of the two functions are proportional to the amplitude of the loop and sense antenna; including the sign, which can be positive or negative. We now have what we need; two signals proportional to the magnitude of the magnetic field vector, including the sign.

To retrieve the amplitude of the two 45 Hz quadrature signals at the AM detector, the output is multiplied by the same functions which modulate signals at the antenna outputs. After multiplication, the result is filtered, or integrated, resulting in a DC level proportional to the amplitude of the loop and sense antennas, including the sign.

The DC level of a conventional AM detector is proportional to the carrier, which was the sense antenna input. This is used for AGC (automatic gain control), since the sense antenna output is not a function of loop position. Once AGC is employed in the receiver, the maximum output from the loop is the same, regardless of received signal amplitude.

With the magnitude of X and Y components of the magnetic field, including polarity, we can generate a vector and create movement in an indicator, or drive an electronic display or autopilot.

There are variants of quadrature multiplexing, including a motorized goniometer, which follows the same fundamentals. Newer direction finders, however, eliminate the fragile and expensive goniometer with techniques just described.

Our direction finder is now fully automatic; the indicator points to the NDB station without manual adjustments. It's called a pointing type ADF because X and Y components of a vector provide an output which drives an indicator that points to the station. The X and Y components are valuable for an electronic display, where X and Y are digitized for the display computer. Another ADF, called the "servo type", requires a mechanical component, either a rotating directional antenna or goniometer.

We have seen the progression of DF from manual operation with a large antenna to a small, unobtrusive loop, to an ADF with a goniometer which removed moving parts from the outside of the aircraft. Finally, there is ADF which can drive an electronic display, all without moving parts.

2.3.1 Local Oscillator

The ADF local oscillator is the first opportunity to discuss the large number of frequencies needed by aircraft receivers and transmitters. In ADF, the range from 200-1999 kHz in 1 kHz increments requires 1800 frequencies. Early receivers had local oscillators with a mechanical capacitor connected to a dial. Accuracy was poor, making it difficult for the pilot to find the NDB. Generating many frequencies with high accuracy is now achieved with a frequency synthesizer.

The ADF local oscillator is a phase locked loop (PLL) synthesizer, providing a resolution of 1 kHz. With few exceptions, the frequency synthesizer is a single-loop PLL, an all-in-one single chip synthesizer. In an up-converting ADF receiver, there is no bandswitching and, consequently, the PLL is single-loop with a narrow frequency range. In older receivers with a low IF (intermediate frequency), such as 140 kHz, the receiver is divided into bands as shown in Table 2.1. The bands were not evident from frequency setting switches and bandswitching occurred internally.

Received Frequency	Local Oscillator
200 kHz – 399 kHz	340 kHz – 539 kHz
400 kHz – 799 kHz	540 kHz – 939 kHz
800 kHz – 1.699 MHz	940 kHz – 1.839 MHz

Table 2.1 ADF bands and local oscillator frequencies

It is difficult to design a VCO (voltage controlled oscillator) for a frequency range of more than an octave (two to one). The term "octave" is borrowed from music, where it also means a two to one frequency ratio. In this example, by dividing frequency bands into octaves, such as the two lower frequency bands, local oscillator range is less than an octave. This is true for high side injection, which is the only way to handle the local oscillator for ADF. High side injection refers to the local oscillator frequency being above the received frequency by the intermediate frequency. The highest frequency band is more than an octave, but the local oscillator is less than an octave.

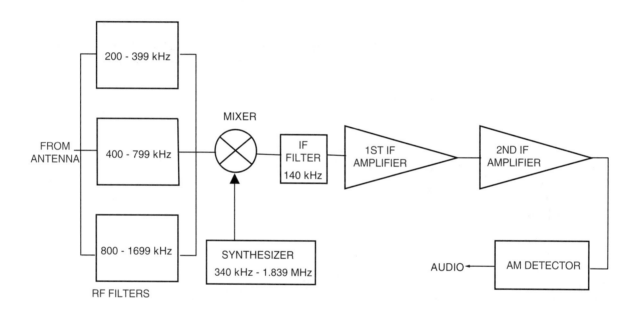

Figure 2.4 Direction finding receiver

This band division is a holdover from when ADF receivers were mechanically tuned. Even though the old variable capacitors covered more than an octave, it was good policy to limit them to an octave. Design problems appeared when oscillator range extended much beyond that. When ADF receivers were first synthesized, receivers were simply fitted with a frequency synthesizer and a varactor-tuned front end.

The synthesizer for the ADF receiver with band arrangements shown in the table requires three VCOs to prevent the tuning range of any one from exceeding an octave. The varactor-tuned RF filter has the same restrictions. The filter was divided into three units for the same reason. In this example, the highest band is slightly more than an octave. Even with this band division, varactors in an early synthesized ADF were supplied as a matched set. If one varactor needed replacement, all diodes in that band were replaced with a matched set. In spite of the problems, early synthesized ADFs performed well and many were produced. Although they are decreasing, there is still a large population of bandswitching ADF's in service.

Later-generation ADF uses up converting, where the IF is higher than the highest input frequency. For ADF, an IF higher than 1.7 MHz should suffice. However, if we chose an IF significantly above the highest input frequency, we could reduce the tuning range of the synthesizer's VCO significantly and simplify the RF filter. The image range, which is removed by the RF filter, is above the highest input frequency. As an example, consider an IF of 5.005 MHz. For an ADF with a frequency range of 200 kHz to 1.699 MHz, the local oscillator spans 5.205-6.704 MHz. Image frequency range is from 10.21-11.709 MHz. This is easily separated from the desired RF range of 200-1699 kHz with a low pass filter. This filter does not need to track the operating frequency. Figure 2.5 shows an ADF using the up converting technique.

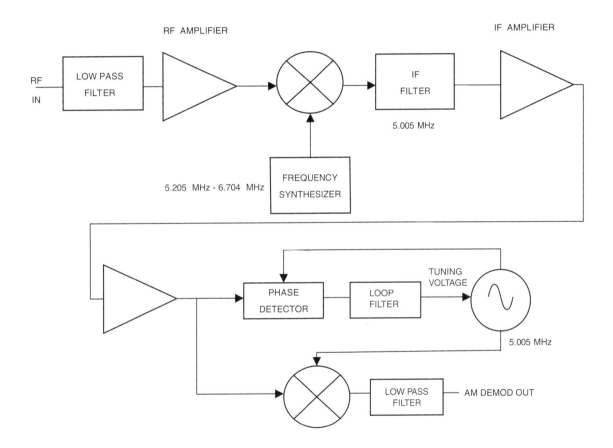

Figure 2.5 Example of up converting ADF receiver using a coherent detector

A significant improvement is the coherent detector. The usual AM detector is a diode which rectifies the AM envelope at the IF output amplifier. When signal level is low, diode detectors distort because a diode is non-linear. Since ADF requires only a carrier to provide the ADF function, it can operate at very weak signals. The coherent detector achieves that function with a phase locked loop which locks on to the carrier component of the IF signal.

The phase locked loop can coast; that is, provide a signal that is phase coherent with the carrier, even when the carrier is temporarily lost. If the time constant of the phase locked loop is a few seconds, the loop continues to provide a clean reference signal for the detector, even when the carrier is extremely noisy or lost. When the PLL time constant is very long, it could take seconds to achieve lock when a new frequency is selected. Therefore, in receivers using a coherent detector, there are two loop time constants; short, when the frequency of the receiver is changed and long when the receiver locks on to a signal.

2.3.2 BFO

In some countries (mainly outside the U.S.), interrupting the carrier to form dots and dashes transmits the Morse code identifier of an NDB station. This is on/off keying, OOK, and was the earliest modulation for radio transmission. For an operator to hear dots and dashes formed this way, a circuit called a beat frequency oscillator, or BFO, is included in the receiver. When two signals are present in an AM detector, non-linearity generates a third signal called a beat. When two signals are CW (continuous wave), or just sine functions, the beat is also a sine function. When the beat is in the audio range it is heard as a tone. Introducing a CW signal in the IF that is 1 kHz above or below the IF frequency results in an audible beat at 1 kHz. When the carrier is removed, the beat disappears. A tone, therefore, makes on-off keying audible as Morse code characters.

A beat frequency oscillator is the classic method of producing an audible tone. There are alternate methods which involve modulating the AGC voltage or using carrier strength to key an audio oscillator. NDB stations in the U.S. and many other countries now emit MCW, or modulated CW. An audio tone is modulated onto the carrier at the transmitting station. This audio tone is detected in the receiver (without a BFO), making it easier for the pilot to identify the station.

2.4 Errors in Direction Finding

There are several sources of error in a direction finding receiver. For the same reason electro-magnetic waves propagate along the earth by conductance, they are distorted by the metal of the aircraft. The effect is cyclic in that an error on one side of the aircraft is countered by an error of the opposite sense on the other side. It's called "quadrantal" error because it's repeated in different quadrants.

Quadrantal errors can be as much as ten degrees and, in many ADFs, a means of correction is provided. Both mechanical and electrical, as well as combination methods have been developed. The latest ADFs have correction factors stored in a non-volatile memory. They are determined by "swinging" the aircraft. The airplane is placed away from buildings and other objects. The NDB transmitting station should be located sufficiently close to provide a strong signal but far enough to lessen the effects of near fields. This eliminates using an NDB on the same airport.

The aircraft is rotated about a central point while observing the ADF indicator. The heading of the aircraft is determined by the aircraft's magnetic compass. Note that the aircraft compass is also disturbed by magnetic properties of the airframe and same swinging maneuver is required to calibrate a compass.

Errors are entered into the ADF as an adjustment or calibration factor in the receiver's memory. Calibration factors generated in the swinging exercise are valid for any ADF installation in that particular airframe with the antenna mounted in the same location. Swinging is an expensive operation, particularly for a large aircraft, so it is desirable to install all ADFs of a particular type in exactly the same way.

There are errors due, not to equipment or installation, but atmospheric effects. The first is skywave interference. The desired path of ADF signals is by ground wave, but some skywave propagation takes place. This occurs primarily at night and is worse at higher frequencies. It is possible to home in on a standard AM broadcast station in the MF band from 540-1750 kHz and most ADF receivers cover this. A clear-channel broadcast station or strong local station provides reasonable ADF operation during the day. At night, the skywave moves unpredictably and produces interference that can render ADF almost inoperable. The phenomenon is called night effect. Beacon frequencies below the broadcast band from 190- 450 kHz do not suffer as much from the night effect.

Another difficulty with ADF is the change in conductivity of the earth. Most pronounced is the shore effect, which occurs when a signal transitions a coast line. The conductivity of water is much greater than that of the ground, with salt water the most conductive. The signal is deflected from a straight line as the wave travels between land and water.

A final problem is atmospheric noise. It is due to lightning discharging from cloud to cloud and cloud to ground. These signals travel thousands of miles and generate noise in the receiver. Since there is always storm activity somewhere in the world, a background noise level is ever present. The level depends on where the noise is measured and season of the year. When the weather is warm, the likelihood of thunderstorms increases and noise levels rise. Because the Northern Hemisphere has summer when it is winter in the Southern Hemisphere, noise is greater in the north in summer. Heavy thunderstorm activity at the equator generates high atmospheric noise all year. The worst case is when a thunderstorm is close to the aircraft because it can severely disable an ADF receiver.

2.5 Static Dischargers

Not only do clouds build up static and electrically discharge to the environment, so do aircraft. Motion through air builds charges on the airframe until the electric potential becomes so high that it dissipates by ionizing the adjacent air. It produces what amounts to a low-energy lightning discharge. Since the discharge is close to the ADF antenna, it produces a strong noise burst in the receiver.

Generating a static discharge is undesirable for a number of reasons. One is that the aircraft may be charged when fueling and could discharge to the fuel nozzle. Proper refueling, therefore, calls for a grounding wire to the aircraft. Another area concerns charges that build on movable surfaces such as ailerons and rudders. These charges tend to travel to the fuselage through moving joints. If the conduction path has a variable resistance, noise may be generated in the joints. Usually, grounding straps solve it through a steady, low conductance path to the fuselage.

To lower the charge that builds on an aircraft, pointy wires known as static discharge wicks are attached to protruding parts. They increase the electric field at the wires' pointed end. This enhanced electric field discharges at a lower voltage, thus reducing the radio noise level. The installation of wicks and low resistance bonding of moving surfaces can reduce radio noise to levels that are virtually undetectable.

2.6 VOR: VHF Omni-Range

The NDB system has interference and accuracy problems that limit the ADF receiver to en route navigation and limited approach and landing guidance. Another major difficulty is that an ADF needle points to the station, but it is difficult to fly because there is often a crosswind blowing the airplane off the course. Through trial-and-error, the pilot must find a heading that will exactly correct for the wind and keep the airplane on a desired track. It is a difficult exercise of combining compass heading and ADF bearing to intercept and fly the course. The A-N range provided easy-to-fly course information but its low frequency suffered the interference problems of NDB. Another problem of the A-N range was that there were only four courses. If the destination did not coincide with one of the courses, the last part of a journey would have to include another navigation system such as an NDB. A new navigation system was needed to provide a large number of courses that were easy to fly and not affected by the vicissitudes of low frequency propagation.

Such a system was designed and accepted for world use in the late 1940s. Known as VHF omnirange or VOR, it provides a continuous selection of courses around a circle with the VOR ground station at the center. Signals are propagated in the VHF spectrum where there is little electrical interference. VHF frequencies , 108.00-117.950 MHz, are not affected by ground or sky waves and propagate in nearly straight lines. A similar system was developed at about the same time but intended for military use. This was the "tactical navigation" or TACAN system. TACAN uses considerably shorter wavelengths and provides distance information as well as course information. Although a military system, TACAN stations were installed in the United States and open for civilian users. Because of the similarity of the systems ,TACANs and VORs were co located or combined into one ground station. Therefore, the VOR and TACAN both defined the same airway rather than having one airway defined by TACAN and another by VOR. When a VOR and a TACAN are co-located the combined facility is called a VORTAC. Most airways in the United States are defined by VORTACs.

The VOR signal is generated by a rotating directional antenna pattern. Note that the *pattern* rotates, not the antenna. A simple analogy uses light signals instead of radio waves. Imagine the rotating beacon at an airport which flashes white when it lines up with the pilot's eye. When the light moves through magnetic north, it causes a second light to illuminate in *every* direction---so every aircraft within range, regardless of position, sees a marker for magnetic north. Each aircraft position may now be determined by measuring the time between seeing the magnetic-north marker to when a flashing light is observed.. The elapsed time is easily converted to position relative to magnetic north in degrees. We don't know the airplane's *distance* from the VOR, but can draw a straight line to the VOR. This line of position (LOP) is called a radial. In air traffic control, 360 radials, or compass courses, fan out from the VOR station.

To make the rotating light into a navigation aid, consider how the VOR signal propagates. RF energy generated by the rotating pattern is called the *variable* signal because it moves around the VOR transmitting tower in a directional emission pattern. The variable signal increases and decreases in amplitude 30 times per second. At the aircraft receiver, it appears 30% amplitude modulated with a sine wave at a frequency of 30 Hz.

Example:

An antenna pattern shows relative signal level, in decibels, as a polar plot. The pattern can be viewed as if the antenna were rotated while a meter in a fixed location measures relative signal strength in decibels. To determine the antenna pattern we find a function that provides a 30% amplitude modulated carrier. That function is

$$G(\theta) = [1+0.3sin(\theta)]$$

Where G(θ) is the antenna gain for an angle θ.

Exercise:

Using MatLab, MathCad, Maple or similar PC-based software, make a polar plot of antenna gain for the VOR rotating antenna.

A reference for magnetic north is required and, as in the light beam example, that signal is transmitted omnidirectionally. Thus far there is an amplitude-modulated carrier at 30 Hz. Rather than measuring time delay, the VOR receiver measures phase. The reference signal must be modulated with a sine wave to make a phase angle measurement. Since the carrier already contains 30 Hz modulation to apply the reference, we cannot further modulate the carrier with 30 Hz ; the two 30 Hz signals would interfere. But a second 30 Hz signal can be placed on another signal called a *subcarrier* and used to modulate the VOR transmitter. The reference signal should not rotate with the variable; it needs to be transmitted omnidirectionally.

The definition of the reference 30 Hz is that it will be exactly in phase with the variable signal when received at a bearing of zero degrees from the VOR transmitter relative to *magnetic* north. VOR radials, therefore, are oriented to local magnetic north.

To prevent 30 Hz modulation on the reference signal from interfering with the variable, a 9960 Hz subcarrier is frequency-modulated with a 30 Hz sine function. The peak deviation of the 9960 Hz subcarrier is 480 Hz and, since the reference is a 30 Hz sine wave, the modulation index is 16. Figure 2.6 shows the spectrum of the carrier with 30 Hz sidebands generated from amplitude modulation produced by the rotating antenna. The second spectrum shows the same carrier frequency in part, except modulated with suppressed carrier double sideband with the 9960 Hz reference signal.

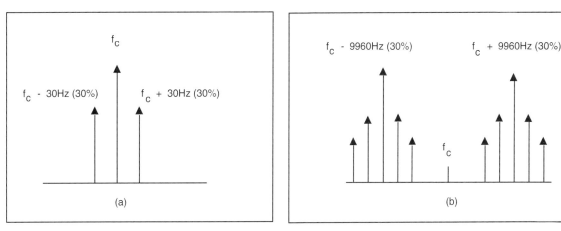

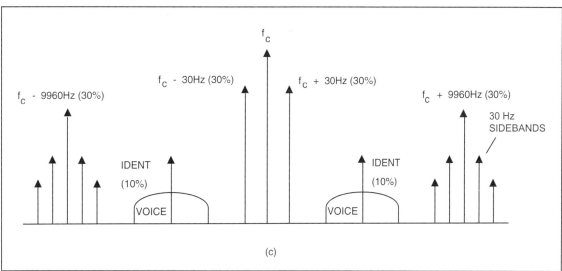

Figure 2.6 Generation of a VOR signal spectrum

If the two signals are radiated so they add in space, the signal arriving at the VOR receiver would be shown in Fig 2.6(c) which is the sum of Fig. 2.6 (a) and (b). Also, voice and a Morse code identification signal are added to 2.6(c). The result is an AM signal where the variable 30 Hz modulation modulates the carrier at 30%, as well as the 9960 Hz subcarrier.

Every VOR station sends out a Morse code identifier. It consists of a 1020 Hz tone and a three-letter station identifier at least every 20 seconds. It is also possible to include voice modulation for other communications. Many VORs use voice to help pilots who do not know Morse code. If only the 1020 Hz Morse code identifies the station, modulation can be as high as 30%. If the 1020 tone and voice are used, the sum of the two may not cause more than 90% peak modulation. Since the 9960 subcarrier and 30 Hz variable represent 60% modulation, the combined voice and 1020 Hz identifier may not exceed 30%.

2.6.1 VOR Indicator

Consisting of three parts, the VOR indicator is shown in Fig. 2.7. The first is the course deviation indicator, or CDI. The second, which indicates the pilot-selected course, is the OBS, or omnibearing selector. Finally, there are flags for TO/FROM and navigation (which shows whether a signal is being received). Often, the TO/FROM and NAV flags are combined into one indicator.

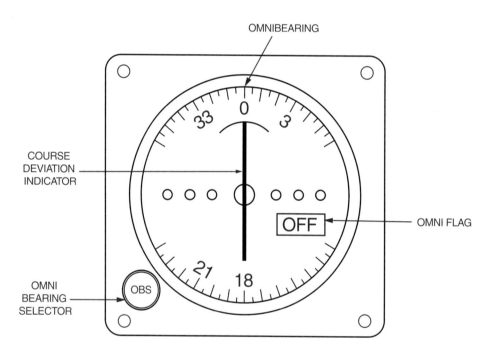

Figure 2.7 VOR indicator

VOR may be used to fly inbound or outbound, meaning towards or away from the VOR ground station on a selected radial. It is far simpler for the pilot to use than an ADF. The pointer is arranged to indicate in the direction of the desired course. As an example, if the course deviation indicator (CDI) points to the left, a correction to the left returns the airplane to the course. The VOR receiver does not employ a directional antenna, nor does it need to know the present heading of the aircraft. A pilot may make a tight 360-degree turn, and the signal to the VOR receiver will not change or cause movement in the CDI. Therefore, if an aircraft is flying left of course while moving toward a VOR station, the maneuver to regain the course is fly to the right. If the aircraft reverses course, the maneuver is to fly to the left. Since the VOR receiver has no knowledge of the aircraft heading some other method is needed to insure that the CDI points in the proper direction.

VOR radials are described by an angular dimension and "TO" or "FROM". Assume we are flying due north and there is a VOR station ahead, as shown in Fig 2.8. Since we are flying due north, the compass heading is 0 degrees plus or minus a wind correction angle. Because we intend to fly north, the OBS is set to 0 degrees. Since the VOR is ahead, we are heading "TO" the station. The VOR indicator shows the selected course, 0 degrees, the course deviation and that we are going "TO" the station.

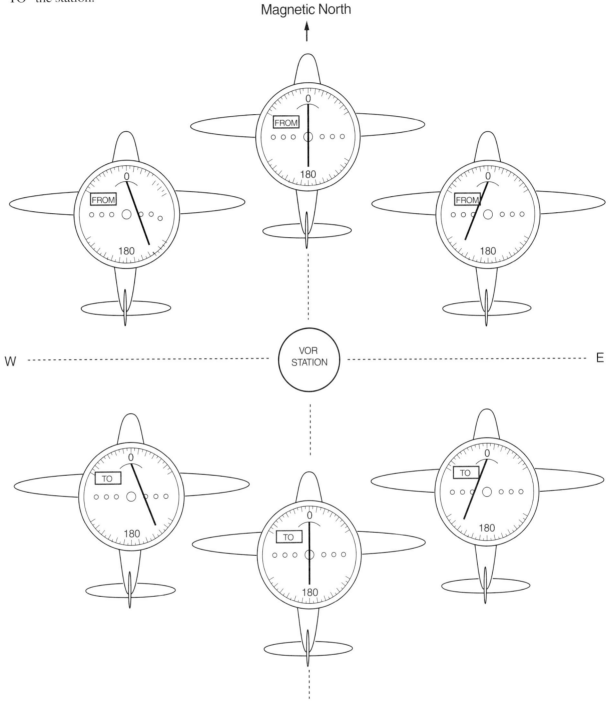

Figure 2.8 VOR indicator for locations around the VOR station

When the airplane flies over the VOR station, the TO/FROM indicator changes to FROM, now that the VOR station is behind us. The rules of flying a VOR are: set the OBS (omnibearing selector) to the desired course, and the CDI and TO/FROM indicators will show the correct indications. As previously mentioned, the magnetic heading of the airplane and the OBS will not necessarily be the same but differ by the crab angle. Remember that the OBS sets the course, while the compass shows the heading of the airplane.

A band of frequencies from 108.000-117.950 MHz is assigned worldwide for VOR stations. This is shared with the instrument landing system (ILS) that operates on frequencies that are MHz plus an odd number of 100 kHz and MHz plus an odd number of 100 kHz plus 50 kHz below 112 MHz. The total for the landing system is 40 frequencies, while the remainder of the 200 channels is for VOR. The frequencies 108.000 and 108.050 are for VOR test stations and not for navigation.

2.6.2 Using the VOR

The VOR system in the U.S. consists of about 1000 stations. Each station has a name and a unique three-letter identifier. When possible, the name of the VOR reflects its location. An example is the VOR at New York's John F. Kennedy airport. Its three-letter identifier is JFK. Across the Hudson River is the on-field Teterboro VOR with the three-letter identifier TEB. VOR stations are the foundation of a system of airways equivalent to highways for automobiles. Airways are numbered with the letter V followed by several digits. As an example V3 is an airway based on a VOR located in Ormond Beach, Florida, near Daytona Beach. This airway is called "Victor Three" using the international phonetic for the letter V, which refers to a VOR-based airway.

The simplest airway is a straight line that connects two VORs. Others may have bends but begin and end at a VOR. As in a highway system, there are intersections to serve as reference points for flight planning and navigation. Above 18,000 feet, where traffic is mostly airline and military , airways are designated by the letter J, for jet routes. The legs are longer and higher power VORs accommodate high-performance aircraft up to 45,000 feet. These VORs, classified "H" for high altitude, may also be used below 18,000 feet.

To understand how the VOR system and airways are used in navigation, let us take a trip from Jacksonville International to Tampa International Airport, two airports in Florida. Figure 2.9 shows the trip as it would appear on a sectional aeronautical chart. Like the VORs, airports have three character identifiers. VOR identifiers are only letters while airports may also have numbers. Jacksonville is JAX and Tampa is TPA.

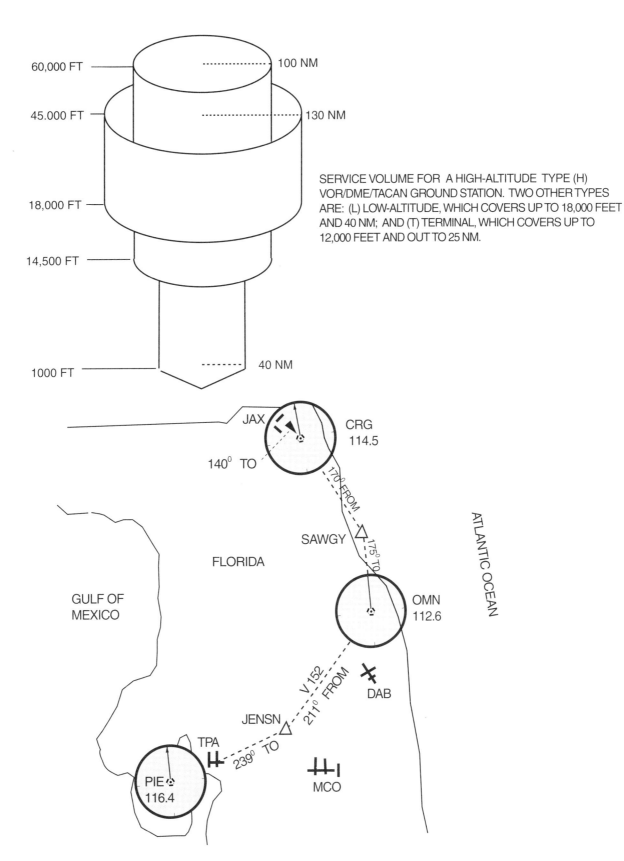

60,000 FT .... 100 NM

45.000 FT .... 130 NM

SERVICE VOLUME FOR A HIGH-ALTITUDE TYPE (H) VOR/DME/TACAN GROUND STATION. TWO OTHER TYPES ARE: (L) LOW-ALTITUDE, WHICH COVERS UP TO 18,000 FEET AND 40 NM; AND (T) TERMINAL, WHICH COVERS UP TO 12,000 FEET AND OUT TO 25 NM.

18,000 FT

14,500 FT

1000 FT .... 40 NM

JAX

CRG
114.5

140° TO

170° FROM

SAWGY

175° TO

FLORIDA

OMN
112.6

GULF OF
MEXICO

ATLANTIC OCEAN

V 152

211° FROM

DAB

JENSN

239° TO

TPA

PIE
116.4

MCO

Fig. 2.9 Trip from Jacksonville Florida to Tampa Florida on an aeronautical chart

When departing JAX, all aircraft should maintain runway heading and intersect the Craig VORTAC, CRG, 140 degree, TO, radial. CRG is south of the airport and the airport is on the CRG 319 degree FROM radial, which corresponds with the 139 degree TO radial. Assume that ILS runway 7 is used for departure. This means we are initially headed east at 70 degrees. Soon after we lift off and gain altitude to receive the CRG VOR we should intercept the CRG 140 degree TO radial. The VOR receiver is set to a frequency of 114.5 MHz and the OBS to 140 degrees. As we lift off and head east, the VOR CDI will swing to the right and continue further in that direction as long as we are heading east. We listen to the Morse code identifier, "ident", which is verified to be the letters CRG. Once clear of the airport traffic pattern, we turn to the right on a southerly course. We select an exact 180 degree southerly course which implies we will intercept the 140 degree radial to CRG at a 40 degree angle. As the CDI begins to approach center we change heading to 140 degrees just as the CDI centers.

We are instructed by JAX tower to take the SAWGY departure, which is one of the published SIDs, standard instrument departures. This involves flying the 140 degree radial from CRG, overfly CRG and continue to the SAWGY intersection. We use a second VOR receiver tuned to the Ormond Beach, OMN, VORTAC at 112.6 MHz. As always, we listen for the ident from OMN to be certain the signal is clear and the letters are OMN.

We continue on a heading of about 140 degrees and make corrections as necessary to keep the CDI centered. When we reach the CRG VORTAC, the TO/FROM indicator begins to flutter and changes to FROM, indicating we have flown over the VORTAC. Visibility is good and we can see the distinctive shape of the VORTAC as we pass over.

The intersection is where the 140 degree FROM radial of CRG intersects with the 175 degree TO radial of OMN. As we approach the intersection, the CDI for the OMN VOR will move from the left to center. At the point when both CDIs are centered, we are at the intersection. Rather than wait until the two CDIs are centered, we begin our change of heading to 175 degrees by turning to the right. Since this takes us off the 140 degree radial from CRG, the CDI for the receiver tuned to CRG begins to move to the left, soon we are on the 175 degree TO radial to OMN.

Intersection names are pronounceable words that are five letters and, if possible, have something to do with the local area. The SAWGY intersection is near St. Augustine Florida. Perhaps we could shorten Saint Augustine to Saint Augie then put the two together to get Saugie, which is six letters. If we change the spelling to Sawgy it would be pronounced the same but with only 5 letters, which qualifies it as an intersection name. It might sound silly, but many a pilot will remember that SAWGY is near St. Augustine Florida.

We continue inbound to OMN on the 175 degree TO radial. As we progress, we change our heading a bit to the east to 170 degrees because of a wind from the ocean. This gives us a 5 degree crab angle. It is our intention to take the victor airway, V-152, which is based on the 211 degree FROM radial out of OMN.

As we approach the VOR station, the TO/FROM indicator begins to flutter a bit and we know we are near OMN. As with the CRG VORTAC, the station is visible ahead of us. We change the OBS to 211 degrees and begin a turn to the right. As we continue, the fluttering stops, the TO/FROM changes to FROM and the CDI indicates we are right of course. We are not at a heading of 211 degrees yet and as we continue, the CDI begins to approach center. We time our turn so that as the CDI reaches center, the heading has just reached 211 degrees. We are heading outbound from OMN on V-152.

Not all victor airways are straight lines and V 152 is an example of an airway with a bend. We locate the bend by tuning the VOR receiver, that was originally tuned to CRG when we departed JAX to the St. Petersburg VORTAC, PIE at 116.4 MHz. We set the OBS to 239 degrees. The bend in V152 occurs where the 239-degree TO radial of PIE intersects with the 211-degree FROM radial of OMN.

Even though the bend occurs at an intersection of two radials from two VORs, it may not be an intersection and have no name. This is called a "cross over point" or COP when navigation along the victor airway is changed from one VOR to another. Even victor airways that do not bend have COPs due to the need to replace a weak VOR signal with a stronger signal. In this example the COP is the intersection JENSN.

Since we are more than 100 NM from PIE when we pass OMN, there will not be a usable signal from PIE. This is indicated by the "nav" flag, which is a red indicator that now says "OFF". If we were to listen to the ident we would only hear noise. Well before we reach the COP the signal from PIE is strong, the nav flag has disappeared and the CDI is pointing to the left. Before we may use the PIE VORTAC we must listen to the ident, as done with the other two VORTACs. Since our 211 degree course is taking us to the 239 degree course required to arrive at Tampa, the CDI slowly becomes centered, whereupon we turn more to the right to a heading of 239 degrees and keep the CDI centered.

The PIE VORTAC is not located at Tampa International but at a nearby, smaller airport. However, the 211 degree radial to PIE passes directly over Tampa International, which is no accident. Since we are heading directly to Tampa we contact Tampa via radio when we are closer and receive landing instructions. We may be told to make a standard approach called the standard terminal arrival, or STAR, the counterpart to a SID.

This hypothetical trip demonstrated the use of the VOR, TO and FROM radials, the TO/FROM indicator, the nav flag, and the audio ident. It described the characteristics of victor airways, COPs, SIDs, STARs and intersections.

2.7 Signal Integrity

An important part of radio navigation is a signal integrity indicator. Radio signals should not be corrupted by interference, a flaw in the ground station or airborne receiver. Radio navigation ground stations are constantly monitored to insure that they remain within the normal range of operation.

In the case of VOR, transmitter voltages and currents are monitored continuously to assure a usable signal to the antenna. Since the antenna is also important, radiated signals are also monitored. Antennas mounted on poles near the VOR station feed monitoring receivers to insure that VOR bearing and other components of the signal are present. There are two monitor types; close in they are called near field monitors, at greater distances they are far field monitors. Should any signal move out of normal limits, the VOR is taken off the air to prevent aircraft from navigating with misleading signals. The monitors are also connected to a computer modem to alert a local FAA office or control tower that the station is off the air.

Newer VOR stations allow a dial-up maintenance inquiry. An autoanswer modem provides a computer with a variety of parameters and allows limited adjustments. It reduces the need to send a technician to the site for maintenance.

Referring to the previous example of a VOR indicator as shown in Fig. 2.6., the indicator is shown with an OBS, a compass card that indicates the selected OBS, a TO/FROM indicator and a Nav Flag to indicate a reliable signal.

2.8 Errors in VOR Navigation

There are several sources of navigation error. One is flight technical error, or FTE. This is generally a fault of the aircrew during such tasks as keeping the CDI centered or setting the OBS to the correct course. Since humans are not perfect, there is always some level of FTE. Effective crew training, and indicators and controls that are easily read and adjusted reduce FTE.

There can be errors at the VOR transmitting station. Like any electrical/mechanical system, adjustment and alignment are needed to keep signals accurate. Ground station errors can be minimized by timely calibration procedures. Near and far field monitors also insure continuous calibration.

Another source of error is in the propagation of signals from the VOR station. The biggest problem with any radio navigation system is multipath propagation, or simply "multipath". You were introduced to multipath earlier, only it was not called that in the discussion of sky wave interference to an NDB station. This form of multipath occurs when two waves arrive at the receiver from different paths; via groundwave and ionosphere.

Consider an example of how multipath can distort a VOR signal. Assume that an airport has an on-field VOR, which is common, and a large hangar. Referring to Fig 2.10, a signal is received directly from the VOR station, which is the desired path. Also, a signal is received from the VOR after a reflection off the hangar. Two waves, therefore, are received at the aircraft; one direct, the other by reflection. The electric fields add at the receiver. Since one path is longer, there is a phase shift due to the time difference. The resulting signals increase or decrease, depending on the time difference. Since the aircraft is moving, the phase angle continuously changes.

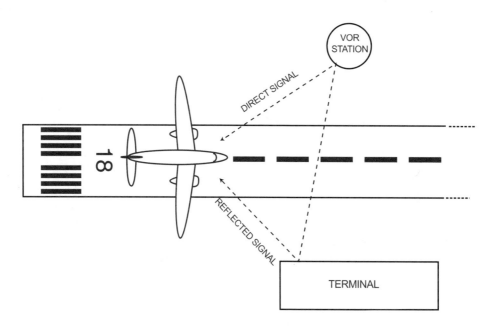

Figure 2.10 Multipath signal propagation from an on-field VOR station

The worst situation occurs when the directional antenna pattern is pointed away from the aircraft and towards the reflector. This results in the weakest desired path signal and the strongest undesired path signal. When the two signals add, the result is the greatest deviation from the normal, multipath-free, signal. The more directional the antenna, the worse the multipath distortion.

There are locations where it is nearly impossible to find a suitable site for a VOR ground station that would not incur serious multipath problems. For example, large metropolitan areas such as New York and Boston are susceptible to reflections from buildings. Mountainous regions also suffer from multipath distortion. For VOR signals, the reflecting objects do not need to be close to the VOR transmitter. When reflectors are very large such as mountains, the VOR station can be 50 miles or more from the reflector and suffer beam distortion.

When the reflector is close to the VOR station, an alternate location can used. This refers to a siting problem and an alternate site is a reasonable solution. When the reflector is a large mountain, other than moving the VOR by tens of miles, there may be no solution. What must be done in these situations is accept multipath distortion and be sure its effects do not compromise safety. Areas where VOR signals are seriously corrupted are marked on aeronautical charts to prevent aircraft from using them. There are usually alternate navigation signals when a VOR is seriously corrupted.

There are situations where a VOR station cannot be easily moved to a location that has less multipath and still provide navigation guidance. This is particularly true of on-field VORs at large airports in big cities. The on-field VOR is expected to provide accurate navigation to the airport and guidance for visual landings. A special VOR ground station that reduces, but not eliminates, multipath problems is used in airports with siting problems.

2.9 Doppler VOR

This improved station is Doppler VOR, or DVOR, which derives its name from the Doppler shift for generating the VOR signal. A highly directional antenna can reduce multipath distortion by directing the signal away from reflecting objects. A non-directional antenna is moderately immune to multipath because there is no situation where the antenna is pointed towards the reflector and away from the receiver. The VOR antenna pattern is mildly directive and it rotates so that it will point away from the receiver and towards a reflector. The DVOR generates VOR signals without directional antennas to reduce multipath interference.

The DVOR station has a fixed omnidirectional antenna and a pair of *moving* omnidirectional antennas, as shown in Fig. 2.11. DVOR signal generation is unique. First, the 9960 Hz subcarrier is now the signal that actually varies as an aircraft traverses the space around the VOR transmitter. The 30 Hz AM modulation is transmitted from an omnidirectional antenna.

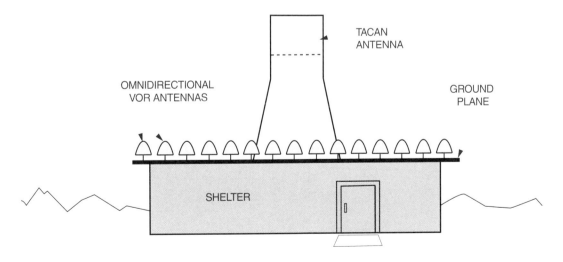

Figure 2.11. The Doppler VOR ground station

The moving antennas rotate along a circular track. Just as the rotating antenna in the conventional VOR does not physically turn, the moving antennas of the DVOR do not actually move. However, to understand how a DVOR works, imagine that the two antennas are rapidly moving along a circular track.

One is driven with a transmitter at a frequency of :

$$F_u = f_c + 9960 \text{ Hz} \tag{2.1}$$

where f_c is the VOR's carrier frequency.

Consider what happens with an aircraft at a significant distance. As the antenna moves *towards* the aircraft, there is an increase in frequency received from the VOR antenna due to the Doppler shift. Similarly, for the antenna moving *away* from the receiving aircraft, there is a reduction in the frequency of the received signal.

The geometry of the doppler shift situation is shown in Fig 2.12. Assume the distance from the aircraft is such that angle f is small. Therefore, the velocity of the moving antenna as perceived at the aircraft is simply the x component of the velocity, which is:

$$V_x = V \sin \theta \tag{2.2}$$

Where V_x is the x component of the velocity in the direction of the aircraft, V is the tangential velocity of the moving antenna and the θ is the angle around the circle measured from the x axis. The amount of doppler shift for sources moving at velocities well below the speed of light is:

$$\Delta f = V_x/\lambda = V_x F_U/c = (VF_U/c) \sin \theta \tag{2.3}$$

Where Δf is the frequency shift, λ is the wavelength of the transmitted frequency, and c is the speed of light.

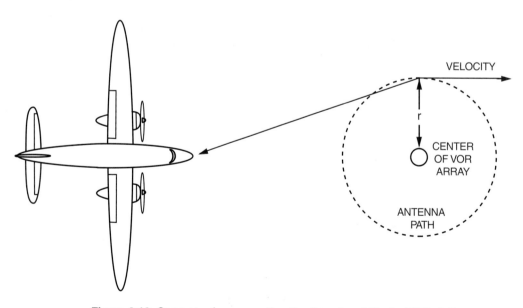

Figure 2.12 Geometry for generating the Doppler shift of a VOR station

From equation 2.3 we see the signal received at the aircraft is frequency modulated with a sine function. If the sine function has a period of $1/30^{th}$ second then the frequency of the modulation is 30 Hz. Assume there are two moving antennas diametrically opposed. The second antenna is fed from an unmodulated source at a frequency of :

$$F_L = f_c - 9960 \text{ Hz} \qquad (2.4)$$

The Doppler shift received from this antenna is the same sine modulation with the same peak frequency deviation except it is 180 degrees out of phase with the other antenna. That is, when one antenna is at the maximum negative peak, the other antenna is at the maximum positive peak. The Doppler shift for the second antenna is

$$\Delta f = V_x/\lambda = V_x F_L/c = (VF_L/c) \sin(\theta + \pi) = -(VF_L/c) \sin(\theta) \qquad (2.5)$$

The airborne VOR receives signals from both moving antennas and the fixed, omnidirectional antenna. The received signal is 30% amplitude modulated with a 30 Hz sine wave at the carrier frequency. There is also an upper sideband at the carrier frequency plus 9960 Hz that is frequency modulated due to the Doppler shift and a lower sideband that is frequency modulated, out of phase, with the upper sideband with the same sine function. The result is the equivalent of a VOR signal received from a conventional VOR station.

Although the signal appears to be the same as that of a conventional VOR, the phase angle of the DVOR that changes as the aircraft moves around the VOR transmitter is not the 30 Hz "variable" signal but the "reference" signal. If we had a precise clock that could provide a phase reference signal we could see this. However, in a VOR receiver we compare the phase of the two signals and it does not matter which one changed phase. It is the phase difference between the two components.

To reiterate, the DVOR produces a signal without directional antennas, but behaves exactly as a conventional VOR signal when received in an aircraft.

To finish the discussion of the DVOR, determine the radius of the track around which the antenna moves. The antenna must make 30 complete passes of the circular track each second. If the radius of the track is R, then the tangential velocity, V, is:

$$V = 60\pi R \qquad (2.6)$$

The peak frequency deviation is 480 Hz according to ICAO annex 10. The peak frequency deviation occurs when the angle, θ is $\pi/2$, when $\sin(\theta) = 1$. Therefore, peak frequency deviation is:

$$\Delta f = (Vf_c/c) = 480 = 60\pi Rf_c/c \qquad (2.7)$$

Here the carrier frequency f_c is used. The actual frequencies are FU and F_L which are slightly different than f_c. Solving for R yields

$$R = (8 \text{ c}) / \pi f_c \qquad (2.8)$$

To find a representative value calculate the actual dimension of R for the mid band frequency of $(108 + 118)/2$ MHz = 113 MHz

$$R = (8 \text{ c})/\pi * 113E6 = 6.76 \text{ meters} \qquad (2.9)$$

Exercise: It is not desirable that each DVOR station be custom sized at the operating frequency for which it will be used. Assume that all VOR stations will be made to the same dimensions;

a radius of 6.76 meters. Determine the errors that would be introduced using this compromise and determine if the design would meet requirements of ICAO Annex 10.

A DVOR station does not have a pair of moving antennas. The forces to rotate two counter-balanced arms, each containing an antenna would be so great the system would be prohibitively expensive, dangerous and unreliable. The antennas are electronically moved.

The center of a DVOR ground station is a horizontally polarized omnidirectional antenna that transmits the carrier with 30% of 30 Hz amplitude modulation. In addition, the Morse code ident and any voice modulation is applied to this transmitter. The carrier power of a VOR station is on the order of 100 watts.

Surrounding the central horizontal omnidirectional antenna is a ring of 56 omnidirectional antennas. These antennas are driven two at a time and switched from one antenna to another to create the moving antenna. One antenna is driven with a CW source at a frequency of the carrier plus 9960 Hz and another at the carrier frequency minus 9960 Hz. These two frequencies must be precise and are generated by heterodyning a 9960 Hz sine function with an oscillator at an intermediate frequency, or IF. As in Fig 2.13, two image rejection mixers generate an upper and lower sideband. The sidebands are filtered, amplified and provided as carrier sources for the moving antennas.

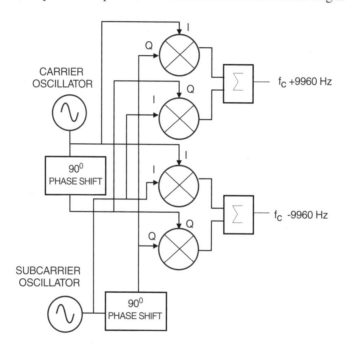

Figure 2.13 Method for generating signals for the Doppler VOR

The upper and lower 9960 sidebands are fed to the omnidirectional antennas at a power of 1/36th of the carrier, which is about 2.8 watts for each frequency for a nominal 100 watt carrier power. The two sidebands are switched from one antenna to the adjacent antenna, completing the entire ring of antennas in 1/30th of a second.

The antennas are switched at a rate of 1680 Hz. The power is switched from one antenna to the next, not with a sudden change but gradually to prevent the switching from causing excessive, spurious sidebands of the switching frequency. Since the signals provided to the switched antennas are the carrier frequency plus or minus the 9960 subcarrier, spurious sidebands are at 9960+1680 Hz and 9960 – 1680 Hz or 11640 Hz and 8280 Hz. If spurious sidebands are not minimized there is a possibility that some navigation receivers will be affected. Also, the sidebands increase the spectrum occupied by the DVOR station.

2.10 VOR Ground Station

The conventional VOR ground station is an interesting study. As mentioned, the conventional VOR uses a rotating antenna pattern at a rate of 30 per second. The physical rotation of a directional antenna at 1800 revolutions per minute, 30 revolutions per second, is not practical. The rate of 1800 RPM is a common motor speed, but rotating something as large as a 108 MHz gain antenna is not reasonable.

It may seem odd that the Doppler VOR ground station is described before the conventional VOR ground station. As it happens, it is easier to understand Doppler VOR than the conventional ground station. For conventional VOR signal generation there are a number of methods that have been used over the long history of VOR. Today only two methods are used. The least common of the two is the use of crossed dipoles and a conventional circular loop. Like the Doppler VOR, it is the easier of the two to understand and will be described first to improve the student's understanding of the more common VOR station.

A common dipole has the familiar figure eight radiation pattern where the null is off the end of the antenna. When the dipole is electrically short, the antenna pattern approaches the polar plot of a cosine function. Electrically short means the antenna is shorter than one half wavelength which also means the antenna is not resistive. To provide power to the short antenna the reactive impedance must be matched to the transmitter One method of achieving this is to employ capacitive loading on the end of the antenna which is adding flat plates to the antenna ends.

In this scheme the crossed dipoles are fed with 30 Hz sidebands only or SBO, while the loop antenna is fed with the carrier and the 9960 Hz subcarrier and 1020 Hz sidebands This signal is called the carrier and sidebands or CSB. If voice modulation is used it is applied to the CSB signal.

The antenna pattern for a dipole will approach the following if the antenna is made very small.

$$V(\theta) = V_E \cos(\theta) \tag{2.10}$$

Where $V(\theta)$ is the magnitude of the electric field intensity and V_E is the maximum electric field intensity which is a function of the transmitter power and the distance from the point of measurement and the dipole antenna. The angle θ is measured from the normal of the dipole antenna. This equation represents a short dipole. The shorter the dipole the closer the antenna fits equation 2.10.

Two dipoles are employed separated by 90 degrees such that the antenna pattern for the second antenna is:

$$V(\theta) = V_E \sin(\theta) \tag{2.11}$$

Sine the two antennas are identical the V_E is the same for both antennas.

One antenna is fed with an SBO signal which is a double sideband suppressed carrier signal that can be expressed as:

$$E_1 = E_0 \cos(60 \pi t) \cos(2 \pi f_c t) \tag{2.12}$$

39

The second antenna is fed with a similar signal except the modulation is in quadrature to the first and can be expressed as:

$$E_Q = E_0 \sin(60\pi t) \cos(2\pi f_c t) \qquad (2.13)$$

Where E_I and E_Q are the in phase and quadrature electric field intensities at a constant radius from the antennas and f_c is the RF carrier frequency.

Realizing the in phase and quadrature antennas are physically offset by 90 degrees the signal in space at a distance R from the two dipoles is given by

$$E(t, \theta, R) = [E_0 \cos(2\pi f_c t)/R][\sin(60\pi t)\cos(\theta) + \cos(60\pi t)$$
$$\sin(\theta)] = [E_0 \cos(2\pi f_c t)/R]\sin(60\pi t + \theta) \qquad (2.14)$$

Equation 2.14 describes a double sideband suppressed carrier signal which is single tone modulated with a 30 Hz signal with a phase angle dependent on where around the antenna array the receiver is positioned. If we add a carrier from an omnidirectional antenna, which means it is the same at all angles of θ, we get the following signal in space:

$$[E_0 \cos(2\pi f_c t)/R][1 + \sin(60\pi t + \theta)] \qquad (2.15)$$

The ICAO requirements for a VOR signal is modulated at 30%. Equation 2.15 represents 100% modulation. The field intensity of the omnidirectional antenna is therefore increased such that equation 2.15 is:

$$[E_0 \cos(2\pi f_c t)/R][1 + 0.3\sin(60\pi t + \theta)] \qquad (2.16)$$

The entire VOR signal includes not only the 30 Hz sidebands but the 9960 Hz reference signal and the 1020 Hz ident signal. These do not vary as a function of θ and are added to the omnidirectional antenna. Thus the entire VOR signal is:

$$E(t, \theta, R) = [E_0 \cos(2\pi f_c t)/R]\{1 + 0.3\sin(60\pi t + \theta) +$$
$$0.3\cos(19920\pi t - 16\cos(60\pi t)) + 0.1\cos(2040\pi t)] \qquad (2.17)$$

To provide the maximum accuracy of VOR signals the ground station must reduce to the greatest extent possible RF energy with vertical polarization. Dipoles have a significant vertical component and, to a smaller extent, loop antennas. An effective way of minimizing the vertical component is to enclose both antennas in a "bird cage". This device is a circular arrangement of half wave resonators that absorb vertically polarized energy.

The crossed dipole VOR ground station is used mainly for portable applications as the antenna array can be made quite small. The circular loop used in the example of the crossed dipole VOR ground station is an inefficient antenna and has some vertical radiation. A much improved omnidirectional radiator of horizontally polarized waves is the Alford loop. The disadvantage of the loop is it is much larger than the circular loop and requires a large ground plane.

Among several types of VOR ground stations a common one uses four omnidirectional radiators. The VOR signal is horizontally polarized. If the signal were vertically polarized, a dipole antenna oriented vertically would produce an omnidirectional pattern in the horizontal plane. In the vertical plane, the antenna pattern is a figure eight with the null directly above the antenna. This is a common antenna and easily visualized. A loop antenna generates the equivalent horizontally polarized omnidirectional antenna. The difficulty in designing a loop antenna is to produce an omnidirectional pattern while still having an efficient antenna. One design that provides both characteristics is the Alford loop.

The common VOR ground station uses four Alford loops arranged in a square. The four corners are oriented northwest, southeast, northeast and southwest. Alford loops are about ¼-wavelength apart and positioned over a large ground plane which launches energy of the array with a slightly upward angle, preventing interaction with nearby structures.

The NW/SE pair of loops are fed a carrier modulated with the ident tone and the 9960 Hz frequency modulated reference. An approximate one-half wavelength delay is introduced between the antennas. The actual delay depends on separation of the antennas. This arrangement results in a figure eight pattern as shown in Fig. 2.14. The same is done with the NE/SW pair, and a second figure eight pattern results. When the two figure eight patterns combine the result is an omnidirectional pattern.

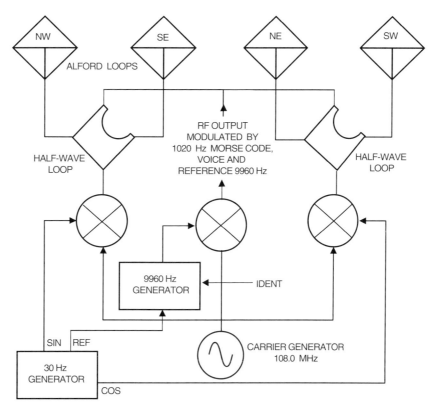

Figure 2.14 Antenna array for conventional VOR

The NW/SE loop pair is also fed with the same carrier but modulated with 30 Hz and in phase. The NE/SW loop pair is fed with a similar signal except the 30 Hz modulation is in quadrature with the NW/SE loop pair. The result is a rotating cardioid antenna pattern, which turns at 30 revolutions per second.

It is interesting to explore how VOR frequencies relate to hardware, particularly when the system was conceived. Many signals were originally generated by electromechanical means. This was true not only of the VOR station but for generating test signals. The basic 30 Hz frequency is tied to the AC line frequency in the U.S. Thirty Hz is 1800 per minute or 1800 RPM, a common motor speed. Some signals for the VOR system were generated with synchronous motors, which required that motor shaft speed be a harmonic of the line frequency. The ident tone frequency is 1020 Hz, not the common ident of 1000 Hz, used for many other purposes. This is because 1020 Hz is exactly 34 times 30 Hz.

The 9960 Hz subcarrier is exactly 332 times 30 Hz, and, of course, the frequency modulation applied to the 9960 Hz subcarrier is exactly the same as the 30 Hz variable. Only the phase angle is different. Therefore, the 30 Hz variable, the 9960 subcarrier, the 30 Hz reference modulation on the subcarrier and the ident tone are all phase locked to the 30 Hz reference. Because of this, VOR test signals and VOR ground station signals could be generated electro-mechanically with a wheel connected to an 1800 RPM synchronous motor.

2.11 VOR Receiver

The VOR receiver is a conventional AM receiver with circuits to demodulate reference and variable signals and provide a course deviation indication, as well as indicate signal integrity. If an AM receiver receives the signal represented by Fig 2.6c, the demodulated output would consist of a 30 Hz sine wave and a 9960 sine wave frequency modulated with 30 Hz. The voice and the 1020 Hz ident would also be present. This signal is called the "nav composite," indicating that it is all components of the VOR signal together. To retrieve the reference 30 Hz from the 9960 subcarrier, an FM demodulator is required, as shown in the block diagram, Fig 2.15.

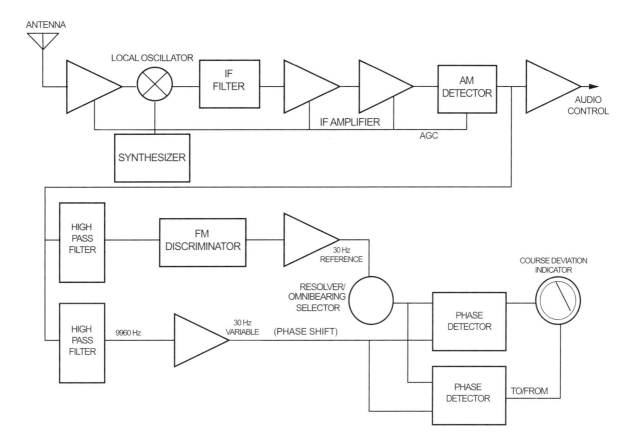

Figure 2.15 VOR receiver and signal converter

Referring to Fig. 2.15, the signals are separated into reference, variable, and audio by filters. A low pass filter separates the 30 Hz variable from the remainder of the nav composite. A highpass filter will perform the same function for the 9960 Hz subcarrier. A combination of high pass and low pass or the equivalent bandpass filter separates the 300 Hz-3 kHz audio, which includes the ident tone at 1020 Hz. The audio band is passed to a headphone amplifier or an audio switching panel and may be used for headphones or loudspeakers. The 9960 Hz subcarrier is fed to an FM demodulator which removes the 30 Hz reference.

There are now two 30 Hz signals where the phase relationship between the two is the omni bearing. Theoretically, the phase angle could be measured between the two 30 Hz signals, and display the omni radial the aircraft is on. However, the goal of VOR is to provide a course deviation indication from a selected course or radial. Rather than measure phase angle, the VOR shifts the phase of one of the 30 Hz signals and then compares the phase to the other 30 Hz signal using a phase comparator. The amount of phase shift is the *selected* course, not the actual course, and the output of the phase detector is the *course deviation* indication. This indication is in angular form, not distance from the desired course. The pilot enters the desired course using the OBS. This sets the phase shifter.

The navigation, or NAV, receiver is usually used for both VOR and localizer The localizer is part of the instrument landing system and covered in a later section. The frequency range of the NAV receiver is from 108.000 - 117.95 MHz. Navigation channels are 50 kHz wide and localizer channels are interleaved with VOR channels below 112 MHz.

The receiver is a common superheterodyne, usually using single conversion. There were exceptions using multiple conversion but these receivers are rare. The local oscillator is probably the most difficult part of the receiver design. This synthesizer must provide 200 channels and an output in the VHF region for the mixer.

The IF of the receiver will determine the frequency range required of the synthesizer. There are as many different IFs as there are manufacturers. One possibility of an IF for a NAV receiver is 29.05 MHz. This requires a local oscillator frequency range from 137.05-147.00 MHz. One reason for selecting this IF is that the local oscillator frequency range does not fall into the VHF communications band from 118.00-136.975 MHz. This lessens the possibility that the VCO for the local oscillator could interfere with a communications receiver in the aircraft.

A phase locked loop is used to generate the local oscillator, which is virtually true of any avionics synthesizer. The block diagram of the navigation receiver synthesizer would be the same as any other synthesizer including the ADF previously discussed. The significant difference is the phase locked loop for the ADF provides frequencies in the range of a few MHz. Most digital logic families can toggle in this frequency range and common logic technologies provide all the building blocks for the synthesizer. In the case of the VHF range required for the NAV receiver synthesizer, common logic elements will not operate without help.

A phase locked loop requires a programmable counter, which divides the VCO frequency down to the reference frequency. This element must operate in the VHF range. The most used logic family at the time of writing is CMOS, including all variations, which cannot provide a variable modulus divider at 147 MHz.

One logic family that can provide the speed to make a programmable divider at 146.95 MHz, and higher, is emitter-coupled logic or ECL. This technology is old and has been around since the early days of integrated circuits. Its advantage is very fast operation, but the disadvantage is the logic consumes considerable power.

Power-hungry logic cannot be integrated in large chips because a lot of power dissipated in a small area increases internal temperatures to dangerous levels. There is a technique that permits very high-speed programmable dividers to be constructed using only one ECL chip with the majority of the circuits in CMOS. This technique is called the dual modulus divider and takes advantage of the high speed of ECL and low power and large-scale integration of CMOS.

The heart of the dual modulus divider is the dual modulus prescaler. This chip is capable of dividing by two moduli, which differ by one. A common chip divides by 10 and 11; another by 64 and 65. One dual modulus prescaler is used to design the programmable divider required for the example of our NAV receiver synthesizer. The synthesizer will use a 50 kHz reference frequency because that frequency is the common denominator of the programmable divider span from 137.05/0.05 = 2741 to 147.00/0.05 = 2940. The block diagram of the dual modulus prescaler is shown in Fig 2.16. Two programmable counters are driven with the output of the dual modulus prescaler. The two programmable counters count up or down but what is important is that they count from a preset to a known state. For our example, assume the counters are down counters, start at a preset value and count down to zero.

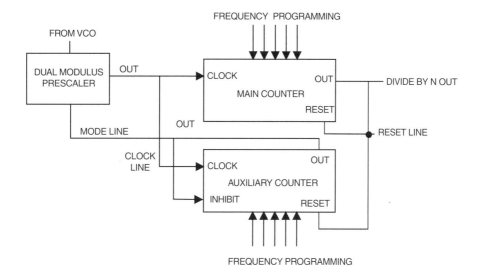

Fig. 2.16 Dual modulus divider

One of the two presettable counters is called the main counter and is preset to the value, M. The other is the auxiliary counter, and preset to a value, A. Both counters are clocked together with the output of the dual modulus prescaler, and both counters are preset at the same time.

When the main counter reaches zero state, both counters are loaded with their preset values. When the auxiliary counter reaches its zero state, it stops counting and changes the modulus of the dual modulus prescaler from N+1 to N. The value of M is always equal to or greater than A.

Consider how many cycles of input are required to go through an entire sequence of this dual modulus divider. It starts when both counters have been loaded with their preset counts and assume that M>A. Both counters count down and the auxiliary arrives at zero before the main counter because M>A. At this point the prescaler modulus is changed from N+1 to N.

It took (N+1)A input cycles to get to this point. There are M-A states left in the main counter in order to take that counter down to zero, reset the two programmable counters and start the cycle again. The modulus is now N and, therefore, it takes (M-A)N input cycles to complete the divider sequence.

The total number of input cycles to complete one sequence of the dual modulus programmable divider is:

$$D = (N+1)A + (M-A)N = MN + A \qquad\qquad (2.18)$$

Where D is the number of cycles to complete one sequence of the programmable divider or the division.

We have not considered the case when M=A. Here, the mode of the dual modulus prescaler would never change to N but remain at N+1. Therefore, the total input cycles to complete the programmable divider sequence would be simply A(N+1). This is what we would get if we let M=A in the equation for 2.17.

Notice that changing M has N times the effect of changing A. For this example a common dual modulus prescaler is used with two moduli of 40 and 41. Therefore, N=40 for this prescaler.

Using this prescaler in the dual modulus divider causes the division to change by 40 for every change of M. A must have 40, or N, different states to allow all possible values of D. From this, M must be equal to or greater than N-1, because A must span from 0 to 39 to be able to "fill in the gaps" between the 40 per steps of M. Since M can never be less than A, the smallest division available from this scheme is when M and A are minimum or 39 and 0 respectively. In a more general way, the minimum division from this dual modulus divider is (N-1)N. In the example, with N = 40, the minimum division is 1560 which is less than the minimum required division of 2741. The division of the circuit is 40M + A. For the lowest frequency of the synthesizer, where D = 2741, which is the minimum division, an M value of 68 is used, which requires A to be 21.

It is interesting to see how changing M changes the *frequency* of the synthesizer rather than the division of the programmable divider. Since the reference frequency is 50 kHz, a change in M causes a 2 MHz change in the synthesizer frequency. Changing the value of A by one causes the frequency to change by 50 kHz. Assigning weights to binary numbers to load main and auxiliary counters:

Main counter

Bit	G	F	E	D	C	B	A
Weight (MHz)	128	64	32	16	8	4	2

Auxiliary counter

Bit	f	e	d	c	b	a
Weight (MHz)	1.6	0.8	0.4	0.2	0.1	0.05

The microprocessor determines the programming numbers required for the synthesizer by the following method. Take the operating frequency, add the IF, truncate to the nearest 2 MHz, divide that number by 2, convert to binary. This will find the value for the main counter. To find the binary value for the auxiliary counter, take the positive difference between the truncated number and the synthesizer frequency in MHz, multiply by 20 and convert to binary.

As a numerical example, let us assume that we will set the receiver to the test frequency of 108.00 MHz. The first step is to add the IF which results in $108.00 + 29.05 = 137.05$. Truncating to the nearest 2 MHz yields 136 MHz. Dividing this number by two yields 68. Converting this to binary yields 0100 0100. This is the binary value for the main counter.

The auxiliary counter is calculated by taking the positive difference between the truncated number and the actual frequency which is $137.05 - 136 = 1.05$. Multiplying by 20 yields 21 which is 01 0101 in binary. The division is $MN + A = 40X68 + 21 = 2741$

Shown below are the M and A values for the first channels of the example receiver:

Channel	Local Osc. MHz)	N	M	A
108.00	137.05	2741	68	21
108.05	137.10	2742	68	22
108.10	137.15	2743	68	23
*****	*****	****	**	**
108.90	137.95	2759	68	39
108.95	138.00	2760	69	00
109.00	138.05	2761	69	01
109.05	138.10	2762	69	02

Notice that A rolls over at 39 while M increments by one. This is the equivalent of "modulo

40" arithmetic. The first application of dual modulus frequency synthesis used 10/11 prescalers which resulted in modulo 10 arithmetic which would interface with the channel selector switches. The modern microprocessor controlled avionics can handle any type of arithmetic and modern dual modulus prescalers use many ratios other than 10/11.

Exercise: Using the algorithm above, determine the binary programming bits to program the example synthesizer to the receive frequency of 112.650 MHz.

From the description and examples, it is seen that the dual modulus programmable divider does divide frequencies, but what is the advantage? Consider the maximum output frequency from the dual modulus prescaler. This occurs at the highest VCO frequency when the dual modulus prescaler is dividing by N rather than N+1. In this example, the highest frequency is 147.00 MHz and N=40. When these conditions occur, output from the prescaler is 3.675 MHz. Relatively low power CMOS circuits can be used at a clock frequency of 3.675 MHz.

The dual modulus prescaler is used at frequencies well in to the GHz region and beyond, and is the only viable frequency division technique for higher frequencies. We will encounter the technique several more times in this text.

2.12 VOR Test Equipment

To test a VOR receiver, a specialized test set is required to simulate the VOR signal. The test set provides not only the nominal VOR signal but modifies the nominal antenna or source of the signal.

An avionics shop has the missing items. It is equipped with control heads, audio amplifiers, speakers, indicators and a signal source. Some airports have special test signals available on the airport surface. These signals are from a 1 watt transmitter that emits a simulated VOR signal only at 0 degrees TO. This is generated without a rotating antenna pattern so the location of the aircraft has no effect on the signal received. The facility, called a VOR test station or VOT, is a high powered test set that can be received on the airport site. Power is not sufficient to receive the signal at more than a few miles.

2.13 DME: Distance Measuring Equipment

The navigation aids discussed thus far, ADF and VOR, are methods of finding a path to a destination. The ADF gives heading information, while the VOR provides course information. Neither tells how far we are from the station unless the aircraft is directly over the VOR and the TO/FROM indicator flips, or over a NDB and the ADF pointer reverses.

We could use two ADF bearings and, by triangulation, find our position. The same can be done with the VOR receiver, in the fashion used to locate an intersection. This measurement, using two angles to find a position, is called a theta-theta navigation because two angles are employed with triangulation. (Actually, triangulation implies three angles. Although not correct, the term is in common use.) Both techniques require multiple receivers, a navigation chart and a procedure that involves calculation. What would be useful is a system that provides continuous position determination without high pilot workload.

Panel-mounted DME. Display is indicating distance (97.9 nm), ground speed, 120 kt and time to station, 48 min. (Narco)

The ADF already has shortcomings as part of a position-determining system because it is difficult for the pilot in flight to calculate course information. (He must add his compass heading to the relative bearing of the ADF to determine his course to the station. This is simplified by a radiomagnetic indicator (RMI) in sophisticated aircraft, but even this takes skill to follow.) The VOR, on the other hand, places an aircraft on a radial, which is the angular part of a polar coordinate system with the VOR station at the origin. To completely specify position in this system, distance to the VOR is required. This form of navigation is called rho-theta, indicating that navigation operates with distance, rho, and angle, theta.

Distance measuring equipment, DME, was developed in 1949 as a part of military system called TACAN, for tactical air navigation. The angular part of TACAN is similar to VOR except measurements are more precise and ground stations can be portable and set up at temporary airfields for battlefield use. DME is the distance part of the TACAN system. The military permits civilian use of TACAN where it is available. In the early 1950s TACAN was installed in a number of permanent installations, but never found significant civil use because of a lack of civil TACAN airborne equipment. TACAN ground stations, however, were located with VOR stations so the TACAN system could be used with civil aeronautical charts. In the mid-1950s, large air transport aircraft began to use the distance portion of TACAN. Since TACAN stations were co-located with VOR or VORTAC , the TACAN distance measurement is available with VOR bearing to determine position.

Determining distance is an obvious application of radio waves. Since their speed is constant, the wave's time of flight enables measurement of distance. Radio signals, as all electromagnetic waves, are absolutely constant in a vacuum. When radio waves travel in matter, they are slower than in a vacuum, but when the material is air, the reduction in velocity is so small it may be neglected for all except the most accurate measurements.

Radar, which stands for radio detection and ranging, uses elapsed time from when a pulse of radio energy is transmitted until a reflected pulse is received, to determine distance to a target. To measure distance to a VOR station, we only need a return signal from the station in response to an airborne transmission. This return signal does not have to be a reflection but transmitted in response to an "interrogation". Because DME measures range, which is an important part of radar, the DME is a "secondary radar" system.

We will study another secondary radar system in Chapter 5. This system operates together with a primary radar and the primary-secondary relationship is clear. The DME has no associated primary radar but otherwise behaves exactly as a secondary radar.

To measure distance, a DME interrogator, the airborne part of DME, transmits an encoded signal. The ground station, containing a "transponder", replies to the interrogation. Some time is needed to process the received interrogation before sending the reply. This delay must be the same for all ground stations in order to have an accurate measurement of distance.

An important term is the "radar mile". This "mile" is not a measure of distance but the time for a radio signal to travel a distance of one nautical mile and return, or the time for a radio signal to travel two nautical miles. A nautical mile is 1852 meters, therefore, a radar mile is:

$$T = (1852 \times 2) / c = 3704 / 3E8 = 12.35 \ \mu s \qquad (2.19)$$

where T is the radar mile in seconds per NM

One type of DME imposes a 50 μs delay from receipt of an interrogation to the transmission of a reply. Therefore, the total delay, measured in the airborne interrogator, is the sum of the time to propagate to the ground station, the delay time and the time to propagate from the ground station. To determine distance from the total elapsed time, subtract the delay time and divide the remaining propagation time by the radar mile. This is shown as:

$$D = (\Delta t - 50 \ \mu s \ )/12.35 \ \mu s/NM$$

where D is the distance in nautical miles, Δt is the total elapsed time in seconds and T is the radar mile in seconds per nautical mile.

The elapsed times for DMEs are not all the same and 50 μs is only one possibility. To make the equation more general, a time delay of T_0 is used:

$$D = (\ \Delta t - T_0 \ ) / T \qquad (2.20)$$

Imagine it is 1949 and we are tasked with developing a system to measure distance using radio waves. First is the choice of a radio frequency. Clearly, any frequency subject to ionospheric propagation is not acceptable. Therefore, the upper VHF and higher frequencies are satisfactory. Since DME is part of TACAN, the frequencies for DME must also suit the bearing part of TACAN.

Frequencies for TACAN are around 1 GHz (from 915-1213 MHz) in the "L" band. The wavelength is on the order of 30 cm, which is important because TACAN requires rotating antenna patterns as does VOR and should be portable. The 30 cm wavelength is acceptable. A higher frequency would have been more suitable but this is 1949, when making transmitters and receivers at 1 GHz is a challenge.

With frequency range selected, next is type of modulation. For measuring time delays, simple modulation is required and it should be pulse type. Some sort of encoding is required so the receivers, airborne and ground, can determine valid signals from noise. The simplest pulse modulation that distinguishes a valid interrogation from a noise pulse is the pulse pair.

Finally, a decision on the pulse shape. Rectangular pulses appear to be the simplest and provide the steep rise to make time measurements. The problem is that the bandwidth of a fast rising pulse is excessive. Among a number of possible shapes for DME interrogations and replies the "Gaussian" pulse was selected. A Gaussian function is found in a number of applications but is used here because of a well-behaved spectrum. This means the spectrum is not overly broad and does not have "regrowth". This means the spectrum continues to decay as the frequency moves away from the carrier frequency.

First, a Gaussian pulse fits an equation of the form

$$V(t) = Vexp(- \pi \ (a \ t)^2 \ ) \qquad (2.21)$$

where V(t) is the Gaussian pulse as a function of time, a is a constant and t is time. The plot of a Gaussian pulse is shown in Fig. 2.17.

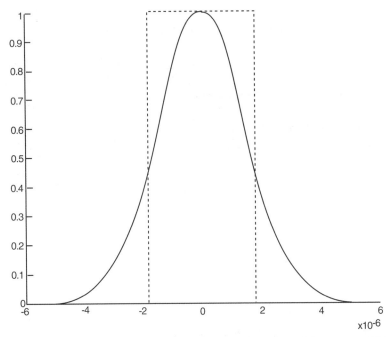

Figure 2.17. Gaussian pulse used in DME and rectangular pulse of the same width.

The spectrum of a Gaussian pulse is also Gaussian. The spectrum of a rectangular pulse is a sinc(x) function. *(Note*: The sinc(x) function is given by sinc(x)=sin(πx)/πx. In many texts, the spectrum of a rectangular pulse is described as a sin(x)/x function. The sin(x)/x function is not defined at x=0 whereas the sinc function is defined to be equal to one. In the limiting sense, as x goes to zero, sin(πx)/πx is equal to 1.)

Compare the spectrum of these pulses in Fig 2.18. Notice how the rectangular pulse spectrum has a number of zeros but pops up again and again. This is the regrowth mentioned previously and causes energy at frequencies far removed from the operating frequency.

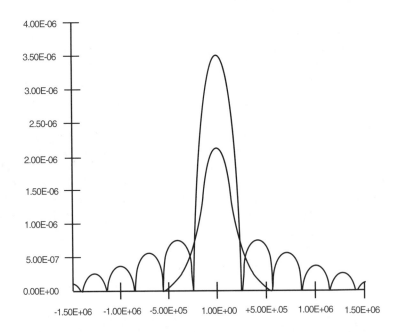

Fig. 2.18 Comparison of the spectrum of a Gaussian pulse with rectangular pulse of the same peak amplitude and pulse width, measured from half amplitude points.

Like any other radio system the Gaussian pulse modulates a radio frequency carrier which, in the case of the DME, is amplitude modulation. Therefore, the envelope of the RF pulse is Gaussian. The equation of the DME transmitter output is:

$$F(t) = V \cos(2\pi f_c t) \exp(-\pi (at)^2)$$

where f_c is the RF carrier frequency.   (2.22)

The Gaussian pulse for DME has a half-amplitude of 3.5 μs and the channels are 1 MHz wide. Knowing pulse width and peak pulse amplitude is sufficient to define the Gaussian pulse. As an example, assume a DME transmitter is operating with a power of 250 watts and the nominal 3.5 μs pulse width. Assuming a 50-ohm transmitter, the peak envelope power is 250 watts which is 112 volts RMS or 158 volts instantaneous peak. Therefore, V = 158. We need to find the parameter, a, and the equation for F(t) is fully defined. We know the half voltage point of the Gaussian pulse. This can solve for a. When the Gaussian envelope is at half amplitude, which occurs at t = 3.5 μs/2, both plus and minus, the envelope is half amplitude:

$$f(t) = (158)\exp(-\pi (at)^2) = 158 \exp(-\pi a^2(1.75E\text{-}6)^2) = 158/2$$ (2.23)

To solve for a, divide both sides by 158 and take the natural log of both sides, we obtain:

$$-0.693 = -\pi a^2(1.75E\text{-}6)^2 \quad a = 268E3$$ (2.24)

Exercise: Using MatLAb or other mathematics program plot the envelope of the DME pulse.
The power spectrum of the DME pulse is

$$|G(f)|^2 = (V/a)^2 [\exp(-\pi (f_c - f)^2/a^2)]^2$$ (2.25)

From this spectrum we can determine the half power bandwidth. This is done by setting the spectrum to be equal to one half the power of the on-channel power.

$$(\exp(-\pi (f_c - f)^2/a^2))^2 = \tfrac{1}{2}$$ (2.26)

$$\exp(-\pi (f_c - f)^2/a^2) = 0.707$$ (2.27)

As before, take the natural log of both sides,

$$(-\pi (f_c - f)^2/a^2) = -0.347$$ (2.28)

substituting the value for a and solving for $(f_c - f)$ we find,

$$(f_c - f) = 89.1 \text{ kHz}$$ (2.29)

The half power points of the Gaussian spectrum occurs at 89.1 kHz above and below the carrier frequency. Therefore, the total bandwidth is twice 89.1 kHz or 178 kHz.

Exercise: Using the Fourier transform, derive the spectrum of the DME Gaussian modulated pulse. Plot the spectrum.

The DME signal is encoded by transmitting two pulses. Because of such simple coding , the

DME receiver cannot completely eliminate false triggering due to noise but encoding does provide some improvement.

A DME interrogation consists of two Gaussian pulses separated by 12 μs for an X channel. We will discuss channels other than X at a later point. The master reference point for making all timing measurements is the 50% amplitude point of the transmitter envelope, as shown in Fig. 2.19. The interrogation is made on an interrogation frequency and received by the DME transponder at the ground station. After a 50 μs delay, the ground transponder transmits a reply with a pulse pair with exactly the same pulse width and pulse separation. The reply, however, is at a different frequency. There are a number of reasons to use separate uplink and downlink frequencies, all associated with reducing interference.

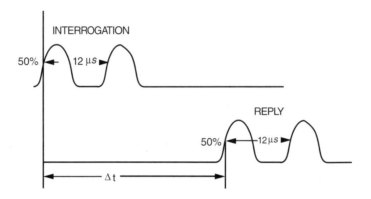

Figure 2.19 Timing reference points for DME calculations

For the X channel, the reply is 63 MHz below the interrogation frequency. The DME interrogation and reply frequency are paired with the VOR frequency of the co-located VOR station. TACAN uses channel numbers and a TACAN-only installation does not require any pairing. When the DME system was first invented and installed, there were only X channels, although they were not called by that name. TACAN was becoming co-located with VOR stations in an ever-increasing rate and by the 1970s virtually every VOR was paired with a TACAN facility. Some that were not were paired with TACAN but just the DME portion of TACAN, are called a VOR-DME. A VOR-only station was becoming rare.

Also in the 1970s, it was evident that the available frequencies for new VOR installations were becoming critically low. It was decided to increase the number of channels by decreasing channels from every 100 kHz to every 50 kHz. The original 100 kHz channel, which is very wide for VOR, was due to early navigation receivers which were tuned with an unstabilized local oscillator. VOR receiver frequency calibration and drift were serious problems. Newer receivers used crystal stabilized local oscillators and did not have these problems.

The original navigation band had a total of 100 channels and the new band was doubled to 200. The number of VOR channels was doubled by adding 100 channels in the VHF navigation band and reducing the channel width to 50 kHz. In the case of the DME, the original 1 MHz channels were not overly wide for the level of technology at that time and it would not be possible to simply cut the channel in half and double the number of channels.

There was another 100 MHz available in the L band, but DME requires two channels to function; an up link and down link. The technique to increase the DME channels was to divide DME into X and Y channels. X channels were the original DME pairings with the 100 kHz VOR

52

frequencies. As an example, the VOR frequency 108.000 has a DME interrogation frequency of 1041 MHz and a reply frequency of 978 MHz. This is the X channel. The navigation frequency of 108.050, which is an added frequency when the number of channels was split, has an interrogation frequency of the same 1041 MHz and a reply of 1104 MHz. Notice the interrogation frequency is higher than the reply frequency for X channels and lower than the reply for Y channels.

Since the same interrogation frequency is used for X and Y channels, something must be done to distinguish one from the other. The technique to make X and Y unique is the spacing between the two interrogation pulses. It is 12 μs for the X channel and 36 μs for Y channels.

The time delay between receipt of an interrogation at the ground station and the transmission of a reply for an X channel is 50 μs. This may be measured from first pulse of the interrogation to the first pulse of the reply, or from the second pulse because reply and interrogation are the same.

For Y channel interrogations, this is not the case. The Y channel interrogation pulse pair is separated by 36 μs, while the reply is separated by 30 μs. For the Y channel, the time delay is 56 μs as measured from first pulse to first pulse and 50 μs when measured from second to second.

There is an advantage from the frequency assignment scheme. Since interrogation and receive frequencies of an airborne DME differ by 63 MHz, regardless of X or Y channels, the frequency source to generate the transmitter's carrier can generate the receiver's local oscillator. This would only work if the DME IF is 63 MHz, which is a reasonable choice for an IF frequency. For X channels, the local oscillator frequency will be above the incoming signal, which is called high side injection. For Y channels, the local oscillator frequency is below the incoming signal or low side injection.

As in many systems, the basic principle sounds simple. But the details are not as easy. In principle, an interrogator transmits an encoded pulse to the ground transponder which returns a reply. The time delay is measured from transmission of the interrogation, based on the 50% amplitude point of the first pulse, to the 50% amplitude point of the first reply pulse. The delay is used in a simple equation and distance is displayed. This is the situation if there were only one aircraft using the ground station. If several aircraft are interrogating, which pulse pairs transmitted by the ground station are your reply?

It is done with a time correlation technique. Assume an interrogation is transmitted by your aircraft. After a period of time the reply arrives at your receiver. The problem is that your reply is received along with pulse pairs with replies intended for other interrogators. If the aircraft does not move significantly between the first and second interrogations, the time delay for the first and second replies is the same.

Let's get a feeling for how far an aircraft moves between interrogations. We will use a rate of 30 interrogations per second or a period of 33.33 ms between interrogations. Consider a fast ground speed of 500 knots. The aircraft moves 0.005 NM in 33.33 ms. For practical purposes, the aircraft has not moved significantly between interrogations.

What about other replies due to interrogations of other aircraft? What would prevent those replies from arriving at the same elapsed time every time the DME interrogates? This would happen if other aircraft interrogated the ground station at exactly the same rate. Why wouldn't they interrogate at exactly the same rate if they were from the same manufacturer and model? We make sure they do not; the interrogation of the ground station is deliberately done at a random rate.

Assume an interrogator is operating at 16 interrogations per second, which is an average. There is not exactly 62.5 ms between each interrogation. The interrogations could be separated by 50 ms one time and 70 the next and so on. Sometimes the interval is longer than 62.5 ms and other times it is shorter but on average it is 62.5 ms. It is important that the time interval be as close to random as possible so no two DMEs can become synchronized. Generally, this is easy by using computer-generated time intervals and a pseudo-random generator. It is necessary to pick out desired replies from all replies received after an initial interrogation. The term initial is used because once the desired reply is found, it can be tracked without having to find the reply.

Assume the maximum distance covered by a DME is 200 NM, a safe assumption because UHF frequencies limit range to line of sight. Using the radar mile at 12.35 μs per NM, the time for the desired reply is 12.35 X 200 or 2.47 ms. We need to add the delay in the ground station but the time is on the order of 2.5 ms. The number of transmissions from a ground station is limited to 2700 pulse pairs per second. Therefore, the maximum number of transmissions that can be received in 2.5 ms is about 7. This means that in the 2.5 ms the DME receiver needs to be active after the transmission of an interrogation, only about 7 transmissions are received. Do not be confused by the term transmission rather than reply. DME ground stations transmit more than replies, which will be discussed in a later section. All transmissions from a DME ground station look alike; replies to your interrogations, replies to other interrogators and non-reply transmissions.

After an interrogation, the aircraft DME records the time of arrival of transmissions from the ground station. The aircraft interrogates again. The time of arrival of the next 7 transmissions is recorded. The only transmission guaranteed to arrive at practically the same elapsed time is your interrogation. It is possible, by chance, that two transmissions arrived at the same elapsed time as the previous interrogation. A third interrogation is made. The likelihood that three random pulses arriving at exactly the same elapsed time is virtually nil. It is possible, however, that the intended reply was missing. This could happen because of interference, a weak signal or other reasons. The ratio of the number of replies to interrogations is called reply efficiency, given as a percentage.

The technique often used is to interrogate about 5 times and look for a reply at the same elapsed time in three out of five interrogations. It is highly unlikely that the reply for another aircraft or noise could occur in exactly the same elapsed time, three out or five. Finding the reply is called locking-on or finding lock. If the ground station has a reply efficiency of 60%, this technique would successfully find the desired reply. If the criterion for determining lock is too loose, the DME could lock on to noise and miss the real replies. If the criterion for locking on is too stringent, actual replies may be overlooked and the DME will not lock on to a usable signal, or take an excessive amount of time to lock on.

There are a number of reasons a DME ground station will not reply to an interrogation. The first and obvious is the interrogator signal is weak in the ground station receiver. If the interrogation is noisy, the receiver will miss some interrogations and not transmit a reply.

Another reason for not replying is when two interrogations interfere. Even though the interrogators are randomized so they will not synchronize, there is a possibility that two interrogations will arrive at the same time. There are also times when specific pulses must be transmitted as a part of the TACAN system and replies will be superceded by TACAN pulses. Thus a DME ground station will not reply to 100% of the interrogations received, even if all interrogations are strong. DME interrogators can operate with reply efficiencies as low as 70%.

The TACAN system requires a constant average number of transmissions from the ground station. Since the DME ground station only needs to transmit when a reply is required, due to receipt of an interrogation, it is possible that if no aircraft is interrogating, the DME station will not transmit. The TACAN system requires the DME pulses to operate. Therefore, the TACAN ground station is designed to transmit an average number of 2700 pulse pairs each second, regardless of the number of aircraft in range. If there are insufficient aircraft to provide 2700 interrogations per second, which is most of the time, random replies called squitter are made. Squitter pulses are injected in random fashion so they appear to be replies to random interrogations of aircraft.

54

As in most radio navigation systems, some form of identification is required to insure that the signal is the correct one. If a DME is off the air, a co-channel DME (same frequency) could be received in its place and cause serious navigation errors. As in many early radio navigation aids, DME contains a Morse code identifier.

The discussion of the DME ground station centered on insuring randomness of the transmissions. For the ident, a regular group of pulses generates Morse code dots and dashes. To make the regular pulse groups, two pulse pairs are separated by 100 µs. This is called a pair of pairs. These pair combinations are transmitted at a regular rate of 1350 pairs of pairs as shown in Fig. 2.20. This results in a repetition rate of 1350 Hz, which is an audible tone for an ident. On the other hand, the pulse pair rate is 2700 pulse pairs per second because the 1350 Hz repetition rate is counted as pairs of pairs.

Figure 2.20 DME ident pulses

In addition to distance, DME can determine ground speed, done by taking the time derivative of the distance. At first it may appear to be a simple mathematical operation. The difference in measured distance between any two interrogations, if divided by the time between the two interrogations, should provide ground speed. Like so many other apparently easy tasks, the problems lie in the details. First, the time between interrogations is on the order of milliseconds. In the latest DMEs, the maximum interrogation rate while tracking a ground station is 16 per second. This is the average rate. Because of the randomness of interrogations, the time is different between any two interrogations. Depending on the ground speed of the aircraft in the direction of the DME transponder, the aircraft will move a small fraction of a mile in the time between two interrogations. The change could be so small that it can not be resolved by the DME. This would indicate that the aircraft has no velocity. Also, depending on noise, multipath and interference, the distance could actually change in the direction opposite to actual travel. This would indicate a velocity with a sign opposite from that of the real ground speed. Because of noise and quantizing error, achieving a realistic ground speed from only two interrogations is not possible.

A number of measurements may be made and the results averaged. Precisely the same results could be achieved by simply extending the time between distance measurements used for ground speed calculations. To understand the problems in calculating ground speed from DME distance consider the following:

Example: How accurate would a ground speed determination be if a DME used interrogations separated by ten seconds? The DME interrogates the ground station 16 times each second and measures distance within 0.1 NM. The ground speed of the aircraft is 150 kts.

Solution: At 150 kts, the ground speed is 0.042 NM per second. Therefore, the distance traveled in ten seconds is 0.42 NM. If the DME were perfect, with no errors, the difference in distance measured in a ten second interval would be exactly 0.42 NM and the calculation would be perfect. However, the DME can only measure distance to the nearest 0.1 mile, which implies the DME can only produce a 0.4 NM difference. Furthermore, because the DME's least significant bit, LSB, is 0.1 NM, there is a quantizing error associated with each distance measurement of plus or minus 0.1 NM. It is quite possible that one distance measurement used for the ground speed measurement is low by 0.1 NM while the other is high by 0.1 NM. Therefore, the differential distance could be accurate to within plus or minus 0.2 NM due to quantizing error. Finally, if the signal is weak or affected by multipath, there could be an additional error of 0.1 NM or more. The final error of the differential distance is plus or minus 0.3 NM.

This implies that the differential distance measured in a ten-second interval would be between 0.1 and 0.7 NM. This range of distance would produce a ground speed calculation between 36 and 252 knots.

It appears the accuracy in a ten-second period is not sufficient to generate an acceptable ground speed. There are techniques to provide a quick and stable ground speed. One that improves matters is to use as small an LSB (least significant bit) as possible. The example of 0.1 NM could be improved to half that or 0.05 NM. It may seem tempting to improve the LSB even more to, say, 0.01 NM. This implies that to make this LSB meaningful, the time reference from the received pulses must be to a similar 0.01 NM or a time accuracy of 0.12 μs or 120 ns. This is difficult and a typical LSB is 0.05 NM.

In the example, we took the worst case of quantizing error. In the ten-second interval, there were 160 interrogations and, if the reply efficiency were on the order of 70%, there would have been 112 replies from which 112 distances could be calculated. We could have used these calculations to predict where the last measurement should have been if it were not for the quantizing error. Averaging, multiple measurement and predicting are all techniques used in filters. The key to fast and accurate ground speed is in digital filtering.

There are other manipulations of distance and ground speed that a DME computer must provide. The first is holding the distance when the signal is lost. This is not rare but occurs often during a normal flight. The most common loss of a signal is when the aircraft banks and the antenna is shadowed from the ground station. The DME processor is designed to coast through such an outage. The technique is straightforward if ground speed is known and it is assumed the DME has been locked on for a while and an accurate ground speed calculated. When the signal is lost, the DME processor predicts DME distance by using ground speed and calculating DME distance. This coasting mode must last a maximum of 15 seconds. When the DME is again received, the actual distance is not different from the displayed distance by more than 1.0 NM.

The DME computer is expected to handle two multipath problems. The first is a multipath signal from the ground station to the airborne receiver. In this case, two characteristics allow the DME interrogator to reject the multipath signal. First, multipath usually has a lower signal level. The airborne receiver operates with a relatively constant signal level and the lower level signal can be rejected. The second is that a multipath signal arrives after the desired signal. When the DME searches for replies, it is important that the process insures that the selected reply occurs before other replies that are correlated in time.

Another problem is echo. This differs from multipath in that multipath is from the down link, and the ground station transmits *two* replies. The station has some multipath reduction techniques, but long multipath signals can cause a false reply. Because the ground station must operate with a wide range of signals, a lower signal level is not rejected. Therefore, a long delayed multipath that could be weak may cause a reply. The airborne interrogator can reject this echo because the signal is correlated in time, but always arrives after the desired reply.

56

2.13.1 DME Indicator

The most important parameter displayed on the DME indicator is distance, followed by ground speed. Some indicators also show time to station (TTS), the time to reach the DME station if current course and ground speed are maintained. There are few controls on a DME; an on/off switch may be provided. If time to station is on the same display as ground speed, there is a switch to select that function, but newer DME's can display them simultaneously. Another knob selects the navigation receiver that will control the DME.

The DME is typically connected to a NAV receiver that controls DME frequency. The DME provides distance to a VORTAC (a combined VOR/TACAN station) and thus the VORTAC frequency also determines DME frequency. There are rare exceptions to this, where a DME is installed as a stand-alone system if a NAV receiver cannot channel the DME.

2.13.2 DME Interrogator

Figure 2.21 shows a block diagram of a typical DME interrogator. As alluded to earlier, the superheterodyne lends itself to a DME interrogator because the transmitter carrier generator is used as the local oscillator for the receiver. This is reflected in the block diagram of Fig 2.21. This synthesizer provides 1 MHz frequency channels from 1041-1150 MHz. The receiver is a single conversion superheterodyne with a 63 MHz IF. The detector is a conventional AM type with a diode or other envelope detector. The DME will receive signals from one ground station although there are replies to aircraft at various distances from the ground station. The replies are relatively constant in amplitude; as the aircraft approaches or retreats from the ground station, signal level changes but will not vary from pulse to pulse.

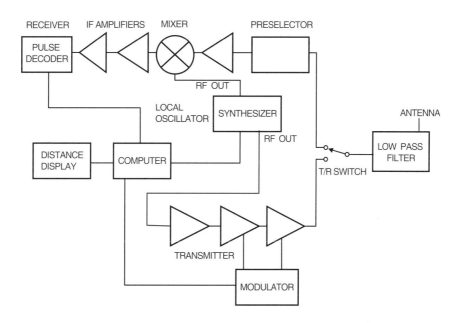

Figure 2.21 Block diagram of DME interrogator

Because the receiver operates over a range of signal levels, an AGC system is required. Like any pulse system, AGC operates at the peak of the pulse. A peak detector is applied to the AM detector and the peak value compared to a reference. The error voltage is fed back to the gain control of the receiver IF amplifier. In addition to controlling gain on the peak of the pulse pairs, many DME receivers enable AGC peak detect circuits only for a pulse pair of the correct separation. This prevents the DME from developing AGC on pulses that are not DME but interference. The L band is shared with other users and an occasional incompatible pulse is common.

The 50% amplitude point of the pulse must be accurately determined. Representing 50% of the peak and the leading edge, it is the timing reference. The dilemma is to find 50% of the peak before it occurs. One technique employs the peak of the first pulse as a reference for the 50% point of the second pulse. This is used on inexpensive DMEs with success, but timing is relative to the second pulse. In a ground station, pulse spacing between first and second reply pulses is usually very accurate and the fact that timing is relative to the second pulse does not seriously affect DME accuracy. The real reason for referencing the rising edge of the first pulse is because it occurs before the arrival of multipath signals. This is not the case with the second pulse. A path length difference of only 2 NM can place the multipath from the first pulse onto the second pulse.

A technique for determining the 50% amplitude of the first pulse is to pass the first pulse through a delay line. Then, the peak of the first pulse is held in real time and the delayed pulse compared to the peak, as shown in Fig. 2.22. In this figure, DME video is peak detected and the video delayed for 10 µs. The delay pulse is fed to a comparator with one-half the peak value of the pulse. Once the delayed pulse crosses the 50% point, the comparator changes state and a logic signal changes state at exactly the half amplitude point. The time when the comparator changes state is the reference point, plus 10 µs, due to the delay line. This additional delay is accounted for in the calculation of DME distance.

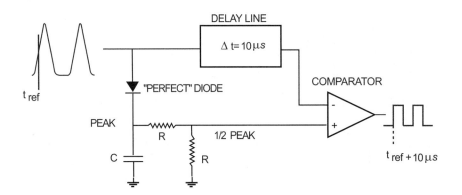

Figure 2.22 Holding peak value of first DME pulse while using that value as a reference for the second pulse for timing measurements.

The DME interrogator transmitter is typically a number of amplification stages that drive a power amplifier to saturation and modulation. The difficulty in DME transmitter design is to achieve the necessary on-to-off ratio while maintaining a Gaussian shape. Modulators use predistortion to overcome non-linearity of the power amplifiers.

2.13.3 Enhanced DME, Scanning DME
DME interrogates only 16 times per second when the interrogator has locked on a ground station. Between interrogations it is possible to rechannel and interrogate a second or even third ground station. In this fashion, one DME can act as three DMEs, providing distance, ground speed and time to station for three different ground stations.

Multiple station DME ranging uses one transmitter and one receiver but requires that AGC voltage be held when the DME receiver retunes another DME. One advantage of the 2700 pulse pairs from a DME ground station is the easing of AGC design. If a DME were receiving three different DME ground stations only 900 pulses per second would be available from each ground station, which is plenty to achieve acceptable AGC action.

One advantage of scanning DME is position determination using three DME distances. Called rho-rho-rho navigation, it is discussed with similar systems in a later section.

2.14 DME Ground Station

DME is the distance part of the military TACAN system. Our discussion of the station will cover only that function of TACAN. There are also DME-only stations and DMEs that are associated with a VOR to form a VOR-DME, but these are rare.

A DME ground station would seem to be similar to a DME airborne interrogator in reverse. Rather than initiating an interrogation and receiving a reply, the DME ground station receives an interrogation and, after a time delay, transmits a reply. To the extent that both interrogator and transponder transmit and receive gaussian shaped pulse pairs in the L band, there is a similarity. There are, however, large differences between ground and airborne systems.

The receiver in the ground station operates with signals from numerous aircraft at various distances and transmitter power. DME interrogators are not synchronized and signals from different aircraft often collide. Compare this to signals uplinked to the airborne receiver; DME pulses received by the airborne interrogator are from one ground-based transponder. Thus, levels vary only slightly due to motion of the aircraft. Even though replies and squitter from the ground station represent random pulses, they do not overlap and collide. In short, signals received from a ground station are much more predictable than interrogation signals from a number of aircraft.

Since the transponder receiver must respond to signals of various levels and unpredictable arrival times, a receiver must respond immediately to signals of wildly disparate levels. Using AGC will not work. The practical solution is that of a logarithmic receiver, which compresses the large dynamic range of received signals. As an example, if a logarithmic receiver has a scale factor of 0.1 volt per dB, a 60 dB range of signals is compressed into a 6 volt range. (Further discussion of the logarithmic receiver is in the description of the airborne transponder.)

To prevent malfunctions due to colliding interrogations, the receiver suppresses further reception once a valid pulse pair is decoded. For a valid interrogation, the receiver is prohibited from receiving for 100 µs. During this period the ground station is preparing to transmit a reply by first delaying 50 µs, then transmitting the reply.

The accuracy of DME/TACAN depends on the transponder's ability to measure the 50% amplitude point of the received pulse pair. Unlike the DME airborne interrogator receiver, it is not permissible to use the first pulse to determine the pulse peak and the second pulse for timing. This is done in airborne interrogators to save cost, but there is no such thing as a low-cost ground station.

DME/TACAN stations operate with a transmitter power output from about 1-2 kW for a range of about 200 NM. DME is sometimes used with landing systems where range is only 20 NM or so and lower power transmitters are used.

Example: If the nominal DME ground station transmitter output power is 1500 watts, the required receiver sensitivity of an airborne unit is –82 dBm, and the nominal DME interrogator transmitter power is 125 watts. What should the DME ground station receiver sensitivity be?

Solution: The path loss from the DME ground station transmitter to the airborne receiver is the difference between ground transmitter power, +61.8 dBm (1500 W), and sensitivity of the airborne receiver, -82 dBm, which is 143.8 dB. The loss is everything in the path between transmitter and receiver antenna; free space loss, receiver antenna, etc. When the ground station receives the interrogation from the airborne DME, it is over the same path. Therefore, for a DME transmitter of +51 dBm, (125 W), minus path loss of 143.8 dB, results in a receiver sensitivity of –92.8 dBm.

Another way of looking at receiver sensitivity is that the receiver on the ground must be more sensitive than the airborne receiver in the same ratio as the difference in transmitter powers. A 125 watt transmitter is 10.8 dB weaker than a 1500 W transmitter, and thus the ground receiver must be 10.8 dB more sensitive.

It is a good design practice that up links and down links fail together. This prevents an overly powerful transmitter from interrogating a DME, where the airborne receiver does not receive replies for lack of sensitivity. This would unnecessarily overload the ground station. The TSO requirements for transmitter power output includes a recommended maximum airborne transmitter output power.

Example:
What is the power duty cycle of a DME ground station compared to a DME interrogator?

Solution: The total number of pulses transmitted by a ground station is 5400 which is two pulses for 2700 pulse pairs. Each pulse has a half amplitude pulse width of 3.5 ms which will be used for the calculation of duty cycle. The total transmit time in one second is 5400 X 3.5µs = 18.9 ms. Since the transmitter emits a total of 18.9 ms in one second, the duty cycle is:

$$DC = (18.9E-3)X \ 100\% = 1.9\%$$

While searching, the interrogator is permitted 150 interrogations per second and 16 interrogations per second while tracking. It is assumed that search is no more than 5% of the time of operation of the DME.

Assume that for every second, 950 ms of that second, the DME is transmitting 16 pulse pairs per second, while for 50 ms, 150 pulse pairs per second are transmitted. Thus, for every second there are 15.2 pulse pairs + 7.5 pulse pairs, or 45.4 pulses. The total transmit time is 158.9 ms. The duty cycle is:

$$DC = (158.9E-6) \ X \ 100\% = 0.016\% \qquad (2.30)$$

The ground station duty cycle, therefore, is considerably higher than the airborne DME transmitter.

Example:
Calculate the true energy per pulse for the 3.5 µs DME pulse by integrating the Gaussian output pulse from a ground station. Assume a peak power of P watts. Using this to determine the RMS output power of the transmitter.

Solution:

The equation of the voltage of a Gaussian pulse is $V(t) = exp(-\pi(at)^2) = exp(-226E9t^2)$. *To convert this to instantaneous power the function is squared and divided by the impedance of the circuit. The Gaussian voltage is given by:*

$$V(t) = V\, exp(-226E9t^2)$$

which had been calculated previously. The instantaneous power is:

$$V^2(t)/R = V^2\, exp(-452E9t^2)/R$$

where R is the circuit resistance. Peak power occurs when the exponential equals 1 and thus,

$$V^2(t)/R = P_{PEAK}\; exp(452E9t^2)$$

To find the energy of the pulse the instantaneous power is integrated over all time and is one of the definite integrals found in common tables. The integral is:

$$\int exp(-452E9t^2)dt = (\pi/452E9)^{1/2} = 2.64E-6$$

Therefore, the true energy per pulse is 2.64E-6 P_{PEAK} (joules).

Let us recalculate the duty cycle for a DME transponder using the true energy per pulse. The ground station transmits 5400 pulses each second for a true power of 14.25E-3 P_{PEAK} or 1.425% which is very close to the 1.9% approximation in the previous example.

2.15 TACAN

We introduced TACAN in the discussion of DME and distance, but not the bearing function. The DME/TACAN transponder transmits an average of 2700 pulse pairs every second. TACAN modulates the amplitude to provide bearing information. As in VOR, the bearing of the aircraft is determined by measuring phase angle between a reference and variable signal. TACAN has two variable signals. One is sine wave modulation of the DME pulse amplitude, with a 15 Hz sine function. A second sine function at 135 Hz is the 9th harmonic of the 15 Hz sine function. The phase of these modulations is a function of aircraft position relative to the ground station. This is the same as in the VOR and modulation is generated by a rotating antenna pattern.

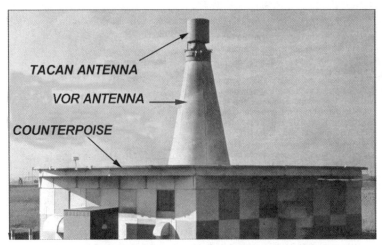

VORTAC ground station. VOR transmitting antenna on roof of shelter emits VOR bearing signals. TACAN, primarily a military system, is used by civil aircraft for the DME function.

Assume that only the 15 Hz sine modulation is applied to the DME pulse amplitudes. After pulse detection in the receiver, the phase is compared to a reference to determine the TACAN bearing of the aircraft.

The reference must be unaffected by the position of the aircraft and is transmitted on a subcarrier and omnidirectionally, as in the VOR system. The reference in TACAN is generated by arranging a group of pulses in the pulse modulation of the DME pulses. A burst of pulses called the north reference burst is generated. The same technique to create an ident pulse is used for the main reference group. Twelve pulse pairs have nominal spacing: 12 μs for X channels and 30 μs for Y channels between pulses in a pair; and 30 μs between pairs, make the north reference burst. To distinguish the reference burst from random squitter pulses, the reference group has regular, not random, spacing between pulses. The north reference burst occurs when the antenna points north, which occurs 15 times each second.

If phase is measured relative to the 15 Hz sine function, the angle is equal to the TACAN bearing. The system works, for all practical matters, exactly as the VOR system and accuracy is similar to that of VOR. TACAN has a second sine function with a frequency of 135 Hz, which is the 9th harmonic of the 15 Hz modulation. Eight auxiliary bursts are a reference for making phase measurements to this 135 Hz sine wave. The required ninth reference burst is shared with the main reference burst.

The auxiliary reference group consists of six pulse pairs with the constituent separation for X or Y channels. The pulse pairs are separated by 24 μs.

One cycle of the 135 Hz sine function only covers 40 degrees of the TACAN bearing. To determine the correct 40 degree segment of the TACAN bearing, the 15 Hz sine function is used as a coarse measurement. All other factors remaining the same, the accuracy of a TACAN system should be nine times better than a VOR system. In practice, accuracy is on the order of three times better.

The main purpose of TACAN, which provides the same information as VOR and DME, is the compact design of portable ground stations for the military. The wavelength, which is about one tenth that of VOR, requires smaller antennas. In the case of VOR it was pointed out that a rotating antenna was not physically possible because of size and rate of rotation. Because of slower rotational velocity and shorter wavelength, TACAN antennas can be mechanically rotated, as shown in Fig 2.23.

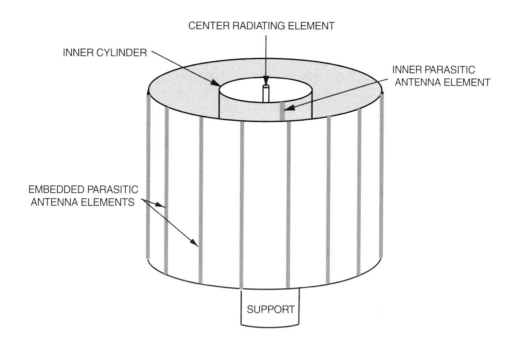

Figure 2.23 TACAN antenna showing rotating directors

The TACAN antenna consists of a central radiating element and nine rotating elements. The rotating elements act as directors in a directional array and are mounted on a dielectric drum-shaped structure. The antenna rotates 15 revolutions per second or 900 RPM, which is not unusually high. Unlike the VOR, the antenna is only about ½ meter in diameter. The 135 Hz fine modulation is generated by embedding 9 director elements in the rotating drum.

The shorter wavelength of TACAN also aids in siting problems. TACAN can operate aboard ships, where VOR would have extreme difficulties with multipath. TACAN can also do air-to-air ranging with airborne transponders.

2.16 LORAN-C: Long Range Navigation

None of the single navigation systems discussed thus far provide navigation for a long distance. VORTAC is good for 100 NM or so and the NDB between 10 and 50 NM. In the continental U.S. and other parts of the world, there are sufficient ground stations to make radio navigation available virtually everywhere. The limited range of the ground station is evident from the airways. To fly a route of significant distance, the path may be serpentine because airways often must not stray out of range of the VOR on which they are based. This is alleviated somewhat by RNAV—area navigation—which computes off-airways routes. RNAV frees aircraft from fixed legs between VOR's, but there is still much flying directly between VOR stations.

Not all air routes fly over populated areas. There are routes over the north pole and vast remote areas. Trans-oceanic routes have no ground-based VOR navigation. When flying over areas with no ground-based navigation separation has been as wide as 60 NM.

A radio-based navigation system, originally meant for ships at sea, called long-range navigation or LORAN, was developed during the Second World War. It was the first of a series of systems based on "hyperbolic" navigation.

The original LORAN system survived more than 20 years. An improved system called LORAN-C was placed on the air in 1958 to cover the east coast of the U.S. The original LORAN was renamed LORAN-A. There was a LORAN-B system but it was a modification of the original LORAN system for special applications and not used to any extent.

LORAN-C is based on a group of transmitters that are time synchronized. The original LORAN system synchronized a group by designating one transmitter as the master. The other stations, called auxiliary transmitters did not transmit until they received the master's signal. An additional time delay from when the signal from the master was received at the auxiliary and when that auxiliary transmitted was called the coding delay. Coding delay was generated by actually receiving the signal from the master and triggering a timer which controlled the transmission from the slave transmitter. This concept of coding delay is not applicable to the modern LORAN-C system. One improvement in LORAN-C is to synchronize the group of transmitters with an extremely accurate atomic clock. Therefore, variations of propagation time from the master to the auxiliary would not reduce system accuracy. Navigating on a hyperbolic system measures *the time difference*, TD, between the receipt of one transmitter relative to another.

To understand hyperbolic navigation, consider two transmitters that are time synchronized as shown in Fig. 2.24. For this discussion, when t=0 the transmitter M emits a pulse. This energy radiates from the transmitter in increasing circles. At a time t =Δ_c(M,X), the X transmitter transmits a pulse. What is important is the energy from the M transmitter passes the X transmitter.

Loran chain for Northeast U.S. The master station, M, is in New York state. Auxiliary stations are at W (Maine) , X (Nantucket) , Y (Carolina Beach) and Z (Illinois). The three star symbols (between M and Z, and W and Y are monitoring stations. Continental U.S. and southern Alaska are covered by a total of 27 master and auxiliary stations.

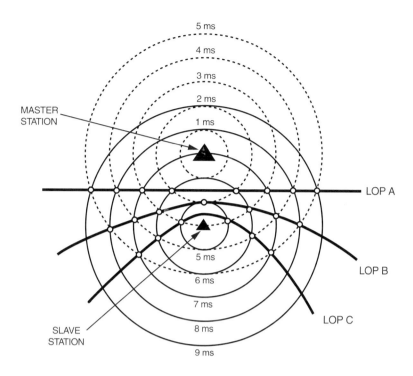

Fig. 2.24 Two time synchronized radio transmitters and elapsed time for propagating waves.

A receiver capable of receiving transmissions from M and X pick up the pulse from M before the pulse from X. Assume the distance from the receiver to M is R_M and R_X is the distance from the receiver to the X transmitter. Velocity of the waves is V. The times involved in transmission and reception of the pulses from M and X are:

Time M transmits	$t = 0$
Time X transmits	$t = \Delta_C(M,X)$
Time M is received	$t = R_M / V$
Time X is received	$t = R_X / V + \Delta_C(M,X)$

Exercise:

Prove that when the wave from the M transmitter passes the X transmitter, the signal from M will always be received before the signal from X. Be sure the proof covers all possible locations in two dimensions. (The proposition is true in three dimensions and the proof would be similar, but LORAN is a two dimensional system.)

Take the difference in time from when the pulse from M and X are received to obtain:

$$\Delta_\tau(M,X) = R_X / V + \Delta_C(M,X) - R_M / V \qquad (2.31)$$

where $\Delta_\tau(M,X)$ is the TD from the receipt of the pulse from M and the pulse from X.

Rewrite the equation to obtain:

$$R_X - R_M = (\Delta_\tau(M,X) - \Delta_C(M,X)) V \qquad (2.32)$$

In this equation V and $\Delta_\tau(M,X)$ are constant. If the receiver is stationary, then $\Delta_\tau(M,X)$ is constant. The velocity of radio waves, V, for the moment is considered a constant.

This equation, which relates a difference in distance to a constant, is the generating equation for a hyperbola. A hyperbola is the locus of all points where the difference in distance to two points, called the foci, is a constant. The "locus of all points" in the formal definition means, from any point on a hyperbola the difference in distance measured from the line to the two foci is a constant, as shown in Fig. 2.24. The hyperbola in the case of LORAN is a LOP (line of position) and the difference in distance to the two transmitters is a constant. Therefore, the transmitters are located at the foci.

The velocity, V, of the LORAN-C signal is not a true constant and can change with seasons and terrain. The transmitting delay, $\Delta_t(M,X)$, is adjusted to improve LORAN-C accuracy. These "constants" change very slowly and the purpose of deliberately changing $\Delta_t(M,X)$ is to compensate for changes in V. The LORAN receiver can make additional adjustments for variations in the velocity of propagation, as discussed later.

Knowing one's position to a LOP is a good start but the goal is to know position to a point. To progress from a line to a point, a third transmitter is synchronized to the other two. This transmitter we will call Y, is arranged so that waves from X and M pass by Y before it transmits. We could take transmitters X and Z and write the same equations as before and derive the same result.

$$R_Y - R_M = (\Delta_t(M,Y) - \Delta_c(M,Y))\, V \tag{2.33}$$

This equation describes a hyperbola with the foci at the location of transmitters M and Y, on which our position must lie. This hyperbola, the MY hyperbola, intersects the MX hyperbola at two points. Since we must lie on both LOPs we must be at one of the two points. This improves our position from a line to one of two points.

There are several methods to determine on which of the two points we lie. If we're on a ship and one of the two points is on land this is a good reason to choose one point over another. Where the equipment has been determining position for a while and the last measurement was close to one point and a considerable distance from the other, we assume we did not travel a huge distance in a short time.

Initially, ambiguity needs to be resolved, then logic applied to remove one of the points. There are transmitters M, X, and Y. Transmitters M and X were used together with M and Y. Each pair produces an LOP. Take X and Y, which will produce a third LOP as defined by:

$$R_Y - R_X = (\Delta_t(X,Y) - \Delta_c(M,Y) + \Delta_c(M,X))\, V$$

The three hyperbolas intersect at one point and a unique point of position is determined. Since position was determined by measuring distances, called rho-rho navigation, where rho refers to distance. Compare this to finding position relative to a VORTAC using VOR and DME, which is called rho-theta navigation.

Example: Determine the distance between the master and X slave in a LORAN-C chain, where the master is located at 54° 59' N; 08° 32' E and the X slave is at 52° 42' N; 06° 22' E.

Solution: The difference in longitude is 2° 10' or 2.167°. The difference in latitude is 2° 17' or 2.283°. By using the law of cosines in spherical geometry we calculate:

$$cos\,(\,c\,) = cos\,(\,a\,)\,cos\,(\,b\,) = 0.9985$$

The angle a is the change in longitude, the angle b is the change in latitude and c is the spherical angle between the master and slave. The "distance" between master and slave is the distance along the surface of the earth on a "straight" line drawn between master and slave. Another description is a "great circle" route between master and slave. This distance is R c, where R is the radius of the earth, which is 3444 NM. Therefore, the distance between master and slave is 3444 arccos (0.9985) = 189 NM.

Even though positions of the stations were given in degrees and minutes, the result of the arccos function must be in radians for the equation to be correct.

Relative to LORAN-C, the transmitter referred to as M, the first to transmit, is called the master. X and Y transmitters are called auxiliary, or slave, transmitters. Together they form a chain. Chains can have more than just two auxiliaries and usually do.

All LORAN-C transmissions use the same modulation and a carrier frequency of 100 kHz. The master station transmits at a well-defined repetition rate. The auxiliaries are timed so the master pulse is received first followed by the X auxiliary, the Y and the Z. If a W auxiliary is used, it is received before the X auxiliary. Since all transmitters in a LORAN-C chain are synchronized, and the master operates at a regular rate, all transmitters, master and auxiliary, transmit at the same rate called the group repetition rate or GRI. There are 40 possible repetition rates and no two LORAN-C chains share the same rate.

Every timing parameter of the LORAN-C system is controlled by extremely accurate clocks. This includes carrier frequency, time of transmissions of the master and all auxiliary transmitters. All transmitters of the chain are monitored and even the smallest clock error is corrected. The master station is corrected to the clock at the National Institute of Standards and Technology, NIST, for US-operated stations. Thus, transmitting times of the master and all auxiliary stations can be accurately predicted.

Assume that our aircraft has an accurate clock as well. Since we know when the LORAN-C station transmitted, we can subtract that time from the time the LORAN-C pulse is received and determine how long it took the signal to travel to the receiver.

Using the velocity of propagation of radio waves the distance to the LORAN-C transmitter is determined . Knowing distance to the transmitter produces an LOP, but rather than a hyperbola, it is a circle with the LORAN-C transmitter at the center.

A second transmitter produces a second circular LOP. Since two transmitters produced one hyperbolic LOP, there is a total of three LOPs, two circles and one hyperbola. There is only one point where the two circles and hyperbola intersect, which is the aircraft's position.

2.16.1 LORAN-C Chain

For hyperbolic navigation, three LORAN transmitters must be received. Therefore, the minimum number of transmitters in a chain is three, a master and two auxiliary stations. Very few chains have the minimum; the typical chain consists of a master, M, and three auxiliaries, X, Y, and Z. It is also common to add a fourth slave called W.

The separation between transmitters is between 150 and 250 NM, making coverage more than 1000 NM across. The areas have irregular shapes, which is a function of the geometry of the stations. To cover continental United States and offshore waters, there are 6 chains. All chains transmit on the same frequency of 100 kHz. Because all LORAN-C is on the same frequency, measures are taken to prevent interference from rendering the system inoperative.

It is a fact that LORAN transmitters overlap and cause interference for short periods at certain locations. LORAN receivers, however, are designed for reliable operation during those occasional collisions. To prevent continuous interference, each chain has a different group repetition interval or GRI. Should two pulses from different chains interfere in a receiver during one instant, those pulses will not coincide during the next transmission. There is occasional interference but it does not persist. Like DME, which does not require a reply from the ground station for every interrogation, the LORAN-C receiver can operate with an occasional missing pulse.

At the time of this writing there are fewer than 40 chains in the world and there is no sharing of GRIs. Therefore, a chain can be uniquely identified by its GRI. They span from the shortest of 49,900 μs to the longest of 99,900 μs. Chains are named to describe their geographic coverage, such as North Atlantic,

North Continental United States (NOCUS) and South Continental United States (SOCUS). The GRI is also an identifier, which is the GRI in μs divided by ten. For example; a chain that has a GRI of 99,800 μs is called the 9980 chain. This is the Icelandic chain, covering the upper North Atlantic Ocean.

Example: The NOCUS and SOCUS chains are adjacent to the central part of continental United States. The GRIs are 8290 and 9610. How often will the two overlap?

Solution: If an overlap occurs, an integer number of cycles of each chain occurs before the two overlap again. Since the interval is 82.9 ms for NOCUS and 96.1 ms for SOCUS, the following equation must be satisfied:

$$T = N(82.9E\text{-}3) = M(96.1E\text{-}3) \qquad (2.34)$$

where N and M are integers. One solution to the equation is N=961 and M=829 which would produce a T = 79.7s. There may be other solutions. To investigate this possibility, the equation is rewritten as N/M = 961/829. This fraction cannot be simplified because 829 is prime. Thus these chains overlap about every 80 seconds.

The 100 kHz operating frequency was chosen to insure that propagation is via ground wave. The original LORAN operated at almost 2 MHz, where ground wave was significant only during the day. At night, much energy propagated via sky wave, which limited the system's ability to provide accurate fixes.

The 100 kHz frequency is better than 2 MHz, but there is still the possibility of sky waves. Like any multipath problem involving pulses, the technique to overcome sky wave distortion is to use the early part of the transmitted pulse.

Another problem with 100 kHz is the significant atmospheric noise at this frequency. The solution is enormous power for LORAN-C transmitters. Typical power outputs are from about 250 kW to over 1 million watts, MW.

Each LORAN-C transmission is a group of eight pulses. They are about 270 μs long, with separation between each pulse of 1 ms, making the length of each transmission 8.27ms. Originally, the master station transmitted a ninth pulse as an identifier but this is not always done.

The LORAN-C pulse is shown in Fig. 2.26. The pulse envelope is closely approximated by the following equation,

$$V(t) = (V_0/4.225E\text{-}9)(\ t \exp(1\text{-}t/65E\text{-}6))^2 \qquad (2.35)$$

Where V(t) is the envelope voltage and t is the independent variable time.

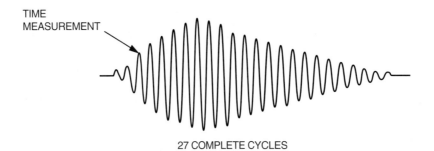

TIME MEASUREMENT

27 COMPLETE CYCLES

Figure 2.26 LORAN-C pulse

Equation 2.35 is for the envelope which amplitude modulates a 100 kHz carrier. As mentioned, every facet of LORAN-C is synchronized to an atomic clock. The pulse is configured to start when t=0 at a zero crossing of the carrier cycle. In many pulse amplitude modulated systems the relationship between envelope and carrier is a random, hit or miss, situation. In systems where time is measured, such as DME, the period of a carrier cycle is short relative to pulse width. In the case of DME, the carrier period is about a nanosecond. Therefore, a DME pulse has more than 3500 cycles between half amplitude points of the pulse. In the case of the LORAN-C pulse, there are only 27 carrier cycles and the zero crossing of the carrier cycle is used for time measurements. Therefore, the relationship between carrier zero crossings and the envelope is important. Distortions of the relationship are called envelope to cycle distortion or ECD.

Two possible phase angles of the carrier may be used. One phase relationship is where the rising edge of the first carrier cycle corresponds with the beginning of the pulse. The other is exactly 180 degrees different, where the falling edge of the first cycle corresponds with the beginning of the pulse. These phase angles both identify LORAN-C transmitters and information sent from LORAN-C stations.

Exercise: Using MathCad , MatLab or other mathematics program, plot the LORAN-C RF pulse. Suggestion: A simple spread sheet can perform this problem. Rather than a sophisticated mathematics program plot the LORAN-C pulse with a spread sheet.

Example: Calculate the energy per LORAN-C pulse for a 1 MW LORAN-C transmitter.
Solution: This exercise gives insight into the actual powers and energies in the generation of a LORAN-C transmission. We could write the equation for a LORAN-C pulse and integrate the square of the pulse over the period of the entire pulse and find the energy. This is valid and will work, except the integration becomes involved. Another approach is to find the energy in each half cycle and add the energies of all 56 half cycles. What makes this technique attractive is that the LORAN-C signal is actually generated a half cycle at a time and the integration gives an insight into parameters in the half cycle generation technique.

The energy of a half sine or half cosine pulse is the same, and is $(\pi/2)V_p^2$, where V_p is the peak voltage of the pulse. The peak voltage of any half cycle is given by the envelope equation:

$$V(t) = (V_0/4.225E\text{-}9)(\ t\ exp(1\text{-}t/65E\text{-}6))^2$$

The peak amplitude of the half cycles is found by evaluating the above equation for t=2.5μs, 7.5μs, 12.5μs etc. These times represent peaks of the half cycles. Since we are interested in the energy per cycle, which is proportional to the voltage squared, the sign of the cycle is not a factor. Therefore, the calculated energy is independent of the phase angle of the LORAN-C pulse. Remember, the phase is changed to transmit information.

The first task is to find out which half cycle has the highest peak power because it is this cycle that the 1MW refers to. Therefore $V(t)^2$ is calculated for the 56 values of t from 2.5μs to 282.5μs in 5μs steps.

This can be done in math programs such as Matlab or a spread sheet program.

As it turns out, the 14th half cycle produces the greatest amplitude of $V(t)^2$. It is necessary to scale the equation to the maximum value, 1.0 MW, the instantaneous peak of the 14th half cycle. Normally, voltage squared must be divided by the resistance of the circuit to find power. In this case we will use a resistance of 1 ohm. The impedance of the LORAN C transmitter may not be 1 ohm but this does not matter for our calculations. The actual voltage is not important, only the power. Therefore, our 1 ohm resistance will simplify calculations.

After scaling the equation of V(t)² so the maximum half cycle produces a 1.0 MW peak, we use the math program to sum the V(t)² values for all 56 half cycles. The energy for a half cycle is

$$(V_{PEAK})^2 / 4E\text{-}5$$

which is found by integrating a half sine or cosine squared pulse over the full half pulse. The total energy for all 56 half cycles is 41.7 joules.

It is interesting to continue this example to calculate average power transmitted by a LORAN-C station. Each transmission consists of 8 pulses. (We are not considering the old protocol of transmitting 9 pulses for a master.) The highest frequency occurs with the lowest GRI which is the 4990 GRI and a frequency of 20.04 Hz. Therefore, there are 160.3 pulses transmitted by the stations in the 4990 chain each second for a total power of 6686 watts.

The master transmission is shown in Fig. 2.27. The eight pulses are the 27-cycle group previously described. There are eight pulses separated by 1 ms. The ninth pulse shown is seldom used but was originally used to designate the master transmission. A typical group received by a LORAN-C receiver is shown in Fig. 2.28. Notice the master precedes the auxiliary transmissions.

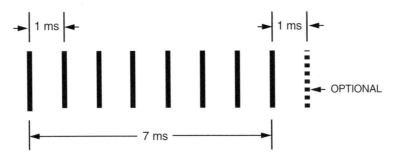

Figure 2.27 Transmission of a LORAN-C master station

Shifting the phase of the carrier between pulses further uniquely identifies LORAN-C transmissions and reduces interference from long delays due to multiple skywave reflections. For every other transmission, each pulse in the master pulse is:

$$0\ 0\ \pi\ \pi\ 0\ \pi\ 0\ \pi$$

where 0 represents an in-phase signal and π represents a signal out of phase with the reference. The next transmission, the phase coding of the master, is:

$$0\ \pi\ \pi\ 0\ 0\ 0\ 0\ 0$$

For auxiliary codes, the two phase relationships are:

$$0\ 0\ 0\ 0\ 0\ \pi\ \pi\ 0 \qquad\qquad 0\ \pi\ 0\ \pi\ 0\ 0\ \pi\ \pi$$

These codes are used by receivers to search and track stations.

70

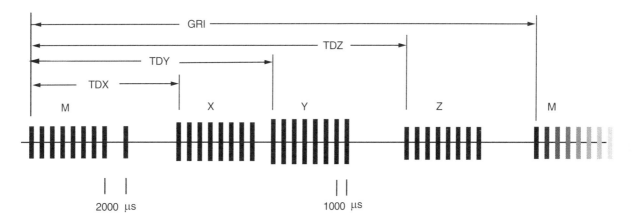

Figure 2.28 Typical LORAN-C chain, as received

2.16.2 LORAN-C Errors

There are several sources of error for the LORAN-C system. The obvious are: incorrect timing in the receiver, distorted signal due to multipath or interference, and errors at the ground station. These errors are no different from those of other navigation systems. Errors in signal detection and computation also cause navigation inaccuracy. For LORAN-C, errors depend on both equipment and location.

Determining accurate LOPs requires that velocity of propagation be known between the LORAN-C station and receiver. The velocity, c = 3E8 m/s, is the velocity of electromagnetic radiation in a vacuum. Radio waves for LORAN-C are not propagating in free space, but through ground waves that partially move in the ground or water, aided by the low carrier frequency of 100 kHz.. Velocity is somewhat less than c and, worst of all, variable. Actual velocity is a function of the path over which the waves travel. As an example, the velocity of propagation over salt water is faster than over fresh water, which is faster than over land. More sophisticated receivers know how much of the path to each transmitter is over water or land and make corrections to improve the position. The receiver finds an approximate position and, referring to a database, estimates the percentage of land, salt water and fresh water to calculate a reasonably accurate velocity of propagation.

Knowing the path over water and land improves position calculation, but other factors are not predictable. Snow cover, for example, affects velocity calculations. The LORAN-C receiver, if it knows the date, assumes that certain paths have no snow, but can't assume that in winter there will always be snow cover. There are other variables that defy prediction in addition to snow cover. To estimate velocity of propagation, monitor stations are placed at known positions. If a monitor knows its position and receives LORAN-C pulses from a particular chain, it can estimate the velocity of propagation. These stations are connected via data links to LORAN-C transmitters and communicate changes in the coding delay of the station. Therefore, coding delays are not fixed, but adjusted to minimize errors at the monitoring stations. This scheme does improve the accuracy of LORAN-C but has shortcomings. The major problem is that coding delay adjustments are based on observations made at the monitoring station. The greatest improvements, therefore, are for users in the vicinity of the monitor, which is placed as close as possible to the center of the coverage area. Even though major improvements are obtained near the monitoring station, there is a benefit over the entire coverage area of the chain.

In Figure 2.29, the drawing on the left shows the intersection of two hyperbolas which locates a LORAN-C receiver's position. The two LOPs intersect at nearly 90 degrees. Assume that because of receiver limitations and the condition of the received signal, the time delay can be measured to within 100 ns. Therefore, the hyperbola is not uniquely determined; it could be anywhere in the region shown in the figure. Assume for this example that the two hyperbolas shown are due to the time delay between the master and X auxiliary, and the master and Y auxiliary. Also assume the time delay error is the same for the two.

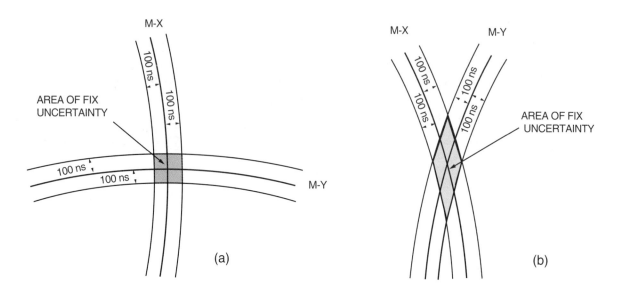

Figure 2.29 Details of dilution of precision (DOP)

The error changes the hyperbola, but for a small section the result moves the line segment toward and away from the focus, as shown in the figure. Therefore, the measured position lies somewhere in the shaded area.

Consider, now, the situation where the LOPs that intersect to produce the position do not intersect at 90 degrees but a much smaller angle, as shown in Fig. 2.29(b). The same 500 ns time delay measurement error produces an area with a shape that is different. The accuracy of position determination is a function of the distance from the actual position to the measured position. Accuracy is a radial or a distance. If we construct a circle of radius r that has at its center the actual position and encompasses the entire area in Figure 2.29, the radius is the worst case error, assuming that 500 ns was the worst case time delay error.

The more rigorous error is a two-dimensional statistical accuracy called the 2D RMS error, discussed in a later section, relative to GPS. The phenomenon introduced at this point is that the amount of error is a function of how hyperbolas intersect, another way of saying the amount of error is a function of position.

A factor called geometric dilution of precision, or GDOP (pronounced gee-dop), is how much an error of time measurement affects the accuracy of a position fix.

GDOP can be so bad, it makes LORAN-C virtually worthless. Most seriously degraded areas are on what is known as a "baseline extension". This is along a line drawn between two transmitters, a master and a slave or two slaves. What occurs is that hyperbolas converge along the baseline extension. In fact, the set of hyperbolas representing LOPs asymptotically converge on the baseline. The larger chains reduce the degradation of performance along the baseline extension with coverage from alternate slaves.

GDOP is not unique to LORAN-C or hyperbolic navigation. It affects other navigation systems such as GPS, which is a rho-rho-rho system. The 2DRMS accuracy of LORAN-C in most of the coverage area is on the order of 0.25 NM. Repeatability, that is the ability to return to the same location after a relatively short period of time, is about 50 to 100 meters.

Since LORAN-C is a time difference measurement, and all LORAN-C transmitters emit the same pulse, the point of the pulse for time measurement could, theoretically, be anywhere. To perform timing, the envelope or cycle zero crossings could be used. It is clear that a zero crossing is preferable to the envelope because transmitter voltage changes more rapidly at a zero crossing. However, we need to find the correct cycle. It would also appear that the greatest amplitude is around the sixth cycle, which is about 65 μs from the beginning of the pulse. The sixth cycle is, actually, not a good point. This is because 60 μs is enough time for a sky wave to interfere with the ground wave. A much better choice is the third cycle.

If the signal is strong and not distorted by multipath or interference, finding the third cycle is done by counting received cycles. The first cycle, however, has considerably less amplitude than the third and, if there is noise or interference, this cycle can be lost during simple counting. If there is a miscount, the fourth instead of third, cycle is used and the TD measurement is off by 10 μs, which considerable. This is called "cycle slip" and causes extreme error.

Many LORAN-C receivers use the envelope of the received pulse to find the third cycle. There are two basic methods to achieve this. The first takes the envelope, delays it and subtracting it from the non-delayed received signal envelope. The zero crossing of the result corresponds with the third cycle zero crossing.

When LORAN-C receivers were first available, the received signal was processed with analog integrated circuits, such as differentiators and comparators. With the advent of inexpensive and fast A/D converters, the LORAN-C pulse may be digitized, complete with noise and interference, and applied to a microprocessor. Digital processing is sophisticated, able to separate signal from noise and accurately measure time delay.

Exercise:
Determine the time delay required to cause the "envelope delay and subtract" technique to cross zero at the rising edge of the third cycle. Hint: This may be done most easily by using a simple mathematics plotting program and adjusting the time delay empirically until zero crossing occurs at zero crossing of the third cycle.

Another approach takes the derivative of the envelope twice to get the second derivative. The point where the second derivative crosses zero with a negative slope is approximately the zero crossing of the third cycle.

Exercise:
Show that the second derivative of the LORAN-C envelope is equal to zero with a negative slope at the third cycle.

2.16.3 LORAN-C Ground Station

Since all LORAN-C transmitters send the same pulse shape and pulse groups, but with different GRIs it is possible to use one LORAN-C transmitter in more than one chain. The same transmitter can be a master for one chain, while serving as an auxiliary for another. LORAN-C ground stations are expensive to build and operate and sharing saves considerable cost. The shared station may be required to transmit for the two chains such that transmissions would overlap. When this occurs, the master transmission takes precedence over the auxiliary. A station can also be an auxiliary in more than one chain.

The original LORAN-C ground stations used vacuum tubes, still the choice for generating very high RF power. The major problem with vacuum tubes is limited lifetime. Although life is measured in thousands of hours, LORAN-C transmitters operate 24 hours a day, 365 days a year and are vital to safe navigation. Original vacuum tube amplifiers were not the most efficient and, when power is as high as one Mw, efficiency is important. Most have been replaced with solid state power amplifiers of unique design. The amplifier is not an amplifier in the normal sense that an input signal is amplified to a high power level, where the output signal is similar in shape to the input. The solid state design has what is called a half cycle generator to provide output power. Since a half cycle is generated, the output is of one polarity and amounts to a pulse generator. Both positive and negative half cycles are required.

As shown in Fig. 2.26, the LORAN-C pulse consists of 27 cycles of a 100 kHz carrier or 54 half cycles. If each half cycle is considered a pulse of 5 μs width, then pulse generation techniques can be used. Only a few LORAN-C half cycles involve peak powers on the order of 1 Mw; most of the 27 cycles are considerably lower power.

The half cycle generators are configured so a standard set of generators can be used for any LORAN-C transmitter. Lower power transmitters require a minimum of 32 generators and higher powers add generators in groups of eight up to a maximum of 64 for a 1 Mw output. Outputs of the half cycle generators are combined with a passive filter network, which couples energy from all half cycle generators to the antenna.

The LORAN-C antenna is a vertical radiator. As discussed in the section on NDB, only vertical polarization supports ground wave propagation. The wavelength of the LORAN-C transmitter is 3000 meters. A resonant vertical radiator is a quarter wavelength or 750 meters. This height is prohibitive, so all LORAN-C antennas are shortened verticals.

There are two basic antennas; the simple monopole and top-loaded monopole. All require an extensive ground plane, which is usually a mesh of copper wire for providing a low resistance path to the earth. When current is fed to the antenna, the return path is through the earth, which is similar to the ground rod used for lightning safety for a telephone or power line at a home. For the ground return of a LORAN-C antenna, very deep ground rods connect to the copper mesh.

The shortened radiator is capacitive, which implies that to absorb power, reactance must be tuned out. Because such tuning involves a large inductance and radiation resistance is very low, the efficiency of the simple monopole is not high.

An improvement in LORAN-C antenna efficiency is obtained by adding a "capacitive hat" to the vertical radiator, as shown in Fig. 2.30. The hat is similar to the ground plane except there are fewer radial conductors. There are also peripheral conductors supported by four towers.

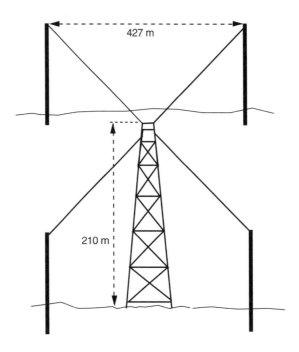

427 m

210 m

Figure 2.30 LORAN-C antenna with capacitive hat

The large five-tower antenna is more expensive because of added construction and real estate. However, due to improved efficiency and lower transmitter power less energy is wasted.

LORAN-C stations usually have an emergency generator that automatically goes on line during a power failure. In addition, most LORAN-C stations have complete redundancy, resulting in a high level of availability on the order of 99.9%.

74

2.16.4 Signal Integrity

As in any airborne navigation, the integrity of signals at the transmitter and receiver should be monitored. At each LORAN-C transmitter, parameters are monitored such as voltages, currents and timing. Should a signal anomaly be detected, the station signal is "blinked" to warn the pilot. This is done by transmitting only 6 of the 8 pulses. The transmitter is not removed from the air because the loss of one element in a LORAN-C chain will make tracking more difficult. For 0.25 seconds all eight pulses are transmitted and then 6 pulses for 3.75 seconds. Receivers in the aircraft have a detector which recognizes the blinked signal.

Monitoring stations, which adjust coding delay, as mentioned earlier, also detect transmissions that are seriously degraded and communicate that condition to the LORAN-C ground station.

2.16.5 LORAN-C Receivers

The receiver is one of the few applications of the TRF, or tuned radio frequency, design. The TRF is an amplifier with tuned circuits followed by a detector. Actually, the TRF predates the superheterodyne and, when broadcasting began in 1920, all vacuum tube receivers, not crystal sets, were TRFs. When the superheterodyne was invented by Edwin Armstrong, nearly all manufacturers converted to the superior design. A few holdouts who refused to pay inventor royalties continued to use the TRF.

The TRF is suited for the LORAN-C receiver because there is only one frequency and signals are strong. Atmospheric noise in the LORAN-C spectrum around 100 kHz is very strong, as are the LORAN-C signals. Therefore, noise figure is not an issue. The antenna is a simple rod type that does not need to be long. The antenna is filtered with a simple bandpass filter. A sharp-skirted filter may not be used because it would distort the signal. LORAN-C shares the spectrum around 100 kHz with other users, mostly narrow band emissions for communications. Since a sharp-skirted filter may not be used, notch filters eliminate specific interfering transmitters. Some receivers use fixed tuned filters, while others have tunable types that filter an interfering signal from a known location

The LORAN-C receiver does not use AGC. This is because signals are received from a number of transmitters and each has its own signal strength. Therefore, the dynamic range of the receiver must be great to handle a strong signal from a nearby station as well as weak transmissions. If the receiver distorts on strong signals, the clipped signals can still be used for processing. When the signal is very strong, locating the zero crossing of the third cycle is not difficult.

Most receivers provide an output which is extracted with a demodulator. The LORAN-C receiver must provide a time reference for calculations. Older receivers employed analog circuits to find the third cycle and provide a time reference output. Typically, an envelope detector, which also could be called an AM demodulator, was used. The envelope was differentiated twice and fed to a comparator. The zero of the second derivative was the time reference to locate the zero crossing of the third cycle.

Older LORAN-C receivers had extensive microprocessors. The processor determined the GRI, performed calculations on time of arrival of LORAN-C signals and computed position. In addition, the ground speed, waypoint information, along track and cross track errors and other parameters were calculated. A large data base was also required, including location of ground stations, GRIs, geographical information and so on. The early LORAN-C receiver had more read only memory (ROM) than any other component!

The modern LORAN-C receiver bears only a slight resemblance to the early models. First, the size of the database has increased, but with newer, much larger, ROM chips. The new receiver has only one or two. Secondly, there are virtually no analog circuits in the modern receiver. As shown in Fig. 2.31, other than amplification and filtering, the output of the TRF is digitized and processed in the microprocessor. The location of the third cycle zero crossing is performed by digital signal processing in the microprocessor.

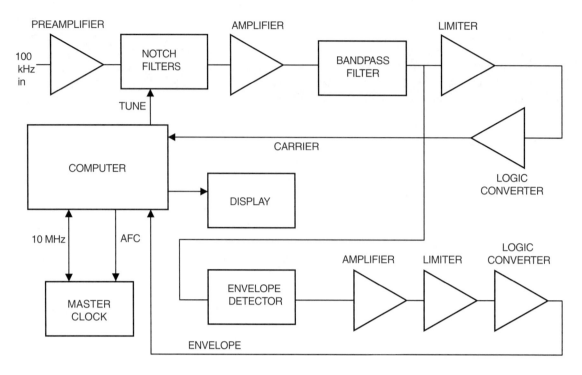

Fig. 2.31 LORAN-C receiver

The receiver operates in several modes. When first powered up, it initializes the computer and display. The second mode is to find and synchronize on pulses from the best chain. Generally, if an aircraft did not move since the previous flight, and the last position is current, the GRI of the best chain is known and easily found .

If the last position is not the same at turn on, the receiver may not find the last GRI, or find that the last GRI is not the best chain for the area. This can occur when the aircraft was moved with the LORAN-C off, a new unit is installed or the receiver was repaired. In this case the LORAN-C receiver must initiate a search. By finding any chain, the receiver calculates a position and determines what GRI is best for the area and that GRI is searched. Once it is found, a more precise and stable position is determined.

The third mode of operation is tracking. Once a position is determined, position is updated, and a ground speed calculated. Other parameters, such as distance, estimated time of arrival and cross track errors, to mention a few, are calculated and updated. As the aircraft moves to areas of decreased coverage such as baseline extensions or simply moving out of the coverage area, the LORAN-C receiver acquires lock on a new chain. Once the new chain provides superior data, the receiver automatically switches chains. Some receivers can track more than one chain and provide an improved position between coverage areas by tracking two chains simultaneously.

Chapter 2 Review Questions

2.1   What electric field polarization is used with a non-directional beacon? Why?
2.2   How is the directional ambiguity of a loop antenna removed?
2.3   Why is the loop antenna of a direction finding receiver enclosed in a conductive pipe?
2.4   How are the signals of the loop and sense antenna combined in one receiver in an ADF?
2.5   Why is up-converting used in the design of an ADF?
2.6   What is quadrantal error?
2.7   What purpose does a static discharger serve in an aircraft?
2.8   How does the VOR solve some problems of the non-directional beacon?

2.9 What is a CDI and what information is available from it?

2.10 An aircraft is heading 270 degrees and receiving the 270 degree TO radial from a VOR. The aircraft CDI is centered and indicates TO. If the aircraft makes a turn and returns on the same course in the opposite direction, what does the CDI and TO/FROM indicator show?

2.11 How does the pilot positively identify a VOR station?

2.12 How does a VOR differ from a VORTAC?

2.13 What could cause a VOR indicator to show "OFF".

2.14 Why are Doppler VORs used?

2.15 A custom-made Doppler VOR ground station was tailored to generate perfect VOR signals for the channel, 108.2 MHz. This station was moved to a new location, where the operating channel is 117.95 MHz. What effect would this have on the resulting VOR signal? How could it be corrected?

2.16 If a VOR receiver uses a 21.4 MHz IF with low side injection, what is the range and frequency resolution of the local oscillator?

2.17 If the local oscillator for the previous problem is generated with a single loop phase locked loop, and a 32/33 dual modulus prescaler, and a 50 kHz reference frequency, what values for the main and auxiliary counters may be used for the synthesizer?

2.18 If a DME operating on a channel of 109.10 MHz receives a reply from a ground transponder 112 µs after the transmission of an interrogation. The time reference for the elapsed time measurement is from the ½ amplitude point of the first interrogation pulse to the ½ amplitude of the first reply pulse. What is the distance to the DME ground station?

2.19 What is slant range?

2.20 What does it mean when a pilot reports a position of 5 miles, DME?

2.21 How does DME relate to the TACAN system?

2.22 A rectangular pulse would have a shorter rise time and would be easier to measure time. However, the DME uses a Gaussian pulse. Why?

2.23 Which navigation channels are X channels? Which are Y channels?

2.24 Relative to the DME transponder, what are squitter pulses? Why are they used?

2.25 How does the DME interrogator locate its reply from all the pulses received in a time period?

2.26 When would a DME transponder not reply to a valid interrogation?

2.27 Draw the block diagram of a DME interrogator.

2.28 Why can the DME interrogator receiver use AGC while the DME transponder cannot?

2.29 What technique is used to prevent two DME interrogators from becoming time synchronized?

2.30 How is the bearing portion of TACAN transmitted?

2.31 How does the TACAN system improve on the VOR system?

2.32 What is a line of position? What would be the shape of the LOPs from a VOR, DME and LORAN-C?

2.33 Why is LORAN-C called a hyperbolic navigation system?

2.34 What basic information is obtained from a LORAN-C system?

2.35 How does the LORAN-C system insure the pulse from the master station will be received before any of the slaves?

2.36 What is a baseline extension? How are LORAN-C signals affected on baseline extensions?

2.37 What elements constitute a LORAN-C chain?

2.38 Why is the third cycle of a LORAN-C pulse used for timing measurements?

2.39 What is GDOP?

2.40 Relative to a LORAN-C ground station, what is a "half cycle generator"? How are these used?

2.41 Relative to LORAN-C signals, what is "blinking"?

References

Forsell, Borje, Radionavigation Systems, Englewood Cliffs N.J., Prentice Hall, 1991

Kayton, Myron and Fried, Walter, Avionics Navigation Systems, 2nd Edition, New York, John Wiley and Sons, 1997

Rohde, Ulrich, Digital Frequency Synthesizers, Upper Saddle River, N.J., Prentice-Hall, 1983

Chapter 3

Terrestrial Landing Aids

3.0 Introduction

Since the beginning, avionics were intended to make landings and departures in bad weather possible. Just how bad is bad? When conditions are good and no electronic aids are required, it is VMC, for visual meteorological conditions. When weather worsens, it becomes IMC, for instrument meteorological conditions. Pilots then fly IFR, under instrument flight rules. Needless to say, there are degrees of IMC; some days are foggier than others. Two parameters to describe the severity of IMC are visibility, and ceiling.

Visibility is the distance one can see horizontally and recognize objects. Ceiling is the height of the bottom of the clouds. Inside clouds visibility is virtually zero. A *precision* landing system is required for visibility less than 2600 feet and ceilings less than 200 feet. A precision landing system must provide both vertical and horizontal guidance along the approach path to the desired runway. ADF provides directional information so an aircraft can head to the NDB ground station. This enables an aircraft to find an airport if the NDB is located at or near the airport, as many are. If visibility is good and the airport in view, a landing is easily made. Just arriving at the airport is not enough, however, when conditions deteriorate. The aircraft should arrive at the touchdown zone of the runway, not 50 meters above, and on the same course as the runway.

If a VOR is located off the end of the runway, flying the radial aligned with the runway enables the pilot to not only locate the airport, but follow the same heading as the runway. A VOR, however, provides no vertical guidance to aid in the descent. Although NDBs and VORs provide "non-precision" landing guidance, they are primarily for en route navigation. These systems do not furnish two essentials for a precision landing, namely high accuracy and vertical guidance.

The precision of an approach---which translates to how low the airplane may descend--- is dictated mainly by ceiling and visibility. In most instances, these are reported by weather observers and broadcast to the pilot, often through the voice feature of a VOR. At large airports with heavy commercial traffic, visibility is automatically measured by a "transmissometer," which sends a light beam alongside a runway and measures how much is lost over a short distance. This results in an RVR, or Runway Visual Range, measured in feet.

The beginning of an instrument approach is often the initial approach fix, or IAF. The aircraft now transitions from the en route to the approach phase. The final approach fix (FAF) is where the aircraft takes the same heading as the runway, and the remainder of the approach is a straight line to the runway.

Today, instrument landings end with a visual touchdown. This implies there is a point in the approach where the flight crew must see the runway to land. This point is usually based on an altitude above the runway elevation called decision height (DH) . (Also used in some procedures is Decision altitude, which is referenced to mean sea level.) If the crew does not make visual contact with the runway at decision height, it must apply power and do a go-around. This is the missed approach point, or MAP. Some aircraft are also equipped for *autoland*---which enables a touchdown and rollout in completely zero-zero conditions (no ceiling, no visibility). There are, however, no airports in the U.S. where the procedure is approved, but that should change in the future.

3.1 ILS: Instrument Landing System

ILS appeared in the late 1930s and has been used for civil landings since 1947. Like VOR, ILS uses VHF frequencies and directional antennas. The entire ILS system consists of horizontal and vertical approach guidance, position marker beacons, approach lights and monitoring and control equipment. There are about 1000 ILS-equipped airports in the U.S. and another 500 throughout the remainder of the world. These installations meet ICAO Standards and Recommended Practices (SARPS) to insure that any aircraft with an ILS receiver may make safe landings at any ILS-equipped airport in the world

Horizontal guidance is provided by a localizer, which produces a radio beam along an approach path that is an extension of the runway centerline. The range of the localizer signal is at least 20 NM. Approach procedures call for an interception of the localizer beam at less than 20 NM from the touchdown point, where the localizer signal is strong and reliable. Once the beam is intercepted, the approach is straight in at the runway's heading. Progress along the path is indicated by marker beacon transmitters which radiate signals vertically. They are received when the aircraft is directly over the transmitter, producing visual and aural signals to the pilot.

The localizer transmits in the VHF navigation band from 108.1- 111.95 MHz using every odd 100 kHz and every odd 100 kHz plus 50 kHz. The frequencies are; 108.10, 108.15, 108.30, 108.35, 111.90, and 111.95 MHz. This is a total of 40 frequencies, of which 38 are used for navigation and two for test purposes. The two test frequencies are 108.1 MHz and 108.15 MHz.

Vertical guidance is provided by the glide slope transmitter, which works in a fashion similar to the localizer. Like the localizer, the glide slope provides one approach path, which is nominally a 3 degree descent measured from the horizontal.

The glide slope operates in the UHF portion of the spectrum from 329.15 to 335.00 MHz. Each frequency is paired with a localizer, as the glide slope is always used with a localizer. Thus, there are 40 total frequencies of which two, 334.70 and 334.55 MHz are reserved for test purposes. These frequencies are the paired glide slope channels for 108.10 MHz and 108.15 MHz.

Frequency pairing does not follow a simple rule because the original number of localizer channels was 20. When this was increased to 40, glide slope channels were inserted how and where they could be, which resulted in an arbitrary distribution. The glide slope receiver is automatically set to the correct frequency by the localizer receiver. Glide slope frequencies are not printed on charts or displayed in the cockpit. No pilot needs to know the glide slope frequency for a particular localizer. Consequently, only avionics technicians know the strange relationship between localizer and glide slope frequency.

3.1.1 Localizer

To understand the localizer, imagine two very narrow-beam, horizontally-polarized antennas. An actual localizer uses a more sophisticated antenna, but the two-beam analogy is a good starting point. Imagine that the localizer feeds one antenna with a carrier that is amplitude modulated at 40% with a 90 Hz sine wave, as shown in Fig 3.1. The second antenna, close to the first, is fed by a signal with exactly the same carrier but with 40% 150 Hz sine wave modulation.

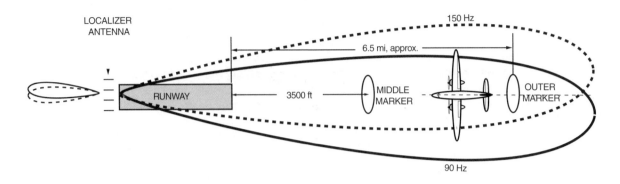

Figure 3.1 Rudimentary localizer beam

Further, imagine these antennas displaced from the runway centerline by a few degrees, as shown in the figure. If a radio receiver is positioned on the extended runway centerline, equal amounts of energy from both antennas are received because of the symmetry. Therefore, the 90 Hz and 150 Hz sidebands are received with equal intensity, and the carrier at twice the intensity since it is received in equal amounts from each antenna.

Receiving twice the carrier intensity is true only if the two antennas are fed with exactly the same carrier. Because the received carrier is due to vector addition, the distance from the receiver to each of the two antennas must be exactly the same. This is necessary, so the carrier adds in phase. This can be assured by placing the two antennas close to each other. As long as the aircraft is not far left or right, the phase angle between the two received signals is zero and the carriers add in phase.

The signal at the receiver on the runway extended centerline is carrier modulated with 20% at 90 Hz and 20% at 150 Hz. You may wonder how two signals originally modulated with 90 and 150 Hz at 40% are received at 20% each. This is because the carrier received on the runway centerline is twice the amplitude received from each antenna individually. The sidebands, being at different frequencies do not add vectorally. The percentage of modulation is reduced because the carrier increases by a factor of two, a result of vector addition, while sidebands remain the same amplitude. It is important to understand how these signals add in space (sometimes called space modulation) and affect percentage of modulation. The localizer system is based on percentage of modulation as generated by space modulation.

If the receiver moves away from the runway centerline, the receiver will experience more modulation of one tone and less of the other. The carrier amplitude may change somewhat, but that is not as important. Remember, the localizer relies on the difference in depth of modulation, DDM, and not the absolute signal strength. When the percentage of modulation of one tone is greater than the other, the localizer receiver will display a course deviation. It is easy to see how the percentage of modulation is the same for both tones only on the runway centerline.

Theoretically, this simple scenario will work but antennas with such narrow beams are not practical. The localizer should be capable of indicating a small fraction of a degree of deviation from the desired course. We did, however, learn some important concepts that will be useful in understanding the modern localizer antenna system.

3.1.2 Localizer Ground Station

Assume, again, that there are two directional antennas. This time the antennas do not need to be highly directional. They are separated by a distance, a, which is an important part of the design and can be adjusted to change the antenna radiation pattern. Assume each antenna is fed with just a carrier; no modulation. The same signal with no phase difference is applied. When the distance from either antenna to the receiver is exactly the same, the two signals arrive at the receiver in phase and the result is twice the field intensity, as would be received from one antenna. If the antennas are arranged as shown in Fig. 3.2, where they are offset from the extended runway center line by the same distance, maximum signal is received on the center line.

If the two antennas are fed with signals exactly out of phase, instead of a signal increase at the extended runway centerline there is no signal, or a null, because of cancellation. An antenna fed with in-phase signals is called a sum antenna, while an antenna fed with signals exactly out of phase is a difference antenna. Both provide numerous peaks and nulls but when the peak occurs on the centerline, it is a sum antenna, and when the null falls on the centerline, the antenna is a difference antenna.

The previous, deliberately simple, example of how a localizer signal could be generated requires very directional antennas. It is difficult to generate narrow beams without resorting to large parabolic reflectors or other exotic techniques. Because of the wavelength, about 3 meters, these techniques are impractical. It is easy, however, to generate sharp nulls with a simple antenna. The modern localizer array uses only moderately directional antennas driven with signals that produce nulls. The nulls are strategically positioned and are the key to the localizer antenna pattern. To appreciate that high gain is not required, let us investigate what happens if two omnidirectional antennas create a localizer signal.

When the distance R is much greater than a, the distances from the receiver to the radiators, r_1 and r_2 are given by:

$$r_1 = R + (a/2)\sin\theta \tag{3.1}$$
$$r_2 = R - (a/2)\sin\theta$$

This is reasonable since the separation between antennas, a, will be a wavelength or a few meters, while the distance to the receiver in an aircraft on approach is thousands of meters. We are interested in the *difference* in distances from antennas to the aircraft. If, for example, the two radiators are fed with signals exactly in phase, when the difference in distance is zero, the two signals arrive at the receiver in phase and add. There is a 6 dB enhancement over the signal received from one radiator alone. On the other hand, if the difference is one half wavelength, the signals, although fed to the antennas in phase, arrive at the receiver out of phase and total cancellation results. The difference:

$$\Delta R = r_1 - r_2 = R + (a/2)\sin\theta - (R - (a/2)\sin\theta) = a\sin\theta \tag{3.2}$$

The two signals combine to increase or decrease the signal as below:

$$E(\theta,R) = [(R_0 E_0)/R](1 + \cos(2\pi \Delta R/\lambda)) = [(R_0 E_0)/R](1 + \cos(2\pi a \sin(\theta)/\lambda)$$

where $E(\theta,R)$ is the magnitude of the electric field intensity at a distance R and an angle θ. E_0 is the electric field obtained from only one antenna at some distance R_0.

To get a feel for the type of radiation pattern this array produces let us plot several antenna patterns for different values of a. It is seen in Fig. 3.2 that as separation increases, but is still integer multiples of a wavelength, the antenna lobe on the runway centerline narrows, while side lobes increase in number. Since we want to cover about plus and minus 20 degrees from the centerline, a separation of 3λ produces a lobe with a half power beamwidth of about plus and minus 20 degrees.

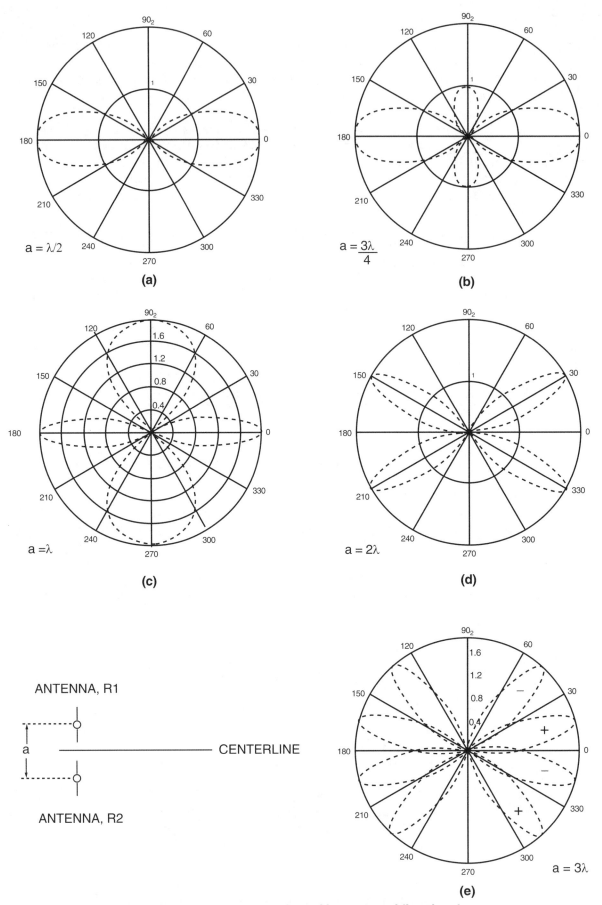

Figure 3.2   Antenna patterns generated by two omnidirectional radiators fed in phase, (a, b, c) and out of phase, (d, e)

82

Next, the antennas are fed with signals that are out of phase. Now there are nulls where there were peaks for the in phase situation. Therefore, there is a null along the runway centerline and a peak to either side, as shown in Fig. 3.2(d, e). Notice, also, the + and - signs in the lobes. These indicate the phase relationships of those nulls.

This discussion related only to a carrier feeding the antennas. Assume the two antennas are "out of phase", with a double sideband suppressed carrier signal, called "sideband only" or SBO. We use 90 Hz single tone modulation. The term "out of phase" is in quotes because there is no carrier to measure phase against. However, the phases of the missing carriers are 180 degrees apart. In other words, carriers that were modulated to provide the SBO signal were of opposite phase. These two new antennas also straddle the runway center line. The sum antenna is also modulated with 90 Hz at 20% which is called "carrier and sidebands", or CSB. The modulation for the sum antenna is normal AM, which has a carrier. Along the runway centerline no signal is received from the difference antennas because the runway extended centerline coincides with the null. Thus, a carrier modulated with 20% of 90 Hz modulation is received.

Consider, next, what happens when the aircraft deviates from the runway centerline. It receives less signal from the sum antenna, which implies that less carrier and 90 Hz sidebands are received. The reduction of carrier and sidebands from the sum antenna is gradual for small angles. We also come out of the null for the difference antenna and receive more sidebands. The null is sharp, however, so a significant increase of sidebands occurs for small changes in θ.

Notice that if there is movement either side of the centerline, there is an increase in sideband energy and an apparent increase in modulation. This is not desirable. . What is required is an increase of 90 Hz modulation with deviation to one side of the centerline and a decrease on the other. If this is achieved with 90 Hz, we can add 150 Hz modulation and do the same on the other side of the runway centerline.

When the antenna pattern was plotted for the difference antenna in Fig. 3.2, there were plus and minus signs for each lobe. An antenna pattern usually is a plot of the magnitude of a signal around an antenna. Usually, the phase of the received signal is not important. Since we are using two arrays, a sum and difference, the sign of the pattern is important. If the difference antenna had a plus sign for the lobe to the left of the runway centerline, deviating to that direction would cause an increase of 90 Hz modulation because it adds in phase with the sum antenna lobe on the centerline. Likewise, when the receiver is to the right of the runway centerline, the negative sign of the difference antenna pattern subtracts the 90 Hz sidebands and reduces the amount of modulation. This is the characteristic we need for the 90 Hz modulation.

Handling the 150 Hz modulation requires that a 150 Hz tone modulates a carrier, which is out of phase with the 90 Hz modulation. When fed to the difference antenna array, the antenna pattern is the same shape, except pluses and minuses are reversed. Therefore, the percentage of 150 Hz modulation increases when the aircraft is to the right of the runway centerline and decreases when to the left Since the null provides the increase and decrease in depth of modulation, the change can be significant for small angles of θ. This produces a narrow localizer beam without a high gain antenna. The signal source for the sum and difference arrays is shown in Fig. 3.3.

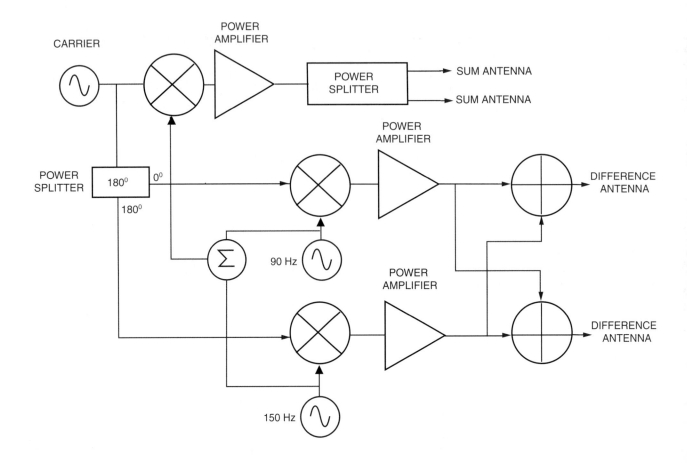

Fig. 3.3. Method of generating signals applied to localizer sum and difference antennas.

The beginnings of a localizer signal are becoming apparent. There is, however, a significant problem; many localizer beams in addition to the desired one along the runway centerline. First, we used the example of an omnidirectional antenna. This is a difficult antenna to make and was discussed for the VOR ground station and Alford loop antenna. It is actually easier to make a somewhat directional antenna. To plot the localizer pattern for an array of directional antennas, multiply the patterns for the omnidirectional case by the antenna pattern of the directional antenna. The typical localizer array uses a log periodic antenna, which has a gain of about 14 dB and significantly reduces the field intensity of false localizer beams to the side of the array, as shown in Fig. 3.4. A localizer beam also emitted from the back of the antenna is not completely eliminated. This is called the back course and discussed in a later section.

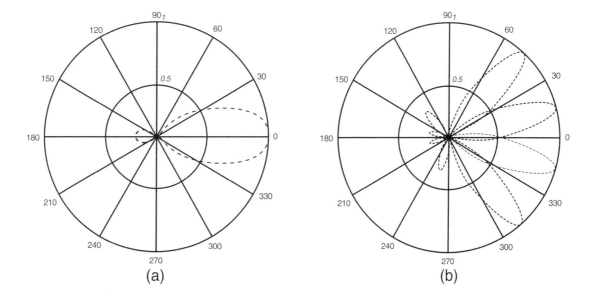

Fig. 3.4. Localizer beams formed by array of directional antennas. Pattern on the left is the directional equivalent of Fig. 3.2(a). Pattern on the right is the equivalent of Fig. 3.2(e).

A directional antenna cannot completely remove false localizer beams from the side of the antenna array. Because the antennas are directional, but not extremely narrow, false beams are much weaker than the desired beam, typically by 20 dB or more. However, if an aircraft is close to the localizer and off course, an apparently normal localizer beam could be intercepted. It would lead to the runway, but the aircraft would not head down the runway centerline. Some means is required to prevent the pilot from flying a false localizer beam. The technique, called a clearance beam, covers up false localizer beams.

If a signal is radiated to cover false localizer beams at the same frequency, additional vector addition of the radiated signals would only cause more false beams. To prevent vector addition, the cover-up signal is at a different frequency. The main localizer signal is the "course" signal and the cover up signal is the "clearance" signal. The course transmitter operates 4.75 kHz above the nominal channel center frequency, while the clearance transmitter is 4.75 kHz below it.

When an AM radio receives two signals, it produces a heterodyne, or beat frequency, which is equal to the difference in frequency. In this case, the difference is 9.5 kHz. This frequency is sufficiently above localizer frequencies 90 and 150 Hz and sufficiently above the 1020 Hz ident tone or any audio on the localizer so there is no interference. The two frequencies cannot be too far apart or they will not pass through the IF filter of the localizer receiver. ICAO Annex 10 recommends that the frequency difference be no less than 5 kHz and no greater than 14 kHz, which implies an offset from the nominal carrier of 2.5 kHz to 7 kHz.

For the clearance signal, there is an additional set of antennas. The clearance signal provides high level modulation at the tone frequency to insure correct CDI (course deviation indicator) deflection . The clearance transmitter and antennas do not provide a guidance signal but a strong "fly left" or "fly right" indication. The signals are single tone- modulated with more than 40% modulation of either 90 or 150 Hz modulation. When the strong clearance signal is received, the "capture effect" causes the localizer receiver to deviate full scale left or right and cover any false localizer beams. This is the "two-frequency capture-effect" localizer.

Performance of the localizer is a DDM (differential depth of modulation) that is linear with angular displacement, plus or minus about 3 or 4 degrees from the centerline. The accuracy of the centerline is approximately 0.1 to 0.5 degrees. The localizer covers about plus or minus 35 degrees from the runway centerline up to about a 7 degree glide path.

To prevent beam bending due to multipath, the localizer should have a narrow antenna pattern. Thus, the typical localizer antenna system consists of 7 pairs of antennas or 14 directional antennas, with larger arrays possible. Individual antennas of the array are log periodic dipoles, mildly directional, and capable of operating on any of the 40 localizer frequencies. The localizer has a Morse code identifier as tone-modulated 1020 Hz. This is applied to the CSB signal on both courses and clearance signals.

3.1.3 Back Course

Older localizers radiated energy from the rear of the antenna. This produced a serviceable beam at the back of the antenna array. The rear facing localizer, called the back course, can be used for departure guidance and for non-precision approaches to the opposite end of the instrument runway. New localizer antennas, however, do not have significant radiation from the rear, and a back course may not be available. Because of the value to navigation, many new localizers install a special array to restore the back course.

There are significant differences in the back course approach. First, signal levels are not as great as on the front course, where antenna gain is higher. Secondly, there is no glide slope for vertical guidance or marker beacons to help the pilot. Consequently, weather minimums must be higher to fly the back course. Many localizer receivers have a back course mode, which reverses the sense of the CDI pointer so it operates in a conventional (fly left, fly right) manner.

The localizer station consists of two transmitters, for course and clearance. They operate on two frequencies and each provides two outputs, CSB and SBO. There is a set of back up transmitters so each localizer station has four transmitters and each transmitter has two outputs. An antenna changeover unit selects one of the two transmitters for the localizer. A monitor checks parameters such as power output, VSWR, modulation level and carrier frequency. If the operating transmitter should go out of specification, the standby transmitter is automatically switched in. The importance of phase angle in radiating localizer signals dictates that the antenna changeover unit may not introduce additional phase delay to the RF signal path.

Because the localizer signal is so crucial to safety of flight, the radiated field is monitored. A receiver is mounted near the approach end of the runway to pick up the localizer signal. The correct DDM for the location is known; the monitor is not necessarily on the runway center line. Should the received DDM change, indicating a bend in the localizer beam, an alarm is sent and the localizer station may be taken off the air.

The two-frequency, capture-effect localizer station described is one of many possible variations, but represents the most advanced design, and the type installed by the FAA at the time of this writing.

3.1.4 Localizer Receiver

A block diagram of a localizer receiver is shown in Fig 3.5. Usually, the receiver is shared with the VOR. This ability is assured by using frequencies in the VOR band for localizers and adopting compatible bandwidth and antenna polarization. In large aircraft it is common to have separate VOR and LOC receivers, but is seldom done in GA (general aviation) aircraft.

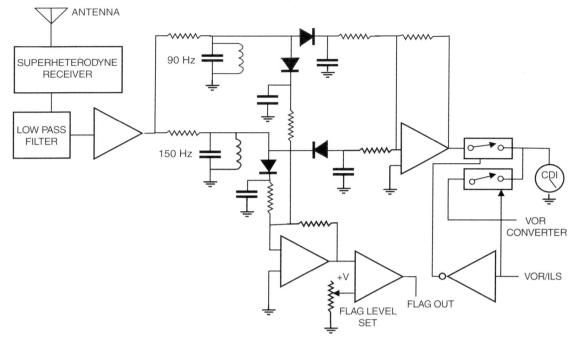

Figure 3.5 Localizer receiver

The shared navigation receiver, called a VOR/LOC, or NAV, receiver automatically switches to the localizer signal converter when a localizer frequency is set into the receiver. The OBS (omnibearing selector) is deactivated, the TO/FROM indicator hidden and the nav flag is used for the localizer.

Demodulated AM is fed to two bandpass filters which filter the 90 and 150 Hz tones. The output of each tone filter is rectified and drives a zero-center meter movement. This is the same CDI as for the VOR. If the aircraft is on course, voltages at the output of the 90 Hz and 150 Hz filters are the same and the meter centers. If the aircraft moves left of course, output from the 90 Hz filter rises. The opposite is true for the other side of the centerline. The simplified block diagram shows inductor-capacitor bandpass filters. In the early days, VOR receivers did use such a circuit but large inductors and capacitors are very unattractive. Modern receivers implement the equivalent circuit using op amps, microprocessors and digital signal processing, DSP.

Signal strength varies as the aircraft moves from side to side, with strength in the center twice that of the far left or right. Meter deflection is proportional to the difference in percentage of modulation of each tone, or DDM (differential depth of modulation).

The LOC (or VOR/LOC) receiver has AGC (automatic gain control) to compensate for changes in absolute signal strength. Therefore, outputs of the tone filters are proportional to the percentage of modulation of each tone. Filter outputs are rectified and subtracted from each other. The meter, therefore, reads DDM.

The two modulating tones are harmonics of 30 Hz. The 90 Hz tone is the third harmonic and the 150 Hz tone is the fifth. This means the two modulating tones are phase locked and their sum has a frequency of 30 Hz.

Exercise:

Using MatLab or other mathematics program, plot the envelope of the localizer signal as received at the center line. Determine the percentage of modulation.

Exercise:
Prove that the localizer envelope is a periodic signal with a frequency of 30 Hz. (Hint: Use the definition of periodicity and write the equation for the localizer modulation.)

The localizer pointer is a course deviation indicator (CDI), the same as for the VOR The sense of the indicator is also the same; the indicator points in the direction of the desired course. Another way of stating this is, the pointer indicates the direction to fly to return to the desired course. As with VOR, the CDI is not a calibrated indicator. It does not give an indication of distance off course but direction and approximate magnitude. There is no practical maneuver that requires sustained flying off the runway center line such as an angled or curved approach. The OBS and TO/FROM indicator are inoperative when the receiver selects a localizer frequency. The NAV flag is used for the localizer.

The localizer has a Morse code ident and may also have voice. The ident always begins with the letter "I" to indicate an ILS signal. The tone is the same as for VOR, 1020 Hz. The ident must repeat no less than every 10 seconds.

3.1.5 Localizer Receiver Signal Integrity

DDM is the metric that enables the localizer receiver to function. The sum of the modulation is nearly a constant and adds to about 37%. To drive the CDI, the *difference* between the amount of 150 Hz and 90 Hz modulation is used to determine if the signal is valid; the *sum* of the 90 Hz and 150 Hz tones is taken. If a centered signal of 0.00 DDM is present and each tone modulates the carrier at 20%, the nav flag is hidden from view, meaning the signal is good. If one of the tones is absent, the resulting percentage of modulation is 20% and the flag would appear. If the signal is a far off-course indication, the signal contains only one tone but the percentage of modulation is 40% and the flag does not appear. For a clearance signal with 80% or higher modulation, the flag does not appear, as this is also a valid signal.

Like the VOR, the localizer suffers problems of multipath interference. As explained, a directional antenna only adds to multipath problems and the localizer requires directional antennas. The localizer system has been in service for more than 50 years and improvements have mainly been in the antenna. There have been advances which permit a single frequency localizer to provide as much accuracy as a dual frequency installation..

Signal integrity is monitored at localizer ground stations. Various transmitter voltages and currents are checked, as well as forward and reflected powers. Because the antenna is an important part of the system, near field and far field monitors continuously monitor signals.

3.2 Marker Beacons

During an instrument approach, the aircraft's position is verified by a marker beacon. It is a 75 MHz transmitter with a directional antenna directed upward. Power output of a marker transmitter is not great, so the signal is only received when the aircraft is directly in the antenna beam. The aircraft is fitted with a 75 MHz receiver and an antenna on the belly. The receiver is not highly sensitive for the same reason that the marker transmitter is not high power. The aircraft should receive the signal only when directly overhead. Most marker receivers have a low sensitivity mode to permit the most accurate determination of position by further reducing sensitivity of the receiver.

There are three types of marker beacons; outer marker, middle marker and inner marker. There was a fourth type called the airway, or "Z," marker but it is no longer used. The inner marker is seldom used and is primarily for a CAT III instrument landing system.

The 75 MHz marker is modulated with three audio tones. The outer marker is amplitude modulated with 400 Hz and identified by 2 dashes per second. The middle marker is modulated with a 1300 Hz tone, with alternating dots and dashes. The inner marker is modulated with a 3 kHz tone, with 6 dots per second.

The marker beacon receiver filters the tones and illuminates one of three lamps on the instrument panel. The outer marker illuminates a blue lamp, the middle marker an amber lamp, and the inner marker, a white lamp. With lamps, tones and dot/dash patterns, the flight crew is alerted to key positions indicated by the marker beacon system. (An outer marker, for example, informs the pilot he is about 5 miles from touchdown; the exact distance is shown on his approach chart.)

Fig 3.6 shows a block diagram of a marker beacon receiver. It is a superheterodyne type, but can be implemented with an old technique called TRF, or tuned radio frequency, shown in Fig. 3-7.

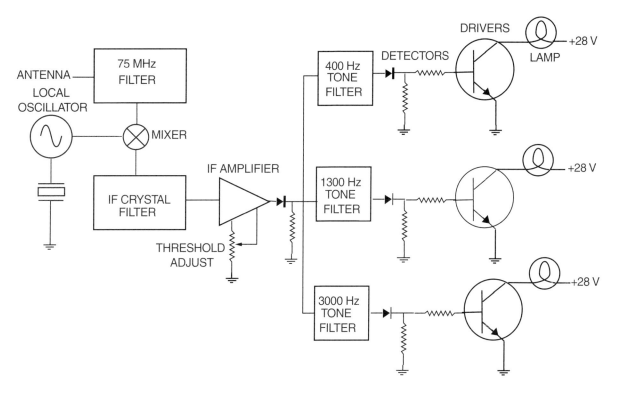

Fig. 3.6   Marker beacon receiver, superheterodyne type

Regardless of receiver technology, demodulated output is fed to filters at 400 Hz, 1300 Hz and 3000 Hz. The tone frequencies were chosen so any harmonic does not correspond with another tone. Some harmonics are close, however; the third harmonic of 400 Hz is 1200 Hz. The bandwidth of the filters is sufficiently narrow to reject the 1200 Hz third harmonic. The tolerance on marker beacon tones is sufficiently tight so 1300 Hz will not vary by more than 10%. Outputs of the three bandpass filters are rectified and drive indicator lamps. Audio is fed to the audio panel and then to the cabin speaker and headphones.

The most difficult part is designing the marker beacon receiver to withstand strong television interference. In the U.S., the marker beacon frequency is surrounded by television channels 4 and 5. Channel 4 extends from 66 to 72 MHz, while channel 5 spans from 76 MHz to 82 MHz. There is a 3 MHz guard band between channel 4 and the marker frequency, but only a 1 MHz gap between channel 5 and the marker. The video carrier for channel 5 is 77.25 MHz. Television broadcasting uses a vestigial sideband which has quite a bit of energy in the 1.25 MHz between the carrier and band edge at 76 MHz. The biggest problem is front end overload and spurious responses in the marker receiver due to the sheer strength of television transmitters. In the U.S., maximum licensed power, which virtually every broadcaster employs, is 316 kw EIRP.

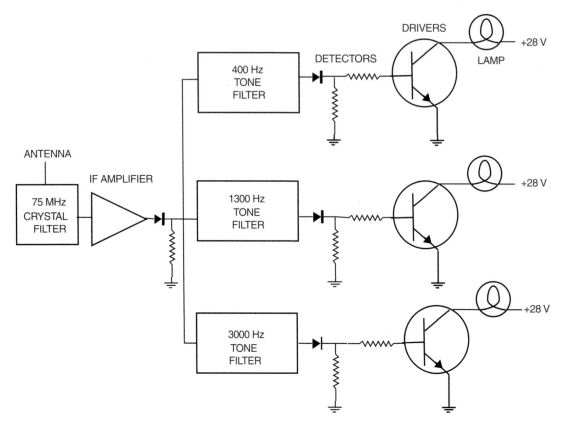

Figure 3.7 TRF marker beacon receiver

Example:

Calculate the level of interference to a marker beacon receiver from a television transmitter operating on U.S. channel 4 at the maximum legal power of 316 kw, ERP, at a distance of 1 NM from an airport. The television tower is in the clear and is line of sight from the airport surface. The video carrier frequency for U.S. channel 4 is 67.25 MHz.

Solution:

The television signal is a mixture of sampled analog, individual television lines and pulses. The pulses synchronize scanning of the picture. There are other sub-carriers, one for sound and a second for color. Television power is specified as peak power, which occurs during the peak of the synchronizing pulse. ERP is effective radiated power, which is the power density generated if a 316 kW transmitter were connected to a dipole. Another form of radiated power is EIRP or effective radiated power relative to an isotropic radiator. Since isotropic radiators are physically unrealizable, the dipole is often used as a reference. The power received by a receiver from a transmitter is given by the following equation:

$$P_{RCV} = (P_T G_T)(\lambda/4\pi R)^2 G_R$$

where P_{RCV} is the power received at the antenna output, P_T is the transmitter power, G_T is the transmit antenna gain, λ is the wavelength, R is the distance from the transmitting antenna to the receiving antenna and G_R is the receiver antenna gain. This equation is often divided into the following terms:

$(P_T G_T)$ is the EIRP

$(\lambda/4\pi R)^2$ is the free space loss

G_R is the receiver antenna gain

In this example, the power specified is not EIRP but ERP, which would be higher than the equivalent EIRP. This is because a dipole has gain over an isotropic radiator. Therefore, the 316 kW must be divided by the gain of the dipole or 1.641.

The antenna for the marker beacon receiver has a gain considerably less than a dipole. This is because a full-length dipole at 75 MHz is 2 meters long. This length is excessive and most marker antenna are much shorter than a dipole. Remember, a marker beacon receiver is not sensitive in the first place. A typical gain is –10 dBd, or 10 dB below a dipole. The antenna gains in the equation are relative to isotropic and thus the gain of the marker beacon receiver is about –7.85 dBi which is 0.164.

We can now insert the numbers into the equation and calculate the signal to the receiver.

$$P_{RCV} = (P_T G_T)(\lambda/4\pi R)^2 G_R = (316E3/1.641)(3E8/(67.25E6 X 4\pi X 1852))^2 (0.164) = 11.5 \ mW$$

An 11.5 mw signal is a strong signal, even for an insensitive receiver such as the marker beacon. As a comparison, the receiver is set to a nominal sensitivity of 1000 µ V, (hard). This translates to a signal power of 5 nW, which is 2.3 million times less than the interfering signal. The TSO test requires the receiver to function with the addition of television signals at U.S. channels 4 and 5 of 3.5 volts, (3.5E6 hard microvolts), peak. This translates to 61.25 mW, which is 7 dB greater than the level calculated in this example. (Hard microvolts are discussed in Chapter 6.)

3.2.1 Marker Beacon Ground Station

The marker beacon is about as simple as a ground station can become. The transmitter is single-frequency, amplitude modulated that provides an output of a few watts. Usually, the power is adjustable so the marker can be used for any of the three classes. The output power is decreased for middle and inner markers since the aircraft is at much lower altitude. As an inner marker, output power is a fraction of a watt.

Markers are heavily modulated, typically 95%, and there is no concern over voice or bearing accuracy. In spite of their simplicity, markers are an important part of ILS and require signal integrity monitoring.

The marker can be replaced with a localizer-DME. As simple as a marker beacon appears, it may be difficult to install. The outer marker is off airport property and it is often difficult to position the transmitter. It is likely that markers will be eliminated in many installations in the remaining time before ILS becomes obsolete.

3.3 Glide Slope

The glide slope provides vertical guidance in a manner nearly identical to the localizer. It is virtually a localizer turned on its side to provide a glide path, as the localizer provides the extended runway center line. There are differences but the principles are the same. First, if the localizer were turned on its side the signal would become vertically polarized. The glide slope is horizontally polarized. The percentage modulation for each antenna is 80%. Therefore, modulation for each tone is 40% at the on-course line. The amount of modulation is twice that found in the localizer. Because the glide slope does not have ident or speech audio, the percentage modulation for 90 and 150 Hz tones is increased.

The glide slope operates in a band of frequencies in the UHF spectrum from 329.15 - 335.00 MHz. The channels are 150 kHz wide in spite of the fact that bandwidth of the signal is only about 300 Hz. This unusually wide channel is a holdover from when UHF receivers and transmitters were not easily stabilized in frequency. There is wasted spectrum in the glide slope band but it would be difficult to change frequencies to preserve spectrum.

There are 40 glide slope frequencies, one for each localizer frequency. Paired with two localizer test frequencies are glide slope test frequencies. Glide slope frequencies are always used with localizer frequencies. A glide slope is never flown alone, with no localizer. This is not the case with the localizer. It is permissible to fly localizer-only in a non-precision approach (one with no vertical guidance).

To achieve pairing of glide slope and localizer, the glide slope receiver is controlled by the localizer receiver. To the pilot, there are no knobs, ident feature or audio. The operating frequency is never displayed. When using the glide slope, hearing the correct localizer audio ident assures that the glide slope is also correct. Signal integrity is checked in the same manner as the localizer. The glide slope receiver also has a separate nav flag and CDI.

3.3.1 Glide Slope Ground Station

In theory, the glide slope is a localizer turned on its side but there are significant differences. The first is that the glide slope is sensitive to reflections from the ground. The localizer beam covers as far from the left as it does from the right. In the case of a glide slope beam, a glidepath is about 3 degrees from the horizontal. Coverage can extend as steeply as 10 degrees or more from the horizontal but, obviously, there is no signal below the horizontal. It was stated in the localizer discussion that multipath causes beam bending. This is avoided by keeping the localizer path clear of large reflective objects such as hangars. The ground is also an ever-present reflector.

Because of reflections there are five types of glide slope ground station. Three use ground reflections in front of the antenna and two attempt to avoid reflections. Stations using ground reflections are sometimes called "image systems". The term refers to the reflection from the ground, as if it were an image reflected from a mirror. Image systems include the null reference, the sideband reference and capture effect system.

Non-image systems are used where ground in front of the antenna is not available or controllable. Such installations occur for airports on mountain tops or pilings over water. Two non-image systems are the waveguide glide slope and end fire array glide slope. Both are expensive and used only when absolutely necessary.

Some glide slope nomenclature is different from that of the localizer. The glide path is generated with the CSB signal and this transmitter is the reference, or REF, signal. This is analogous to the course, CRS, signal in the localizer. Course is horizontal guidance, while the glide slope provides vertical guidance, which is not a course.

The null reference glide slope uses two horizontally polarized reflector-style antennas. The lower antenna is 4.25 meters from the ground while the upper antenna is twice the height at 8.5 meters. These heights are critical as this is an image system which depends on reflections from the ground. The CSB signal is transmitted from the lower of the two antennas. The SBO signal is transmitted from the upper antenna. The direct and ground reflected signals combine to form a glide path at the desired angle.

Operation of the null reference system depends on reflectivity of the ground ahead of the glide slope antenna. Where reflectivity is bad and the ground (or water) in front of the antenna is subject to change, the null reference system can not be used. An alternative is the capture effect system. This uses three antennas and is similar to the localizer capture effect technique using CLR antennas. As with the localizer, the capture effect system requires two transmitting frequencies.

The sideband reference system requires only one transmitting frequency and two antennas at a height less than the null reference system. This is more immune to terrain effects than the null reference system and is often used for runways where the terrain falls off rapidly near the runway.

Glide slope coverage in the vertical is from about 0.45θ to 1.75θ where θ is the glide path angle. Lateral coverage is plus or minus 8 degrees from the runway centerline.

The glide slope transmitter is similar to the localizer. There are the same CSB and SBO transmitters, antenna changeover units and monitors. Far field monitors are employed and the transmitter checked for signal integrity. The most significant difference is, there is no voice modulation or ident tone. Three-image glide slope systems are the most common while non-image systems are rarely used and only for situations where ground conductivity in front of the antenna cannot be assured.

3.3.2 ILS Categories

Instrument approaches come in two basic types; precision and non-precision. A major feature of a non-precision approach is no vertical guidance (glide slope). Several radio navigation aids such as NDB, VOR, DME or a combination provide non-precision guidance.

Precision approaches always include vertical guidance, and use all elements of the ILS; localizer, glide slope, marker beacons and approach lighting . Should one element be inoperative, such as the glide slope, the approach reverts to non-precision, and landing minimums are raised (higher ceiling and visibilities required for the landing).

Precision approaches are divided into categories: CAT I, CAT II and CAT III, in order of decreasing visibility and ceiling. CAT III is further divided into three subcategories, CAT III A, CAT III B and CAT III C, again in order of lowering visibility and ceiling. Category III C, also known as "zero-zero", for zero visibility and zero ceiling, is as bad as it gets. Not only does the aircraft require guidance down to the surface of the runway, it needs guidance to flare, decrab, touch down and rollout. Once the aircraft stops, further guidance is required to taxi to the terminal. There are no certified installations of CAT III C in the world at the time of this writing.

CAT I, the most common ILS, is found at hundreds of airports in the U.S and the world. Even regional airports have at least a CAT I ILS for landings during ceilings of 200 feet and a half-mile visibility.

CAT II landings are limited to ceilings of 100 feet and an RVR (runway visual range) of 1200 feet. This requires all equipment aboard the aircraft for a CAT I landing, plus a second localizer receiver and second glide slope receiver. A radar altimeter is also required, as well as a crew of two. In the U.S., large airports are commonly equipped for CAT II approaches.

CAT III A is for conditions at or better than a ceiling of 100 feet and an RVR greater than 700 feet. This permits the flare and landing to be done visually. In addition to equipment for a CAT II approach, an autopilot is required. Some aircraft have been certified to use a head up display, HUD, in lieu of an autopilot. This ILS category is found in airports with frequent low visibility such as London's Heathrow and Gatwick, and airports in Alaska where alternate airports are at extreme distances.

CAT III B is for conditions as low as a ceiling of 50 feet and an RVR of 150 feet. Guidance is provided to flare and land, but there is enough visibility for taxiing. Landings in CAT III B require all equipment for CAT III A, plus an autopilot capable of an automatic landing, including rollout to taxiing. Very few airports are equipped for CAT III B approaches as are few aircraft.

To make an instrument approach, everything in the process is certified, such as airborne receivers and autopilots. This implies that equipment meets TSO requirements. The installation of instrument equipment is also certified. Even TSOd avionics incorrectly installed will not provide the performance for a successful landing. This certification occurs during the initial installation and continues as a part of a maintenance program. Pilots must have instrument ratings, training and recent experience with instrument landings in real or simulated IMC.

The airport, in addition to required ground equipment, is also certified. This requires inspection by the FAA. A test involves flying the approaches at the airport in a specially-instrumented aircraft to insure ILS beams are straight, signals are strong and, in general, all components of the ILS are functioning properly. All signal integrity monitoring equipment must be operating to make ILS landings. Higher-category landings require more accurate far-field and other monitoring equipment.

The difference between CAT I, II and III ILS equipment is that CAT III is apparently more accurate. To a certain extent this is true, but more important than accuracy is reliability. The difference between CAT I and

CAT III is availability; the amount of time the signal is present at the required accuracy. As an example, if the localizer transmitter of a non-precision installation fails or goes out of spec, the transmitter is turned off and a repair crew dispatched. Until the transmitter is fixed, aircraft divert to an alternate airport, wait until conditions are suited for a visual approach or until repairs are made. A spare localizer transmitter could be provided, but this is not required.

In the case of precision approaches, spare transmitters are required. The localizer signal may not be out of tolerance or missing for more than 10 seconds for a CAT I installation and for no more than 2 seconds for a CAT III installation. The spare transmitter for a CAT I installation typically remains unpowered and is turned on and brought on line when needed. Therefore, it is necessary to determine an out-of-tolerance condition, apply power to the spare transmitter, wait for circuits that need to stabilize and place the spare transmitter on the air, completely in tolerance, in ten seconds. Although not trivial, it's possible.

In the case of CAT III, it is not possible to do all these tasks in 2 seconds. In the CAT III localizer, the spare transmitter is fully powered, feeding its output to a dummy load. The internal signals of the transmitter are continuously checked and known to be in tolerance. Therefore, when the transmitter is put on the air, it is known to be good. This is called a "hot spare" and is found on other radio navigation systems. There are similar requirements for the glide slope except the CAT I glide slope must not be out of tolerance for more than 6 seconds, while the CAT III has a maximum of 2 seconds.

3.4 ILS Errors

Errors in ILS signals are from the usual sources, with multipath at the top of the list. It usually results in bending of the beam. Some small bends are not serious, providing they are significantly far from the runway so when the aircraft arrives, it is close to the centerline and pointed down the runway.

In ILS, errors are in three dimensions and can be due to the localizer and glide slope. Errors in the marker beacon signal, called along track error, ATE, are not as critical as cross track errors, XTE, which are errors of altitude and deviation from the extended runway centerline. The concept of a tunnel is used to categorize errors in approach and landing; with two intersecting tunnels converging at the touchdown point as shown in Fig. 3.8

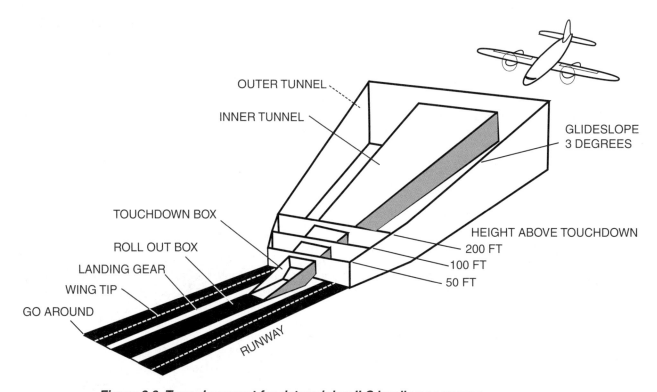

Figure 3.8 Tunnel concept for determining ILS landing accuracy

One point should emerge for localizer and glide slope ground stations; they are sensitive to phase disturbance, particularly the glide slope. Anything that shifts phase in a radiated signal causes beam bending. Five types of glide slope are in operation to deal with these problems. Sophisticated localizer antennas are large and need careful adjustment. Non-image glide slope antennas are also large. In general, any type of disturbance will bend the ILS beams.

ILS has been in operation for more than 50 years with continuous improvement, but there are weaknesses. Multipath, again, is at the top of the list. There are sites where even the most advanced antenna and two frequency glide slope or localizer cannot totally eliminate beam bending. This usually happens in mountainous areas where an accurate ILS is most essential. There are significant differences in the back course approach. First, signal levels are not as great as on the front course, where antenna gain is higher. Secondly, there is no glide slope for vertical guidance or marker beacons to help the pilot. Consequently, weather minimums must be higher to fly the back course. Many localizer receivers have a back course mode which reverses the sense of the CDI needle so it operates in a conventional (fly left, fly right) manner.

Another problem is lack of channels. There are only 40 ILS frequencies and, since each ILS runway requires its own frequency, an airport with multiple ILS requires a frequency for each runway. In the case of instrument approaches to both ends of an ILS runway one frequency can be used for either end. This is because only one approach is allowed at one time and only one of the two ILS systems is activated. There are strict safety requirements to insure that the two ILS systems can never be powered simultaneously.

Another problem is interference from high-powered FM broadcast stations. The highest carrier frequency for FM broadcasting in the U.S. and other countries is 107.9 MHz. The lowest localizer frequency for navigation is 108.30 MHz. The lowest localizer frequencies are 108.10 and 108.15 MHz which are reserved for testing in the U.S.

The effective radiated power, ERP, from broadcast stations can be as high as 500 kW (outside of the U.S.). Like airports, broadcast towers tend to be just outside of town. It is possible that an aircraft will receive high field intensity from a broadcast transmitter while on approach to an ILS runway.

There are several ways a high-powered broadcast transmitter interferes with a localizer signal. The first is energy near the localizer carrier frequency due to modulation of the broadcast station. The frequency difference between the highest broadcast channel and the lowest localizer is 400 kHz. Energy from the broadcast transmitter 400 kHz removed from the carrier frequency should be well down from the carrier power. The carrier power , however, is 500 kW ERP and even 60 dB down is equivalent to 0.5 watts radiated power. A 0.5 watt transmitter at a few miles, line of sight, is a strong signal.

Exercise:
The signal intensity for a localizer transmitter and antenna required by recommendations of ICAO Annex 10 is a minimum of 100 μV/m at 10 NM from the touchdown point. For a broadcast tower 2 NM from the approach, what is the effective radiated power due to spurious output from the broadcast transmitter at the localizer frequency, that would be 20 dB below the localizer signal?

Another way a high-powered broadcast transmitter interferes with a localizer receiver is overload. There are two common types; the first is a reduction in sensitivity of the receiver by presenting so much power the RF amplifier is overwhelmed and cannot handle weak signals in the presence of strong signals. NAV receivers usually have varactor-tuned RF amplifiers and large signals cause rectification and serious interference. Another common overload is intermodulation. This requires two strong signals. Together they generate a third signal in the front end of the receiver which falls on the localizer frequency. For two signals to generate interfering intermodulation, the following relationship must hold:

$$f_{loc} = 2f_1 - f_2 \qquad (3.3)$$

where f_{loc} is the localizer frequency; f_1 is one of the two interfering frequencies and f_2 is the other. This equation gives the frequency for third order intermodulation, the most troubling. The frequencies f_1 and f_2 can be reversed and should the equation be satisfied intermodulation is generated at the localizer frequency.

Example: Will two strong signals at 107.90 MHz and 107.50 MHz cause an intermodulation at a localizer frequency?

Solution: The equation 3-4 will be evaluated with either frequency substituted for f_1 and f_2

$$f = 2X107.9MHz - 107.50\ MHz = 108.3\ MHz$$

$$f = 2X107.5MHz - 107.9MHz = 107.1\ MHz$$

The first calculated frequency is a localizer frequency while the second is a frequency in the FM broadcast band. Adjacent broadcast channels are not assigned to the same community and the two channels in this example are not adjacent. There are communities that have broadcast stations on both of these channels.

As seen from the example, there are combinations of broadcast frequencies that cause intermodulation on a localizer frequency. One solution is simply not assign a localizer frequency to an airport where there is possible intermodulation from local broadcast transmitters. There are locations where this solution is more difficult than it sounds. As an example, in the New York metropolitan area, every possible FM channel is assigned. In addition, most FM transmitters are in sight of three large airports; JFK, LaGuardia and Newark and a number of smaller airports. Virtually every available localizer frequency is assigned to an airport within sight of an FM broadcast tower. There are other areas where this problem exists. In Europe it is heightened by broadcast stations in adjacent countries.

Even though ILS antennas have been developed to a fine art, the cost is high. Accuracy of ILS must be flight-tested on a regular basis. The glide slope is affected by the ground plane ahead of the antenna and this can change. The construction of buildings, roads, bridges, etc., in the beam of the glide slope affect beam accuracy. It is not uncommon to have to adjust a glide slope antenna after a flight test. Keeping an ILS system in good adjustment is time-consuming and expensive. Four major problems with ILS:

1. Interference from FM broadcast
2. Lack of available frequencies
3. Inability of an ILS to be installed at some difficult sites
4. Cost of checking and adjusting an ILS antenna array.

3.5 Microwave Landing System (MLS)

Because of ILS's shortcomings, there was a need to develop a new landing system. Further, a new system should permit approaches other than straight-in on a constant glide path. The microwave landing system, MLS, was proposed in the early 1970s as the ILS replacement and several sites selected for beta testing. Performance was good and the system was about to be installed world-wide. Another development, however, eclipsed MLS; it was the rapid rise of the Global Positioning System, GPS.

The U.S. military and some European countries use MLS, and it has provided landing guidance for NASA's Space Shuttle. There are a few installations in the U.S., including Alaska, for non-public use. For the military, MLS has the advantage of portable ground stations which can be quickly installed without siting problems. The effects of multipath are considerably less than that experienced with ILS. An MLS can be transported to a temporary military landing field without extensive flight tests and antenna adjustments .

At the time of this writing, satellite navigation (SATNAV) is not capable of guiding a CAT II or CAT III landing. Satellite CAT I landings are performed at select airports and there are plans to install augmentation systems that raise performance to CAT III. Some in the industry are concerned about the vulnerability of GPS to incidental and deliberate interference and many are suggesting a non-GPS back up landing system. It is possible MLS will reappear in the future.

For civilian airports outside the U.S., MLS is the least expensive and effective way to achieve CAT III capability. Where siting is a problem, MLS is the only way to achieve CAT III. In the most difficult sites, it might be needed for an approach of any category. Because MLS is currently in service and could see additional use, it is included in this text.

MLS is based on a time reference scanning beam, TRSB. During its development different schemes were proposed but after extensive trials, TRSB was accepted by ICAO. MLS provides azimuth (course), elevation (glide path) and distance. Unlike ILS, any azimuth or elevation is available for an approach to an airport. The on-course indication of glide slope or localizer is accurate because there is only one beam.

As its name suggests, TRSB MLS operates with a scanning beam, with a carrier frequency in the 5 GHz region. There are 200 MLS channels from 5031.0 - 5090.7 MHz. To understand MLS operation, consider the azimuth function. This is analogous to the localizer in ILS, which guides the pilot to the runway centerline.

An understanding of MLS geometry will aid the description of MLS transmission. The geometry is mostly referenced to a desired flight path that is, laterally, an extension of the runway center line. Vertically it creates a nominal 3 degree glide path. MLS is flexible and it is possible to fly an approach that is not the nominal, including curved approaches.

The MLS approach line intersects the surface of the runway at the MLS datum point. This is at the approximate touch down several hundred meters in from the approach end of the runway. This is also the location of the MLS elevation antenna and DME.

The approach azimuth antenna is beyond the stop end of the runway and is capable of providing guidance along the entire length of the runway. Unlike ILS, there is no guidance beyond the azimuth antenna; i.e. , no back lobes of the MLS antenna. For departure guidance there is a separate back azimuth antenna before the touchdown end of the runway.

The MLS ground station transmits an unmodulated microwave carrier from a directional antenna with vertical polarization. The carrier is turned on as the directional beam sweeps through an angle of about 60 degrees. The actual sweep angle is not important at this point, but the center of the sweep is the runway centerline. Thus the sweep is plus and minus 30 degrees from the centerline. An aircraft in the arc of this beam receives a pulse of energy as the antenna sweeps by. The shape of this received signal is a pulse that is essentially the antenna pattern of the antenna. It may have sidelobes, as well as a main lobe as shown in Fig. 3.9.

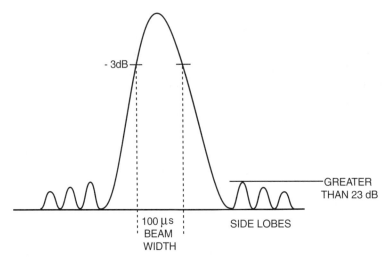

Figure 3.9 Envelope of received MLS scan signal

The maximum sweep angle depends on the airport. If there is the possibility of severe multipath distortion due to nearby mountains, for example, the scan angle can be limited to prevent this. The maximum sweep is plus and minus 62 degrees from the runway centerline.

After the antenna sweeps the approximate 60 degrees, the carrier is removed for a short period and the antenna sweeps in the reverse direction. Once again the aircraft receives the pulse as the antenna returns to the starting point. The sweeps are called TO and FRO. If the time between TO and FRO is measured, the angular position of the aircraft may be determined. Consider an aircraft that is far right of the runway centerline, and another is far left. The aircraft to the right is the first to receive the TO scan and the last to receive the FRO scan. The aircraft to the left is the last to receive the TO scan and the first to receive the FRO scan. The time between pulses for aircraft to the right of the runway centerline is longer than the time between received pulses for aircraft on the left of the centerline.

If the rate of scan of the beam is known, the angle of an aircraft relative to the runway centerline is given by:

$$\phi = (T_0 - t)V/2 \qquad (3.4)$$

where ϕ is the azimuth or elevation angle in degrees, t is the elapsed time between the TO and FRO scans, T_0 is the time delay when the aircraft is on the glide path or the runway centerline and V is scan velocity in degrees per second. Table 3.1 shows ICAO standard values for MLS parameters.

Function	Max Scan Angle (Degrees)	Value of t for Max Scan Angle	To	V Degrees/ μs
Approach AZ	-62 to +62	13 ms	6.8 ms	0.020
Hi Rate App AZ	-42 to +42	9.0 ms	4.8 ms	0.020
Back AZ	-42 to +42	9.0 ms	4.8 ms	-0.020
Approach EL	-1.5 to +29.5	3.5 ms	3.35 ms	0.020
Flare EL	-2 to +10	3.2 ms	2.8 ms	0.010

Table 3.1 MLS Parameters

Referring back to DME, it was apparent that when measuring time delays between pulses it was important to determine reference points carefully. Also, it was important to use an early part of the pulse to prevent inaccuracy due to multipath interference. The shape of the DME pulse must be well-controlled so reference points are kept precise.

In the case of MLS, the pulse is generated by the antenna pattern, which includes sidelobes. In addition, there is the possibility of multipath contamination. The pulse generated by the TO scan is exactly the same as the FRO except reversed in time. As observed in the aircraft, the TO pulse is generated by the scanning beam passing from right to left, while the pulse generated by the FRO pulse is generated by exactly the same beam scanning left to right. If the received signal is contaminated by multipath, the same contamination exists on both scans.

To determine the time delay between TO and FRO, the TO scan is sampled, stored, reversed in time and compared to the FRO scan. The time delay is adjusted so the absolute value of the difference between the two pulses is minimized. This results in a time difference that is insensitive to multipath and the shape of the antenna pattern.

The azimuth angle relative to the runway centerline is measured. This is different than the localizer, where only an approximate angle may be determined from the localizer signal in space. An elevation angle is provided by a similar scanning beam. In this case, the scan is up and down rather than left to right. The scans are still called TO and FRO. For elevation guidance, the center reference is the nominal glide slope, which is about 3.0 degrees from the horizontal.

The same scheme provides back course guidance. There are special scanning beams to aid in flare (raising the nose just before touchdown). There is provision for 360 degrees of azimuth, which helps intercept the approach path and provide navigation in the airport vicinity.

Another difference between ILS and MLS is that all MLS scanning beams share the same carrier frequency. The functions are separated by time sharing. This maximizes the 200 channels assigned to MLS. However, as received in the aircraft, the scanning beams all look alike, so a method is provided to identify each transmission. This is done with a packet of digital data transmitted immediately preceding the TO scan. More than just the identity of the following scan is included. In the case of azimuth, runway heading and airport identity are transmitted. In the case of elevation guidance, the angle of the glide path is included.

The MLS identity signal was long debated during development. With digital data available, the obvious ident was a digital word that could be decoded and displayed on the instrument panel. However, Morse code was used for virtually every navigation aid and pilots were used to listening for idents. During the landing phase it was not desired to search a display for an ident. The MLS data word, therefore, includes tone on and off data bytes to operate a tone oscillator in the aircraft. The audio spells out the MLS ident in Morse code.

Digital data for MLS functions is transmitted via differential phase shift keying. This is a moderately spectrum-efficient modulation that does not require a precise clock to decode. It is also more immune to Doppler shift.

Example: How much Doppler shift would exist for a 5.03 GHz signal received by an approaching aircraft moving at 135 knots ground speed?

Solution: The Doppler shift for velocities that are small compared to the speed of light is

$$\Delta f = v/\lambda$$

where Δf is the Doppler shift, v is the velocity of the aircraft and λ is the wavelength of the received signal. A 5.03 GHz carrier has a wavelength of 0.06 meters. The velocity, 135 knots, is 69 meters per *second. Therefore the Doppler shift is:*

$$\Delta f = 69 / 0.06 = 1150 \, Hz$$

Relative to the carrier frequency, this amount of Doppler shift is rather low, but relative to the bandwidth of the MLS signal this amount of Doppler shift is significant.

Differential phase shift keying is a method of angle modulation that does not require a clock extraction technique or transmission of a reference signal. (We meet this method of modulation again in the discussion of the secondary radar system called mode-S.)

As a matter of review, there are two basic methods of modulating a carrier; amplitude and angle. We discussed navigation aids using amplitude modulation such as NDB, localizer, glide slope, VOR and DME which is pulse amplitude modulation. A sinusoid has an amplitude and an angle. When the frequency of the sinusoid is constant, the angle changes at a regular rate, which is called frequency, f. A constant frequency sinusoid is given as:

$$V(t) = A \sin (2 \pi f t) \qquad (3.5)$$

where V(t) is a sinusoid voltage; for this example, f is the frequency of the function and t is the independent variable, time. The term in parentheses is an angle, the argument of the sine function. In the parentheses is a function of time so let us write the equation in a different form:

$$V(t) = A \sin (\theta(t)) \qquad (3.6)$$

where $\theta(t)$ is an angle that is a function of time. If $\theta(t)$ were a constant multiplied by time, the sinusoid is an unmodulated carrier with an angular frequency equal to the constant. In the previous example the constant was 2π f which is called the angular frequency while f is called the frequency. If we change $\theta(t)$ so it is not a constant time, we are angle modulating the carrier.

One way the angle can be changed is to suddenly shift phase. The largest change that may be implemented is 180 degrees or π radians, which is the phase angle used in the MLS system. Whenever phase is measured, or modulated, there must be a reference which represents no phase shift. Whenever information is transmitted with phase modulation, a phase reference must be provided. Sometimes this is done in the beginning of a transmission with a reference phase. The receiving system locks an oscillator on the reference phase and holds the phase reference for the duration of the transmission. If data are short, the stability of the reference oscillator does not need to be great. If the message is long, the phase reference must be stable.

When transmission is from a moving platform, serious difficulties arise. Due to the Doppler effect, the angle of the local phase reference and the transmitting unit is constantly changing. If motion is at a constant velocity, Doppler shift is present in the transmitted phase reference and the local phase reference adjusted for the Doppler shift. When velocity changes, that is acceleration is involved, the constant frequency phase reference is not accurate. The more time that elapses from receipt of the reference signal, the less accurate the reference.

There are solutions to this problem. One is to make messages as short as possible to minimize the time delay from when the reference is sent to when the last bit is transmitted. Another is to use the previous bit as a reference, which reduces the time delay from reference to data bit to a minimum. This is called differential phase shift keying.

Any number of phase angles may serve but for MLS only two, in phase and out of phase, or 0 and π are used. This form of modulation is called binary DPSK. It requires each bit to have a time slot. To locate the slots, a time reference signal is transmitted, which is usually a part of a preamble.

To decode a DPSK transmission, the phase of the received signal in a time slot is compared to the previous time slot. If the phase is different, meaning π radians in the case of MLS, the bit is a logic 1. If the phase is the same, the transmitted bit is logic 0. Note that one more time slot than bits to be transmitted is required because the first bit requires a previous time slot to decode. This extra time slot is included in the preamble. An example of the MLS data transmission using DPSK is in Fig. 3.10

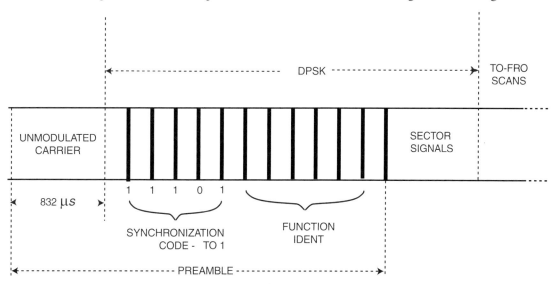

Figure 3.10   MLS data transmission

Before a scan is transmitted, a DPSK data transmission identifies the to-be transmitted scan. The time slots in the MLS DPSK transmission are 64 μs in duration and each message is 12 time slots. The first five time slots transmit the preamble, which is 11101. The next five bits are data. The last two are parity bits. Generally, a parity bit provides little error detection but two parity bits operating on selected data bits offer significantly more protection. Also, scans are transmitted repeatedly so if a DPSK message is received with an error, a retransmission occurs in short order.

3.5.1 Precision DME

The information provided by MLS thus far involves angular displacements from a glide path or runway centerline. The possibility of curved approaches was mentioned but to calculate and fly a curved approach, an actual position must be determined. Also, MLS removes the need for marker beacons. To accomplish this, MLS provides precision DME (PDME), which increases accuracy over conventional DME.

Precision DME operates on the same channels and uses the same principles to determine distance. The aircraft interrogates a ground transponder, which sends replies. The time delay is measured and distance calculated. The difference between conventional and precision DME is the shape of pulses and the point on the pulse where time is measured.

When precision DME was developed for MLS, there were no frequencies so it was decided to use existing DME frequencies. Should the need for PDME occur again, the decision to use the same frequencies as existing DME would be appropriate.

PDME is about ten times more accurate than standard DME. If existing DME is scaled to generate pulses one-tenth the width of the 3.5μs pulse, or 0.35μs, the same techniques and circuits can be used as in normal DME. However, a pulse of one tenth the width implies that the DME interrogator and transponder require ten times the bandwidth. It could be inferred that ten conventional DME channels are required for PDME. The 1 MHz DME channel is much wider than required by modern standards, and only about 6 normal DME channels would be required for a PDME if it were simply a scaled up or down version of normal DME, depending on whether pulse width or bandwidth is being scaled.

PDME was designed to not only operate on the same frequencies but to have the same bandwidth and operate with normal DME interrogators. The technique chosen uses only the lowest part of the DME pulse for precision time measurements. There is nothing limiting the ability to measure distance very accurately using pulsed radio frequency carriers. The difficulty lies in accurately determining a time reference from a pulse that has a finite rise time. One of the biggest obstacles to precision measurement is multipath contamination of the received signal.

For PDME, only the lowest part of the pulse from 5% to 30%, called the partial rise time, is used for time measurement. This represents about 250 ns of the leading edge, which insures there will be no significant multipath arriving that close to the beginning of the pulse. A Gaussian pulse does not have a sharp rise time suitable for precision time measurements. The spectrum for DME requires a pulse similar to the Gaussian shape, but there are no requirements that the pulse be Gaussian. Therefore, pulses for PDME are a combination of cosine and cosine squared. This new pulse has a spectrum within the existing channels and fast rise time on the leading edge.

The normal reference for timing pulses is the half amplitude point. This is from 0.5 to 1 μs from the beginning of the pulse and would be vulnerable to multipath contamination. The reference point for DME time measurement is called the virtual origin. This where the pulse would cross zero if it were perfect. It is the beginning of the pulse where there can be no multipath contamination. The reference point has zero amplitude and therefore cannot be measured. The point is determined by projecting where the pulse would have crossed zero from the early part of the received pulse.

The cosine/cosine squared pulse would serve both PDME and normal DME. What has to be taken into account in the time reference point is the virtual origin for PDME and the half amplitude point for normal DME. With the exception of the reference point, when comparing PDME to normal DME, the pulses are compatible, the channels are the same and the concept the same. Thus, the same interrogator can serve both PDME and normal DME. There must be a way the ground transponder knows which mode, precision or normal, an interrogator is operating so the transponder can choose the time reference from half amplitude to virtual origin. This is done by different pulse separation for the interrogation pulses. The normal DME uses one set of pulse spacings for X channels and a second for Y channels. The PDME introduces two new spacings, W and Z channels.

Channel	Mode	Interrogation Pulse Separation	Reply Pulse Separation
X	IA	12μs	12μs
X	FA	18μs	12μs
Y	IA	36μs	30μs
Y	FA	42μs	30μs
W	IA	24μs	24μs
W	FA	30μs	24μs
Z	IA	21μs	15μs
Z	FA	27μs	15μs

Table 3.2 DME Interrogations

The two new modes are the initial approach fix, IA, and final approach fix, FA. In addition to the reference point for measuring time delay, several other things change between interrogations IA and FA. Notice the X initial approach and the Y initial approach modes have the same pulse separations as normal DME modes X and Y. The ground station provides the mode of operation requested by the airborne interrogator. PDME is used only with MLS installations. It is possible that will change in the future but PDME is only required for landing. At an airport with MLS and ILS, the same DME transponder can serve both facilities. Since X and Y initial approach modes are the same as normal DME, the transponder will reply with a normal DME transmission when interrogated. Only when the transponder is interrogated with the FA mode will the ground transponder make time measurements relative to the virtual origin.

3.5.2 Precision DME Accuracy

The accuracy of navigation systems discussed thus far is based on static measurements that require a constant display. As an example, to determine accuracy of the localizer, a simulated localizer signal is applied to the equipment under test and the indicator observed. For a DDM of zero, the indicator should center, with a maximum deviation as a percentage of full scale.

The applied signal in this case is steady and the receiver expected to provide a steady indication. However, in the real world this is not the case. An aircraft is moving, the signal may vary in strength and possibly be distorted with multipath. In the ILS, the aircraft typically follows a straight-in approach where the received signal has a constant DDM. In the case of MLS, approaches may be curved, where received signals are constantly changing. To realistically test an MLS, which includes PDME, a dynamic input signal is used and the system evaluated by dynamic measurements.

Another important aspect of MLS and many ILS installations is that approaches are flown on autopilot. The true evaluation of an MLS landing is how well the aircraft follows the desired path with MLS connected to the autopilot. A parameter that describes this is called path following error, or PFE.

There is another parameter to describe the ability of MLS to direct an autopilot landing. Imagine two cars traveling on a highway. One is driven by a skillful driver and remains centered between white lines on the road. The other wanders between the lines, constantly turning the steering wheel to correct errors. Neither car has left the roadway, nor crossed the white lines, so both vehicles could have a very small path following error. But the less-skillful driver does it with numerous small motions.

In an aircraft, controls make corrections to the path of flight. An autopilot flying an approach moves the controls to keep the aircraft on course, but if it is like our less-skilled car driver, the controls move a lot, creating what is called control motion noise, or CMN. What separates control motions required to keep the aircraft on course and CMN? The difference is frequency. PFE is a low frequency component of control motion and noise a higher frequency component.

To measure CMN and PFE of a system using MLS, a dynamic signal, one that is changing as an aircraft would receive in flight, is applied to the unit under test. Steering commands that drive an autopilot are monitored and compared with those that occur if the autopilot flew the desired course without error, and the difference is extracted. The difference is filtered with a low pass and a high pass filter. The low pass signal is the PFE, while the high pass signal is the CMN. Cutoff frequencies of low pass and high pass filters are specified for the test, and are a function of type of aircraft.

These tests are performed with computer-driven test equipment and can be sophisticated. The filtering and differencing is done with a computer, as well. Such tests are necessary to assess how a system will function in an aircraft.

3.6 Comparison of MLS and ILS

With this understanding of ILS and MLS, it is useful to compare them to see how MLS provides better performance at less cost.

The high sensitivity of ILS antennas (glide slope and localizer) to their environment in terms of multipath has been discussed. How does MLS overcome these problems? It, too, operates with directional antennas. MLS does not require precise space modulation as do glide slope and localizer. MLS depends only on amplitude. In addition, should the MLS beam be distorted by multipath, it compares TO and FRO scans, each with the same distortion and subtracts distortion out of the measurement.

When equipment cost is compared, the first MLS installations were more expensive, but this is misleading. MLS was never installed in large numbers or benefited from economy of scale. Also, there was little competition between suppliers of ground stations. Finally, solid state microwave devices have been around for a long time, but significant advances were made in the last decade. The same can be said of airborne receivers. Only a few manufacturers made MLS receivers and since the system is obsolete in the U.S., there will be no new suppliers.

The ILS system, ground station and airborne, is based on old technology. There are thousands of ILS installations at airports world wide and hundreds of thousands of airborne installations. The major cost of ILS is continuing maintenance.

Maintenance is not a matter of replacing components or making adjustments. One high cost item is preparing the earth. It may sound unusual but remember that a glide slope signal received by an aircraft depends on the ground in front of the glide slope antenna. The surface for hundreds of meters must be flat to prevent bends in the glide path. This area must also be kept clear of vehicles and buildings. The cost of property, keeping it free of vehicles, removing vegetation, insuring flatness and frequent flight testing to verify CAT III performance, exceeds the cost of maintaining the electronics.

In many cases, airports cannot provide a CAT III ILS because of siting problems. For locations where it is installed, the cost of a cancelled or diverted flight is so high it that avoiding only a few per year justifies a CAT III landing system.

3.7 Radar Altimeter

The radar altimeter, sometimes called radio altimeter, provides an indication of height above ground. This is a measured height rather than a reference to an aneroid altimeter and correcting for ground elevation. The radar altimeter is superior to the barometric altimeter, having an accuracy to within ten feet or less. It operates by measuring the time of flight of a signal from the aircraft to ground and return, then calculating distance. The time measurement uses pulses similar to DME, radar and TCAS.

The first radar altimeters transmitted narrow pulses of about 20 ns; the time delay divided by the velocity of radio propagation produces altitude above the ground. The difficulty is that the minimum distance to be measured is a few feet. (This discussion uses feet for distance rather than meters because ICAO specifies altitude in feet.) The approximate propagation of electromagnetic waves is one ns per foot. If altitude is four feet, the time delay is eight nanoseconds which is 4 ns to the ground and another 4 ns to return.. The RF pulse width to measure altitude that low would require a pulse width of less than 8 ns. This assumes the receiver can be activated and ready to receive the return signal in near zero time.

Generating a pulse of RF energy with a width of less than 10 ns is difficult. In addition, the narrow pulse has a spectrum which requires a broad bandwidth receiver, with a resulting increase in

Radar Altimeter Display

noise level. One method to measure low altitudes with a pulse type radar altimeter is a delay line in the altimeter. This is a length of coaxial transmission line which increases the time delay between transmitted and received pulse. As an example, if a length of coaxial cable which provides an additional 20 ns of time delay is inserted at the transmitter output, the time delay for an altitude of 4 feet is approximately 28 ns. The additional delay allows a much wider pulse and a longer time between transmission and the time to receive the pulse.

A radar altimeter can use one or two antennas. With two, the transmitter is connected to one antenna while the receiver uses the second. The important advantage is no need to change the antenna from transmitter to receiver. The two-antenna scheme, therefore, does not require a transmit/receive, T/R, switch. The receiver would be overloaded when the transmitter sends and requires protection or an ability to recover quickly from overload.

A major advantage of the two-antenna radar altimeter is the ability to separate the receiver from the transmitter. The very fact that two antennas are mounted a few meters from each other on the fuselage introduces significant isolation between the transmitter and receiver. When installed on a large air transport aircraft, it is not difficult to find locations for transmitter and receiver antennas. The antennas are usually of the horn type and the mounting holes rather large. But even when the systems are triple-redundant, which occurs often on air transport aircraft, there is room for 6 horn antennas.

This is not the case for smaller aircraft. Cutting a large opening in the fuselage of a small aircraft can have a significant effect on the structural integrity of the airframe. There have been several models of single antenna radar altimeters available for general aviation but the trend for all aircraft is the dual antenna altimeter.

The frequency band for a radar altimeter is 4200 - 4400 MHz. There are no channels and all radar altimeters operate on the same range of frequencies. It would appear that a 200 MHz band provides sufficient spectrum to transmit pulses as narrow as 10 or 20 ns. Theoretically this is true but unless a transmitter is crystal controlled, some frequencies must be used as a guard band to allow for transmitter drift. Regardless of stability, narrow pulses require wider receiver bandwidth and a less sensitive receiver. This is overcome by a more powerful transmitter. In spite of the disadvantages, the pulse type of radar altimeter appears in a number of products. It is virtually obsolete, however, in favor of a simple concept using a frequency modulated transmitter

3.8 FMCW Radar Altimeter

Assume a transmitter is frequency modulated with a linear modulation waveform. This is transmitted to the ground from the aircraft and received after a delay due to altitude. A block diagram of this type of radar altimeter is shown in Fig. 3.11. The transmitter is a frequency modulated oscillator which feeds an antenna. The oscillator also serves as the receiver local oscillator.

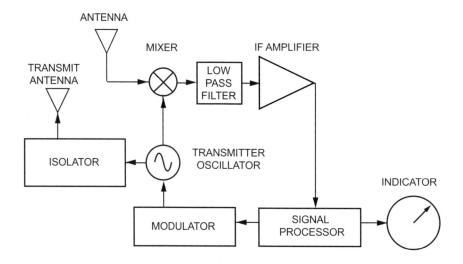

Fig. 3.11   FMCW radar altimeter

The frequency modulation is at a low frequency so we can consider the transmitter as continuous wave, CW, without sidebands. Because the reflected signal is the transmitter signal, it also is CW. Therefore, the output of the mixer is a CW signal. Due to time delay, the signal received is what the transmitter output was a short time ago. Because frequency is constantly changing, there is a frequency difference between transmitter output and received signal.

Referring to Fig. 3.12, the frequency difference is constant except at the peaks of the modulation. If modulation is slow compared to the time delay, the time where the frequency difference is not a constant is a very small proportion of the total time. Therefore, the output of the mixer can be low pass filtered and counted.

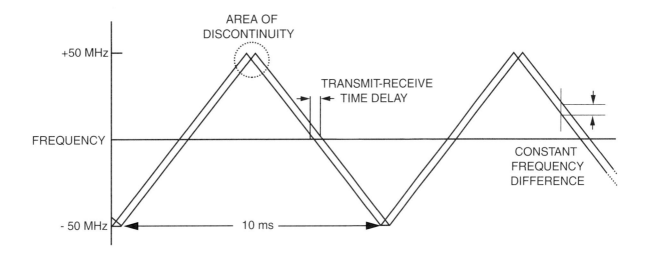

Figure 3.12. FMCW Radar Altimeter: transmitted and received frequencies as a function of time

Altitude is proportional to the frequency of the mixer output, and is given by the following formula:

$$D = 0.984 \Delta f / 2R \qquad (3.7)$$

Where D is altitude in feet, Δf is the constant frequency difference at the mixer output and R is the modulation rate in Hz per nanosecond. Because only the frequency of the returned signal is important, output of the receiver mixer is limited as an FM receiver.

This is strictly an FM system so the IF amplifier which follows the mixer is a limiting type, the system requires no AGC. However, signals from the greatest altitudes have the least energy and the filter following the mixer often has a rise favoring the higher difference frequencies which are due to the weakest signals.

This type of radar altimeter has been successful for many years. As with any altimeter, the greatest difficulty in measuring occurs at the lowest altitude. As altitude decreases the frequency difference decreases until it goes to zero. The use of a delay line prevents the frequency difference from equaling zero, but there is a decrease in frequency, which makes counting the frequency difference difficult. Rather than counting frequency, the altimeter may measure the period of the output cycles to determine altitude. Most FMCW radar altimeters both count the difference frequency, measure the period and switch from one measurement to the other when altitude crosses below a threshold. The difficulty in design is to seamlessly switch from one measurement to the other.

An FMCW altimeter that overcomes the problem of accurate measurement at low altitudes causes the modulation rate to change in order to keep the frequency difference constant. Returning to the equation relating frequency difference to altitude, $D = 0.984 \Delta f / 2R$, the frequency difference, Δf, is kept constant while the rate is changed.

To gain an understanding of how this affects modulation, let us investigate the rate of modulation near the maximum range, say, 2000 feet and a low altitude of 10 feet. The constant frequency deviation is 12 kHz. For the case of 2000 feet the equation is:

$$R = 0.984 \Delta f / 2D = 5904 / D = 2.952 \text{ Hz/ns}$$

107

For an altitude of 10 feet the rate is 590 Hz/ns. Most altimeters use a peak frequency deviation of 50 MHz, which implies that total frequency deviation is 100 MHz. The excursion for one cycle of modulation is 200 MHz. This can be visualized by considering the modulation cycle from the −50 MHz peak, which requires the frequency to go from −50 MHz to +50 MHz, an excursion of 100 MHz, and back to −50 MHz, a second 100 MHz excursion. The frequency has changed 200 MHz in the time of one cycle. If the modulation were a triangle wave at a frequency of f_m and produced a peak deviation of 50 MHz, the rate of change of the modulation would be (200MHz) f_m. Therefore, for an altitude of 10 feet f_m is:

$$f_m = (590 \text{Hz/ns})/(200 \text{MHz}) = 2.95 \text{ kHz}$$

The modulation frequency at 2000 feet is 14.75 Hz. In this technique the higher modulation frequency occurs at the lower altitude where most accuracy is needed.

Regardless of technique, no radar altimeter can operate with a zero delay between transmitted and received signal. Zero delay does not occur because in an aircraft there is some minimum time delay due to transmission lines connecting the altimeter to its antenna(s). Further, there is always a distance between the antenna(s) and ground. The zero altitude reference is when the aircraft main landing gear is about to touch the runway; the altimeter should read zero. Technically, if gear and tire compress after the aircraft weight is supported by the landing gear, the altimeter should read slightly negative. This is splitting hairs and most altimeters cannot read altitude to this resolution. The zero reading is important and altimeters must be adjusted for each installation to indicate an accurate zero altitude.

Understanding what "zero radar altitude" is suggests that altimeter antennas be mounted close to the main landing gear. This is important so the angle of attack of the aircraft does not have an effect on the radar altimeter. The angle of attack can be different for various situations such as aircraft loading and wind conditions.

3.8.1 Aircraft Installation Delay

When an altimeter reads zero this does not indicate the delay from transmitter to receiver is zero. There is the delay of the transmitter transmission line, the delay from transmitter antenna to the ground and back to the receiver antenna and the delay in the receiver transmission line. These external delays are different for each aircraft and are called "aircraft installation delay" or AID. A radar altimeter can be adjusted for it, usually in steps of 5 feet. The altitude between steps is adjusted by trimming the length of transmission lines. As an example, assume a radar altimeter is to be installed in an aircraft, which uses two antennas. The antennas are 5 feet from the runway surface and the minimum distance between antenna and radar altimeter is 7.5 feet. The transmission line has a velocity factor of 0.66 which indicates that radio energy travels at 2/3 the velocity of electromagnetic waves in a vacuum. Every foot of cable provides a delay of 1.5 feet in air. The minimum AID is 5+1.5(7.5)= 16.25 feet which occurs for minimum length antenna cables.

Switches on the altimeter can only be set to exact five foot increments so the transmission line is increased for an AID of 20.0 feet. This requires lengthening the transmission line by 2.5 feet. Don't forget that each foot of transmission line adds 1.5 feet of AID because the velocity constant is 0.66.

3.8.2 Multiple Altimeter Installations

The radar altimeter is an important component of CAT II and CAT III landings, which require extreme reliability. Radar altimeters, therefore, are doubly and triply redundant. Each operates in the same band of frequencies. They are synchronized, ironically, not so they all transmit the same frequencies but that they are *not* synchronized.

These external delays are different for each aircraft. If two altimeters are transmitting so one is sweeping up in frequency while the other is sweeping down, the two frequencies will cross at a rapid rate. Mutual interference will be short lived because they are sweeping away from each other. On the other hand, if two altimeters are sweeping in the same direction with nearly the same rate, the frequency difference would be nearly a constant and overwhelm the altimeter.

With two altimeters, their sweep must be out of phase. With three, when two altimeters sweep in the same direction, the difference frequency is so great it falls beyond the cutoff frequency of the receiver IF filter.

Multiple altimeter installations always provide sensor information for a computer. Don't expect to see three indicators, one for each system, in the instrument panel or one indicator with a switch to select the desired system. Redundancy involves comparing all three outputs to insure integrity. Methods of redundant systems are covered in a later section.

3.8.3 Radar Altimeter Indicator

The radar altimeter is a simple single-arc indicator with a range from zero to about 2500 ft. Often the indicator is non-linear with a resolution of 10 feet at the lower end and 100 feet at the upper end. The indicator is not a meter movement and is usually a motor-driven servo indicator which does not suffer from bounce in rough air.

The indicator has the ability to set a reference "bug" which causes an indicator lamp to illuminate when altitude becomes less than the set altitude. This is for setting the decision height, DH, which is a critical altitude in a precision landing. If the flight crew cannot make the remainder of the approach visually at decision height, the instrument landing must be aborted and a "missed approach" procedure initiated. As with any navigation indicator, if the signal is not reliable a flag must be provided; usually the servo system pulls the pointer out of view.

3.8.4 Testing and Evaluating Radar Altimeters

Testing the radar altimeter involves probably one of the simplest test sets in the avionics industry. To simulate the radar altimeter's signal environment is nothing more than a time delay and a reduction in the signal power. Therefore, an attenuator and length of transmission line connected from transmitter to receiver is all that is required to test an altimeter. Of course, a shop test set would offer a number of simulated altitudes and attenuations for extensive evaluation and troubleshooting.

The simplicity of a test signal allows for a very useful self-test mode. Most radar altimeters provide an internal time delay, attenuation and a method of switching to perform a self-test function. The self-test function can be automatically enabled or by the crew using a push switch. The typical self-test is a 50 ft indication.

3.9 Ground Proximity Warning System

Controlled flight into terrain, or CFIT (pronounced "see-fit"), is a major cause of aircraft accidents "Controlled" means an aircraft was being flown under normal control at the time of impact and a system failure was not a cause of the crash. This means the air crew was flying a perfectly functioning aircraft, unaware of the proximity of the terrain. Most CFIT accidents occur in the terminal area and for this reason ground proximity warning systems are covered in this chapter.

The first system to lessen the likelihood of an encounter with the ground was based on the radar altimeter. These systems, called ground proximity warning , or ground prox, systems analyzed only the altitude above ground (AGL) available from the radar altimeter.

CFIT accounted for nearly one-half of all airline fatalities in the decade of the 1980s. Recognizing the problem, the FAA mandated the use of a radar altimeter-based system to alert pilots of close encounters with the ground. The reduction in CFIT incidents was very gratifying for U.S. carriers. Progress in the rest of the world was not as good and in 1979, ICAO mandated the use of ground prox systems throughout the world and similar reductions were noticed.

One of the major problems of any ground proximity warning system, GPWS, is the fact that aircraft often operate in proximity to the ground. Obviously, an aircraft on approach for landing is indeed on a controlled fight *to* terrain, rather than *into* terrain. The dilemma is to recognize legitimate flight in close proximity to the ground and avoid false alarms at critical moments of flight; takeoff and landing. A ground proximity system that is prone to false alarms, like any system, will be ignored after a while. On the other hand, CFIT crashes do occur on takeoff and landing and if the warning system is not fully functional during these phases of flight, the warning system will not be effective. Simply using radar altimeter data is prone to false alarms.

There are a number of clues that an aircraft is on approach or on climb out, and these clues can be used to alter the criteria for terrain warning. For example, the status of flaps, and gear could be used to determine a landing configuration. En route flight is evident by airspeed and barometric altitude. Thus the configuration of an aircraft selects a "mode" of the GPWS. The main input to the ground proximity warning system, however, is from the radio altimeter. Other inputs are used to select a mode of operation suitable for the flight configuration.

There are a number of variations; GPWS is the basic system. Later, more sophisticated systems are called *Enhanced* Ground Proximity Warning Systems, or EGPWS. Another name for EGPWS is Terrain Awareness and Warning System, or TAWS, which is the nomenclature of choice for recent TSOs and ARINC characteristics.

The solution to differing aircraft situations is the adoption of "modes" which are determined by information available to the GPWS. The purpose of modes is to alter the algorithms which determine the issuance of an alarm to suit the operation of the aircraft. Alarms are aural and GPWS was one of the first systems to recognize the need for aural warnings. Aircraft already had more horns, buzzers, whistles, klaxons and gongs than a pilot could decipher. A GPWS warning is most likely to occur on approach, an intensive period when the crew's attention is fully dedicated to the task at hand. The warning must be interpreted without error in a matter of seconds.

3.9.1 Ground Proximity Modes

Mode 1. This mode is based on excessive barometric descent rate at low altitude. This mode is enabled at 2400 ft AGL, where most radar altimeters function. Most GPWS systems alert for descent rates of over 4000 ft per minute at the 2400 foot altitude. This decreases linearly to about 2000 feet per minute at 500 feet AGL or about 15 seconds to impact. Exceeding these limits results in an aural warning of "sink rate" . Higher descent rates triggers a "pull up" warning in mode 1. There are variations in the limits that trigger warnings depending on the certification of the GPWS. The rates given in this paragraph are approximate.

Mode 2. This mode is based on the rate of change of radio altitude, called closure rate, as compared to the descent rate of mode 1. The closure rate required for a warning depends on the configuration of the aircraft; en route is mode 2A, landing is mode 2B. Again, there are a number of criteria depending on the certification of the GPWS. At approximately 1500 feet AGL a closure rate of 3500 feet per second triggers a "terrain-terrain " warning. If the closure rate is not reduced, or the rate increases, the warning is repeated and changed to "terrain-terrain, pull up".

Mode 3. This mode detects failure to gain altitude on takeoff to about 700 ft AGL. The altitude is determined from the barometric altimeter. A 10-ft altitude loss at 50 feet above ground, increasing linearly to 100 ft loss at 1000 feet , triggers the aural alarm, "don't sink". Mode 3 is terminated for altitudes higher than 1500 feet AGL. The actual maximum altitude depends on the certification of the GPWS.

Mode 4. This mode alarms when the AGL altitude is insufficient for the configuration of the aircraft. Early Mode 4 systems had a gear up detector; alarming for altitudes of less than 500 feet AGL with gear up. Later versions included flap settings, airspeed, and descent rate to prevent false alarms. For higher airspeeds the warning is "too low, terrain". The lower airspeed warnings are "too low, flaps" and "too low, gear".

Mode 4 operates on take off simultaneously with mode 3 but alerts on altitude, rather than altitude loss. The mode 4 alarm on takeoff is "too low, terrain".

Mode 5. This mode alerts when an aircraft is well below the glide path as determined by the ILS glide slope. When the aircraft is above 150 feet and 1.3 dots below the glide path, the warning is "glide slope". At lower altitudes and greater deviations below the glide slope, the same warning is given but at a higher audio level; "GLIDE SLOPE!" Aircraft not using a glide slope receiver will not operate in this mode.

Mode 6. This mode is for various routine annunciations such as "radio altimeter" indicating the aircraft on approach has descended to an altitude where the radio altimeter has a valid signal. Also "decision height" or, alternatively, "minimums," indicates the point where the airport should be visually sighted on an instrument approach. This latter warning is usually sounded by the second pilot in the crew. This warning is an important characteristic of the modern flight deck that permits single-pilot certification of aircraft.

Mode 7. The final mode is for alerting the possibility of wind shear. A variety of parameters are used to predict wind shear and, if an aircraft is so equipped, the warning is "windshear, windshear, windshear".

3.9.2 Terrain Awareness and Warning System (TAWS)

GPWS attempts to eliminate CFIT incidents by analyzing the AGL altitude as measured by a radar altimeter for trends that would indicate a potential for collision with the ground. Modes 1 through 5 alert the aircrew to potential problems related only to the aircraft's altitude. In many situations, by the time the rise in terrain is noticed, it is too late to issue a warning because the terrain is rising faster than the aircraft can climb. The space under surveillance is directly below the aircraft but the most critical terrain is ahead of the aircraft. The situation is also such that turning is not an alternative to climbing because nothing is known of the terrain to the right or left of the track. Very often, the terrain lateral to the aircraft is not any better. What is required is a method of assessing the terrain near the aircraft, most importantly ahead of the aircraft, at a "look ahead distance."

Another deficiency of GPWS is that warnings give very little information about the terrain. The only avoidance maneuver issued from a GPWS system was "pull up". If surveillance is extended forward and to the side of the aircraft, this information may be used to perform other, possibly more effective, avoidance maneuvers. A plan view showing significant terrain would permit the aircrew to see and avoid terrain and to plan the most effective maneuvers.

Military aircraft that use terrain following navigation, have sophisticated side looking radar systems to give an accurate view of the terrain, not only below the aircraft but in front and to the sides. Side looking radars are so incredibly expensive that even air transport aircraft cannot justify their installation. CFIT accidents are not unique to the largest and most expensive aircraft and a reasonably priced system to prevent CFIT accidents in all aircraft is desired.

With the advent of large computer memories and modern data compression techniques, entire maps can be stored in resident computer memories. If an accurate position of the aircraft were known, the map display can show the local area relative to the present position of the aircraft. This is the idea behind the moving map display.

Some of the first moving map displays presented a conventional aeronautical chart, which was already familiar to the pilot. The orientation of the chart was either north up, track up or heading up to insure the map would be in a convenient orientation for the aircrew.

The idea of a pictorial navigation system is an old one. The VOR had a visual display that pointed to the desired course. The HSI was an improvement in that it would give a visual display of the aircraft's position relative to the desired course and would take into consideration the heading of the aircraft.

By including terrain features in the moving map the air crew would be aware of proximate and potentially dangerous terrain. Not all terrain information is needed to make the air crew aware of potential dangers, just that which is near the altitude of the aircraft.

We may take this one step further. By knowing the instantaneous velocity and, possibly, instantaneous acceleration of the aircraft, the future position of the aircraft may be predicted using one of the curve-fitting mathematical tools. We can now calculate just how close the predicted path of the aircraft will come to the elements of the terrain stored in the terrain map. If the aircraft is predicted to come closer than safe flight allows, an alarm may be issued to take proactive maneuvers.

Predicting the position of an aircraft in the future using current data is tricky at best. We must realize that there are, also, inherent errors in the data concerning the aircraft at the present time. Therefore, we must consider the prediction to be not of a point in space but an ever increasing volume ahead of the aircraft, such as a cone. If we were to predict the position of an aircraft, the further away from the present position, the greater the error. The TAWS system defines a volume, which can be a cone with the present position at the apex. This volume is called the protection volume. The length of the cone is the look ahead distance, while the angle of the cone depends on how precise the predicted aircraft position can be. The terrain data stored in the database is compared to the space occupied by the calculated protection volume to see if any terrain penetrates the protection volume. If it does, the system activates an alarm.

There are alternative methods of determining a terrain threat. One is opposite to that described; a volume is constructed around the terrain and the predicted flight path is compared to determine if a collision is possible. Both methods achieve the same results; two entities plus their statistical errors are compared to predict whether they occupy the same space at the same time.

TAWS can be time based or distance based. Determining an alarm could be based a minimum time to impact or a distance to impact. Time and distance are virtually interchangeable if an accurate ground speed is known. Alarms can be based on the reaction time of the crew, the time constant of the aircraft as well as the time to complete an evasive maneuver. Alarms could also be based on a simple minimum approach distance. In order to insure consistency of TAWS systems the FAA has created test scenarios to which all TAWS systems must be subjected.

Most systems have more than one alarm category depending on the time to impact any terrain that penetrates the protection volume. If a potential conflict exists so far in the future that avoidance maneuvers can be made as simple adjustments, this does not warrant an alarm and emergency procedures. The problem with GPWS was by the time some alerts were sounded, there was no time to avoid an incident. Therefore, for TAWS, providing terrain information before the situation becomes critical is a salient part of the system.

For aircraft with a flight management system, FMS, a flight plan is stored in the FMS. A TAWS system can compare the flight plan to the stored terrain data base and predict terrain conflicts hundreds or even thousands of miles from the present position. Also, having a flight plan simplifies the prediction of future aircraft position. It can be assumed an aircraft adhering to the flight plan will continue to do so and deviations from the flight plan can trigger more predictive algorithms.

A GPWS system with look-ahead enhancements was found to be so effective that the FAA passed regulations to require such systems in larger aircraft. All new aircraft of more than 15,000 kg or with 30 or more passenger seats built since October 2001 were fitted with TAWS. By March 2005 all aircraft operating under part 121, all turbine aircraft with 6 or more passenger seats under part 135 and part 91 must have TAWS as defined by TSO 151B .

TAWS, as defined by the TSO, has the "classic" GPWS functions plus forward looking terrain avoidance features. The TSO also defines two classes of TAWS, A and B. The classes are different mostly in the inputs provided to the system as outlined in the table below.

Input	Class A	Class B
GPS	yes	yes
Heading	yes	yes
Radar Altitude	yes	optional
ILS	yes	optional
Gear	yes	optional
Flaps	yes	optional
Air Data	yes	optional
Map Display	yes	optional

The first observation from the table above is that should all the options of Class B be set to yes, we will have a class A system. If none of the options are set to yes the system is the "classic" GPWS without the need for a radar altimeter. The radio altitude is derived from the GPS solution and the ground elevation from the database. What distinguishes TAWS from GPWS more than anything else is the TAWS system has a terrain database.

A class B system with few options will be limited in features. As an example, a class B system without an ILS interconnection will not provide the mode 5 "below glidepath" alert.

A class A system provides all the classic GPWS warnings and adds two forward looking terrain avoidance alerts. Primarily, the forward looking terrain is displayed on a plan view with color indicating the severity of the terrain. Essentially, severity is a matter of time to impact and the ability to make an evasive maneuver. In addition to the plan view, one alert is issued which is premature descent. This alert is only issued in the vicinity of an airport and indicates the altitude is too low for an approach.

A block diagram of a typical EGPWS is shown in fig. 3.13. One evident feature is the large number of interfaces. EGPWS probably has more interfaces than any other system in the aircraft except the flight management system. Having no sensors of its own, EGPWS is nothing more than a computer.

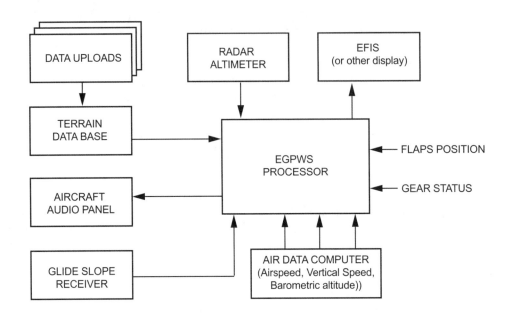

Fig. 3.13 Typical TAWS (Terrain Awareness and Warning System).

3.9.3 Determining Terrain Hazards

In modern aircraft, including small airplanes, accurate position is readily available from a GPS receiver. Aircraft position is also available from an inertial navigation system, INS, but this tends to be installed only in larger aircraft. Many GPS receivers calculate the velocity vector and some the acceleration vector which is used to predict future position of the aircraft. The GPS-derived velocity and acceleration vectors are long term calculations. The INS, on the other hand, provides nearly instantaneous velocity and acceleration vectors. By using data from both systems TAWS can calculate the most accurate predicted flight path.

The closest that an aircraft can approach the terrain depends on a number of factors. First is the type of aircraft and its ability to perform maneuvers. As an example, a large air transport aircraft is not capable of performing highly evasive maneuvers and therefore should give any terrain a wide berth. On the other hand, a small aircraft could perform highly evasive maneuvers because of its slower airspeed and smaller size. In the extreme, military aircraft can make very tight maneuvers even at high airspeeds.

As mentioned previously, crew reaction time and aircraft response time are also a part of the alerting process. In the case of a very maneuverable and fast military aircraft crew response time becomes a major limiting factor.

The biggest problem with any collision avoidance system is to eliminate false alarms. If a system gets a reputation for issuing false alarms, air crews will tend to ignore future alarms. TAWS has a unique problem in the terminal area as it is the object of the aircraft to "collide" with the ground.

114

Clearly, a landing is controlled flight into terrain (CFIT). Of course it is a well-controlled flight in to a specific part of the terrain, the runway! However, unless the TAWS system knows that an aircraft is landing, the system will sound endless alarms during a perfectly safe landing.

The GPWS had a similar problem but since the system uses a much simpler algorithm, preventing false alarms was easy. TAWS is a three dimensional system and would require a three dimensional algorithm and three dimensional display.

The elimination of false alarms is simplified by providing two modes of operation for TAWS; en route and terminal. Clearly, if an aircraft is not in the terminal area, any close terrain is a danger. The GPWS system reduced false alarms using these two modes. However, in the case of GPWS determining when the aircraft was in the terminal area was not a trivial task. A number of signals were used to determine the operating mode of the GPWS such as flap setting, the receipt of a localizer or glide slope signal or gear position. Determining operation in the terminal area in the future may become a problem when more landings are made with GPS or INS, and some of the usual signals, such as glide slope and localizer may not be present. However, there will always be some sort of "landing configuration" that can be sensed.

Determining en route or terminal mode for TAWS is extremely simple since the position of the aircraft is known at all times. As a requirement for TAWS, in addition to terrain data, a database is added with the coordinates of all airports. By comparing the airport location database to the position of the aircraft, the proximity of the aircraft to an airport is calculated. In addition to airports the location of initial approach fixes (IAF), markers and final approach fixes (FAF), can be stored and a very reliable determination of the phase of flight calculated.

3.9.4 The Terrain Data Base

The terrain database for TAWS is from the National Imagery and Mapping Agency, NIMA, a part of the United States Federal Government and formally called the Defense Mapping Agency. NIMA provides the FAA charts and approach plates and is the source of data for privately-published navigation charts and plates. NIMA sells to the public a terrain database called Digital Terrain Elevation Data.

The NIMA Digital Terrain Elevation Data, DTED, is 10E12 data points evenly spaced over the Earth's surface. DTED level 1 is a data point every 3 arc seconds. DTED level 2 is a data point every 1 arc seconds and DTED level 0 is every 30 arc seconds.

The distance between data points is a function of latitude. Recall, the historic origins of the nautical mile was that one nautical mile of distance represented a change of longitude of one minute of arc at the equator. As we increase latitude the distance represented by one minute of arc decreases as the cosine of the latitude. This is because the lines of longitude converge at the poles. This relationship was the very first equation in this text, 1.1 and is:

$$D = \theta \cos \phi \qquad\qquad\qquad 1.1$$

DTED 0 represents a data point at approximately every 0.5 NM at the equator. DTED 1 represents a point every 0.1 NM and level 2 is a point every 0.03 NM or every 62 meters.

Data are organized in the terrain databases as a function of latitude and longitude. Each datum is the highest elevation that lies within a latitude and longitude boundary. This organization of data is compared with GPS and INS sensors that produce position information in terms of latitude and longitude relative to WGS-84. At the equator the data space is nearly square. But the shape approaches triangular and becomes much smaller as latitude increases. To adjust the terrain database to be more in line with a Cartesian X-Y arrangement, modifications are made to the NIMA database when used in the TAWS system. The major advantages of the modifications is to reduce the amount of data stored and to simplify calculations. As an example a 15 second terrain database could be reduced in accordance with the table below.

Latitude Range (degrees, north or south)	Adjusted Longitude Separation
0 - 45	15 arc seconds (no adjustment)
46 – 66	30 arc seconds
67 – 74	45 arc seconds
75 – 78	60 arc seconds
79 – 83	90 arc seconds
84 – 86	180 arc seconds
87	300 arc seconds
88	450 arc seconds
89	900 arc seconds

An inspection of the table shows that for latitudes between 46 and 66 degrees only half of the available data are stored with no loss of spatial resolution.

Example:

Relative to the table above what would be the minimum and maximum distances in nautical miles for the longitude separations shown?

Solution: In the first category, 0 – 45 degrees, the distance at the equator represented by one minute of longitude is one nautical mile per minute of arc. Since the data resolution is 15 arc seconds or ¼ of an arc minute the resolution is ¼ nautical mile or 463 meters.

At the most northward or southward extreme at 45 degrees of latitude the distance represented is determined from equation 1.1 and is 0.707 nautical miles per minute of arc or a resolution of 327 meters.

In the second category the data are compressed to 30 arc seconds. In the lower end of this range of latitude each minute of arc represents (1 NM) cos (46 degrees) = 0.695 NM/ arc minute. The data resolution is ½ arc minute and thus the separation is 644 meters.

In the upper range of this category the separation is 524 meters. It is left as an exercise to the student to verify the spatial resolution of the remaining categories

For airports surrounded by particularly difficult terrain a more comprehensive database, the Airport Safety Modeling Data, ASMD, is available for selected airports, worldwide, where dangerous terrain is in the vicinity of the terminal area. This database was initiated in 1997 by the President of the United States after the loss of the Secretary of Commerce in a CFIT crash.

The terrain information in the database is stored as a grid, based on latitude and longitude. The surface of the earth is divided into squares where the boundaries are lines of latitude and longitude. The size of each grid square is on the order of one second of longitude by one second of latitude. Each grid square is a memory location and the data word for that memory location is the highest altitude in that square. Larger blocks of data, such as a square measuring 16 minutes by 16 minutes would also have one number representing the highest elevation in that block. The larger block contains 256 of the smaller blocks. For terminal operations the data are extracted using the smallest elements while for en route situations the larger block can be used, and significantly increasing data storage efficiency.

The coordinate system for organizing the data in the grid is the WGS-84, which is the same system used by GPS. This insures compatibility with GPS and INS systems, which are key players in the TAWS system.

3.9.5 Special Problems of the Terminal Area

Just how close an aircraft can approach terrain without danger depends on the performance of the aircraft, as previously discussed. Regardless of performance, an envelope of protection around the aircraft is projected towards the direction of flight. The envelope is relative to the aircraft and is along the predicted flight path of the aircraft. If any terrain in the map should penetrate the envelope an alarm is issued.

A number of factors are involved in generating the protection envelope. For en route flight the performance of the aircraft and current flight conditions are the major factors to generate the envelope of protection. Also, since TAWS is based on predicting the location of the aircraft, the protection envelope must be widened to insure that errors in the prediction of the aircraft's position due to a variety of other errors does not allow for a dangerous situation to exist without the issuance of an alarm. In the terminal area the protection envelope becomes much more complicated.

A model for generating the protection envelope and a model with which the TAWS system must be compatible is the "terminal instrument procedures" or TERPS. This document along with the United States Standard of the same name, insures obstacle clearance for instrument approaches. The obstacle clearance surfaces extend away, towards the ground, from the nominal glide path. This assures that an aircraft on the approach glide path can be assured that obstacles are a safe distance below. As the aircraft approaches the runway, the distance below the aircraft where the highest terrain could be present decreases. The obstacle clearance surface extends laterally from the nominal glide path to allow for aircraft to be off the glide path by small amounts. The protection surface is a "trough" with inclined sides. The floor of the "trough" is inclined so that it reaches the ground just before the point of touchdown. This structure means the following: terrain and obstacles directly below the aircraft and within a relatively short distance from the aircraft but still generally below must become shorter as the aircraft approaches the touchdown zone. This is very evident in many ILS approaches. Within a mile or so of the runway it is not uncommon to see single story buildings. Closer, there are no buildings with nothing higher than a fence. Just before touchdown there is usually a cleared area with not even as much as tree.

It is necessary to limit the height of obstacles laterally off the runway centerline as well. Aircraft exercising a missed approach may be climbing while turning away from the runway centerline.

Essentially, the TERPS insures that no obstacles encroach the described envelope. If a TAWS system used the same envelope the same guarantee would apply. Generally, the TAWS envelope is somewhat more conservative to compensate for any possible errors made in the calculations. The envelope cannot be made too conservative. A situation where an obstacle is outside of the TERPS envelope but inside of the overly conservative TAWS envelope, would cause an alarm when executing a perfect instrument approach.

Table 1: Required Terrain Clearance

Phase of Flight	Required Obstacle Clearance -*TERPS*	Required Terrain Clearance (TAWS)	
		Level Flight	*Descending*
En route	1000 feet	700 feet	500 feet
Terminal	500 feet	350 feet	300 feet
Approach	250 feet	150 feet	100 feet
Departure	48 feet/NM	100 feet	100 feet

The TERPS insures a certain clearance for various phases of flight. For example, it insures that no obstacle is within 250 feet of the nominal glide path on approach. The signals provided by the ILS should allow a properly functioning airborne ILS receiver to keep the aircraft well within 250 feet of the glide path. However, due to malfunctioning equipment or flight technical error, an error greater than 250 feet can occur and result in a CFIT incident. The TAWS alarm will occur at 100 feet from the nominal glide path and provide the additional time/airspace to correct the problem.

3.9.6 TAWS Displays

Most TAWS systems display proximate terrain using a color contour display. In this way the air crew can see potentially dangerous terrain long before it becomes a problem. The terrain displayed is limited to less than 2000 feet below the aircraft. This is to prevent the display from becoming cluttered and difficult to read. The display, however, is not a true topographic display. Terrain shown in yellow or orange represents a potential collision hazard. Terrain shown in red is a more immediate hazard and needs an immediate reaction. As an example, very high terrain aft of the aircraft may not even be displayed at all because the current predicted flight path will not take the aircraft to the terrain.

In the first TAWS systems, before the system was TAWS but enhanced GPWS, the indicator of choice was the weather radar display. This was the first use of a color graphics display in aircraft and was the indicator for a number of systems before the widespread use of EFIS. In most aircraft the display for TAWS is the EFIS display. The modern display includes a moving map, TAWS, including man made obstacles such as towers and buildings, navigation aids, course and track information and weather information. Such a display can become a human factors nightmare and some information can be suppressed. When flying en route the likelihood of terrain information appearing is low. On the other hand, when flying in the terminal area, when terrain begins to appear there is less reason to display weather.

Chapter 3 Review Questions

3.1   Which radio navigation systems are used in the instrument landing system?

3.2   What are characteristics of the received signal from a localizer navigation aid on the runway extended centerline?

3.3   How would the received localizer signal change if an aircraft deviated from the extended runway centerline to the left while on an approach? How would the signal change if the deviation were to the right?

3.4   What type of indicator may be used for the localizer?

3.5   Why is a second carrier frequency used in the two-frequency localizer?

3.6   What is a "back course"?

3.7   How is a localizer station identified so the aircrew is sure the correct signal is being received?

3.8   What causes a "NAV flag to appear when the navigation receiver is tuned to a localizer frequency?

3.9   What is the purpose of a marker beacon?

3.10   What is the carrier frequency and nature of modulation of a marker beacon?

3.11   Where is a marker beacon antenna mounted on an aircraft?

3.12   Why is not desirable to design a very sensitive marker beacon receiver?

3.13   How is the glide slope signal similar to the localizer? How does it differ?

3.14   What type of audio ident appears on a glide slope signal?

3.15   What is the "image" in the image type glide slope ground station?

3.16   How do CAT I, CAT II and CAT III ILS systems differ?

3.17   What problems associated with the ILS does MLS avoid?

3.18   What is TRSB, relative to MLS?

3.19   What technique does MLS use to transmit several guidance signals on the same radio frequency?

3.20   How does MLS reduce the effects of multipath?

3.21   What system provides distance information in an MLS approach?

3.22   An FMCW radar altimeter sweeps with a linear saw tooth waveform from 4240 to 4360 MHz at a repetition rate of 100 Hz. The aircraft installation delay is 17 feet. If the difference frequency is 180 kHz, what is the altitude?

3.23   An FMCW altimeter using two antennas is to be installed in an aircraft. The distance from the antenna to the runway surface is 3.5 feet and the minimum coaxial cable to span the distance from altimeter to antennas is 6.5 feet. There is an AID switch on the altimeter of 5, 10, 15, and 20 feet. If this altimeter is connected using Teflon cable with a $V_p = 0.71c$, where should the switches be set and what is the length of each cable?

3.24   What is CFIT?

3.25   What does "zero" altitude mean as indicated by a radar altimeter?

3.26   A 3 arc second terrain data base is available for Daytona Beach International Airport, DAB at N29 degrees W 81 degrees. What is the dimension in nautical miles of the grid square of the data base?

Chapter 4
Satellite Navigation

4.0 Introduction

Space-based navigation was not only the first method of long-distance navigation, but is the most advanced today. The earliest travelers followed sun and stars with reasonable accuracy, but there were disadvantages. Solar navigation does not work at night and stellar navigation is impractical during the day—and neither works when it's cloudy. Then came the discovery that radio waves penetrate both clouds and darkness. For the last 70 years navigators relied on radio transmitters located on land. But a new navigation system based on satellites began development in the 1970s. It proved superior in accuracy en route and sufficiently precise to guide aircraft to landings. The system is all-weather, immune to precipitation static and propagates predictably through the atmosphere. It is available to vehicles and people on foot. These were the objectives of the US Department of Defense (DoD) when it set about developing a system to meet the needs of military forces throughout the world. It also provides navigation where hostile forces would not permit ground stations. Locating transmitters out of reach is easily solved by satellites.

Another benefit is that radio waves arrive in a straight line. There is no over-the-horizon propagation or ionospheric bending of signal tracks at higher frequencies. Although satellite signals travel long distances, most of the trip is through the emptiness of space There are disturbances to the signal, but this can be corrected. Availability is assured by having enough satellites in view anywhere on earth at all times. Accuracy depends on the method of transmitting signals and effects of the atmosphere. It is also necessary to adjust the satellites to correct orbital errors.

4.1 GPS: Global Positioning System

The system to meet these needs was originally called Navstar, but today is known as the Global Positioning System, or GPS. Originally for the military, not all features are available to civilian users. Orbiting satellites transmit coded signals on two frequencies, and two levels of accuracy; the Standard Positioning Service, SPS and the Precision Positioning Service, PPS. The SPS mode can receive only one of the two transmitting frequencies. The PPS mode acquires both. The PPS mode is available only to military users who can decode it. Accuracy of the civilian version varies from about 100 to a few meters, while the PPS is about 7 times more accurate. The "civilian" part of GPS is also used by the PPS to decode a highly-encrypted signal in the Clear/Acquisition or C/A mode. The PPS is also called P mode or P code, where "P" refers to precision.

Earlier attempts at satellite navigation included a system called Transit. It was more of an experiment to gain experience than practical worldwide navigation. The technique was a

Doppler shift in the carrier transmitted by the orbiting satellite. Doppler shift increases frequency of the carrier as the satellite approaches, then lowers it as the satellite retreats. At the moment the shift changes from an increase to a decrease, the receiver location on earth is perpendicular to the path of the satellite. The satellite could be directly overhead or lower on the horizon. This provides a line of position (LOP). A second satellite in a different orbit adds another line of position. Two satellites in different orbits, therefore, are required to fix a position. Even more limiting was that satellites were not in view at the same time. It was necessary to use dead reckoning to estimate a vessel's position relative to the first LOP, until the second satellite became available.

Transit was intended for ships at sea as a method of updating their inertial navigation systems. The number of satellites in orbit allowed a position measurement only about every one and a half hours. For a large, slow ship this may be sufficient to update inertial navigation but hardly acceptable for aircraft.

The GPS system consists of three basic components; ground segment, user segment and space segment. Consider, first, the space segment since it's the most familiar. The space segment consists of 24 orbiting satellites, called space vehicles, SV, in 6 circular orbits inclined at 55 degrees relative to the earth's equatorial plane, as shown in Fig. 4.1. Of the 24 SVs, 21 are required for global coverage. Three SVs are spares in case of failure. Rather than viewing GPS as a 21-satellite system with three spares it should be viewed as a 24 satellite system that can provide full performance even with three failed satellites.

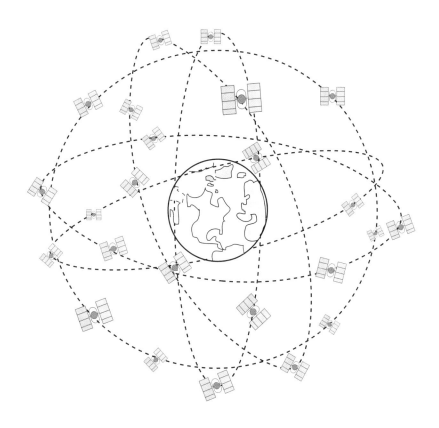

Figure 4.1 GPS space segment

The first SVs for GPS were orbited early 1978. Called Block I, they were launched until late 1985. Each satellite was assigned a space vehicle number, or SVN. There were 11 block one SVs numbered from SVN-1 to SVN-11. The block I SVs were developmental but performed admirably with the last block I SV decommissioned in 1995. Block II were the first operational satellites and covered SVNs from SVN-13 to SVN-21. (SVN-12 was lost). Block IIA SVs bearing SVNs 22-40 brought the GPS constellation up to full operational capability, FOC. Twenty four satellites constitute an operational system, according to the FAA. Each subsequent block brought improvement, along with advances in the clocks carried aboard each satellite.

SVNs 41-66 are block II R, where the R represents "replacement" Having reached FOC subsequent SVs will replace failed or obsolete SVs.

The ground segment of GPS consists of monitoring and control stations. Although signals come from space, the SVs are under control of the ground. The remaining portion, the user segment, comprises GPS receivers in ships, aircraft, vehicles and hand carried portables.

4.1.1 Finding Position With Orbiting Satellites

The basic principle of GPS is rho-rho-rho (determining a fix from three distances). The technique is based on the position of SVs in known orbits. Each SV transmits a navigation message that contains the exact time of day the message is sent. The GPS receiver has a time of day clock and compares its (local) time against the time the message was transmitted. From this information, the en route time for the SV message is calculated. Once elapsed time is known, and assuming the velocity of radio waves is known, distance to the SV can be calculated. This distance is called *pseudorange*, or R_p. The prefix "pseudo" is used because the distance determined from this first approximation contains errors that are corrected later.

The position of the SV is known because the orbit is predictable. Distance to the satellite is also known, so the user can determine a surface of position, which is a sphere with a radius of R_p with the satellite at the center, as shown in Fig. 4.2(a).

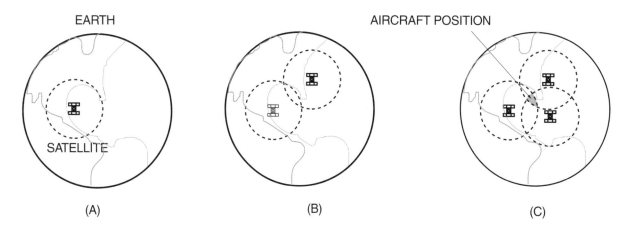

Figure 4.2 Finding position using satellites

Unlike Transit, at least 6 GPS satellites are visible at any time; there is no waiting for the next one. As the second GPS SV is received, its position is also known, which permits a second pseudorange measurement and a second surface of position. The two spheres intersect on a circle, which is a line of position, as shown in Fig 4.2(b). As in LORAN-C, two transmitters produce a LOP. The difference is that in GPS the LOPs are in three dimensions, rather than two.

When a third SV is received, a third surface of position is determined, as shown in Fig. 4.2(c). Designating the SVs as A, B, and C, we can determine three surfaces of position, and three LOPs by taking the SVs two at a time: A and B; A and C; and B and C. There is only one point where the three circles intersect and that is the receiver's position. Three satellites, therefore, are required to find a position. This system sounds simple, and, in theory, it is. But, as mentioned earlier, "the devil is in the details."

First, three spheres of position to derive the LOPs had a satellite at the center of the sphere. The accuracy of the position on earth depends on the accuracy of the satellite position. Let's investigate orbital dynamics to see the challenges in knowing satellite position with great accuracy.

4.1.2 Orbits

Satellites are held in orbit by balancing two forces: gravity, pulling the satellite towards the earth, versus centripetal force, which would fling the satellite into space. The orbits are elliptical, according to Kepler's laws. Kepler (1571-1630) discovered that orbiting bodies sweep out equal areas in any equal elapsed time period. He was not calculating orbits of artificial satellites, of course, but attempting to understand orbital dynamics of planets around stars, and moons around planets. Kepler formulated his law empirically by analyzing extensive data gathered by another astronomer, Tycho Brahe. Before Kepler, astronomical orbits were believed to be circular. Kepler's discovery of the elliptical orbit was interesting because a circle is a form of an ellipse with an eccentricity of zero. GPS satellites are in circular orbits, which is important, as they provide a constant distance from earth and an easily predicted ground track. A ground track is the path on the surface of the earth directly under the satellite. The point directly below the satellite is called the subsatellite point. GPS satellites move relative to the surface of the earth, which is unlike the geostationary satellite, which is always directly overhead one spot on earth.

GPS orbits are inclined 55 degrees to the equator to provide global coverage. No satellite passes directly over the North or South Pole, which would require an inclination of 90 degrees. It is not necessary for a satellite to pass directly overhead for coverage; so an aircraft flying over either Pole can pick up sufficient satellites lower on the horizon.

In a circular orbit, gravity is in the direction of a radial from the center of the earth to the satellite, and centripetal force is along the same radial direction, except directed away from earth. The forces act along the same radial line except in opposite directions. Also, traversing a circular path involves a constant *magnitude* of acceleration, not constant acceleration, because the *direction* of the acceleration vector changes. Therefore, we can write an equation using only the magnitude of the forces, realizing that forces are actually vectors.

Using Newton's law, the force on the satellite due to gravity is:

$$F = g \, (M_e M_s)/R^2 \qquad\qquad (4.1)$$

Where M_e is the mass of the earth or 5.983E24 Kg, M_s is the mass of the satellite, g is the universal gravitation constant, and R is the distance from the satellite to the center of the earth. To be rigorous about this equation, distance R should be measured to the center of mass of the earth. The geometric center and center of mass are very close but this will be discussed later.

The amount of centripetal force is

$$F = M_s R \omega^2 \qquad (4.2)$$

where M_s and R are as before and ω is the angular rate at which the satellite orbits in radians per second. Now, equate the centripetal force to the gravitation force.

$$F = g (M_e M_s)/R^2 = M_s R \omega^2 \qquad (4.3)$$

Notice that the mass of the satellite appears on both sides of the equation. Therefore, satellite mass is eliminated from the equation and the equation solved for radius, R.

$$R = [g M_e/\omega^2]^{1/3} \qquad (4.4)$$

For a circular orbit, R must be a constant. Since g is a constant and M_e is a constant, ω must be a constant. Since the term gM_e is used often in orbital mechanics it is convenient to introduce a constant which we may call $\mu = gM_e = 398601$ km^3/s^2. Notice that the constant as stated here does not use standard SI units but uses km rather than meters. This is common and results in all orbital mechanical equations using km rather than meters. With the large distances encountered in satellite orbit calculations having results in km is preferable. However, other equations involving satellites such as path loss and time delays will not use km and it is necessary to be vigilant.

The value of ω will set the height of the orbit. However, there are values of ω that make the GPS system easier to use. We want the satellite path to be easily predicted. If the satellite took the same ground track every day, this would make calculation of position easier.

We, as the user segment, "orbit" the axis of the earth every day. We make a circular path around a point for every rotation of the earth on its axis. Imagine that a satellite orbited twice for every one orbit we made. The satellite must make two orbits for our one we would see the satellite constantly moving away from us. If we would observe the satellite at certain time of the day, at approximately 24 hours later the satellite would return to exactly the same point because its orbit is synchronized to our "orbit". If we were to plot the path taken by the satellite by projecting a line from the satellite to the center of the earth, the satellite will always take the same path every day. This is a geosynchronous orbit.

If the satellite made two orbits per day it would trace out one path over the surface of the earth each day. If the satellite made three orbits per day it would trace out 2 paths over the earth before repeating and so on.

Do not confuse geosynchronous with geostationary. A geostationary orbit is one where the satellite makes one orbit per day just as we do on the earth's surface. Furthermore, the satellites must be in the equatorial plane. Thus if we observe a satellite with one orbit per day positioned over the equator it will remain stationary.

GPS satellites are not over the equator but inclined at 55 degrees. The satellites come up from the southern hemisphere, pass the equator at a point called the ascending node, and go north over the northern hemisphere. To an observer on the other side of the globe, the satellite is seen coming down from the northern hemisphere and traveling towards the southern hemisphere. When the north to south track passes the equator this is the descending node. An observer at any location on the earth, at any time, will see GPS SVs ascending and descending.

Where the satellite passes over the equator is an important parameter. Even though satellites are orbiting, their path can be specified without reference to earth. Imagine that a satellite orbits about a point, an infinitesimally small piece of collapsed matter with the same mass as earth. The orbital dynamics would be the same as orbiting the earth because equations used thus far describing an orbit involve the earth's mass and not its size or shape. Since the satellite is orbiting a point we must describe the orbit relative to other objects in the universe. A coordinate system relative to a distant star could serve this purpose. The motion of the distant star is extremely small, approaching zero. It can be considered stationary relative to the universe. This is called "inertial space," which is a coordinate system fixed in space.

Where the satellite crosses the earth's equatorial plane is the right ascension of the ascending node. This angle is measured from the reference angle called the vernal equinox. The reference is a line in inertial space drawn from the center of the earth to the sun at the time the line crosses the equator. Here on earth, the vernal equinox is the first day of spring. In locating this line we did not consider the surface of the earth or any lines of latitude or longitude which are creations of man. We were considering only the orbit relative to the collapsed matter point which, like the earth, orbits around the sun. Therefore, the vernal equinox is a point relative to the inertial reference system. The actual time when this line crosses the equatorial plane varies from year to year and spring arrives one year in the middle of the night and the next year during the morning. Likewise, the actual location relative to the surface of the earth of the vernal equinox changes from year to year.

Now, consider the orbit over the rotating earth. The right ascension of the ascending node is a characteristic of an orbit; which is a line in space. This does not imply that the satellite crosses the equator at a longitude equal to the right ascension of the ascending node. Remember, the vernal equinox was a line drawn from the center of the earth to the sun at the time of equinox and had no reference to latitude or longitude. The parameters of the orbit are easily described in inertial space but to be useful on the surface of the earth the orbit must have certain characteristics relative to latitude and longitude. In the case of GPS, there are four satellites in each orbit and all four satellites share the same ascending node. However, each satellite has its own equatorial crossing longitude. The longitude where each satellite crosses the equator depends on where the satellites are in the orbit. This is called phasing.

In the GPS constellation, the right ascension of the ascending node of the six orbits are equally spaced. The right ascensions are 32.847, 92.847, 152.847, 212.847, 272.847, and 332.847 degrees, or every 60 degrees. The longitude at which the satellites cross the equator depends on phasing. As an example, for the 32.847 degree orbit, longitude of the equatorial crossings are 169.73, 54.57, 103.62, and 119.69 degrees. Also, there are two equatorial crossings for each satellite each day. These are separated by 180 degrees so the first satellite listed will cross at 169.73 degrees and again at 349.73 degrees.

Phasing is not done to equalize the longitude of equatorial crossings. It can be seen from the previous example that equatorial crossings of satellites in orbit are not regular. Phasing is adjusted to insure adequate coverage at all points on earth at all times. This requires irregular equatorial crossings. To insure that the ground track of each satellite repeats every day, the angular orbital rate must be an integer multiple of the earth's angular rate. The GPS rate was chosen to be exactly twice the earth's angular frequency.

We used the term "day" when referring to the repeating GPS ground track. Many people define a day as the time it takes the earth to rotate once on its axis. That is a day but a *sidereal* day. The normal concept of a day is from noon to noon at a fixed position on the earth. But the apparent movement of the sun as observed on earth is controlled by two factors; the earth's rotation on its axis and orbiting of the earth about the sun. Imagine, for a moment, that rotation of the earth around its axis ceases. First, how would we know? We could sight a distant star and measure movement in the sky. In other words, we could compare motion of the earth to the inertial coordinate system. The star used as a reference remains stationary in the sky if there is no rotation of the earth.

What else would happen if the earth's rotation ceased? We would have one very long day lasting about a year (365.25 days to be more accurate. The 0.25 day extra is the reason we have leap years.) What is interesting, however, is that the sun would rise in the west and set in the east! This means that orbiting produces motion of the sun contrary to what we perceive when earth rotates about its axis. The sun rises and sets 365 times in what we call a year, and rises and sets 366 times every fourth year for an average of 365.25 sunrises and sunsets in each year. The earth must rotate on its axis one more time than 365.25 to counteract the contrary motion of the sun due to the earth's orbit about the sun.

We spotted a distant star to know whether the earth is rotating about its axis. A distant star could also determine how often the earth rotates in the inertial coordinate system. One rotation of the earth about its axis relative to a distant star is a sidereal day, where sidereal means reference to the stars. The term "day" means solar day, the same time our clocks show and is the motion of the sun perceived on earth. To have a repeating ground path, GPS satellites orbit the earth twice each sidereal day.

Let us calculate the time for one sidereal day. The earth rotates on its axis 366.25 times each year. In this case a year is conventional, or solar, time because we measured a year relative to our perceived motion of the sun. The earth requires 365.25 days to complete an orbit around the sun. The orbit about the sun makes the seasons and sets the length of a year. If we did not account for the extra ¼ day in the year, in about 700 years the seasons would reverse; cold in June in the northern hemisphere and hot in January.

The time required for one complete rotation about the earth's axis is 365.25 solar days divided by 366.25 revolutions or:

$$365.25/366.25 = 0.9972696 \text{ solar days} = 86{,}164.1 \text{ seconds} \qquad (4.5)$$

Twenty-four hours is 86,400 seconds so the sidereal day is shorter than the solar day by 235.9 seconds or 4.93 minutes.

Calculate the satellite's angular velocity, which is two revolutions in a sidereal day:

$$\omega = 4\,\pi \,/\, 86.164\text{E3} = 145.8\text{E-6 rads/sec.} \qquad (4.6)$$

With a value for ω we calculate the radius of the GPS orbit:

$$R = [g\,M_e/\omega^2]^{1/3} = [6.673\text{E-11} \times 5.983\text{E24}/(145.8\text{E-6})^2\,]^{1/3} = 26.58\text{E6 meters} \qquad (4.7)$$

The radius is measured from the center of the earth. To find the altitude, subtract the mean earth radius, 6378 km, from the radius which yields 20,202 km or 10,908 nautical miles.

To draw the ground trace of a GPS satellite we plot the position of the point directly below the satellite, called the subsatellite point. Starting at any location, the position of the subsatellite point is plotted until it returns to the starting point, after which the plot repeats. The ground track would cross the equator and head north to a latitude of 55 degrees. This is because the satellite is inclined at 55 degrees. The track then heads south, crosses the equator and continues to a southerly latitude of 55 degrees and returns to the starting point. Because the satellite makes two orbits in one sidereal day, the ground track will travel north to 55 degrees and, likewise, south twice for each orbit. Because the earth rotates once for the satellite's two orbits, the ground track makes only one pass in the east-west direction each day.

Another way of visualizing this is to consider the geostationary satellite. In this case, the satellite makes one orbit per day. So does the surface of the earth. Thus, the satellite is stationary relative to the surface of the earth. If the satellite were viewed from space, that is to say, in the inertial coordinate system it would be seen to orbit once per sidereal day.

4.1.3 Perturbations of the GPS Orbit

Consider how the mechanics of an orbiting satellite affect the GPS system. First, accuracy of a satellite's position sets the accuracy of GPS position determination. An orbit that is perfect, one that can be calculated by assuming the earth is perfectly spherical and homogeneous, and there are no other celestial bodies such as the moon and sun to influence the orbit with their gravity forces, is called a Keplarian orbit. The equation describing a Keplarian orbit is simple, the equation of an ellipse where the circle is a special case. In satellite orbital calculations a set of parameters called Kepliarians are used to calculate the perfect elliptical orbit, then the effects of perturbing forces are applied. Taking a look at the equation, there are two constants, gravitational constant, g, and mass of the earth, M_e. Gravity is a constant of nature and does not degrade GPS accuracy. The mass of the earth is another factor. The earth is not homogeneous; its shape not a perfect sphere, but it is close. The earth is flattened at the poles, another way of saying it has an equatorial bulge. The amount of flattening at the poles is small; the radius of the equator is only about 0.34% greater. This difference is so minor it may be overlooked when calculating an orbit. However, GPS must measure to a high level of precision.

The earth is oblate, meaning it is not perfectly spherical. A satellite makes two passes each day and the force due to gravity changes slightly. The orbit experiences slight perturbations due to the non-uniform gravity vector. Errors are small, realizing that satellites are almost 11,000 NM from the surface of the earth and gravity varies inversely with the square of the distance from the center of the earth. The biggest problem is that errors accumulate. If a single pass causes slight perturbation from a circular orbit, each pass adds more to the perturbation. Because the orbit frequency is twice that of rotation of the earth, the problem is one of harmonic distortion.

Errors produced by oblateness of the earth are calculated by a complex equation for the gravitational potential of the earth using a set of empirically-derived parameters called zonal harmonics. Without delving into this equation, two major effects are predicted. The first is steady drift of the ascending node. To recall, the ascending node is where the ground track passes the equatorial plane while the satellite is ascending north. This drift may be removed by reducing the theoretical orbit radius a small amount so the satellite orbital period is a bit shorter and compensates for drift.

There is another effect to orbits due to the oblateness of the earth called apsidal rotation but it only affects elliptical orbits. Since the GPS satellite orbit is circular the major perturbation due to the oblate earth is the drift of the ascending node.

There are higher-order, meaning minor, effects attributable to the gravitational potential equation involving higher harmonics. These perturbations are not steady and become complex. The gravitational attraction of sun and moon also have a small effect on orbits, which are not simple harmonics of the orbital period. There is also radiation pressure from the sun. All these effects are slight, difficult to calculate and cumulative. Shown below are the relative effects of several perturbing forces on a GPS orbit. The earth-mass attraction is relative to a homogeneous earth and is the desired force.. The other forces are undesired and are responsible for a distorted orbit. The major perturbation is the second zonal harmonics which is due to the oblateness of the earth.

Force	Acceleration m/s^2	Displacement from desired orbit in one hour
Earth Attraction	5.65E-1	0 m
Second Zonal Harmonic	5.3E-5	300 m
Lunar Gravity	5.5E-6	40 m
Solar Gravity	3.0 E-6	20 m
Fourth Zonal Harmonic	1E-7	0.6 m
Solar Radiation Pressure	1E-7	0.6 m
Gravity Anomalies	1E-8	0.06 m
All Other forces	1E-8	0.06 m

Table 4.1 Relative Perturbing Effects on a GPS Orbit

This introduces the need for the GPS control segment. All satellites eventually must have their orbits "straightened out." This is called stationkeeping. When an orbit becomes so badly distorted it can no longer serve the intended purpose, the satellite is moved by firing small rockets to fix the orbit. This is done by ground stations that monitor the satellite and transmit command signals to the spacecraft. Satellites are only moved when absolutely necessary because it uses rocket fuel. Should fuel be wasted, the satellite cannot be moved and can become worthless. The orbit of the GPS satellite is extremely critical. But, if the satellites are fixed, say, every day, the amount of rocket fuel to implement this level of stationkeeping would be prohibitive. Instead of adjusting GPS orbits constantly, information on the level of perturbation is made available to the user so corrections can be made. Stationkeeping is only carried out when the orbit has become seriously degraded. These correction factors are called ephemeris data or ephemerides.

It was important to discuss orbital dynamics to understand why *ephemerides* are part of the system. Ground stations monitor satellite orbits and adjust for errors by providing ephemerides to the user segment. Because of the cumulative nature of orbital distortions, ephemerides are constantly changing and growing. A satellite orbit is first calculated to be Keplerian, then corrected using ephemeris data. The ephemerides are uplinked to the SV and become a part of the SV navigation message.

To summarize; the orbits of GPS satellites are stable with small perturbations. Information on perturbations is transmitted to the user segment. Verifying range, however, requires measuring a time delay and assuming that the velocity of radio waves is constant.

4.1.4 Determining Range

The GPS system relies on the accurate measurement of range from a number of SVs. Measuring range with radio signals involves the speed of those radio waves. The velocity of electromagnetic waves is an absolute constant in a vacuum. Most of the nearly 11,000 nautical miles the GPS signal travels is space, which is about as close to a vacuum as one could imagine. During the last few nautical miles the signal passes through the atmosphere and slows slightly in velocity. Because GPS must be accurate, even such small changes affect range. This hints at the need for more corrections, as discussed in a later section.

128

4.2 GPS Clocks

Another factor in elapsed time between satellite and GPS user is accuracy of the clocks; both in the satellite and user equipment Accurate clocks have been a part of navigation for over 100 years. If you know where on the earth you are, celestial bodies can be used to tell time. An example is the sundial. If you know what time it is, the sundial tells longitude by turning the dial until it reads the correct time. What if you know neither time nor location? You can't use the same sundial to do both. To navigate on sun or stars requires a mechanical clock.

About the time European explorers were traveling to the New World, accuracy of a mechanical clock (around 1750) was 1 second per day, which is one part in 86,400, or 12 parts per million. For sailing ships, achieving such accuracy was a challenge for clock makers and a handsome reward was offered for a time piece capable of this accuracy aboard a sailing ship. Accurate clocks were usually made with a pendulum for a time-keeping oscillator. A massive pendulum in a vacuum can achieve an accuracy of 1 part in a million but hardly on a rolling, pitching ship. The breakthrough came with the invention of the chronometer, which used an ingenious design of hair spring, escapement (a see-saw device which ticked off accurate time intervals even as the wind-up spring weakened) and temperature-compensated metals that provided great accuracy under severe conditions at sea. Although the chronometer revolutionized marine navigation in the 18th century by providing a means of determining longitude, its accuracy is measured in miles. A landing aircraft needs accuracy measured in meters to descend to a touchdown point on a runway.

The advent of electronics in the early 1900s brought forth oscillators of unparalleled stability based on quartz radiators. Oscillations in quartz are actually mechanical but the clock is treated as an all-electronic device. Using temperature stabilized quartz resonators, electronic clocks are capable of one part in 10^9 or a thousand times better than the best mechanical clock.

GPS is often called a one-way ranging system. Compare this to DME, which requires a transmission to a ground transponder, which then replies. The round trip time delay is measured, which includes propagation time and an internal delay for the ground transponder. The airborne transponder in conjunction with air traffic control radar determines range in the same manner. Primary radar measures the time delay from transmission of a high power pulse to receipt of back-scattered energy. These are examples of two-way ranging, where distance is measured by the time delay between outbound and returned signal. The range, R, is:

$$R = \Delta t \, c/2 \qquad\qquad (4.8)$$

where Δt is elapsed time for the round trip and c is the speed of radio waves. In this equation the distance measurement is as accurate as clock accuracy. This assumes the velocity of radio waves is constant, which it is not. Energy is propagating through the atmosphere and, although velocity is close to that in a vacuum, it is not exactly the same. For DME and radar, the small difference in velocity of radio waves has an imperceptible effect.

If an inexpensive 10 part per million, PPM, clock measures range of a DME or radar, the error introduced by the clock for a DME distance of 100 NM is 0.001 NM. Clearly, an inexpensive clock is more than sufficient for DME. The main difference in time measurement is that a two-way ranging system measures time delay directly, while one-way ranging determines time delay by using two time of day measurements.

One way ranging, therefore, requires an accurate time of day clock. Any inaccuracy is proportional to the time when the time of day clock was last set. The GPS space segment has 24 accurate clocks synchronized to a master clock located at a master control station. The station keeps what is called GPS time. It is used only for GPS and not adjusted to be in step with UTC, universal coordinated time. Also, atomic clocks for UTC and GPS are not precisely coordinated with solar time. UTC is occasionally adjusted to agree reasonably close to solar time by "leap seconds". It is not desirable to adjust GPS time with large changes of as much as one second and UTC and GPS are slowly drifting apart.

In the GPS satellite, clocks are not reset. Deviation from GPS time is measured and correction data uplinked to the satellite twice each sidereal day. This means the worst case clock error develops over 12 hours. Extremely stable atomic clocks, however, drift only a few nanoseconds in 12 hours. .

What accuracy is required for GPS clocks? To get a feel for this, electromagnetic energy takes 3 ns to travel one meter. Assume the satellite clock introduces no more than 10 meters to the error in GPS ranging. Therefore, the clock must be within 30 ns. The clock, however, could have been last checked 12 hours, or 41,100 seconds ago. Clock accuracy to insure less than 30 ns error after one half day is a part in 1.37E12.

Even though satellites contain accurate atomic clocks, they tend to drift. What is important is that all satellite clocks report the same time. This is achieved by monitoring at ground stations and comparing SVs to the master clock and GPS time. GPS time and universal coordinated time, UTC, are essentially the same at present (early 2002), but slowly drifting apart. Because GPS must disseminate precise time signals, the difference between GPS and UTC can be simply published or broadcast for making corrections. The drift of satellite clocks is compensated by uploading corrections twice every day. The elapsed time measurements use clock offsets to determine the precise elapsed time.

Einstein proposed that time was not the same everywhere and it can be affected by acceleration and gravity. These theories, when introduced early in the twentieth century, were criticized by scientists as preposterous. This is no longer the case. Working with atomic energy and particle accelerators, scientists are true believers in the theory of relativity. High-energy physics push the velocities of sub-atomic particles to within a fraction of a percentage point of the speed of light. The effects of relativity are easy to see at these velocities.

In the aviation world, high velocities are not rare but even the speed of the fastest aircraft is a small portion of the speed of light. However, in GPS there is a need for extremely accurate measurement for very small differences.

The GPS clock and its location in space requires corrections for relativistic effects. These are primarily due to the earth's gravitational field and the relative motion between satellite and user. Clocks aboard the SV actually appear to run faster than they really do. This is probably the first system, exclusive of scientific experiment, where relativistic effects are significant. To compensate for them, clocks in the satellite are deliberately offset to a lower frequency.

Few clocks can provide a level of accuracy suited for GPS, except for the atomic clock. SVs are equipped with cesium and rubidium clocks and hydrogen masers for an accuracy of 1 part in 10^{13}. This number to describe accuracy of a clock is simplistic. Clock stability requires measurement of short and long term accuracy. Even though the ultimate controlling device is a quartz crystal phase locked to the atomic standard, there are short-term "Allen" variances to be considered.

The challenge was that an atomic clock had never been launched into space before. One unknown during development was whether an atomic clock could survive the launch, then operate five to ten years in space. The clock is such a key item that GPS SVs are provided with two or three redundant clocks. Block I SVs had three rubidium clocks on board. Block IA SVs had three rubidium and one cesium. Recent SVs have two rubidium and two cesium.

These clocks are expensive and heavy, making them impractical for installing aboard aircraft. Thus, there must be a way to provide accurate time-keeping on the airplane without a mega-dollar system. There is a clever method of determining correct time in the user equipment without an atomic clock.

Let us go back to finding a position. Three SVs are used and the range from each is measured. The resulting spheres of position from each range measurement produces a position fix. Assume that a fourth satellite is used and a fourth sphere of position is determined. If the satellites are A, B, C, and D, four positions may be determined. This is from the combinations of ABC, ABD, BCD and ACD. Each combination should produce a position fix and, if there are no errors, they should all be the same. If there are any errors, the points will be scattered about.

Assume that an inexpensive quartz crystal clock has an error. If we change the on-board clock in the correct direction, that is, toward the true time, the spread of the position fixes will narrow. If we continue to change the on-board clock, the spread of points decreases and as we pass the actual time, the points begin to spread out again. We can never reduce the spread to zero because other error sources can set the on-board clock to the correct time by minimizing the spread of points.

A typical quartz crystal clock can have an error of 1 to 5 parts per million. To maintain a range measurement accuracy of 1 meter, the clock must maintain correct time to within 3 ns. A drift of 1 part per million causes an error of 1 μs in one second or will take only 3 μs to accumulate an error of 3 ns. To reduce the time drift, the on-board time base is adjusted to reduce the drift. The GPS system can provide more than navigation but is used for precision frequency and time of day transmission as well.

The ranges to the SVs are called *pseudoranges* because of uncorrected errors. The setting of the clock is the first step in changing pseudorange to range.

4.2.1 GPS Time

The major application of GPS for aviation is position determination. Another is disseminating precise time. GPS provides a highly accurate clock to synchronize LORAN-C stations. GPS can also provide accurate time for air traffic control centers, as well as aircraft. GPS time will synchronize future airborne digital communications systems. The dissemination of precise time will find increasing application in the future.

It is necessary to first understand the concept of universal time. Accurate timekeeping implies there is a master clock by which all others are compared. There are a number of master clocks throughout the world. The U.S. National Institute of Standards and Technology, NIST, maintains a master clock for the U.S. For many years, the National Bureau of Standards, precursor of NIST, maintained an accurate pendulum clock and transmitted time signals via HF radio. The clock was compared to motion of the sun and periodically adjusted to agree with solar time.

In the 1940s, the pendulum clock was augmented by a quartz resonator electronic clock which, like the pendulum clock, was checked against solar time. There were many master clocks throughout the world, essentially one per industrialized country. In the U.S. there was a second master clock at the Naval Observatory in Washington, D.C. It made sense to place master clocks at observatories because the sun calibrated the clocks and equipment was at the observatory. One significant observatory is in Greenwich England situated at the zero meridian. Standards bureaus of the world adjusted their master clocks to agree with time determined at the Greenwich observatory, which is called Greenwich Mean Time or GMT

In the 1950s quartz clocks were replaced with clocks regulated by emissions from atoms. Atomic clocks have an accuracy many orders of magnitude better than quartz clocks. Only certain frequencies of oscillation, in the microwave spectrum, are available from an atomic clock An integer number of cycles of microwave radiation defines the time of one second. It is not possible to generate a precise "solar second" with an atomic clock.

It is important to understand solar time to appreciate problems associated with accurate timekeeping. Solar time is relative to the position of the sun as observed on earth. The best reference is high noon, when the sun reaches its maximum position in the sky. This time varies enormously. If an observer is on the east boundary of a time zone, high noon occurs about 1 hour ahead of high noon as observed on the western boundary. Consider high noon as observed at Greenwich, England, which sits on the zero meridian. Even here, high noon will not occur exactly 24 hours after the previous noon. This is because the motion of the earth is not perfect. It is affected by the gravitational pull of other celestial bodies. Also, the earth's rotation is slowing down. It is a very small amount but accurate time keeping must consider the phenomenon.

Atomic clocks are not affected by celestial bodies or other phenomenon. As solar time varies and slows, the atomic clock ticks off seconds in a stable manner. Eventually, the atomic clock and a clock set to the motion of the sun drift apart. The standard for most applications, which does *not* include GPS, is Universal Coordinated Time, or UTC. (The abbreviation is UTC rather than UCT, because the internationally-accepted abbreviation is based on the French translation of Universal Coordinated Time.) UTC is kept with an atomic clock. To prevent drifting so far from solar time that high noon could take place at 11 AM, the atomic clock is adjusted periodically to bring UTC more in line with solar time. It would take thousands of years before high noon occurred at 11 AM, but there are applications requiring accurate time, such as solar navigation, where a few seconds are noticeable.

To keep atomic time in line with solar time, leap seconds are added to UTC. This occurs only every few years but the need is there. Until leap seconds are added, NIST and other standards bureaus worldwide, publish the difference between solar and UTC time.

GPS uses its own standard called GPS time. Leap seconds are not used because seconds added to every GPS receiver will show enormous, but temporary, errors. It is also likely that the receiver will lose lock. Instead, GPS and UTC time are kept within a few microseconds except for integral leap seconds. Another way of stating this; the two time systems are different only by an integer amount of leap seconds, plus or minus a few microseconds. GPS time and UTC will continue to drift apart in jumps of a second and, after a hundred years or so, could be as much as a minute different.

GPS clocks in SVs are not exact and have small drifts. The ground segment monitors the SV clocks and determines offsets from GPS time. These errors are included in the navigation message to account for the GPS space segment clock error. GPS SV clocks are adjusted from the ground segment, but only when the error grows large.

4.2.2 Finding Position From Time Measurements

Consider the geometry that determines a position on earth based on time measurements from GPS SVs. SVs move in a circular orbit around the center of the mass of the earth. The surface of the earth is approximately that of a sphere with its center at the center of mass. "Approximately" because the earth is not a perfect sphere but oblate, with mountains, valleys and tides For understanding GPS geometry, begin by assuming the earth is a perfect sphere.

With circular orbits having a center at the center of mass of the earth (not the geometric center), a coordinate system is constructed with the origin at the center of mass. This an earth centered, EC, coordinate system. The goal is position information, or latitude, longitude and altitude. If the coordinate system is rotated and one of the three axes anchored to the earth's zero meridian, the earth is fixed within this coordinate system. This is the earth centered, earth fixed, ECEF, coordinate system.

Rotating coordinate systems are not a new concept to engineers, particularly electrical. A phase diagram, the so-called phasor diagram, for alternating current, AC, is based on a rotating coordinate system.   ECEF coordinates are a Cartesian system with the X axis passing through the zero meridian and equator. We will use this ECEF coordinate system in the following discussion.

4.2.3 Correcting the User Clock
Let us assume our user clock, not being a highly accurate atomic variety, has an error, which we will call clock bias. If our clock is slow, that is to say the clock shows an earlier time than the correct time, it would appear that signals from the SVs have taken less time to arrive at our receiver than the true time. On the other hand, if our clock is fast it would appear it took more time to arrive at our receiver. There would be an error in the range measurement that is directly proportional to our time error, which may be given as:

$$\Delta R = \Delta tc$$

If our clock is slow or Δt, our clock error, is negative we must add the clock bias as a distance from the actual measured range, or pseudo range to get the actual range.

It is important to understand that the clock bias error is the same for each pseudo range measurement made for each SV. This is because we take the difference between the time in the navigation message which was based on GPS time to which all SVs are locked, and our user clock.

Assume we measure the pseudo range from four SVs. Each measurement includes the same clock bias expressed as a distance. Therefore, we have four equations and four unknowns as:

$$R_1 = (\ (X_{S1} - X_U)^2 + (Y_{S1} - Y_U)^2 + (Z_{S1} - Z_U)^2\ )^{1/2} + \Delta R \qquad 4.9(a)$$
$$R_2 = (\ (X_{S2} - X_U)^2 + (Y_{S2} - Y_U)^2 + (Z_{S2} - Z_U)^2\ )^{1/2} + \Delta R \qquad 4.9(b)$$
$$R_3 = (\ (X_{S3} - X_U)^2 + (Y_{S3} - Y_U)^2 + (Z_{S3} - Z_U)^2\ )^{1/2} + \Delta R \qquad 4.9(c)$$
$$R_4 = (\ (X_{S4} - X_U)^2 + (Y_{S4} - Y_U)^2 + (Z_{S4} - Z_U)^2\ )^{1/2} + \Delta R \qquad 4.9(d)$$

Where R_N is the range to the Nth SV, X_{SN}, Y_{SN} and Z_{SN} is the X , Y and Z coordinates of the Nth SV, X_U, Y_U, and Z_U are the X, Y and Z coordinates of the user. The X, Y and Z coordinates of all four SVs are accurately known because the orbits are very predictable and we have the necessary ephemerides to insure precise orbital determination.

Notice that ΔR, the error due to the user clock, appears in all four equations and affects the measured range the same way for each SV. The range measured without the clock correction is called pseudo range.

The unknowns of the equation are the X, Y, and Z coordinates of the user in the ECEF coordinate system and the ΔR, the clock bias. Thus, we have four equations, and four unknown and a solution. The user clock is corrected by using $\Delta R = \Delta tc$ and the user clock shows a precise time of day. These equations show how GPS is not only a precision navigation system, but a time dissemination system.

Having precise time, say to within nanoseconds, is important to laboratories and so-phisticated military operations but it is not evident what practical applications of such precise time exist on an aircraft. In a later chapter we will discuss a future time division multiplexed, TDM, communications system that takes full advantage of GPS time.

Four SVs are needed to generate the four equations to have a full solution to the GPS message. Once the user clock is corrected, the ΔR, clock bias, can be equated to zero and only three equations or SVs are needed to determine a fix. As previously discussed the user clock is a quartz oscillator which, while not an atomic clock, is reasonably stable and will permit the use of only three SVs for short periods of time.

If more than four SVs are received, which is usually the case, it is possible to improve the accuracy of the system by averaging.

4.3 Earth Model

GPS determines position relative to the center of the satellites' orbits. It is a three dimensional system with latitude and longitude for two dimensions and altitude relative to sea level as the third. To physicists, GPS is a four dimension system; X, Y, Z and time. Since most navigation is not done by physicists, we will discuss GPS as a three dimensional, 3D, system. To provide altitude requires the radius of the earth to mean sea level, MSL, be known. If the earth were a perfect sphere, this would be simple, due to a constant radius from the center of mass to MSL. The earth is not a perfect sphere, but the deviation is not extreme. The earth is nearly spherical with a flattening at the poles. The mean radius of the equator is 6378 km while the radius at the pole is 21 km less , a flattening that must be considered when making altitude calculations. A 21 km error in altitude is excessive.

An earth model must include irregularities. One example is the WGS-84 earth model, generated by the World Geodetic Survey of 1984. It is sufficiently detailed for GPS to provide all three dimensions, latitude, longitude and altitude, with reasonable precision. However, the least precise is altitude, partially due to the earth model.

4.4 Space Vehicle

Versions of the GPS SV have changed over the years, but some areas are common to all. The space vehicle is divided into the following sections:
1. Clock
2. L Band Communications
3. Cross Links
4. Mission Data Unit
5. Telemetry, Tracking and Control, Stationkeeping

The atomic clock is one of the most expensive and failure-prone parts of the SV. After many early failures, great improvements were made in this component. There are two types, rubidium and cesium, and both may be found on GPS SVs. Cesium standards are larger and heavier, weighing about 20 pounds and consuming 20 to 25 watts. Rubidium standards weigh about 14 pounds and consume about 15 watts.

An L-band communications section of the SV provides L1 and L2 down link signals. These are radiated from a directional array of circularly polarized antennas pointed toward earth. Carrier generation, modulation and power amplifiers are included in the L-band section. The navigation message is transmitted from the mission data unit.

The L-band antenna is an array of helical antennas with a directional pattern that beams most energy towards the user. Each SV has 12 helical antennas positioned in two concentric circles. The pattern increases signal strength to users who observe the SV low on the horizon. This accounts for greater signal loss through the atmosphere and longer propagation distance.

Cross links provide communications and ranging between SVs. Recall in the discussion of the GPS system, SVs are under control of the ground. There is a back up mode called autonomous navigation, autonav, where a SV that loses command signals continues to operate by communicating with other SVs in the constellation.. The first operational SVs could provide positioning data for 14 days without contact from the control segment. The latest SVs will provide a minimum of 180 days of positioning service in the autonav mode.

The mission data unit is the major controlling computer. Some tasks performed are:

1. Compose the navigation message
2. Generate the PRN
3. Generate selective availability, SA
4. Provide anti-spoof, AS
5. Operate the SV in the autonav mode
6. Perform self checks of the spacecraft
7. Provide timing and synchronization of other subsytems on the spacecraft
8. Receive and store uplink commands from the control segment

Telemetry, tracking and control, TT and C, and the stationkeeping section keep the SV in the correct orbit, and oriented toward earth. Commands from ground stations are transmitted to the SV and orbital corrections made by firing retro-rockets on the space vehicle. Stationkeeping keeps solar arrays pointed toward the sun for power, and antennas pointed toward earth.

4.5 GPS Signals

Two carriers are modulated by GPS signals: 1575.42 MHz, the L1 frequency, and L2 at 1227.6 MHz. Two are required to perform corrections due to the ionosphere and to transmit PPS (precision positioning service) signals. Only L1 and L2 are transmitted from SVs at the time of this writing. However, a new frequency, L5, will be included in SVs launched after about 2002. L5 is covered in a later section.

Next, consider how the message modulates the carrier, and establishing a time reference. GPS modulates with the technique of *spread spectrum*. Every SV uses the same pair of operating frequencies in a method called code division multiplexing, CDMA.

There are two ways for many users to occupy the same set of frequencies. Most common is frequency division multiplexing. Each user has an assignment, which is a band of frequencies broad enough to pass information, but only on a small portion of the entire band. A familiar example is FM broadcast which has 100 channels, each 0.2 MHz wide, from 88.1 MHz to 107.9 MHz. The band carries 100 potential users in the 20 MHz band of frequencies.

There are restrictions. If two stations in the same community have adjacent channels there are two strong signals close in frequency which can cause interference. This is solved by not assigning adjacent channels in the same area. For one community there is not a total of 100 channels but only 50.

There is another problem. If some stations are not on continuously, their frequency channels are wasted when they are off the air. For broadcasting, this is not a major problem because most broadcasters are on continuously. In the two-way radio industry, a channel is often used only a few minutes. When the inactive time is added over a day, the quiet time becomes significant.

The technique of spread spectrum, as the name implies, deliberately spreads the spectrum of a user from a narrow band to a width that occupies the entire assigned band. As an example, take the FM broadcast signal. The channel assigned to each broadcaster is 200 kHz wide. Spread spectrum modulation would increase the bandwidth to the entire 20 MHz range. This is a one hundred-fold increase in bandwidth. The advantages of spread spectrum are a function of the amount of increase in bandwidth and a parameter called the spreading gain, or processing gain, defined as:

$$G_s = 10 \log (BW_s / BW_u) \qquad (4.10)$$

where BW_s is bandwidth of the signal after it has been spread and BW_u the bandwidth before it was spread. For our example of FM broadcast; since bandwidth increased by a factor of 100 the spreading gain is 20 dB.

There are two methods of spreading a spectrum. Continuing the FM example: For every station to occupy the entire band, each station could jump from one channel to another in random fashion so it would occupy every channel at least once. Randomness is required so two or more stations will not become synchronized and jump to the same channels. Even in a random pattern, two stations will occasionally occupy the same frequency. If there are a lot of channels the chances diminish. If the number of stations is high, the probability increases. When two transmitters are on the same frequency there is a short period where the two signals interfere. Since all transmitter frequency patterns are random, the times when interference occurs is also random. This means that interference is much like noise. Therefore, as the number of users increases, the noise level goes up. This method of spread spectrum is called frequency hopping.

To receive frequency-hopped spread spectrum, the receiver must hop in the same order as the transmitter to the same frequencies. Herein lies a problem. If frequency hopping is random, how does the receiver know which frequency to select? The "random" frequencies are not truly random. True randomness is a non-deterministic system, where the next frequency cannot be calculated by any method. The "random" frequency schedule, rather, is a pseudorandom sequence which can be predicted with a formula. The pseudorandom sequence has characteristics of random noise but is predictable. Pseudorandom sequences, also called pseudorandom noise or PRN, are used in the GPS system.

There is another method for generating spread spectrum and it's the method used with GPS. It's called the direct-sequence method. As shown in Fig 4.4, a carrier is modulated with information for the navigation message. For GPS, the modulation is binary phase shift keying. This uses two phase angles; 0 and π radians. One phase represents a logic one, while the other is a logic zero. This modulation is similar to, but not the same as, the modulation for MLS data transmission, which was *differential* phase shift keying

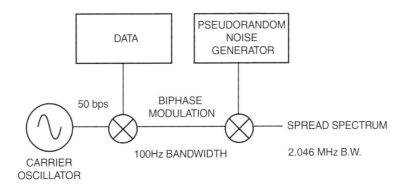

Figure 4.4 Direct sequence spread spectrum modulation

The data rate of the C/A (coarse acquisition) navigation message is low, about 50 bits per second, bps, and bandwidth is about 100 Hz. This narrow bandwidth is "spread" by binary phase modulating the navigation message signal. The process, called the spreading function, is a pseudorandom sequence of zeros and ones. The clock rate is 1.023 MHz, which results in a bandwidth of 2.046 MHz. Bandwidth has been increased from 100 Hz to 2.046 MHz for an increase of 20,460 or 43 dB of processing gain. The P (precision) code has a clock ten times the frequency and the navigation message is the same. Thus the processing gain is 53 dB. The higher the spreading gain the more effective are the advantages of spread spectrum.

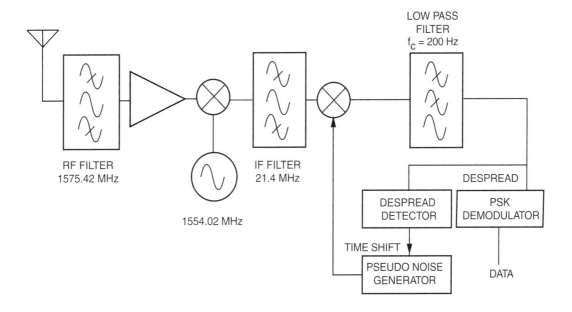

Figure 4.5   Direct sequence spread spectrum receiver

To communicate with spread spectrum, two characteristics must be met. First, the desired signal is received and, second, other signals may not interfere. All transmitted signals occupy the same spectrum and cannot be separated by the usual techniques, such as filtering.

A block diagram of a direct sequence spread spectrum receiver is in Fig. 4.5. The key to receiving a spread spectrum signal is to despread the signal. Once this is accomplished, it can be handled with conventional circuits for demodulation.

Generating direct sequence spread spectrum takes a carrier modulated with the message and spreading it to a much wider frequency range. In GPS, the message modulates the carrier with binary phase shift keying, but modulation could be anything; AM, FM or phase modulation. To spread the signal, the modulated carrier is multiplied by +1 or –1, which is another way of viewing binary phase shift keying.

If the spread signal is multiplied by the same sequences of +1 and –1 at the same time the result is the signal before it was spread. As an example, assume the signal is multiplied by +1, -1, -1, +1, -1. When the spread signal is received it is multiplied by the same sequence with the same time relationship. The first +1 means the signal was unaffected by the spreading signal since it is multiplied by one. At the receiving end, the signal is multiplied by +1 or not affected at all. The next multiplier is –1. At the receiving end, the signal is multiplied by a –1, which inverts the phase a second time and undoes the phase shift applied at the transmitter. Every time the spread signal shifts in phase, the phase is shifted again, which negates the phase shift applied at the transmitter end. The result is that the spreading function is removed, in a process called "de-spreading".

There are three normal PRN codes that may be transmitted by the SV; the C/A code, the P code and the Y code when anti-spoof is activated. There are two "abnormal" codes called non-standard codes that are used when a SV is not reliable, called the non-standard C/A and the non-standard Y code. These codes will not despread in a GPS receiver. This insures that a deficient SV will not be used.

The difficulty is determining proper alignment of the despreading function. Despreading and spreading are the same and generating the spreading function in the receiver replicates the generation in the transmitter. The spreading function in the GPS C/A code lasts 1023 clock cycles and repeats. Because the sequence repeats, the code is not truly random, as a random code would never repeat. The code is called a Gold code and the method of generation discussed later. The clock for the C/A code is 1.023 MHz, causing the code to repeat every 1 ms. The 1 ms time is called an epoch. There are other epochs in the GPS system and this epoch is the C/A code epoch.

The Gold code for C/A (coarse acquisition, also called "clear" acquisition indicating the code is not encrypted but in the clear), is a string of 1023 bits. To despread a received spread spectrum signal the local code must be perfectly aligned with the code in the spread message. The receiver tries all possible alignments until despreading occurs. Before alignment is tried, however, the correct alignment of the code is determined. If the output is despread, the phase of the output changes in no less than 1/50th second, because data is at 50 bits per second. The clock of the despreading function is 1.023 MHz and the most time there will be no phase change is 10 clocks. This is a characteristic of PRN. If there has been no phase change in 10 clocks of the PRN sequence or slightly less than 10 μs, it is known that the code is aligned. If all possible alignments of the PRN code are tried, where a 10 μs period of no phase change would signify proper alignment, it takes a maximum of 1023 X 10 μs, or 10.23 ms, to test all possible alignments.

There are techniques to speed the process. One is simultaneously trying 8 different alignments of the PRN by passing the code through a shift register. This reduces the time to slightly more than 1 ms. Once proper alignment is found, the GPS receiver is said to have "locked on" the SV and the received signal tracked without re-acquiring the PRN alignment. The despreading process, however, can be disturbed by noise or interference.

Once the correct alignment is found the receiver must track the SV as the code alignment will constantly change due to the relative motion between the SV and the user. One popular method is the "code locked loop". The incoming signal is compared to three versions of the PRN for the SV. One is one clock early, one is the nominal and the third is one clock late. These are called the early, prompt and late PRNs. When correctly aligned only the prompt PRN will despread the signal. If the time delay changes, either the early or late despreading will begin to show some results. The receiver computer introduces a time delay to produce despreading only with the "prompt" PRN. This technique is analogous to a phase detector in a phase locked loop.

If the PRN matches the PRN of the received signal, and the two codes are perfectly aligned, the received signal is despread. If the PRNs do not match, the signal is spread further. This should not be hard to prove because it was the same process of multiplying a signal by a PRN, using biphase modulation, that generated the spread signal in the first place. All GPS SVs transmit on the same two frequencies. Of every SV in view, only the SV that has a PRN that matches the receiver's PRN is despread and demodulated.

The GPS receiver knows which SVs are accessible and tries only PRN codes associated with available SVs. The receiver knows approximately where it is on earth to know the available SVs. When a receiver is turned on, it assumes it is at the same location as before. If the receiver is removed from an aircraft and sent to a repair shop, it may get "lost" and not quickly find the expected SVs. When this happens, the receiver performs a "sky search", which is to try every PRN code until it finds a SV. This narrows the search and the receiver looks for nearby SVs. Note that the GPS receiver must be able to predict where any SV is at any time. The sky search may take more than a minute to demodulate sufficient SVs to determine an accurate position.

4.6 Generating PRN Codes

The PRN is a set called Gold codes. The heart of the Gold code is a shift register with linear feedback. Consider the four-bit shift register arrangement shown in Fig. 4.7.

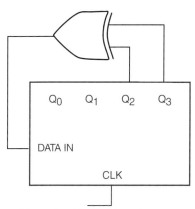

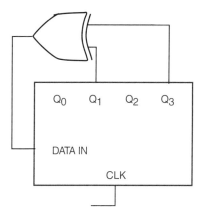

Figure 4.7 Maximal length sequence   *Figure 4.8 Sub-maximal sequence*

If the shift register starts at the state of all ones, it generates the sequence in Table 4.1. It can serve as an exercise to verify that the sequence shown is generated by the circuit. Once the shift register returns to all ones, the sequence repeats.

State	Q0	Q1	Q2	Q3	Q0	Q1	Q2	Q3
1	1	1	1	1	1	1	1	1
2	0	1	1	1	0	1	1	1
3	0	0	1	1	0	0	1	1
4	0	0	0	1	1	0	0	1
5	1	0	0	0	1	1	0	0
6	0	1	0	0	1	1	1	0
7	0	0	1	0	1	1	1	1
8	1	0	0	1				
9	1	1	0	0				
10	0	1	1	0				
11	1	0	1	1				
12	0	1	0	1				
13	1	0	1	0				
14	1	1	0	1				
15	1	1	1	0				
16	1	1	1	1				

Table 4.1 PRN codes generated with a shift register and linear feedback

What would happen if the shift register is loaded with all zeros? Two zeros X-ORed produces a zero which, when fed back, keeps the shift register at all zeros. Therefore, the shift register will never change. Of 16 possible states of the four bits of the shift register, one combination, all zeros, cannot be used. The maximum length a sequence can have for the 4 bit shift register example shown is 15.

What would happen if a different pair of bits are X-ORed to produce the feedback? As a matter of demonstration, Fig 4.8 shows a different feedback arrangement. As mentioned previously, feedback must include the last bit of the shift register. If not present, the last stage of the shift register plays no role and the same results could be obtained with a three bit shift register. To have an N bit PRN sequence generator, the Nth shift register stage must be included in the feedback.

Notice that this feedback combination does not provide a 15 state PRN, as shown in Table 4.1. This example repeats after 5 clock cycles. Now to extend the four bit example to shift registers of any length with linear feedback.

1. The maximum length of the PRN sequence is 2^N-1 clock cycles.
2. Not all combinations of feedback provide a maximal length sequence.
3. Even when feedback produces a maximal length sequence, there is one state the shift register may not assume.
4. Feedback must include the Nth stage of the shift register.

These characteristics of a PRN generator using a shift register apply to shift registers of any length.

It was shown in the 4 bit example that not all possible combinations of feedback produce a maximal length sequence. The PRN sequence in the GPS C/A mode is to have 1023 states before repeating, which requires a ten-stage shift register. Only 60 feedback arrangements produce a maximal length sequence. Of the 60, half are mirror images of the remaining half. In reality, there are only 30 unique sequences.

Since the GPS constellation consists of only 24 SVs, perhaps simple linear feedback could produce a suitable code. This would only allow for an expansion of 6 SVs to a total of 30. Further, the codes have too much similarity. Some codes have excessive cross correlation. (Correlation is discussed in a later section.)

To increase the number of codes and improve cross correlation, two maximal length sequences are generated and X-ORed together. Exclusive ORing is also called "modulo two addition", which is essentially binary adding without a carry. As before, the sequence has a length of $(2^N – 1)$, where N is the length of the shift register to generate maximal length sequences. There are, however, with this method of generating PRN sequences, $(2^N – 1)$ different sequences. This is because two sequences may be X-ORed with $(2^N – 1)$ different time delays.

For the 1023 state code required there are 1023 different alignments of any pair of codes. Since there are 30 independent codes that can be taken two at a time, there are 435 combinations. For each there are 1023 time delays for a total of 445005 possible combinations. Some combinations do not produce codes with low cross correlation characteristics and are not used. Most possible codes produce useful, low cross correlation codes perfectly suited for GPS.

4.7 PRN Codes

One method of qualifying PRN codes is autocorrelation. Take a sequence of zeros and ones that appear to be random. What makes it random? First, there should be as many zeros as ones, because the likelihood of one state or the other should be the same, or random. There should be a certain number of two ones together or three ones together or four, etc. This means there should be narrow pulses, medium wide pulses and wide pulses. The number of narrow pulses relative to wide pulses may not be immediately apparent. If we were to picture the Gaussian or normal distribution which is characteristic of a random process there is a high probability of one value and the probability diminishes for events that are significantly different. Therefore, the most likely pulse width is one logic one and this diminishes where the very wide pulses are very unlikely. The Gaussian distribution is a two sided plot which is accounted for by the fact that there are groups of logic ones as well as groups of logic zeros.
What shows randomness is the autocorrelation function. Take a series of zeros and ones, which represents a finite length sequence and compare the sequence to itself but offset by one bit, two bits, three and so on. Compare, in this sense, means perform an exclusive NOR function, where the output is a logic one when the two inputs are the same. Take as an example the sequence:

$$0\ 1\ 0\ 0\ 1\ 0\ 1\ 0\ 0\ 1\ 1\ 1\ 0\ 1\ 0$$

This was chosen "at random" by the author by writing down a sequence of ones and zeros. If this sequence is correlated with itself, it would always be the same and output of the exclusive NOR would be a solid one. We would then say correlation is perfect; it correlated with itself. Now offset the sequence one bit and correlate again. Shown below are two sequences offset by one bit:

$$0\ 1\ 0\ 0\ 1\ 0\ 1\ 0\ 0\ 1\ 1\ 1\ 0\ 1\ 0$$
$$0\ 1\ 0\ 0\ 1\ 0\ 1\ 0\ 0\ 1\ 1\ 1\ 0\ 1\ 0$$

Notice the rightmost bit on the offset sequence has extended beyond the top sequence. The sequence repeats so the bit will move to the left side. Shown below are two sequences which result exclusive NOR-ing.

```
0 1 0 0 1 0 1 0 0 1 1 1 0 1 0
0 0 1 0 0 1 0 1 0 0 1 1 1 0 1
1 0 0 1 0 0 0 0 1 0 1 1 0 0 0
```

In this exercise, there are 5 ones out of 15 comparisons or an average of 0.33.

Now, offset the codes by an additional bit:

```
0 1 0 0 1 0 1 0 0 1 1 1 0 1 0
1 0 0 1 0 0 1 0 1 0 0 1 1 1 0
0 0 1 0 0 1 1 1 0 0 0 1 0 1 1
```

In this case, autocorrelation produces 7 ones out of 15 for an average of 0.47. Because we have 15 bits we could never have an average of exactly 0.5. Therefore, 0.47 is as close as we can get. There can never be an autocorrelation of exactly 0.5 for any PRN because the sequence is always an odd number. This is because the maximal length sequence is (2^N-1) which is always an odd number. This is more in line with what is expected from a true random sequence. If a true random set of ones and zeros is offset and compared, the likelihood of two bits being the same is as likely as being different for an average of 0.5. Let us offset the sequence another bit.

```
0 1 0 0 1 0 1 0 0 1 1 1 0 1 0
0 1 0 0 1 0 0 1 0 1 0 0 1 1 1
1 1 1 1 1 1 0 0 1 1 0 0 0 1 0
```

For this delay, the bits are the same 9 times out of 15 for a result of 0.6.

Continue the process by offsetting the two codes a bit at a time:

```
0 1 0 0 1 0 1 0 0 1 1 1 0 1 0
1 0 1 0 0 1 0 0 1 0 1 0 0 1 1
0 0 0 1 0 0 0 1 0 0 1 0 1 1 0 = 0.33
```

```
0 1 0 0 1 0 1 0 0 1 1 1 0 1 0
1 1 0 1 0 0 1 0 0 1 0 1 0 0 1
0 1 1 0 0 1 1 1 1 1 0 0 1 0 0 = 0.53
```

```
0 1 0 0 1 0 1 0 0 1 1 1 0 1 0
1 1 1 0 1 0 0 1 0 0 1 0 1 0 0
0 1 0 1 1 1 0 0 1 0 1 0 0 0 1 = 0.47
```

```
0 1 0 0 1 0 1 0 0 1 1 1 0 1 0
0 1 1 1 0 1 0 0 1 0 0 1 0 1 0
1 1 0 0 0 0 0 1 0 0 0 1 1 1 1 = 0.47
```

```
0 1 0 0 1 0 1 0 0 1 1 1 0 1 0
0 0 1 1 1 0 1 0 0 1 0 0 1 0 1
1 0 0 0 1 1 1 1 1 1 0 0 0 0 0 = 0.47
```

```
0 1 0 0 1 0 1 0 0 1 1 1 0 1 0
1 0 0 1 1 1 0 1 0 0 1 0 0 1 0
0 0 1 0 1 0 0 0 1 0 0 0 1 1 1 = 0.40
```

142

```
0 1 0 0 1 0 1 0 0 1 1 1 0 1 0
0 1 0 0 1 1 1 0 1 0 0 1 0 0 1
1 1 1 1 1 0 1 1 0 0 0 1 1 0 0 = 0.60

0 1 0 0 1 0 1 0 0 1 1 1 0 1 0
1 0 1 0 0 1 1 1 0 1 0 0 1 0 0
0 0 0 1 0 0 1 0 1 1 0 0 0 0 1 = 0.33

0 1 0 0 1 0 1 0 0 1 1 1 0 1 0
0 1 0 1 0 0 1 1 1 0 1 0 0 1 0
1 1 1 0 0 1 1 0 0 0 1 0 1 1 1 = 0.60

0 1 0 0 1 0 1 0 0 1 1 1 0 1 0
0 0 1 0 1 0 0 1 1 1 0 1 0 0 1
1 0 0 1 1 1 0 0 0 1 0 1 1 0 0 = 0.47

0 1 0 0 1 0 1 0 0 1 1 1 0 1 0
1 0 0 1 0 1 0 0 1 1 1 0 1 0 0
0 0 1 0 0 0 0 1 0 1 1 0 0 0 1 = 0.33
```

Compare this to a pseudorandom sequence generated with a shift register and linear feedback.

```
1 0 0 0 1 0 0 1 1 0 1 0 1 1 1
1 1 0 0 0 1 0 0 1 1 0 1 0 1 1
0 1 1 1 0 0 1 0 1 0 0 0 0 1 1 = 0.47

1 0 0 0 1 0 0 1 1 0 1 0 1 1 1
1 1 1 0 0 0 1 0 0 1 1 0 1 0 1
1 0 0 1 0 1 0 0 0 0 1 1 1 0 1 = 0.47

1 0 0 0 1 0 0 1 1 0 1 0 1 1 1
1 1 1 1 0 0 0 1 0 0 1 1 0 1 0
1 0 0 0 0 1 1 1 0 1 1 0 0 1 0 = 0.47

1 0 0 0 1 0 0 1 1 0 1 0 1 1 1
0 1 1 1 1 0 0 0 1 0 0 1 1 0 1
0 0 0 0 1 1 1 0 1 1 0 0 1 0 1 = 0.47

1 0 0 0 1 0 0 1 1 0 1 0 1 1 1
1 0 1 1 1 1 0 0 0 1 0 0 1 1 0
1 1 0 0 1 0 1 0 0 0 0 1 1 1 0 = 0.47
```

```
1 0 0 0 1 0 0 1 1 0 1 0 1 1 1
0 1 0 1 1 1 1 0 0 0 1 0 0 1 1
0 0 1 0 1 0 0 0 0 1 1 1 0 1 1 = 0.47


1 0 0 0 1 0 0 1 1 0 1 0 1 1 1
1 0 1 0 1 1 1 1 0 0 0 1 0 0 1
1 1 0 1 1 0 0 1 0 1 0 0 0 0 1 = 0.47


1 0 0 0 1 0 0 1 1 0 1 0 1 1 1
1 1 0 1 0 1 1 1 1 0 0 0 1 0 0
1 0 1 0 0 0 0 1 1 1 0 1 1 0 0 = 0.47


1 0 0 0 1 0 0 1 1 0 1 0 1 1 1
0 1 1 0 1 0 1 1 1 1 0 0 0 1 0
0 0 0 1 1 1 0 1 1 0 0 1 0 1 0 = 0.47


1 0 0 0 1 0 0 1 1 0 1 0 1 1 1
0 0 1 1 0 1 0 1 1 1 1 0 0 0 1
0 1 0 0 0 0 1 1 1 0 1 1 0 0 1 = 0.47


1 0 0 0 1 0 0 1 1 0 1 0 1 1 1
1 0 0 1 1 0 1 0 1 1 1 1 0 0 0
1 1 1 0 1 1 0 0 1 0 1 0 0 0 0 = 0.47


1 0 0 0 1 0 0 1 1 0 1 0 1 1 1
0 1 0 0 1 1 0 1 0 1 1 1 1 0 0
0 0 1 1 1 0 1 1 0 0 1 0 1 0 0 = 0.47


1 0 0 0 1 0 0 1 1 0 1 0 1 1 1
0 0 1 0 0 1 1 0 1 0 1 1 1 1 0
0 1 0 1 0 0 0 0 1 1 1 0 1 1 0 = 0.47


1 0 0 0 1 0 0 1 1 0 1 0 1 1 1
0 0 0 1 0 0 1 1 0 1 0 1 1 1 1
0 1 1 0 0 1 0 1 0 0 0 0 1 1 1 = 0.47
```

Notice the results of the PRN generated with the shift register is perfect in the autocorrelation while the "random" numbers written down by the author, although they did not autocorrelate too badly, is far from perfectly random. Next, plot the average of the exclusive NORing as a function of bits of offset and use both positive and negative bits. In this case a −1 bit as an offset is the same as a plus 15 because the example sequence is a pseudorandom sequence and repeats every 15 bits. A minus 2 bits is the same as 14 and so on. We will also plot the pseudorandom sequence, with the results shown in Fig. 4.9.

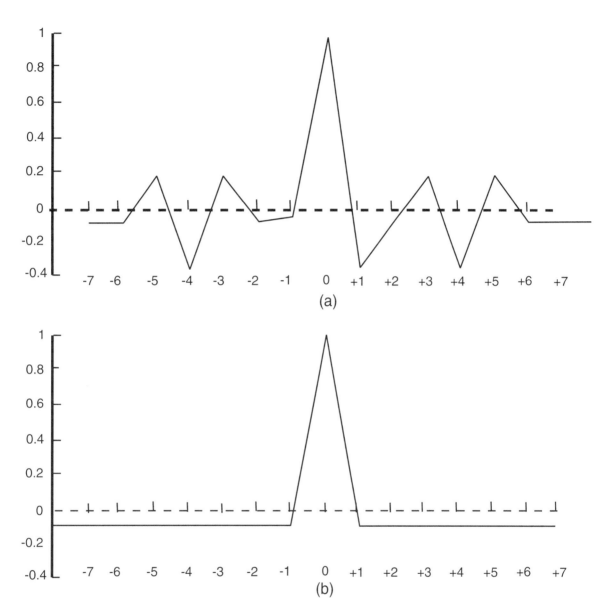

Figure 4.9 Correlating a PRN sequence

Let us change from a discrete step plot, which can only have integer time delays to a plot with fractional time delays. What if two sequences are perfectly lined up? The result is a steady logic one or an average of 1.00. If time is offset by a fraction of a clock, the output of the output would have some zero states rather than a solid logic one. The average output voltage decreases linearly until the time delay is exactly one clock, whereupon the output is 0.47 average. Therefore, a straight-line segment is drawn from 1, where the time delay equals zero to 0.47, to where the time delay equals 1 clock.

The remainder of the plot is a straight line; there are straight-line segments connecting data points of 0.47 each. In reality, once the time delay exceeds 15 bits, the output of the exclusive ORing returns to 1 and the plot repeats. This is called the autocorrelation function of the pseudorandom sequence. The only difference between this plot and a true random sequence is that the true random sequence never repeats.

If a pseudorandom sequence does not correlate, the result of the exclusive ORing results in a value of exactly 0.5. This is because inputs to the exclusive OR are the same as much as they are different. The average can never be exactly 0.5 because the sequence is an odd number. In the example of an exclusive OR function to determine correlation, the result is offset by one half. In a true mathematical autocorrelation, the comparison produces a 1 if the inputs are the same and a -1 when different.

Another characteristic of pseudorandom sequences is they never correlate with other pseudorandom sequences. This characteristic is called "orthogonality". GPS uses orthogonal codes. To test for orthogonality, two different codes are correlated, which is called cross correlation, rather a correlation with itself, which is autocorrelation.

The 15 bit PRN sequence in the previous example was generated with a 4 bit shift register and linear feedback. There are only two combinations of feedback that produce maximal length code using linear feedback. We shall use the other PRN to check for orthogonality between the two codes.

The other PRN available from a 4 bit shift register is:

1 1 1 1 0 1 0 1 1 0 0 1 0 0 0

To correlate this with the code of the previous example:

$$
\begin{aligned}
&1\ 1\ 1\ 1\ 0\ 1\ 0\ 1\ 1\ 0\ 0\ 1\ 0\ 0\ 0 \\
&\underline{1\ 0\ 0\ 0\ 1\ 0\ 0\ 1\ 1\ 0\ 1\ 0\ 1\ 1\ 1} \\
&1\ 0\ 0\ 0\ 0\ 0\ 1\ 1\ 1\ 1\ 0\ 0\ 0\ 0\ 0 = 5/15
\end{aligned}
$$

$$
\begin{aligned}
&1\ 1\ 1\ 1\ 0\ 1\ 0\ 1\ 1\ 0\ 0\ 1\ 0\ 0\ 0 \\
&\underline{1\ 1\ 0\ 0\ 0\ 1\ 0\ 0\ 1\ 1\ 0\ 1\ 0\ 1\ 1} \\
&1\ 1\ 0\ 0\ 1\ 1\ 1\ 0\ 1\ 0\ 1\ 1\ 1\ 0\ 0 = 9/15
\end{aligned}
$$

$$
\begin{aligned}
&1\ 1\ 1\ 1\ 0\ 1\ 0\ 1\ 1\ 0\ 0\ 1\ 0\ 0\ 0 \\
&\underline{1\ 1\ 1\ 0\ 0\ 0\ 1\ 0\ 0\ 1\ 1\ 0\ 1\ 0\ 1} \\
&1\ 1\ 1\ 0\ 1\ 0\ 0\ 0\ 0\ 0\ 0\ 0\ 0\ 1\ 0 = 5/15
\end{aligned}
$$

$$
\begin{aligned}
&1\ 1\ 1\ 1\ 0\ 1\ 0\ 1\ 1\ 0\ 0\ 1\ 0\ 0\ 0 \\
&\underline{1\ 1\ 1\ 1\ 0\ 0\ 0\ 1\ 0\ 0\ 1\ 1\ 0\ 1\ 0} \\
&1\ 1\ 1\ 1\ 1\ 0\ 1\ 1\ 0\ 1\ 0\ 1\ 1\ 0\ 1 = 11/15
\end{aligned}
$$

$$
\begin{aligned}
&1\ 1\ 1\ 1\ 0\ 1\ 0\ 1\ 1\ 0\ 0\ 1\ 0\ 0\ 0 \\
&\underline{0\ 1\ 1\ 1\ 1\ 0\ 0\ 0\ 1\ 0\ 0\ 1\ 1\ 0\ 1} \\
&0\ 1\ 1\ 1\ 0\ 0\ 1\ 0\ 1\ 1\ 1\ 1\ 0\ 1\ 0 = 9/15
\end{aligned}
$$

$$
\begin{aligned}
&1\ 1\ 1\ 1\ 0\ 1\ 0\ 1\ 1\ 0\ 0\ 1\ 0\ 0\ 0 \\
&\underline{1\ 0\ 1\ 1\ 1\ 1\ 0\ 0\ 0\ 1\ 0\ 0\ 1\ 1\ 0} \\
&1\ 0\ 1\ 1\ 0\ 1\ 1\ 0\ 0\ 0\ 1\ 0\ 0\ 0\ 1 = 7/15
\end{aligned}
$$

```
1 1 1 1 0 1 0 1 1 0 0 1 0 0 0
0 1 0 1 1 1 1 0 0 0 1 0 0 1 1
0 1 0 1 0 1 0 0 0 1 0 0 1 0 0 = 5/15

1 1 1 1 0 1 0 1 1 0 0 1 0 0 0
1 0 1 0 1 1 1 1 0 0 0 1 0 0 1
1 0 1 0 0 1 0 1 0 1 1 1 1 1 0 = 9/15

1 1 1 1 0 1 0 1 1 0 0 1 0 0 0
1 1 0 1 0 1 1 1 1 0 0 0 1 0 0
1 1 0 1 1 1 0 1 1 1 1 0 0 1 1 = 11/15

1 1 1 1 0 1 0 1 1 0 0 1 0 0 0
0 1 1 0 1 0 1 1 1 1 0 0 0 1 0
0 1 1 0 0 0 0 1 1 0 1 0 1 0 1 = 7/16

1 1 1 1 0 1 0 1 1 0 0 1 0 0 0
0 0 1 1 0 1 0 1 1 1 1 0 0 0 1
0 0 1 1 1 1 1 1 1 0 0 0 1 1 0 = 9/15

1 1 1 1 0 1 0 1 1 0 0 1 0 0 0
1 0 0 1 1 0 1 0 1 1 1 1 0 0 0
1 0 0 1 0 0 0 0 1 0 0 1 1 1 1 = 7/15

1 1 1 1 0 1 0 1 1 0 0 1 0 0 0
0 1 0 0 1 1 0 1 0 1 1 1 1 0 0
0 1 0 0 0 1 1 1 0 0 0 1 0 1 1 = 7/15

1 1 1 1 0 1 0 1 1 0 0 1 0 0 0
0 0 1 0 0 1 1 0 1 0 1 1 1 1 0
0 0 1 0 1 1 0 0 1 1 0 1 0 0 1 = 7/15

1 1 1 1 0 1 0 1 1 0 0 1 0 0 0
0 0 0 1 0 0 1 1 0 1 0 1 1 1 1
0 0 0 1 1 0 0 1 0 0 1 1 0 0 0 = 5/15
```

From this exercise it is seen that the two codes never correlate when shifted relative to each other. Correlation is indicated by all ones from the output of the exclusive NORing. The output does get close with two outputs of 11/15 but that is still not correlated. The examples shown are two short codes; the longer codes approach the theoretical. Recall that one characteristic of the Gold code is excellent cross correlation. In other words, Gold codes are very orthogonal.

4.7.1 GPS PRN Generator

The previous discussion used as an example a four stage shift register as it would be nearly impossible to demonstrate the characteristics of PRN with the actual ten stage shift register used in the GPS. Two ten stage shift registers generating two maximal length sequences called G1 and G2 are modulo two added as shown in fig 4-10. A time delay between G1 and G2, which can be as small as 5 clocks and as much as 950, determines which SV PRN will be generated. It is important that the C/A PRN be synchronized with the X1 epoch of the P code.

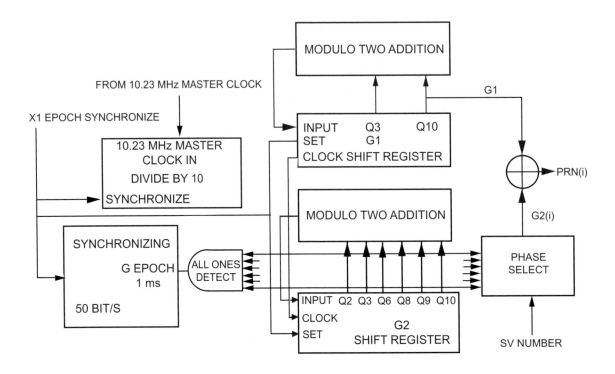

Figure 4.10 Generation of the C/A PRN

4.8 Navigation Message

The data rate for the navigation message is 50 bits per second and the entire message takes 12.5 minutes to transmit. That would imply there are a lot of data in the message and to a certain extent that is true. Some of the data are updated more often than once every 12.5 minutes. Included in the navigation message are certain timing and synchronizing words, the ephemerides, as discussed previously. Also included are telemetry data relative to the health of the satellite, clock correction factors and other correction factors.

The complete navigation message, all 12.5 minutes of it, is called a "superframe". This superframe is divided into 25 frames, sometimes called a page, of 1500 bits taking 30 seconds each to transmit. Finally, each frame is divided into five subframes of six seconds each. Since the data rate is 50 bits per second, each subframe consists of 300 bits.

Each subframe contains ten 30 bit words and starts with a preamble used for synchronizing the navigation message. The first word of the ten is the preamble and telemetry. The second word in the subframe, the handover word or HOW, is probably the most important data of the GPS system as it transmitted every subframe.

The HOW includes the time of week (TOW), the key to the GPS system. In addition to the TOW the HOW includes flags, identification and parity. Timekeeping in the GPS system is through a running count called the Z count of the X1 "epochs" of 1.5 seconds each. The Z count started when the GPS satellite was initiated on 0000 January 6/7, 1980, GPS time, and is a 29 bit number.

The TOW is the 19 least significant bits of the Z count. These 19 bits return to zero after one week. Since one week is 7 days of 86,400 seconds each total time of week is 604,000 seconds or 403,200 X1 epochs. Since the HOW is transmitted every 6 seconds the two LSBs of the TOW are not included in the HOW. Therefore, the HOW is a truncated TOW being the 17 most significant bits of the 19 bit TOW. This gives the HOW an LSB of 6 seconds and spans from zero to 100,799 and rolls over. Notice the 29 bit Z count is not a pure binary number. A 17 bit binary number rolls over after a count of 131 071, not 100,799.

The remaining 10 MSBs of the Z count are the week number. Since ten binary bits can count 1024 weeks, in 19.625 years the entire Z count rolls over. Thus, on the 31st week of 1999 the GPS Z count rolled over.

The HOW word gets its name from the fact the HOW is used achieve synchronism with the P code sequence. The HOW is available without any encryption or "in the clear" and is used to acquire lock to the P code PRN sequence. This is the reason the SPS mode is also called C/A mode for clear/acquisition mode.

Following the HOW in the navigation message are 8 data words each containing 24 bits of data and 6 parity bits. The 8 data words provide various data which are summarized below:

Each 30 bit word plus the last two bits of the previous word are encoded into a (32,26) Hamming block code with 32 symbols and 32 "information" bits. Since two of the "information" bits are from the previous data word they are not true information bits. The 6 parity bits are generated by p=Hd where p is the 6 bit parity word, H is the (24X6) parity matrix and d is the 24 element data vector.

The parity check detects all errors of less than 4 bits and essentially detects all errors for bit error rates, BER, of less than 10^{-3}.

4.8.1 Determining the Time Delay

It may not be readily apparent how a data transmission of only 50 bits/s could disseminate the time of day to within, literally, nanoseconds. Let us investigate the time of day from the MSB down to the LSB.

The HOW provides the time with a 6 second LSB. Each subframe, in which the HOW is present consists of 300 bits of 20 ms. Each bit can be identified and counted to improve the time resolution to 20 ms; the time of one bit. During the time of one data bit, the C/A PRN code repeats 20 times. By counting the number of 1 ms C/A code epochs improves the time resolution to 1 ms. Finally, the period of chip clock of the C/A code is 1/1.023 MHz or 978 ns. By measuring the time delay between the local PRN chip clock and the received signal chip clock the time resolution is improved to a few nanoseconds.

Absolutely everything in the GPS system is phase coherent and synchronized. Timing can be achieved by determining the "phase" of the PRN epochs, the PRN clock and even the carrier cycles themselves.

4.9 PPS: Precision Position Service

The PPS signal is similar in construction to the standard , SPS, signal. The differences are in the accuracy of the time transmission for the navigation message and that PPS signals are encrypted to prevent unauthorized use.

The PRN of the PPS is transmitted at a 10.23 MHz chip rate, which implies a ten fold increase in accuracy. PPS does not achieve the theoretical maximum but is capable of a seven fold increase in accuracy because of other factors that prevent a ten fold increase. One factor is that P code operates with less power density at the user antenna and is more vulnerable to noise.

PPS PRN code is much longer than the 1023 clock cycle of SPS. PPS code repeats in 2.36E14 clock cycles, which is 38.1 weeks. The code for both the PPS and SPS is a matter of public knowledge and is published in the GPS interface control document, ICD. What is not known is where the P code is reset at the beginning of the week. When desired by the U.S. DoD, the PPS PRN code is encrypted with a secret Y code not known to the public.

The use of the secret Y code is twofold. First, it denies unauthorized receivers precision navigation, which is a benefit during hostile action. Second, it prevents an enemy from transmitting a signal similar to the PPS PRN code and causing GPS receivers to malfunction. GPS can reject interfering signals but lose this ability when jamming signals are identical or similar to the desired signal. This technique of jamming with a look-alike signal is called "spoofing" and the use of encrypted code is "anti-spoofing," or AS. Because a P or Y code may be used for PPS, it is often called the P/Y code.

Every week at midnight (Saturday night/Sunday morning), GPS time, the code is reset—not back to zero but at various points in the cycle. At the beginning of the week, the time of week (TOW), count is set to zero concurrent with the resetting of the P code.

The L1 frequency is modulated by both the C/A and P/Y code. It is done by quadrature biphase modulation. The L2 frequency is normally biphase modulated, with either the P code or encrypted Y code. The modulation may or may not contain the navigation message. Having the same code modulate L1 and L2 is necessary to determine the ionospheric group delay. It does not matter if the navigation message is present, or that the P/Y code cannot be deciphered, as only the time delay of the modulation is determined.

4.10 Almanac

Part of the data transmitted is the almanac. GPS is a dynamic system; SVs are launched, some become faulty, others are taken out of service. Included in the almanac are reports on the health of other SVs. These data are relative to the accuracy of the navigation message, particularly the HOW, and signals from the SV. These data would be important in calculating DOP (dilution of precision) or, if the SV is in poor health, its signal may not be used to solve the position equation. The approximate ephemerides are provided for all SVs as an aid to quick position determination. The almanac data also includes approximate clock corrections for all SVs. The difference between GPS time and UTC is transmitted in the almanac.

4.10.1 Clock Corrections

Several sets of clock corrections are uplinked to the satellite and the satellite transmits the correction parameters to the user segment. These corrections must be used with prediction algorithms because the SVs are uplinked only twice every day. The clock correction algorithm involves the PRN clock and are the phase error, frequency error and rate change of frequency error. Coefficients of a polynomial, which are K_0, K_1, and K_2: the phase error of the space vehicle PRN, frequency error or phase velocity error, and rate change of frequency or phase acceleration error, are broadcast by the satellite. The phase error, as a time is given by the equation:

$$\Delta t_{SV} = K_0 + K_1 (t-t_0) + K_2 (t-t_0)^2 + \Delta t_R$$

where Δt_{SV} is the space vehicle phase error as a time, t_0 is a reference time and Δt_R is the relativistic correction. The relativistic correction involves another calculation using broadcast data from the

150

satellite. This equation is identical to the classic equation from basic physics describing uniformly accelerated motion where the object started at a position K_0 at time t_0.

4.10.2 Ephemerides

As discussed in an earlier section, ephemerides are data describing the perturbations of the orbit of the SV. Listed below are parameters to calculate the precise orbit of a SV:

> Mean anomaly at epoch
> Deviation from computed mean motion
> Eccentricity
> Square root of semi major axis
> Longitude of ascending node at epoch
> Inclination
> Argument of perigee
> Rate of right ascension
> Rate of inclination
> Harmonic correction terms
> Time of epoch

As discussed previously, the ideal GPS orbit is circular, inclined at exactly 55 degrees and spaced exactly every 60 degrees. Because of the earth's oblateness and other factors, the orbit will change. First, the orbit will not be exactly circular, which means that eccentricity is not 0 but some small value. The orbit must be treated as elliptical and the argument of perigee required to describe an elliptical orbit.

The inclination can change. Orbital calculations must use the actual inclination rather than 55 degrees. To estimate the actual inclination between updates of the ephemerides, the rate change of inclination may be used with a polynomial in a manner similar to the clock corrections discussed previously to calculate the current inclination. The same is true of the right ascension.

4.10.3 Ionospheric Corrections

Ionospheric corrections are data concerning the state of the ionosphere for predicting the time delay in the ionosphere. These parameters will be used in algorithms discussed later.

4.10.4 UTC Corrections

The current time difference between UTC and GPS time is used to provide accurate UTC from the GPS system.

4.10.5 Signal Integrity Monitoring Concerns

There is an important consideration about signal integrity. There are many data transmitted from SVs on the health of other SVs. It would appear that an FAA requirement for signal integrity monitoring would be available from GPS. The problem is that the entire navigation message takes 12.5 minutes to complete, which is too slow. Even if an SV is detected out of specification and data immediately up-linked to an SV, it could take as long as 12.5 minutes to receive the warning. This assumes the warning could be uplinked immediately, which is not how the GPS system is configured. It is necessary that an SV be in view of a ground antenna to receive updates. Typically, GPS SVs are updated only twice a day. Compare this time delay to the ICAO-required elapsed time of 2 seconds to display a warning or replace a defective CAT III localizer. The GPS system in and of itself does not provide for suitable signal integrity monitoring but auxiliary systems have been developed to provide this function and are discussed in a later section.

4.11 Relationship Between GPS Frequencies

All GPS frequencies have as a common denominator the C/A PRN clock frequency. The master oscillator is the 10.23 MHz P/Y-code. The C/A clock is derived by dividing 10.23 MHz by 10 for 1.023 MHz. The L1 frequency is 10.23 MHz X 154 = 1575.42 and L2 is 10.23 MHz X 120 = 1227.6 MHz. Even the 50 bit per second data rate of the navigation message is 10.23 MHz divided by 204,600.

In generating carrier frequencies and clocks in the SVs, all signals are phase coherent. Ultimately, all signals are phase locked to the master atomic clock aboard the SV. This is important for a high precision mode called carrier phase tracking, used for ultra precise applications such as surveying. It's called real-time kinematic or RTK .

The 10.23 MHz source is derived from the atomic, or "master" clock. It was mentioned earlier that the precision of GPS is so fine that it is one of the few electronic systems where relativistic corrections are required. The GPS system requires that carrier frequencies , the clock rate of the PRNs, the times of epochs and all other frequencies be received at precise frequencies. Because of the earth's gravitational field, the actual frequency in the SV must be slightly lower than the desired. The SV 10.23 MHz clock is offset by –4.567 mHz, (*milli*hertz, not megahertz!) This means the 10.23 MHz master clock is actually 10.2999999543 MHz to an observer on the SV, but 10.2300000000 MHz to an observer on earth.

4.12 Monitor and Control Stations

The success of GPS depends on accurate parameters. There are five monitor stations located at Hawaii, Colorado Springs, Ascension Island in the Atlantic Ocean, Diego Garcia in the Indian Ocean and Kwajalein Island in the Pacific Ocean. Each monitor has multiple channel receivers capable of receiving L1 and L2 from all SVs in view. Each has redundant cesium clocks. All data from SVs is "time tagged" and transmitted to the master control station in Colorado Springs. Time tagging indicates the precise time data from the SVs was received. When data is transmitted to the control station, the time delay through the data communications system is now known.

An operational control station receives data from the monitor stations and formulates navigation data for uplinking to the space segment. The data includes ephemerides, health messages, clock corrections and others. The uplink to the SV is through four ground antennas using S-band transmitters. These antennas are co-located with monitor stations at Ascension, Diego Garcia, and Kwajalein. The fourth is at the Kennedy Space Center in Florida. This ground antenna is only used during the launch because radio transmissions are limited at launch sites. Navigation messages are linked to the ground antennas and uplinked to the SVs as they pass over. These transmissions are highly encrypted to prevent damage to the GPS system by hostile forces.

4.13 GLONASS

GLONASS, which is "Global Orbiting Navigation Satellite System", was built by the former Soviet Union (now Russia) and declared operational in 1996. The system operates in a similar fashion to GPS but with some significant differences. There is a constellation of 24 satellites but in three orbits of eight satellites each. The time of orbit is not exactly twice each sidereal day but at a slightly faster rate. Rather than the ground track repeating after only two orbits, the GLONASS satellite ground track repeats every 17 orbits.

Instead of CDMA, (code division multiple access, spread spectrum), GLONASS satellites each have an assigned channel frequency with a bandwidth of 562.5 kHz. Each satellite transmits on two frequencies, L1 and L2, using FDMA (frequency division multiple access). Two bands are assigned. LI channels span from 1597–1617 MHz, while L2 channels lie between 1240–1260 MHz.

The GLONASS system uses a PRN code, but not to enable all satellites to operate on the same frequency. It's for time synchronization, based on two codes, C/A (coarse acquisition) and P (precision). The C/A code, the same for all satellites, is a 511 state maximal length code generated in the usual fashion using a 9 bit shift register with linear feedback. The feedback taps are 5 and 9. The clock is 511 kHz so the sequence repeats every millisecond.

The GLONASS P code is also the same for all satellites and, like GPS, had not been published by the Soviet Union, but was analyzed several years ago. The code operates at ten times the C/A rate at 5.11 MHz and generated by a 25 stage shift register with linear feedback. The code, however, is not sequenced to the entire length. It is reset every second, which implies there are only 5 110 000 states of the code.

The PRN codes biphase-modulate the carrier frequency generators, along with the navigation message. The codes spread the bandwidth of GLONASS signals and, in that sense, it is a spread spectrum system. The important difference from GPS is that GLONASS satellites operate on different frequencies and the PRN codes, which are the same for all satellites, are used for time synchronization. GPS satellites all operate on the same frequency and have different codes. The code is what allows a specific satellite to be demodulated, which is the basis of CDMA. The GLONASS navigation message is different from GPS but serves the same purpose.

The status of GLONASS has been uncertain. With the breakup of the Soviet Union, the system has been in various states of operation and not suitable as a sole source of navigation. In spite of these problems, GLONASS could enhance GPS. There has been concern that GPS may have periods of insufficient coverage at some locations. Although GPS availability is excellent and GLONASS has been poor, together they might enhance availability better than either system alone. GPS would be the backbone of a combined system.

4.14 Selective Availability

The techniques for denying unauthorized users the high precision PPS mode were outlined previously. However, the lesser precision from the SPS mode could still be used for hostile action. The U.S. DoD has provided for a method of degrading accuracy of SPS to any level under control of the ground segment. This is achieved by introducing random errors into the PRN code. The phase of the clock is changed in a random fashion sometimes called clock "dithering". The C/A PRN code uses a 1.023 MHz clock with a period of 978 ns . If the clock is dithered up to half the period this introduces a random error of 489 ns. Electromagnetic waves travel 1 meter in 3.3 ns so the peak-to-peak error of 489 ns introduces a distance error of 148 meters peak to peak. The amplitude of these errors can be set to any value by the ground segment but is typically on the order of 100 to 300 meters. This is called selective availability, or SA.

SA does not affect the military because the hand over word, HOW, is not affected and the military receiver determines position using the P/Y code. Also, the P/Y code clock is not dithered.

SA can be controlled from the ground, the error adjusted and SA removed. Ironically, SA *was* removed during one military action, Desert Storm. Military forces were using civilian GPS receivers because of an inadequate supply of military P-code receivers! Beginning May, 2000, Selective Availability was removed completely. The U.S. Department of Defense announced it had developed techniques to turn SA back on in limited regions of the globe if national security warranted it.

4.15 Ionospheric Propagation Delay

It was mentioned that the velocity of radio wave propagation is constant in a vacuum. In the atmosphere, however, velocity is slower, depending on conditions. Slowest velocity is in the ionosphere, a layer of the earth's atmosphere characterized by a high density of charged particles. This is caused by ionization of atmospheric gasses due to ultraviolet radiation from the sun. The amount varies from night to day and from winter to summer with the seasonal tilt of the earth on its axis. Finally, ionization changes with the 11-year sun spot cycle. Ionospheric slowing can add as much as 300 ns to the transit time from SV to earth.

In addition to different ionization levels at various locations on earth, even the amount of atmosphere the GPS signal passes through is not the same for all SVs. When a SV is low on the horizon its signal travels through more atmosphere and more ionosphere. SVs directly overhead see a shorter path to earth. A first order approximation of ionospheric delay is made by knowing SV location relative to the user. The GPS receiver has a time of day clock and can make approximations for time and season. To take full advantage of GPS, however, it must account for the slowing of the velocity of electromagnetic waves in the ionosphere.

Wave velocity in the ionosphere is a function of frequency. The two-frequency GPS receiver has the advantage of comparing the difference in arrival of the L1 and L2 frequencies to determine the additional delay in the ionosphere. For two carrier frequencies with the same modulation, there is a time difference between their arrival at the receiver. Both signals propagate at the same velocity, $c = 2.9979E8$ m/s, when traveling through nearly empty space and much of the lower levels of the atmosphere. Therefore, the total time delay is:

$$\Delta T_{L1} = T + \Delta t_{L1} \tag{4.11}$$

and

$$\Delta T_{L2} = T + \Delta \tau \Lambda 2 \tag{4.12}$$

where ΔT_{L1} is the total time delay of the L1 signal, ΔT_{L2} is the total time delay of the L2 signal. T is the time it takes either signal to traverse the distance from the SV if there were no ionosphere. Δt_{L1} is the additional propagation time through the ionosphere of the L1 frequency, and Δt_{L2} is the additional ionospheric propagation time of the L2 frequency for the same SV to user path.

Ionospheric delay, to a first order approximation, is inversely proportional to the square of the frequency in the frequency range of L1 and L2. If the difference in the time of propagation between L1 and L2 signals is measured in the GPS receiver:

$$\Delta T_{L2} - \Delta T_{L1} = \Delta t_{L2} - \Delta t_{L1} \tag{4.13}$$

Because velocity of propagation in the ionosphere is inversely proportional to the frequency of the electromagnetic waves squared, there are two equations using a constant, K;

$$\Delta t_{L1} = K/(1575.42 \text{ MHz})^2 \quad \Delta t_{L2} = K/(1227.6 \text{ MHz})^2 \tag{4.14}$$

Using the previous equation,

$$\Delta t_{L2} - \Delta t_{L1} = K(1/1.5070E18 - 1/2.4819E18) = (2.607E\text{-}19)K$$

Since $\Delta T_{L2} - \Delta T_{L1} = \Delta t_{L2} - \Delta t_{L1}$ is the time delay between the receipt of the two carriers, we solve for K and use that value to determine the ionospheric propagation time. But K is not really a constant. It is a function of the ionosphere, which changes. Solving the equation for K has to be done periodically to account for the changes in K.

Since we care only about the ionospheric delay at L1, solve for that using K:

$$\Delta t_{L1} = K/(1575.42 MHz)^2 = (\Delta t_{L2} - \Delta t_{L1})/(2.607E-19)(1.57542E9)^2 = 1.5455(\Delta t_{L2} - \Delta t_{L1}) \qquad (4.15)$$

By measuring the time difference between receipt of L1 and L2, the atmospheric delay is found.

GPS carrier L1 at 1575.42 MHz is modulated with the C/A spread spectrum signal and simultaneously with the P/Y code signal. The two modulations are in phase quadrature. The L2 carrier is modulated with just the P/Y code. The time difference between receipt of the L1 and L2 provides the input to calculate the time delay of the GPS signal in the ionosphere. It is not necessary to know the P/Y code to make the time delay measurement because the same P/Y code modulates both carriers. The two received signals are compared or correlated and the delay required between the two to cause the two codes to be the same is the time delay. This method is called a codeless method. If the two received signals are used in a feedback loop, the system is called a delay locked loop.

Single frequency GPS receivers (nearly all civilian receivers), cannot use the two frequency method described. An alternative method models the ionospheric delay as a half cosine. Because much of the ionospheric activity ceases at night, the delay can be modeled as a half cosine beginning at approximately local sunrise and ending at approximately local sunset. The equation for this model is:

$$\Delta_I = F(\theta) \left[5E-9 + A(\phi) \cos(2\pi t - 50,400 \ \omega(\phi)) \right] \quad \text{for day} \qquad (4.16)$$
$$\Delta_I = F(\theta) \left[5E-9 \right] \quad \text{for night} \qquad (4.17)$$

where Δ_I is the time delay due to the ionosphere, $F(\theta)$ is a factor which accounts for the longer path through the ionosphere for lower elevation angles, θ, $A(\phi)$ is the amplitude of the half cosine model as a function of geomagnetic latitude, ϕ and $\omega(\phi)$ is the frequency of the half cosine as a function of geomagnetic latitude.

The geomagnetic latitude is relative to the magnetic north and south poles and not the geographic poles. The earth's magnetic field affects the nature of the ionosphere. What makes the ionosphere unique is the concentration of charged ions. Charged particles moving in a magnetic field experience forces, and thus tend to migrate. The density of charged particles in the atmosphere varies with the magnetic field of the earth and is responsible for the dependence on the ionospheric slowing on geomagnetic latitude.

The ionosphere varies not only from day to night but from season to season and over an 11 year sunspot cycle. Furthermore, sudden and temporary changes can occur during high solar activity such as a flare. The GPS SV includes, in the message, factors for determining $F(\theta)$, $A(\phi)$ and $\omega(\phi)$.

Because the half cosine model for slowing in the ionosphere uses constants that are up loaded to the SV, sudden changes in the ionosphere can cause large errors that remain until updated constants are received. The single frequency receiver can detect changes in the effects of the ionosphere by comparing the change in group delay and carrier phase shift of the received signal. As mentioned previously, the ionospheric delay is a function of carrier frequency. Define a group delay $\Delta g(\omega)$, in seconds which is:

$$\Delta g(\omega) = K/\omega^2 \qquad (4.18)$$

where ω is the carrier frequency in radians per second and K is a constant which is dependent on the electron density of the ionosphere and the path length through the ionosphere.

By definition group delay is the derivative of the phase delay of the modulated carrier relative to frequency or:

$$\Delta g(\omega) = d\Phi(\omega)/d\omega = K/\omega^2 \qquad (4.19)$$

where $\Phi(\omega)$ is the phase shift in radians of the carrier from a reference phase.

By rearranging equation 4-19 and solving for $\Phi(\omega)$ by integrating both sides of the equation, we obtain:

$$\int d\Phi(\omega) = \int \left(k/\omega^2\right)d\omega$$

$$\Phi(\omega) = -K/\omega \qquad (4.20)$$

Equation 4-20 is rewritten as a time delay of the carrier, $\Delta c(\omega)$, rather than a phase delay;

$$\Delta c(\omega) = \Phi(\omega)/\omega = -K/\omega^2 \qquad (4.21)$$

This equation is a bit misleading. Equation 4.21 was derived because time delay and phase delay are a function of frequency in the ionosphere. However, for a single frequency receiver $\omega = 2\pi f$ is a constant. It is in fact K that is the variable because of changes in the ionosphere. With this in mind we rewrite 4-18 and 4.21 as functions of K and note that,

$$\Delta c(K) = -\Delta g(K) \qquad (4.22)$$

Equation 4-22 shows that the group delay and the carrier phase delay are the same magnitude but opposite signs. Therefore, the difference between the group and phase delays is twice the delay through the ionosphere. Because there is no reference phase for measuring the carrier phase delay, comparing the group to phase delays can only provide changes in the ionospheric delay.

4.16 Differential GPS

Ionospheric delay is one of the more important contributors to GPS error but not the only one. Even when the most sophisticated ionospheric delay correction algorithm is employed residual delays remain. There are other contributors to GPS errors. Tropospheric delay, although much less than ionospheric delays is just as variable, unpredictable and thus can be a significant error source for demanding applications of GPS such precision approach and landing.

Other error sources are clock errors. Even though clock corrections are included in the navigation message, short term drifts of the space vehicle clock can add to the GPS error. Multipath propagation is another source of error.

In a differential GPS system a GPS receiver placed at a known position on earth becomes a "reference locator." Knowing its position and position of the SV, the receiver can calculate the real range to the SV. As in any GPS receiver, the reference locator sets its time of day clock to high precision using four or more SVs. Since the reference locator is fixed, i.e. has no accelerations, and operates 24 hours a day, the reference locator determines time precisely by averaging a large number of observations.

The reference locator calculates range from the SV, measuring pseudorange and correcting it for ephemerides, clock errors and relativistic corrections. These corrections are made from the received almanac data. No corrections are made for ionospheric propagation. This range is compared to the calculated range and any differences are due to ionospheric propagation and SA. This differential is time tagged with the Z count and formatted to be transmitted by datalink to aircraft or other vehicles using differential corrections.

The corrections are relative to a specific SV and for a specific area. The amount of error introduced by SA is the same everywhere for the specific time. Ionospheric corrections are most accurate when the aircraft using the DGPS correction receives signals that travel through the same atmospheric path. The reference locator provides corrections for SVs that are in view for the locator's GPS receiver.

The closer the user is to the reference locator, the better the corrections. In the case of ionospheric induced errors, the error is not the same everywhere. The atmosphere is not homogeneous and effects in one location are not the same as elsewhere. Thus, for the most accurate corrections, the reference locator should be near the DGPS user.

Corrections for SVs in view should be the same as for SVs in view by the user. If corrections are not available for an SV, that SV cannot be used because it would increase error of the fix. The reference locator GPS antenna, therefore, is placed in a clear location to receive the maximum number of SVs.

The concept of DGPS works well. Problems arise when a datalink is configured. As with any radio service, obtaining worldwide frequencies for differential corrections is difficult because of congestion. The Federal Radio Navigation Plan has scheduled radio navigation aids such as VOR, localizer, and NDBs for elimination. One source of frequencies for DGPS datalinks is VOR channels that are vacated. The problem is that VORs have not yet been eliminated and GPS is to replace VOR. To remove a VOR from the air, a DGPS system should be in place and fully operational. Thus, a datalink should be operational before VORs are decommissioned.

There are other plans for disseminating corrections that use SVs. Data would be generated on the ground and relayed to a satellite, where it would be transmitted back to earth. The problem is that DGPS can overcome the effects of SA and, once the correction signal is broadcast from a satellite, a hostile force can overcome the protection that SA provides. In the case of ground-based DGPS datalink, range is deliberately limited so corrections are received only within 10 to 50 NM. Any hostile action that approaches its target within this distance should have been detected by early warning radar . This argument could be also be posed for SA.

4.16.1 WAAS and LAAS

There are two DGPS systems under development in the United States, a wide area augmentation system, WAAS, and a local area augmentation system, LAAS. In Europe a similar program is underway to augment the Galileo system; it's called EGNOS, the European Galileo Navigation

Overlay System. WAAS was commissioned 10 July 2003 and at the time of this writing has 25 WAAS reference stations, WRS. There are 20 stations in the continental United States, CONUS, three in Alaska, one in Puerto Rico and one in Hawaii. The generic term adopted by ICAO is the Satellite-Based Augmentation System, or SBAS.

Three categories of WAAS approaches are available:

WAAS Lateral Navigation, or LNAV, with a minimum descent altitude of 400 ft AGL;

WAAS Lateral and Vertical Navigation, or LNAV/VNAV, for descents to 350 ft AGL;

WAAS Localizer Performance with vertical guidance, LPV, for descents to 250 ft, AGL;

The LPV approach is just short of being a CAT I approach in that the ILS CAT I can provide a 200 foot decision height while the LPV minimum descent altitude is 250 feet.

Before a WAAS approach can be used at an airport, the FAA must design and certify approaches for WAAS signals in space. Designing an approach insures that the intended flight paths provide for the minimum obstacle clearance distance and does not place approaches or departures over restricted air space, and so on. Once an approach is designed, it is necessary to publish approach plates and provide electronic data files to distributors of databases. Existing approaches can be used, which minimizes the planning process, but flight testing for signal integrity is still required. Approach plates are modified to add the approved WAAS approach. This process can take years to generate approaches for large airports in the United States and longer for smaller airports.

The 25 WAAS reference stations, WRS, determine correction data and provide that data via the WAAS data network to the wide area master station, WMS. WAAS master stations are located in Leesburg, Virginia and Pasadena, California. The WMS calculates corrections from the collected data and uplinks them to a geostationary communications satellite via the geostationary uplink system or GUS. The WAAS correction message is broadcast on the GPS L1 frequency, 1575.42 MHz, using the same form of modulation, spread spectrum, BPSK, used by the GPS constellation.

As of fall 2006, the WAAS GEO network included:

Satellite	Location		PRN	NMEA #
Inmarsat	Pacific Ocean Region, POR	178 deg E	134	47
Atlantic	Ocean Region west, AOR-W	142 deg W	122	35
Anik		107.3 deg W	138	51
PanAm		133 deg W	135	48

PRNs and future satellites for the European EGNOS use;

Satellite	Location		PRN	NMEA#
Inmarsat	Atlantic Ocean Region, east, AOR-E	15.5 deg W	120	33
	Indian Ocean Region, west, IOR-W	64 deg E	126	39
	Indian Ocean Region, east, IOR-E	64 deg E	131	44
Artemis		21.5 deg E	124	37

Note: the PRN number is the NMEA (National Maritime Electronics Association) ident number plus 87.

In continental United States there is sufficient overlap so at least two geostationary satellites are in view at any time.

Corrections for wide area augmentation are divided into long term and short term. Examples of long term corrections are for clock errors, ephemeris errors and ionospheric models. Short term corrections are mostly for clock errors because there are both long and short clock errors. These corrections are mostly addressed in individual SV navigation data messages. The difference is these corrections from the SV are for that particular SV but not for one particular location. As an example, the ionosphere has different properties at different locations on the earth. WAAS corrections will be for specific user locations. Also, SV data are uplinked only twice per day, while WAAS corrections are uplinked continuously. This is an important attribute because of FAA requirements on signal integrity monitoring.

Geostationary satellites do not have full global coverage and lack coverage at the poles. However, the purpose of the WAAS correction is to improve GPS accuracy for CAT I landings. Geostationary satellites provide coverage to about 70 degrees of latitude. Since at high latitudes geostationary satellite will be nearly at the horizon, any obstruction that prevents viewing the horizon, such as buildings or mountains, will prevent coverage. More than 95% of the world's airports are covered by geostationary satellites and for airports not covered, LAAS may be used.

WAAS data are transmitted at 500 symbols per second. The data stream is modulo two added with a 1023 state PRN using binary phase shift keying, BPSK. The PRN is synchronized to the C/A code epochs with a WAAS data block of 250 bits. Therefore, 0.5 second is required to transmit the entire WAAS message. The signal in space is right hand circularly polarized, RHCP, just as the GPS signal. The WAAS spread spectrum signal is fully compatible with GPS signals and can be received, demodulated and decoded by a GPS receiver.

WAAS corrections can improve accuracy of the GPS system from about 20 meters to 2 meters or less. In addition, the WAAS system alerts users to GPS system deficiencies for the area of interest and can respond to a failure within 6 seconds. At the time of this writing there are over 600 LNAV/VNAV WAAS approaches and more are added each year.

LAAS will follow WAAS with similar data. Plans are to provide VHF data links using an 8 level differential phase shift keying, D8PSK, modulation scheme. This system is very similar to the future VHF data link discussed in chapter 6 and to the SCAT-1 system discussed in limited detail in this chapter.

Another enhancement provided by LAAS is called "pseudolites". A pseudolite is a ground-based transmitter that sends a signal exactly the same as that of an SV. The pseudolite does not orbit so there is no need for ephemerides. Transmitting a navigation message with the time of day, the signal can be used for additional ranging. Strategically positioned, pseudolites can improve the navigation solution near an airport to reduce DOP (dilution of precision), particularly VDOP (vertical dilution of precision).

Pseudolites have a problem due to the rapidly changing distance between them and the aircraft. As an example, a pseudolite 1 NM from an airport might be used for the initial approach at a distance 20 NM. As the aircraft approaches, distance decreases to 1 NM, a 20 to 1 change. This represents a 26 dB variation of signal level. Under no conditions does the signal strength of an SV vary by that much, and there is danger of overloading the GPS receiver.

A solution is to provide pseudolites for short distances only. In the previous example, SV signal strength could be reduced so the signal is received only in the last mile of the approach, where augmentation is most important. Thus, the aircraft would receive the signal at a distance of 2 NM from the pseudolite and 1 NM at the airport. This would cause a signal variation of only 6 dB.

A problem is that a GPS receiver closer to the pseudolite will have a variation much greater than 6 dB unless the pseudolite is positioned so that users cannot get too close. Notice that this affects any user type---aircraft, automotive and hand held units. This phenomenon, where the pseudolite overloads a GPS receiver that gets too close, is called the "near-far" problem.

One DGPS system in limited operation is called special category I, or SCAT-I. It provides a landing aid that appears as a CAT I ILS approach, but data is generated only with GPS signals. This means that airports with no ILS can have ILS-type approaches at almost any runway. This also implies that DGPS can provide additional precision approaches at airports already equipped with ILS. Few airports, including the largest, have ILS approaches for all runways. Precision approaches may also be available where an ILS can never be installed, such as seaplane bases and roof-top helicopter pads. The SCAT-I system can also solve severe problems at airports where ILS cannot be installed.

An airport, however, must also have other equipment for precision approaches, such as approach and runway lighting and markings. Precision approach paths need to be free of obstructions such as mountains and large buildings. Finally, approaches must be designed and approach plates published for public dissemination. Compared to purchasing and maintaining a CAT I ILS system, however, these costs are minimal.

The SCAT-I system uses a conventional reference locator, typically at the airport, plus VHF data link using eight level differential phase shift keying, 8DPSK. The datalink carrier frequencies are offset VOR frequencies. The offset is 25 kHz and the VOR frequency is not assigned for local use. SCAT-I transmitter power output is about 10 watts and the datalink ground transmitter antenna deliberately not mounted on a high tower. This limits range of the datalink so there is no interference to the VOR.

The deliberate reduction of SCAT-I range also limits versatility of the system. If range could be extended to a 50 NM radius, the SCAT-I augmentation signal could serve a number of airports. Remember, the SCAT-I signal is most important at touchdown, and it is ground range that counts, not ground to air. The SCAT-I system is useful for multiple airports only where airports are close together.

SCAT-I is presently installed in a few locations throughout the world and permitted only for private use. There is reluctance to add new SCAT-I systems because LAAS will be in more widespread use. However, the future of LAAS is uncertain for a variety of reasons, including funding. On the other hand, contracts awarded by the FAA may lead to a SCAT I –like LAAS in the future. Because SCAT-I is a certified system and in operation, it has been described as an example of local DGPS for this text. The fundamentals of DGPS are similar in SCAT-I, and LAAS.

4.17 Signal Integrity Monitoring

The GPS system has several signal integrity monitoring systems, but not all are suited for civil operations controlled by the FAA. GPS was developed and is owned by the U.S. DoD so the definition of signal integrity monitoring is different from that of the FAA.

Each SV transmits the "health" of all GPS SVs. This information is uploaded to the SV several times each day and available to all users. Recall the discussion of higher category ILS systems such as CAT-II and CAT-III. One important difference in higher category landing systems is how quickly a fault can be repaired or alarmed. For the CAT-III system, only 2 seconds are allowed from when a system goes out of tolerance until the spare transmitter is on the air. The concept of signal integrity monitoring as applied to CAT-III ILS is not like GPS. The GPS navigation message takes 12.5 minutes just to transmit and the message updated only twice each day. Clearly, the notification of a failed SV would take too long to be included in the navigation message to satisfy FAA requirements for signal integrity monitoring. Something had to be done to bring GPS signal integrity monitoring closer to ILS, VOR or other FAA-approved navigation aids.

For normal GPS (not DGPS), there is a system called receiver autonomous integrity monitoring, or RAIM (pronounced nearly like "rain"). There are several ways to implement RAIM, but the basic concept is to make several calculations of position and check if they agree. As an example, a certain amount of RAIM is inherent in any GPS receiver. Recall that four SVs allow three different position determinations. These three correct the system clock. However, if one of the four SVs is completely off, any measurement made with that SV is far removed from the other measurements. Typically a GPS receiver can receive more than four SVs.

As an example, assume five SVs are received. Therefore, ten independent position measurements can be made. The logic of RAIM implies that if ten positions are close, signals from the SVs must be reasonably good. If the spread is great, and adjusting the receiver's clock cannot reduce the spread, it is a simple matter to calculate position minus one SV and see if results improve. When running RAIM algorithms, GDOP (geometric dilution of precision) must be considered. Some SVs with good signals but bad geometry can negatively affect the navigation solution.

RAIM is a compromise. Any data relative to the SV transmitter does not enter in to RAIM calculations. For VOR and ILS, transmitter abnormalities are immediately handled by bringing a spare transmitter on line or shutting down the ground station. Normal GPS, not differential, is used for en route navigation and RAIM is sufficient for that purpose. When DGPS is used for landing guidance, the reference locator provides more than simple precision enhancement, but additional signal integrity monitoring. With the development of WAAS and LAAS the long time signal integrity monitoring problem of GPS may be solved.

The ground reference locator has the advantage of knowing exactly where it is and that the velocity of its GPS receiver is zero, referenced to earth. Thus, SV signals can be individually checked for reasonable range and velocity. Data link indicates which SVs are not trustworthy with minimal delay. Thus, ground differential correction stations not only improve accuracy of GPS navigation, but reliability as well, an important part of any instrument landing.

On the other hand, correction signals must also have integrity. Receiving corrupted correction signals could degrade GPS navigation rather than enhance it. This is done by normal methods of digital data error detection and correction.

4.18 GPS Signals in Space

The two GPS carriers (L1 and L2) are transmitted as a circularly polarized wave. Circular polarization is required because the field orientation of the receiving antenna varies; the users are in moving aircraft, ships, vehicles and on foot. Polarization is right hand circular, meaning the electric field rotates counter clockwise when viewed leaving the SV. The polarization is generated by a helical antenna. An array of helical radiators provides nearly uniform signal intensity over the overage area, as shown in Fig. 4.11.

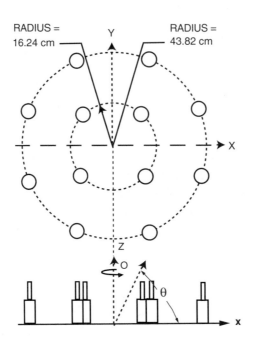

Figure 4.11 GPS satellite antenna

Advanced Problem:
Calculate the free space loss, exclusive of ionospheric effects, for GPS satellites.

Solution:
When the satellite is directly overhead, the distance is the shortest, at 20,187 km. Therefore, the loss at that point for the L1 frequency, the greater loss of the two frequencies, is:

$$L_{FS} = 10 \log [(1/4\pi)(\lambda/R)^2] = 10 \log [79.6E\text{-}3 (89.0E\text{-}18)] = -161 \, dB$$

The loss at the point of greatest distance, 25,788 km, when the satellite is low on the horizon, is 20 log (25,788/20187) = 2.1 dB, more or –163 dB. Notice how little the GPS signal varies due to different distances. The total loss is the free space loss plus the atmospheric loss. The maximum atmospheric loss is about 2.1 dB and is often less than 1 dB Thus, the worst case total path loss is about 163 dB.

The GPS SV provides a signal level to an antenna at the ground with a minimum carrier level of –160 dBW. This is based on receiver antenna gain of 0 dBic, which is gain over isotropic with circular polarization. The antenna for GPS receivers has a pattern that is close to hemispherical. If the antenna has no losses and is perfect, it would have a gain of 3 dB over isotropic since it covers only half the sphere. Because of circular polarization and losses in implementing the antenna, the actual gain of a patch antenna for GPS receivers is about 3 dB less than the theoretical, or 0 dBic.

This level of –160 dBW represents the entire signal power, as if the signal were measured with a very wideband power meter. There are sidebands associated with the signal due to modulation but the total power is –160 dBW. In order to pass the entire GPS signal, a bandwidth of 2.048 MHz is required. After the GPS signal is demodulated, bandwidth of the baseband signal is 1.024 MHz. It is after demodulation where signal to noise is measured. The thermal noise in this bandwidth is:

$$P_{th} = -228.6 \text{ dBW/K Hz} + 10 \log(1.024 \text{ MHz}) + 10 \log T_S =$$

$$-168.5 \text{ dBW/K} + 10 \log T_S$$

where T_S is the receiver system noise temperature.

A typical T_S is 220K. Therefore, the equivalent noise power of a GPS receiver is:

$$P_{th} = -168.5 \text{ dBW/K} + 10 \log (220K) = -168.5 \text{ dBW/K} + 23.4 \text{ dBK} = -145.1 \text{ dBW}.$$

Notice that noise power is 14.9 dB greater than the signal received from the SV. It would appear that this signal could not be retrieved from the noise. This calculation shows quantitatively why spread spectrum is used for covert communications. A conventional spectrum analyzer or other spectrum-scanning receiver would not detect a signal 14.9 dB below the thermal noise. However, signal processing gain increases signal to noise ratio by an amount approximately equal to the processing gain. Therefore, the equivalent signal to noise level of a GPS spread spectrum receiver is the signal to noise ratio plus the 43.1 dB processing gain or +28.2 dB. In other terms, after the signal is despread it is 28.2 dB above the noise. Demodulating a BPSK signal with a 28.2 dB signal to noise ratio produces virtually an error-free output.

A –160 dBW signal, however, is weak and should be handled with care. For this reason, low noise receivers with amplified antennas are often used with GPS receivers. These sensitive receivers are susceptible to interference from strong transmitters so GPS antennas need careful placement.

4.19 GPS Receivers

The GPS receiver was intended to be small and light weight for troops in the field. It does not require large, expensive components such as atomic clocks, cavity filters, high gain antennas or large computers. The major civilian market for GPS is divided into marine, road vehicle, aircraft and hand-held. There are significant differences in form factor, power requirements and displays, but signal processing is generally same for all. Airborne GPS provides outputs based on the location of conventional radio fixes, airways and airports, as well as altitude. This is a significant difference from marine GPS where altitude is of no value.

Displays and databases for a marine unit are different from the airborne unit, but there are other internal differences. An airplane moves at greater velocity and acceleration, requiring a computer capable of tracking the GPS PRN.

The GPS user antenna is right hand circularly polarized to match polarization of the SV antenna, and is typically a microstrip patch. This is well suited for aircraft because of a flat profile. The antenna usually has a preamplifier to make up the loss through the transmission line to the receiver. There are antennas without preamplifiers (on a hand held receiver, for example) where there is a short, low-loss coaxial cable between antenna and receiver.

The most desirable antenna pattern covers the visible sky but not below the horizon or toward the ground. SVs close to the horizon are less useful for navigation. It is best if they are not received because they are more likely contaminated with multipath interference. SVs more than about 10 degrees above the horizon are desired, and the antenna pattern is arranged to be less sensitive at low angles. This is the mask angle and is typically between 10 and 15 degrees. In a turn some desired SVs will not be received when they fall below the mask angle, and undesirable SVs low on the horizon are received. This is temporary and the GPS receiver computer should continue to provide navigation using available SVs, then quickly lock on to SVs that return when the bank angle is reduced.

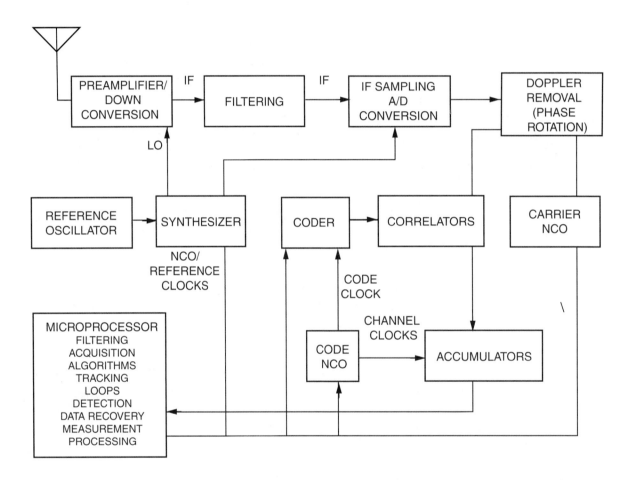

Figure 4.12   GPS receiver

A block diagram of a GPS receiver is shown in fig. 4-12. The receiver topology is that of a superheterodyne but not in the classical sense. In the GPS receiver the GPS signal is converted to a lower frequency and immediately digitized and processed. In the block diagram the antenna feeds a "pre filter", which filters out strong interfering signals. The GPS signal, when the P-code is considered, is over 20 MHz wide. The low noise amplifier, LNA, follows the filter. It is important the pre filter have low loss to preserve the noise figure of the LNA. As in any superheterodyne, the RF frequency is converted to an IF which is sufficiently high to encompass the bandwidth of the GPS signal, C/A only or C/A and P code, depending on the application. An IF filter follows the downconversion along with an IF amplifier.

In the block diagram the IF amplifier is followed by an A/D converter. In most receivers this A/D conversion is a one-bit conversion which is nothing more than a hard limiter. Some later receiver designs have used 2 bit A/D converters and it would be reasonable to assume 3 and even 4 bit A/D conversions may exist in the future.

Most of the GPS receiver is single digital VLSI chip which contains the signal processing and other functions. Once the GPS signal is in digital form, (the output of the A/D converter), all signal processing is performed in one VLSI chip.

After A/D conversion, the first process applied to the GPS signal is separating the in-phase and quadrature carriers. This is done by multiplying, exclusive ORing, the GPS signal with two carriers equal to the IF. These two carriers are in-phase quadrature.

A Costas loop is used to insure phase coherency and the I and Q signals are generated with a numerically controlled oscillator, NCO. This technique is also known as "direct digital synthesis". Because it is important to use only digital signals to process the GPS signal, functions that would normally be implemented with analog circuits, such as the Costas loop or a voltage controlled oscillator are implemented in digital circuits.

Once the I and Q carriers are separated, the GPS signal is still spread spectrum but where the I and Q modulations are separated. The GPS signal is despread by multiplying the GPS composite signal with the PRN of the satellites to be tracked. A GPS receiver is said to have a certain number of channels, N. This implies the receiver can despread N different SVs. A discussed earlier, 4 SVs must be tracked to determine the four unknowns, latitude, longitude, altitude and time. Six satellites is the usual minimum number of satellites visible and 12 is the maximum number of satellites visible. Receivers typically have between 6 and 12 channels.

The receiver generates a C/A code for each satellite tracked. The C/A code has three variations; an early code, a prompt code and a late code. The early and late codes are nothing more than the nominal C/A code but shifted one chip clock early and one chip clock late.

The GPS signal is multiplied by the PRN for a particular SV which is PRN_K where K is SV number. There are three versions of this PRN; PRN_{KE}, PRN_{KP} and PRN_{KL}, PRN early, prompt and late for satellite K. The phase of the PRN is adjusted so that any despreading from the early and late are equal, which means the phase of the PRN is centered between early and late. If the phase of the PRN begins to advance, there will be increased despreading of the "early" output. Likewise, if there is a phase retardation there will be increased despreading of the "late" output. By sensing the amount of signal present in the early and late outputs and using that information to control the phase of the PRN chip clock generated with the NCO, the PRN phase can be adjusted to be in exact phase. This is called a code-locked-loop. There is one code locked loop for each "channel" of the GPS receiver.

A civilian GPS receiver would receive only one of the L band frequencies an decode only one PRN for the Kth SV's C/A navigation message. Future GPS receivers will decode L1 and L5 and would involve 2 local oscillator frequencies.

Correct demodulation of the GPS signal involves the phase of the NCO and the PRN to be correct. We could consider the phase of the NCO and the phase of the PRN as two variables. If we plot the effectiveness of demodulation of the navigation message as bit error rate as a function of the two variables, we have a three dimensional plot. The X axis is the phase of the local oscillator which separates the quadrature multiplexed carriers. The Y axis is the phase of the PRN and the Z axis is the probability of a bit being correctly received. This plot has peak values where the demodulation of the navigation message is most effective. In this context, effective means data is obtained with minimal errors.

This plot would have false peaks where NCO and PRN phase errors produce an apparent improvement in demodulation effectiveness, but never sufficient to be useful. A software search routine must eliminate locking on to a false peak.

When the GPS receiver is turned on, the almanac lists SVs in view. This assumes the receiver is in nearly the same location it was when turned off, the GPS clock has been running and the receiver knows the time. The receiver tries to despread the IF signal using the PRNs for SVs in view.

The IF signal appears to be noise. The IF signal is, in fact, several SVs and noise. The SVs are noise-like signals with the addition of thermal noise, which accounts for the noise-like appearance of the IF. If the IF is multiplied by a PRN of a SV signal included in the IF noise, where the PRN has the correct time relationship, part of the IF signal is despread and produces a narrowband output from that SV. The other SVs and thermal noise are further spread.

The almanac provides the PRNs, and the time relationship must be found. A direct technique is to move the PRN code in time and watch the output of the despreader, then stop the variable time as soon as despreading is detected.

Consider how despreading is detected. The navigation message is sent at 50 bits per second, which means that each bit lasts 20 ms. The PRN has 1023 states in the sequence and the clock is 1.023 MHz which implies the PRN repeats every 1 ms. Therefore, the PRN repeats 20 times during the time of one data bit. The simplest way of detecting this is to low pass filter the correlator output. If the time relationship of the PRN is correct, a logic one or zero appears at the output and lasts a minimum of 20 ms. If the time relationship is not correct the output is midway between logic one and zero levels.

If we try one complete PRN sequence, 1 ms, and test the output of the correlator for a steady logic one or zero, a solid one or zero is a good indication of correlation. There are 1023 different time orientations of the PRN sequence. Using this simple technique, we would have to try up to all 1023 time delays and wait 1 ms to test each one. The attempt at despreading would take up to 1.023 seconds. This is the worst case. On average, it takes half that time or about one-half second to test a PRN.

This process can be speeded up considerably. First, simultaneous correlations can be performed. For example; eight correlations for eight different time delays or eight periods of the 1.023 MHz clock increase speed by a factor of eight. A PRN could be checked, on average, in 63 ms.

When the receiver has been turned off or geographically moved, so the almanac is not correct, correlation will not be successful for PRNs as expected. In this case, all PRNs for active SVs are examined to find which are available. This may be time consuming because all 24 PRNs must be tried. Once SVs are located, the position of the GPS is found and almanac data restored. This is more of a problem for a portable GPS since it is more likely to be transported while turned off. It usually doesn't happen with airborne units because GPS is operating when the aircraft is flown.

4.20 GPS Accuracy

To understand accuracy, it is important to consider its nature. Foremost is that accuracy is a statistical measurement. As an example, a navigation system is WW% probable to provide an accuracy of XX for YY% of the time. Assume we investigate the accuracy of a VOR ground station. This station is not perfect and, in certain areas, there are problems with multipath distortion. However, if the problems occur in only 5% of the area and the system otherwise provides one-degree accuracy, we could say accuracy is plus or minus 1 degree in 95% of the coverage area. It is equally probable that an aircraft will be in any one part of the coverage, including the area with multipath distortion, and reword the accuracy statement as; "95% probable that accuracy is plus or minus one degree".

Further, assume the VOR is an older station and tends to drift with temperature. Every winter when the temperature goes below –20C accuracy goes down. Since this happens only a few nights each year, it can be said that 99% of the time the station meets the specification. Accuracy can now be specified as; "95% probability that accuracy is plus or minus one degree for 99% of the time".

Availability, in some circumstances, is more important than accuracy. Our descriptor, 99% of the time, specifies what percentage the specified accuracy is available. If the most accurate navigation system is operational only half the time, its accuracy is of little use. GPS was not declared suitable for sole means of navigation until the entire system was functional, with a constellation of 21 operating SVs and three spares. Before the entire constellation was launched, GPS was used where available.

Typically, six SVs are in view from any location on earth at any time. Four SVs are needed to obtain an initial position and three can be used for short periods. It would appear that six would be more than necessary.

Certain combinations of SVs provide better results than others. When SVs are low on the horizon they may not provide a good fix when used with other SVs. This was discussed relative to mask angle. If SVs are directly overhead, they will not combine for a good fix. Better results occur with SVs directly overhead and two or three others between about 15 and 75 degrees. Generally, the more SVs, the better the position determination. Of six SVs in view, it is possible that some will cause a deterioration, rather than an improvement, in accuracy.

SVs of less than optimum geometry cause PDOP, for position dilution of precision (pronounced "P-dop"). Another is called GDOP, for geometrical dilution of precision (pronounced "G-dop") and includes effects of position and time measurement errors. The effect of PDOP is given by:

$$\Delta P = PDOP (\Delta R) \qquad (4\text{-}23)$$

where ΔP is the RMS position error and ΔR is the RMS ranging error. Even though the local clock can be set for excellent accuracy and calculations made to remove SV position and clock errors, some level of range error remains, which is ΔR. PDOP is a number that ranges from one, perfect geometry, to 6 which is about the limit. With the constellation of 21 active and 3 spare SVs, it is not possible to always use an ideal arrangement of SVs. On average, PDOP is about 2.0. If a GPS receiver corrects pseudorange to within 1 meter because of PDOP, on average the actual position output of the GPS receiver is 2 meters, RMS.

Because GPS is three-dimensional , accuracy should be specified in three dimensions. This implies that a GPS fix is contained within an "error sphere". This is called the "spherical equivalent probable" or SEP. An example is a 90% SEP for the minimum radius sphere that contains 90% of the GPS position measurements.

167

If we specify a minimum PDOP and revisit availability, simply having four SVs is not enough. There must be sufficient SVs with good geometry to provide a reasonable fix for the task. If a high-altitude en route leg is flown, a SEP of a few hundred meters is acceptable. On the other hand, navigate in a terminal area preparing to land, and a few hundred meters is insufficient.

At this time the vertical component of a GPS fix is the least accurate of the three dimensions. A few hundred meters accuracy is acceptable if altitude is determined by another means. This is, in fact, often the case. High en route altitudes are specified as pressure altitude and determined by an aneroid (pressure-driven) altimeter. Assuming that altitude is determined via aneroid altimeter, a horizontal error of a few hundred meters is acceptable for en route flight. GPS errors in the horizontal plane are called HDOP (horizontal dilution of precision).

The required DOP affects the availability of the GPS system. It was mentioned that the average PDOP is 2.0. If availability is specified for situations with a PDOP of 2.0 or less, availability is about 50%. Half the time for a fixed location, PDOP would be below 2.0 or, at any fixed time, half the locations on earth would have PDOP less than 2.0. To use GPS just for horizontal navigation, with barometric altimetry for vertical guidance, an availability of 99% is achieved by accepting an HDOP of 2.7. If HDOP is 4.5 there is an availability of 99.9%. An HDOP of 6 assures availability of 99.99%. A PDOP of six may not be suitable for many phases of navigation.

These examples are for GPS without augmentation. By adding an augmentation system timing errors decrease and accuracy improves. PDOP is still present because the augmentation system cannot improve bad geometry.

4.21 GPS Navigation

The GPS receiver determines latitude, longitude and altitude—which comprise position. This combines with waypoints, airways, destinations and other factors affecting the flight. GPS receivers provide amazing calculation capability and include data bases with the location of navaids such as VOR and NDB. This enables the GPS receiver to follow the same routes formed by the National Airspace System, NAS. One difficulty with the database in GPS receivers is that information changes. Airports are modified and the airport reference point (usually near the center of the field) can change. Although rare, VORs and NDBs are moved, shut down or added. Most GPS receivers, therefore, provide a method for updating their database.

In large aircraft, the calculation to solve the navigation equation is performed in a central computer which receives the GPS position input. Using this technique, the GPS may not require its own data base; the central computer stores it.

When navigating with GPS, a flight path or routing is selected. This can be to a waypoint, which is usually entered by keying in the alphanumeric identifier shown on an aeronautical chart. This provides latitude and longitude for 2 D navigation to the waypoint. For more critical maneuvers, such as an instrument approach, the fixes are pre-stored in a computer memory and displayed in correct sequence to the pilot When used with advanced navigation systems for landing, course deviation indication is both vertical and lateral.

There are no course indicators unique to GPS. Most GPS receivers drive conventional instruments such as the CDI and HSI. Because flight crews are familiar with them, they will be in service for many years. As an example, the SCAT I system, which is a DGPS landing system, behaves exactly like a CAT I ILS. A flight crew would not know the difference from the instruments if a SCAT I or CAT I approach were flown. The (VOR/LOC) NAV receiver is not used and there is no Morse code identifier.

168

4.22 Improved GPS for Civilian Use

GPS was first and foremost a military system and no one expected it to become the mainstay of civilian navigation. When augmentation was first considered the military owners of GPS were deliberately degrading the signal with selective availability, while the FAA was designing methods of undoing the damage done by selective availability. Finally, selective availability was turned off. To gain the full accuracy of the GPS system, two frequencies were required, L1 and L2 to determine the ionospheric corrections. L2 is the basis for the military-exclusive PPS and civilian users cannot take full advantage of that service. There were proposals to add another frequency for GPS SVs which would permit civilian users to enjoy the full capabilities of the GPS system but during a time of national emergency the civilian frequency could be deleted or degraded as needed.

An additional frequency was attractive for another reason. Some problems with interference had been noticed after GPS use became widespread and an additional L band down link frequency would make it more difficult to intentionally or unintentionally jam the GPS service. A new "civilian" L5 frequency was established at 1176.45 MHz or 115 X 10.23 MHz. L band frequencies, L3 and L4 are for military-only non-navigation applications of GPS.

At the time of this writing, no SV is transmitting the L5 signal. Newer SVs will be equipped with the L5 signal The latest block of space vehicles, block IIR which are space vehicles number 41 to 66 will be the last to not have L5 capability.

The L5 carrier is modulated in a very similar fashion but not identical to L1 and L2. Two carriers, in quadrature, at 1176.45 MHz are BPSK modulated with two bit streams. The in phase carrier is modulated with a modulo two addition of the downlink data transmission called the NAV data, a synchronizing sequence and a PRN ranging code. The other carrier, the quadrature carrier Is modulated with a PRN ranging code and synchronizing sequence. The in phase and quadrature PRNs are different. As with L1 and L2, the PRN is unique to the SV and is used to identify the SV. There are also nonstandard codes, not assigned to any SV, to prevent the use of a corrupted L5 signal, which is also the same as L1 and L2..

The chip rate for the L5 PRN is 10.23 MHz. The codes last 10,230 chips and thus repeat after 1 ms. The PRNs are Gold codes and of the more than 4000 possible different codes only 74 are used. This represents 17 in-phase PRNs and 17 quadrature PRNs. Of the 37 pairs of PRNs only 32 are assigned to SVs and 5 are reserved for such applications as WAAS.

The L5 signal is right hand circularly polarized and produces a minimum level of -154 dBw for either in-phase or quadrature carrier into a circularly polarized 3 dBi antenna with the SV at an angle of 5 degrees above the horizon.

Of the possible 64 different message types, only 5 are defined at the time of this writing. The L5 data is mostly the same as L1 and L2 but with a different format and parity algorithm. Messages are 300 bits at 50 bits per second for a total time of 6 seconds. Each message starts with a preamble, 10001011, followed by a 6 bit message type identifier. Seventeen bits of TOW is next, which represents the start of the next message. A one bit "alert flag" immediately follows the TOW which when set, indicates SV accuracies may not be trustworthy. In message types 1, 3, 4, and 5, the PRN number follows.

The CRC parity generating polynomial is a CRC-24Q which is different than that used for L1 and L2.

The message types are: message 1, clock health and accuracy; message 2, ephemeris Data; message 3, UTC, ionospheric parameters and other data; message 4, almanac data; message 5 is reserved for special messages as needed by operating command. Message 5 can accommodate up to 29 eight-bit ASCII characters. The permitted ASCII character s are upper case alphabetical, numerical and some punctuation.

Chapter 4 Review Questions

4.1   What are three basic elements of the GPS system?

4.2   Describe the GPS satellite orbit.

4.3   How many satellites are required to find a position?

4.4   What is pseudorange? How does pseudorange become range?

4.5   Assume that a system uses satellites that orbit the earth three times each sidereal day. What is the altitude of the satellite?

4.6   What types of clocks are used in the SVs?

4.7   What type of clock is in the normal GPS receiver?

4.8   What is an earth model? Which model is used for GPS?

4.9   What is processing gain? How much processing gain is required in GPS?

4.10   Why is spread spectrum used for the GPS system?

4.11   How is a Gold code generated?

4.12   What is autocorrelation?

4.13   What characteristics should a PRN sequence have?

4.14   What is selective availability?

4.15   What errors can differential GPS offset?

4.16   Draw a block diagram of a differential GPS system.

4.17   What is RAIM? How does it work?

4.18   What system(s) would make RAIM unnecessary?

4.19   For what reason (s) is a new L5 carrier desired?

4.20   What is the major communications link for LAAS?

4.21   What is the major communications link for WAAS?

4.22   What is a pseudolite?

4.23   What is the kinetic energy of a GPS satellite per kg of mass?

4.24   What is the potential energy of a GPS satellite per kg of mass?

References

Farrell, Jay, Barth, Matthew, <u>The Global Positioning System and Inertial Navigation</u>, New York, McGraw-Hill, 1999

Chapter 5

Surveillance Systems

5.1 Introduction

Historically, after navigation the second requirement for aviation electronics was communications—to control traffic, prevent collisions, disseminate weather and handle operational messages. An air traffic controller could contact an aircraft and request its location, which the flight crew determined from its navigation systems. Maintaining separation depended on a flight crew knowing its position, often by noting station passage over a VOR, crossing an intersection or estimating position by dead reckoning. Altitude was determined by an aneroid instrument.

Because position was not highly accurate, aircraft flying under air traffic control (ATC) were widely separated. There was always the possibility that an aircraft not in contact with ATC would stray into controlled airspace. Some method of locating aircraft that required neither crew participation nor voice communication would be a great improvement.

Radio detection and ranging, *radar*, was developed during World War II for the same purpose. One problem, however, was the inability of radar to provide a three dimensional fix, that is, aircraft position and altitude. There are height finding radars, but they are only effective for short distances.

A second problem was that aircraft could not be positively identified. Radar returns from enemy and friendly aircraft looked the same. The solution was IFF, for identification friend or foe. The first radar system, which worked on reflections from the skin of the airplane, was known as primary radar. The IFF enhancement is called secondary radar. Although IFF has undergone much refinement, it still operates much the way it was implemented in the 1940s.

This section will discuss primary and secondary radar, a collision avoidance system based on secondary radar, airborne radar for detecting weather, ground proximity and a collision avoidance system using GPS data.

At the time of this writing, major changes are happening. The system that has been operating for more than 50 years is called "air traffic control", or ATC. As its title implies, aircraft are controlled from the ground An air crew can request a route but before the route may be flown it must be cleared by ATC.

5.2 Free Flight

In recent years, ATC has increasingly allowed airplanes to fly off published airways (a type of flight known as "area navigation" or "random navigation," abbreviated as RNAV), but the system is mainly based on fixed airways and the aircraft changes course when over a station or intersection. This results in fuel and time wasting "doglegs" and funnels aircraft into the same path. It has been argued that if all aircraft simply flew where they wished, because of their random location and destinations, safe separation would result. Only when aircraft converge on a major hub, control may then be necessary. During the en route phase it would only be necessary to monitor aircraft. This would predict a loss of safe separation and only aircraft involved in a potential collision would be asked to change course or altitude. Most aircraft would be free to fly directly to their destination at any altitude or route. This concept *manages* rather than *controls* air traffic. The program is called "free flight", and is in development at the time of this writing. However, much of the free flight concept has been specified and hardware has been built and demonstrations have been carried out. Free flight is moving towards implementation. Because of free flight air traffic control, ATC, will be mostly replaced, except in terminal areas, with ATM, for air traffic management.

Computer models have proven the free flight concept. Pilots can file a flight plan and make en route changes without contacting ATM. This freedom allows the crew to select the shortest, most fuel-efficient route or a more comfortable flight level. Free flight, however, can only be effective if aircraft are equipped with accurate position determination equipment, collision avoidance and data communications. ADS-B (automatic dependent surveillance-broadcast) is a method of surveillance that uses GPS position information, and is one key to the free flight concept. Although most air traffic is presently under control of ATC, the term ATM—the next-generation system—will also appear in the remainder of this text.

Since much of the decision making is being transferred from ground-based air traffic control to the cockpit, the aircrew must be provided with sufficient and accurate data to make good decisions. As an example, many flight path changes are based on weather. Current technology provides three sources of weather information. The first is visual observation from the flight deck. The second is weather radar information from the on board weather radar. And, finally, there are weather briefings from a flight service station.

The information from the aircraft is good for only a few nautical miles of visual observations and up to 200 NM for airborne weather radar. It is very important to realize these are observations, not forecasts. Realizing an aircraft with a tail wind can travel 200 NM in about 20 minutes, course changes based on radar data extending only 200 NM could require course changes every 20 minutes.

Providing weather observations as well as forecasts to the flight deck for the entire route will permit minimal course changes. This involves uplinking of digital weather data and graphics displays to the aircraft.

Another reason for a course change is to avoid a conflict. The same situation exists here. TCAS has a range of about 20 NM and it is collision avoidance system not a flight planning system. Another free-flight tool is the cockpit display of traffic information or CDTI. Unlike a TCAS display or primary PPI (plan position indicator) display, the CDTI includes direction of flight and intent. If the intended track of an aircraft is known, flight planning can avoid conflicts. This enhanced traffic information system is based on a system of surveillance called automatic dependent surveillance, ADS, of which ADS-B is a variant, and is discussed in more detail later in this chapter.

5.3 Primary Radar

Primary radar uses a network of ground-based stations with two classes of operation; terminal and en route. A radio signal transmitted in a beam strikes the aircraft and reflects back to a receiver at the same position. If the beam is narrow, it is known that the reflector (the aircraft) is in the beam because energy returns to the radar site. If a short pulse is transmitted, it is possible to measure elapsed time and determine the range or distance. Aircraft in the beam are detected and their range determined, thus the term *radar*, for radio detection and ranging.

We need to go back and revise this simple description and the term "reflected". When radiated energy encounters an obstruction, called "illuminating a target," energy is not reflected in the sense of a mirror. Some energy passes around the target and is not reflected. Some energy is reflected in all directions and only a small amount is reflected in the direction of the radar. The phenomenon is called "scattering." If energy is returned to the transmitter, it is called "backscatter." Received at the radar site, backscatter is used to detect the target.

How well a target produces backscatter is its "radar cross section," or RCS. To understand how RCS relates to backscatter, imagine a mirror which reflects radio waves completely; there are no reflections to the side and no energy can pass through the mirror. Although this is a theoretical device, a flat piece of conducting material such as aluminum or copper comes close to it.

Assume a radio mirror of one square meter in area. By definition this target has an RCS of 1 square meter. All energy is reflected back to the transmitter. If an aircraft backscatters the same amount as the 1 square meter radio mirror, the aircraft has an RCS of 1 square meter.

Radar cross section depends on the shape of the aircraft; relatively large airplanes can have an RCS of only a few meters. A small business jet may have an RCS of 1 square meter. Military aircraft are designed to have very small RCSs, using techniques called "stealth".

The concept of radar, therefore, transmits a pulse of energy from a directional antenna in a particular direction. The same antenna receives backscattered energy and the time delay is used to determine range. The strength of the signal from a target is a function of distance, antenna gain and transmitter power.

Assume a transmitter providing power to an "isotropic radiator". This device, which for coherent radio waves, is only theoretically possible, radiates equally well in all directions. For a narrow pulse, energy propagates in all directions and is contained in a sphere of radius R. Power density, which is the power per unit area, is:

$$P(R) = P_T/4\pi R^2 \qquad (5.1)$$

Where P(R) is power density at a distance, R, from the transmitter, and P_T is transmitter power.

A radar transmitter uses a directional antenna to concentrate energy into a cone of solid angle. A measure of how well it does this relative to the density from an isotropic radiator is called antenna gain or G. For a directional radar antenna energy density is now given by:

$$P(R) = GP_T/4\pi R^2 \qquad (5.2)$$

Once this signal illuminates the target, backscattered energy reverses direction and propagates back to the transmitter. Essentially, the target becomes a transmitter with a transmitted power of:

$$(RCS)GP_T/4\pi R^2 \qquad (5.3)$$

The power density of the backscattered signal decreases as the $1/R^2$, as any radiated signal. The phenomenon is the same whether the radiator is a transmitter or a scattering target. The signal power density at the radar transmitter is inversely proportional to the distance of the fourth power or :

$$P(R) = (RCS)GP_T/(4\pi R^2)^2 \qquad (5.4)$$

Energy returned to the radar site is intercepted with the same antenna used for the transmitter. The ability of an antenna to turn radiated into conducted energy is called capture area. As an example, if a power density of 1 mw per square meter illuminates an antenna with a 1 meter capture area, the antenna provides one mw of power at the output connector.

Multiplying power density by capture area results in the power level at the antenna output. Multiplying antenna capture area A, by energy density, E(R) results in power to the receiver at the radar site;

$$AP(R)=P_R(R) = A(RCS)GP_T/(4\pi R^2)^2 \qquad (5.5)$$

where $P_R(R)$ is the power from the antenna available for the receiver.

This equation contains two factors for the same antenna; capture area, A, and gain G. There is a relationship between capture area and gain, which is:

$$A = G\lambda^2/4\pi \qquad (5.6)$$

Where λ is the wavelength of radiated energy. Substituting the above for A results in the "radar equation";

$$P_R(R) = (RCS)G^2\lambda^2 \, P_T/4\pi(4\pi R^2)^2 \qquad (5.7)$$

This equation reveals problems faced by early researchers in radar. A serious one is that the signal decreases in power with the distance to the target to the fourth power. In other words, the signal becomes very weak quickly as range increases. Also, the signal varies with wavelength squared. Another way of looking at it; the signal decreases with shorter wavelengths. Short wavelengths are essential in radar to obtain backscatter from targets. Long wavelengths tend to travel around small targets.

Example: Calculate the signal to a receiver from a radar system that has a 36 dB antenna gain, a transmitter power of 1000 watts, an operating frequency of 5. 65 GHz, from a business jet target with an RCS of 1 m^2 at a distance of 75 NM.

Solution: To solve this problem first calculate λ from the frequency
$\lambda = c/f = 3E8/5.65E9 = 0.053$ m

Second, convert 75 NM to meters.
R = 75X1852 = 1. 39E5

Third, antenna gain, given in decibels, is the one way of specifying antenna gain

174

converted to a number:
$$G = 10^{3.6} = 3.98E3$$

The solution is obtained by substituting values in the equation:

$$P_R(R) = (RCS)G^2\lambda^2 \, P_T/4\pi(4\pi R^2)^2 = 6.03 \text{ X } 10^{-18} = -142 \text{ dBm}$$

A signal of 6.03 X 10^{-18} watts returns from a 1E3,watt transmitter. The loss in dB is transmitter power, +60 dBm, which is 202 dB greater than the received signal.

This example shows that to make radar work, huge antenna gain is required, as well as high transmitter power and sensitive receivers. As an interesting comparison; the one-way free space loss from the moon to the earth is only 219 dB at 5.65 GHz! In fact, engineers experimented with bouncing signals from the moon using surplus WWII radar equipment.

5.4 Secondary Radar

Radar locates a target by knowing the antenna angle when the transmission is made and elapsed time when the backscattered signal is received. Range to the target is calculated by the time delay, which allows the target to be located on a polar coordinate display, with the radar site at the origin. This display, a plan position indicator, or PPI, is in two dimensions, while aircraft exist in a three dimensional world. Two additional data are added to the PPI by secondary radar.

Secondary radar is more appropriately a communication system, rather than radar. It requires equipment in the aircraft that communicates with secondary radar, namely a transponder, or transmitter/receiver, that receives and responds to pulse encoded transmissions.

The transponder in the aircraft receives pulse amplitude modulated signals called "interrogations". When an interrogation is valid, the transponder replies on a different frequency. Readers who covered DME in this text will notice a similarity; DME is a secondary radar system as well. In the case of DME, however, the transponder is located on the ground and the interrogator in the air. DME determines range only and does not derive bearing information. DME uses omnidirectional antennas at both ends; on the ground and airborne.

Secondary radar described here is associated with the Air Traffic Control Radar Beacon System, or ATCRBS (pronounced "at-crabs"). The airborne equipment is also called the ATC transponder or Mode A/C transponder, which will become apparent later.

Secondary radar is a communications system but there is another difference between primary and secondary radar. The signal strength of a communications system varies inversely with distance to the *second* power, compared with primary radar which reduces with the *fourth* power. The reason is that secondary radar adds energy to the system. When a primary radar signal illuminates a target, energy from the radar has already decreased as the inverse of the distance squared. Backscattered energy also decreases inversely with the distance squared. When a transponder receives an interrogation, the energy has reduced with the inverse of the distance squared. But the transponder transmits a reply which regenerates the signal. Therefore, secondary radar can have the same range as primary radar with significantly less transmitter power. The typical ATCRBS interrogator achieves the same range as primary radar with as little as 1000 watts radiated power, compared to megawatts for primary radar.

There are two types of interrogations in the ATCRBS secondary radar system; modes A and C, which provide identity (A) and altitude (C). It is unfortunate that mode A is identity and not altitude because many people confuse the A with altitude. Although mode B was planned, it has never been used for civil aviation. ATCRBS is shared with the military, where a variety of additional interrogation modes are used.

Since ATCRBS is similar to DME, we can build on DME to gain insight into ATCRBS. The interrogations are pulse amplitude modulated at a carrier frequency of 1030 MHz. An interrogation consists of two pulses for the same reason DME uses two; to distinguish an interrogation from a noise pulse. (A third pulse is involved in the interrogation, but is not a part of the interrogation.) ATCRBS pulses are 0.8 ms in width and close to rectangular in shape. A perfect rectangular pulse has zero rise time, which implies the system must have infinite bandwidth. This is not possible and actual rise time is on the order of 10 to 50 ns.

Advanced Problem: Calculate the spectrum of a transponder interrogation pulse with a rise time and fall time of 10 ns. Consider the pulse measured between half amplitude points. Compare the spectrum of the transponder pulse to a Gaussian pulse of the same half amplitude width by plotting the spectra.

The receipt of a valid interrogation causes the transponder to reply and include data in the transmission. There are no data transmitted by the DME transponder other than the ident and TACAN modulation. The reply is used by the airborne DME interrogator to calculate distance to the ground station.

Two types of data words may be requested by the ground interrogator, and transmitted by the transponder. The first is identity. This identifies the aircraft either uniquely (with a 4-digit code issued by an ATC controller) or categorically, such as an aircraft flying under visual flight rules (the code is "1200"). The other information from the transponder is altitude of the aircraft.

The interrogator antenna on the ground is physically atop the primary radar so the ATCRBS interrogator rotates exactly as the primary radar. Because primary and secondary radar share antenna location and pointing, the returning backscatter signals from the primary radar and replies from the transponder can be correlated. With the exception of the time it takes the transponder to respond to an interrogation, the elapsed time from a ground radar station until the reply is received is the range to a target. It is possible to know, therefore, which target of the primary radar is associated with the secondary radar reply This can only be done if every transponder has precisely the same delay, which they do.

Let us take a moment to understand how secondary radar enhances the PPI display of the air traffic controller. With secondary radar, the display contains not only targets detected by primary radar but two other important pieces of information; an aircraft's identity and altitude. The controller now has the equivalent of a three-dimensional display and knows, positively, which blip represents which aircraft.

An additional feature of the ATCRBS transponder is an "identity" or ident feature. This is in addition to the identity provided by a dialed-in "squawk "(a code assigned by ATC). When the controller says "Ident" the pilot presses a button on the transponder and transmits an additional pulse in the reply. This causes the aircraft's blip on the radar to brighten and bloom, making that target easily apparent to the controller. As the world transitions to the new ATM, the role of the controller and use of the ident button will diminish.

One common feature of the ATC radar display is a specialized form of PPI (plan position indicator) called the moving target indicator, or MTI. It solves the problem of radar returns from stationary objects such as buildings and towers. There are also returns from slow moving

176

airborne objects such as clouds. These undesired responses are called clutter and may be eliminated by displaying only targets in motion. There are, however, slow moving objects such as airships, helicopters, free balloons and light aircraft that should be displayed. The transponder on these slow-moving targets provides a positive identity and prevents them from being removed from the PPI display.

In the secondary radar system, it is desired that only transponders in the beam of the antenna respond—and not those within the antenna's back and side lobes. Although modern antenna designs minimize radiation from back and sides, some persists. When the IFF system, precursor to ATCRBS, was developed during World War II, side lobes were prevalent. To prevent aircraft moderately close to the interrogator's antenna from receiving a valid interrogation and replying off the main beam, a system of side lobe suppression, SLS, was developed.

SLS transmits a third interrogation pulse, which is a reference for determining reception from side lobes. The envelope of an interrogation is shown in Fig 5.1. P1 is the first pulse of an interrogation, and is transmitted from the directional antenna. The second pulse, P2, is transmitted from an omnidirectional antenna with a signal level greater than the signal from any side lobe. If the amplitude of P2 is greater than P1, the interrogation is being received from a side lobe and should not cause a reply. The third pulse, P, is the same level as P1 because it is transmitted from the same antenna.

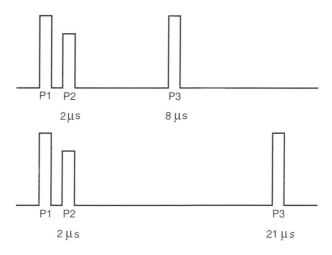

Figure 5.1 Transponder Interrogation

The time delay from P1 to P3 designates the type of interrogation. The delay between P1 and P2 is always 2.0 μs. When P1 and P3 are separated by 8 μs, a mode A, identity, reply is expected. When the separation is 21 μs, a mode C, altitude, reply is expected.

If a P2 pulse is received after a P1 pulse, where the level of P2 pulse is 1 dB below P1 or greater, the transponder will not reply and not recognize any pulses for 35 μs, plus or minus 10 μs after receipt of P2, which is called "dead time" or "suppression time". This prevents the transponder from responding to multipath signals. Generally, when an aircraft receives a side lobe transmission, it is relatively close to the interrogator, a region where multipath signals are strong.

The transponder replies 3.0 μs from receipt of P3 to the transmission of F1 as measured from the half amplitude point of the pulses. This delay is critical and affects the ability of the secondary radar system to determine position.

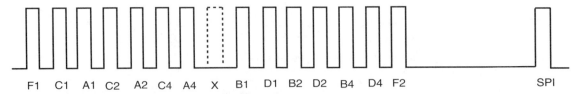

F1 C1 A1 C2 A2 C4 A4 X B1 D1 B2 D2 B4 D4 F2   SPI

Figure 5.2 ATCRB replies

5.5 Replies

The transponder replies with a pulse-amplitude modulated, PAM, transmission at a carrier frequency of 1090 MHz. The reply consists of two framing pulses 20.3 μs apart as shown in Fig. 5.2. Framing pulses are always present and mark the beginning and end of 15 time slots, which are assigned to data bits. The first framing pulse is the reference for measuring delay time of the transponder. The time slots are separated by 1.45 μs and the pulses are 0.45 μs wide. Notice that the framing pulses are separated by an integer multiple of 1.45 μs. There is a maximum of 14 binary data bits that may be transmitted in the reply, although there are 15 time slots. The 15th time slot is called the X bit and intended for some future purpose. For more than 45 years, however, the X bit was never used and finally declared a zero.

A logic one is transmitted by providing a pulse in a time slot. A logic zero is indicated by no pulse. This has been called "pulse existence modulation," PEM, by this author. If a logic one is transmitted, a pulse exists in the time slot. If a logic zero is to be transmitted the pulse does not exist. Since there are 14 time slots for a reply, and two are occupied by framing pulses, only $2^{12} = 4096$ different data words may be transmitted. Clearly, there are more than 4096 aircraft in the world and the aircraft population must share 4096 possible identity codes. Aircraft are assigned an identity only while in communication with ATC.

There are generic codes not assigned by the air traffic controller, such as 1200 for aircraft flying under visual flight rules (VFR). These aircraft may not be in radio contact with ATC. A code dialed into a transponder is commonly called a "squawk".

The transponder provides four switches for setting the squawk, entered as an octal number, shown below. The squawk ranges from 0000 to 7777, where each octal digit spans from 0 to 7. Each handles 3 bits, and four digits cover the required 12 bits.

D4   D2   D1   Least Significant Digit
C4   C2   C1
B4   B2   B1
A4   A2   A1   Most significant Digit

Example: The octal number 4564 is given as D4=1 D2=0 D1=0 C4=1 C2=0 C1=1 B4=1 B2=1 B1=0 A4=1 A2=1 A1=1. Notice that designating the D digit to be the least significant while the A digit is the most significant is the opposite of modern convention. Note, however, that the ATCRBS system evolved from IFF, invented in the 1940's. There were few conventions for binary systems at that time.

A mode A reply is shown in Fig. 5.3. Framing pulses are always present and the X pulse always missing. The data pulses are present when a logic one is to be transmitted and not present when a logic zero is to be transmitted.

178

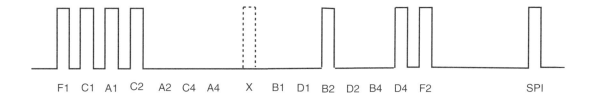

F1 C1 A1 C2 A2 C4 A4 X B1 D1 B2 D2 B4 D4 F2 SPI

Fig. 5.3 Mode A reply

The same 14 time slots transmit altitude as well as identity. The only way the ground interrogator can distinguish altitude from identity is by the interrogation. That means if a mode C interrogation is transmitted, the reply is assumed to be altitude.

An extra pulse, called the special pulse identity, SPI, is transmitted 4.35 µs, or 3 times 1.45 µs, after the last framing pulse implements the ident of the ATCRBS transponder. Pressing the ident button on the transponder enables this pulse. The transponder contains a timer that removes the ident pulse after about 20 seconds.

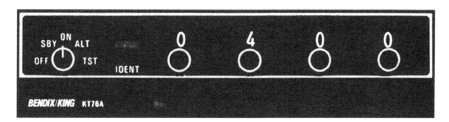

ATCRBS Transponder

5.6 Mode C

Before discussing altitude, we need to consider different altitudes used in air navigation. The most obvious is "above ground level," or AGL. This is the altitude a tape would measure if stretched from aircraft to ground. This altitude is used mostly for landings and is measured from the aircraft by a radar altimeter. (Aviation weather reports also state ceilings in AGL.)

The second altitude is "mean sea level", MSL. This is height above mean sea level which takes into account variation due to tides. This altitude is usually measured with an aneroid altimeter. Until recently, MSL was measured only with an aneroid altimeter; with the advent of satellite navigation, however, altitude may be measured electronically.

For an aneroid instrument to read altitude, it needs to be adjusted for atmospheric pressure. The altimeter has a barometric pressure adjustment usually called a "baro-set" knob which enters local sea level barometric pressure. Now the altimeter reads the correct altitude. In the air, the pilot obtains sea level barometric pressure from a ground facility via radio.

There are problems in using the baro-set of an altimeter. First, sea level pressure changes from one location to another. If the barometer is set at the departing airport, it may not be correct at the arrival airport. Also, the barometer changes with weather conditions. The setting, even at the same airport, will not be valid on returning from a flight. There is also human error in setting an altimeter. For this reason, altitude transmitted from the transponder is "pressure altitude". This is the altitude an altimeter shows if the baro-set is adjusted to 29.92 inches of mercury.

Encoding altimeter contains pressure sensor to drive altimeter pointers and altitude encoding device for transponder

There are two types of altimeters for providing altitude information to the transponder. One is an "encoding altimeter," which is viewed by the flight crew for normal altimetry. This indicator has a baro-set to allow adjustments for MSL readings. Part of the same system is an altitude encoder to provide the electrical output for the transponder. The encoder is attached to the altimeter instrument before the baro-set knob so transponder output is unaffected by the baro-set.

The second type of encoding altimeter is the "blind encoder". This device has no external dial, thus the "blind" designation. It provides only electrical outputs for the transponder and other devices (such as an air data computer) that require altitude information. Since there is no dial, there is no baro-set and the encoder provides only pressure altitude.

Altitude is encoded into binary words of 11 bits from –1000 feet to 126,700 feet with a least significant bit of 100 feet. It is called the Gilham code, which is an example of a Gray code. This code has a unique characteristic in that only one bit changes between subsequent values. This is used for mechanically-encoded data to reduce the size of possible errors.

Example: What range of altitudes may be represented by an 11-bit binary data word with a 100-foot least significant bit?

Solution: There are $2^{11} = 2048$ different combinations of 11 binary bits. Therefore, 204,800 feet of altitude could be encoded with 11 binary bits.

The reason that only 127,700 feet of altitude is encoded is because the Gilham code does not permit all combinations of the possible 2048.

ATCRBS interrogations and replies have no error detection or correction; not even the simplest parity. Therefore, more than one interrogation is typically received by an aircraft as the interrogator antenna beam sweeps past the aircraft and replies are compared. If the majority of replies are the same, that reply is assumed to be correct. This is not spectrum efficient, but the system is more than 50 years old. Problems such as this prompted the development of a more efficient system.

There are other problems with ATCRBS secondary radar. One is garble, which occurs when two aircraft are the same distance from an interrogator antenna. The two transponder replies arrive at the interrogator at nearly the same time and mutually interfere. The aircraft may be well separated, for example, by several thousand feet of altitude, but still be at the same distance from the interrogator antenna. Another problem is the limited number of identity codes. There should be enough codes for every aircraft in the world.

Because of increasing air traffic the problems of ATCRBS were becoming severe. It was determined by the FAA that an improved system was essential. The new system would call transponders selectively so two aircraft in proximity would produce only one, correct reply. The data field was increased so every aircraft in the world could have a unique identity. The system is also capable of transmitting data other than identity and altitude. The system is called the mode S transponder, where S refers to "selective." It can selectively address single transponders. Other aircraft in the vicinity will not reply.

5.7 Mode S System

Mode S was developed to reduce garble and enhance air traffic control radar. Because the system is being phased in over years, it meets these requirements during the transition:

1. Selectively interrogate transponders.
2. Provide altitude and identity data to the interrogator.
3. ATCRBS interrogators must operate with mode S transponders without modification to ATCRBS interrogators.
4. Must interrogate ATCRBS transponders.
5. Cause a transponder to reply with its identity when identity is not known.
6. Provide additional data other than altitude and identity.
7. More spectrum-efficient than ATCRBS.

Item 1, selective address, is the basic requirement of the mode S system. Item 2 will insure the mode S system is, at least, as good as ATCRBS. Item 3 is required because the mode S system will be phased in, which implies that during the transition both ATCRBS and mode S interrogators are present. The mode S transponder must reply to an ATCRBS interrogation as if it were an ATCRBS transponder.

In Item 5, a transponder cannot be selectively interrogated if the address of the transponder is not known. There must be a way of determining the address of a transponder before it is selectively interrogated.

Item 6 insures that mode S can be used in more advanced surveillance systems, including collision avoidance.

The last item, 7, insures that mode S does not cause the amount of interference on transponder frequencies experienced with ATCRBS.

5.8 Mode S Interrogations

Divided into two categories, mode S interrogations are selective and non-selective. The non-selective are the simplest and include familiar techniques. Figure 5.4 shows the 6 non-selective interrogations. The interrogations are pulse amplitude modulation because the ATCRBS transponder must react to these interrogations. The first two non-selective interrogations, in Fig. 5.4 a and b, show the normal ATCRBS A and C interrogations, and are not mode S interrogations.

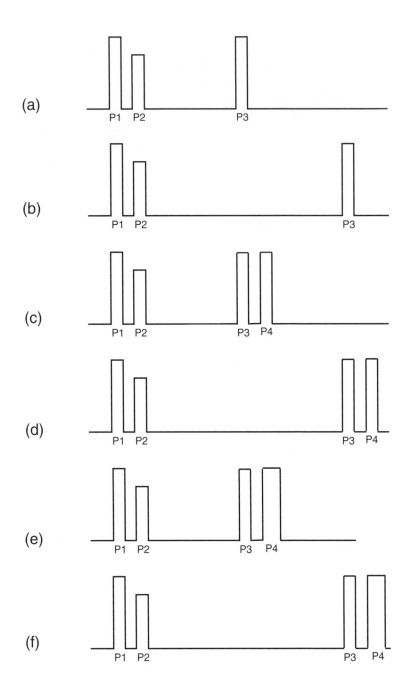

Figure 5.4 Mode S non-selective interrogations

The mode S transponder responds to these interrogations as if it were an ATCRBS transponder. This insures that the transponder is compatible with ATCRBS .

Figure 5.4c and d show two mode S interrogations; the ATCRBS-only, A and C all calls. An "all call" implies that all mode S transponders reply. What about the ATCRBS transponder? The interrogation is almost a standard ATCRBS interrogation except there is an extra pulse, P4. ATCRBS transponders are required to reply 3 μs from receipt of the rising edge of a valid interrogation. This means the ATCRBS transponder is transmitting most of the time P4 is being received. When an ATCRBS transponder receives a valid interrogation, it no longer receives until 50 μs from the rising edge of P3 of the valid interrogation. Thus, the ATCRBS transponder replies normally to the ATCRBS/mode S all call with either a mode A or mode C reply, depending on the interrogation.

182

The mode S transponder, on the other hand, replies after a much longer delay time, 128 μs, measured from the half amplitude point of P3 to the first pulse of the reply and is capable of receiving the P4 pulse, which follows 2 μs after P3. The ATCRBS/mode S all call results in a reply from the mode S transponder. The reply, however is a mode S reply, which includes the address of the mode S transponder. Therefore, the ATCRBS/mode S all call is a mode S interrogation because the mode S transponder replies with a mode S reply. The mode S transponder, seeing P4, recognizes the interrogation as mode S . If there were no P4, the mode S transponder would produce an ATCRBS reply.

The fifth and sixth non-selective interrogations, shown in Fig 5.4 e and f, are ATCRBS /mode S A and C all calls. As explained, the ATCRBS transponder does not receive P4 and replies with a mode A or C transmission depending on the interrogation. The mode S transponder knows the interrogation is not an ATCRBS interrogation due the existence of P4, and by measuring the width of P4, finds the wider 1.6 μs pulse and will reply with mode S.

The second broad category is selective interrogation, which requires the address of the transponder to reply. It is enlightening to understand how selective and all call interrogations are used in the mode S system. Assume a new mode S system is turned on for the first time. Air traffic control radar operates around the clock and a cold start is uncommon. The cold start, however, shows how mode S uses all interrogations.

The mission of the mode S interrogator at turn on is to locate and identify all aircraft within range. Some transponders are ATCRBS, while the remainder are mode S. If the mode S interrogator transmits ATCRBS mode A and C interrogations, all transponders, mode S and ATCRBS, reply. If there is no garbling, it locates and identifies all aircraft within range. In this case, the identity is the ATCRBS squawk and not the mode S address for aircraft equipped with mode S transponders.

Mode S identity is obtained by transmitting an ATCRBS/mode S all call. For this interrogation, mode S transponders reply with their address. At this point, the interrogator has located all aircraft in the coverage area, with altitude information, and knows which are ATCRBS and which are mode S. The mode S address of each aircraft is also known. Having this information, future interrogations of mode S transponders may be made with mode S selective interrogation. The ATCRBS only all call may interrogate ATCRBS transponders, which results in only ATCRBS transponders replying. This reduces the amount of transmission on transponder frequencies.

Assume there is garbling from several transponders when the mode S interrogator is turned on from a cold start. If the sequence of interrogations is the same, starting with ATCRBS mode A and C, both interrogations result in a garbled reply.

The second interrogation in the sequence was the ATCRBS/mode S all call. This results in two garbling transponders; the ATCRBS transponder with an ATCRBS reply and the mode S transponder with a mode S reply. The delay from receipt of an interrogation to transmission of the reply from an ATCRBS transponder is 3 μs and 128 μs for the mode S. Because of this, the two transponders that garbled on the ATCRBS interrogation will not garble on the mode S all call.

What if two transponders garble on a mode S all call interrogation, where one transponder is mode S and the other ATCRBS? These transponders will not garble on an ATCRBS interrogation and, therefore, the ATCRBS mode may be used until the two aircraft separate. This garble scenario is for a cold start situation. If two aircraft, one mode S and the second

ATCRBS, move into a garble situation after they are identified, the mode S transponder is selectively addressed, which prevents the ATCRBS transponder from replying. On the other hand, an ATCRBS only all call can be used in place of the ATCRBS interrogation and the mode S transponder will not reply. Thus, garbling is prevented in this situation.

Once the mode S interrogator has been operating a while, the procedure is different. Rather than having to identify all aircraft in the coverage area, ground radar must keep track of aircraft entering and leaving. All mode S aircraft are listed on a "roll call" and selectively interrogated. These aircraft are tracked and, when an aircraft leaves, it is removed from the list. ATCRBS aircraft can be interrogated with normal ATCRBS interrogations but every so often a series of mode S all calls are transmitted to be sure that a mode S equipped aircraft did not slip into the coverage area without being identified.

The secondary radar interrogator performs various other signal processing such as a moving target indicator to eliminate returns from stationary objects such as clouds or buildings. There are also undesired returns in the secondary radar system called fruit. The term, from the IFF system, stands for Friendly Replies Unsynchronized In Time. The replies are from friendly transponders but to another interrogator. The repetition rate of interrogators is deliberately different so two ground interrogators can never synchronize. This is similar to what was done in DME where interrogations were random in nature. Secondary radars, since they are at fixed locations, may be assigned specific repetition rates, whereas the airborne DME interrogator can be anywhere and a random interrogation sequence is required.

Removing fruit is the job of the "defruiter," which operates the same as would DME, separating the desired reply from squitter. It is known that the range of a transponder will not change by a large amount from one interrogation to the next. There is a time window in which the reply from a specific transponder will arrive. Occasional fruit appears in the time window but is highly unlikely after the next interrogation. Unlike DME, this tracking must be carried out, not just for one ground transponder but as many as 100 aircraft. Defruiting is the same; the secondary radar must repeat the process a number of times.

5.9 Mode S Selective Call

The ability to elicit a reply from only one aircraft is accomplished by selective call in the mode S system. A selective interrogation consists of two short pulses followed by a long pulse. The two short pulses are simple pulse amplitude modulation which silence ATCRBS transponders. The long pulse, which is P6, contains the DPSK modulation of the selective interrogation. Notice the two pulses are separated by 2 µs and are the same amplitude. These pulses appear as a side lobe interrogation to an ATCRBS transponder, which ignores the interrogation.

The long pulse, shown in Fig. 5.5, contains phase shift modulation, which is the selective interrogation. The modulation for selective interrogation is differential phase shift keying or DPSK.

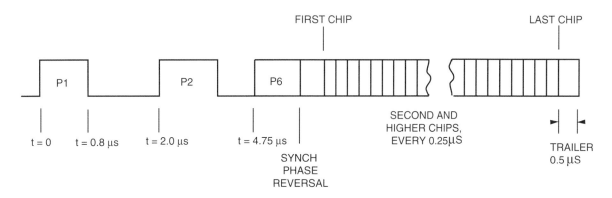

FIRST CHIP
LAST CHIP

P1   P2   P6

t = 0   t = 0.8 μs   t = 2.0 μs   t = 4.75 μs

SYNCH
PHASE
REVERSAL

SECOND AND
HIGHER CHIPS,
EVERY 0.25μS

TRAILER
0.5 μS

Fig. 5.5 Selective mode S interrogation

To transmit DPSK, each bit has a 250 ns time slot. The phase of the RF carrier within the time slot determines if a logic one or zero is transmitted. A phase comparison is made with the phase of the previous time slot. In normal phase shift keying or PSK, a phase reference determines logic ones or zeros. The phase reference must be derived from the transmitted signal and remain steady during the transmission. It is not difficult to make a steady phase reference for the time of the mode S transmission. What makes conventional PSK difficult in a moving platform such as an aircraft is the change of phase due to aircraft movement.

Example: An aircraft is flying 250 knots directly towards a mode S interrogator. How much phase shift would occur on a 1030 MHz carrier in 250 ns due to motion of the aircraft?

Solution: First convert the 250 kts which is 250 NM per hour to meters per second or 128.6 m/s. In 250 ns the aircraft has moved 3.215E-5 meters.

The wavelength of a 1030 MHz carrier is 0.29 meters. Therefore, the aircraft has moved 1.11E-4 wavelengths or 0.04 degrees.

Example: If a mode S interrogation is transmitted with PSK, the phase reference would have to be held for the entire mode S message. The long interrogation is 30 μs in length. How much would the phase reference drift for an aircraft with a velocity, in the direction of the interrogator, of 550 kts?

Solution: Next, the problem is changed from DPSK to PSK and increased airspeed to 550 kts (a common cruise for jet transports). The velocity, 550 kts is 283 meters per second. As in the previous example, wavelength is 0.29 meters. The aircraft moves 8.5 mm in 30 μs, the time of the transmission, which is 0.03 wavelengths or 10.5 degrees.

What is the effect of Doppler shift? This drift in reference can be corrected by changing the frequency of the reference to compensate for Doppler shift. These techniques are used in some systems. However, when acceleration is present these techniques become difficult.

5.10 Checking for Errors

ATCRBS has no error detection or correction. The only method to insure that a reply is correctly received is the interrogator transmits numerous times for each antenna pass and compares the received replies. If replies are the same, the reply may be assumed to have been received correctly. But how many replies are sufficient to declare an error-free reply? Would ten or a hundred be sufficient? Ten or more replies would not be unusual for an ATCRBS transponder to provide for a single antenna pass. With effective error detection one reply would be sufficient. The amount of time a transponder transmits can be reduced by a factor of more than ten when error detection is used. The error detection scheme for mode S is called a cyclic redundancy check, or CRC. This treats a digital message as a number and performs mathematical manipulations, adding check bits before transmitting data.

The mathematics involve division but it is not the quotient that is important but the remainder. To understand this technique, assume a message represented by the decimal number 253. Exactly how the message was reduced to a simple number is not important at this time. The number 253 should be reliably transmitted to the receiving end and reliably mapped back to the original message. We choose a number that divides into 253 and append the remainder to the number. Let us choose 8 as the divisor. Thus 253 divided by 8 is 31 with a remainder of 5. We now *append*, not add, the remainder, 5, to the number to get 2535. The numbers 2, 5, and 3 represent data and the last 5 represent the error check digit. Since the divisor is 8, the remainder can never be greater than 7 and only one digit is required to add the check bits.

At the receiving end, the first three digits are divided by the same factor 8 and the remainder compared to the last digit. If the remainder is the same, it is highly likely the message was received without error. The term ”highly likely” is used in this context because it is possible to have errors that go undetected. Assume the number with the check bits is received with an error. The number was received as 2435 rather than 2535. Dividing 243 by 8 yields 30 with a remainder of 3, which is not the same as 5 and the error is detected.

Why choose 8 as the divisor? Try, for example, 10. We can still append only one digit for the check because division by 10 produces remainders up to 9. Consider the same example of a corrupted transmission. The data word is 253 which, divided by 10, produces a remainder of 3. This results in the transmitted data plus error check of 2533. Next, see what happens if the same digit is corrupted, i.e. 2433 is received rather than 2533. The number 253 when divided by 10 yields a remainder of 3 which matches the check digit. Notice that any error in the first two digits will not be detected! It is clear that using 10 as the divisor is a bad idea. The number used in the example was a decade number, which implies that each digit has a weighting of ten times the previous digit. This is why a generating polynomial which is a multiple of ten is not a good choice. For binary numbers, generating polynomials that are multiples of 2 are poor choices.

Now apply the same techniques to binary numbers. A binary message representing letters, numbers, signs, altitudes, etc., is a series of ones and zeros. It easy to imagine this series as a number on which mathematical operations can be performed. The message is divided with a binary number called a generating polynomial because it generates error detection bits. A unique division is employed called modulo two. This is division that does not use carries or borrows. As an example, use a generating polynomial of 1 0 1 0 1 and a data number of 1 1 0 1 1 1 0 1 0 1 1 0.

Divide the data number by the generating polynomial:

```
                       1 1 1 0 1 0 0 1
      1 0 1 0 1 ) 1 1 0 1 1 1 0 1 0 1 1 0
                 1 0 1 0 1
                   1 1 1 0 1
                   1 0 1 0 1
                     1 0 0 0 0
                     1 0 1 0 1
                       0 1 0 1 1
                       0 0 0 0 0
                         1 0 1 1 0
                         1 0 1 0 1
                           0 0 1 1 1
                           0 0 0 0 0
                             0 1 1 1 1
                             0 0 0 0 0
                               1 1 1 1 0
                               1 0 1 0 1
      Remainder               1 0 1 1
```

In this example there are a 12 bit data word and a 5 bit generating polynomial. The remainder is 5 bits, but the first bit is always zero. Thus, there are 4 remainder bits. The remainder has a length of one less bit than the generating polynomial.

Let us consider how, using logic elements, we can actually perform this division. First, when a bit of the data word is a one, the generating polynomial is exclusive ORed with the first five bits of the data number. This can most easily be done serially, which is one bit at a time. If the second bit of the data word is a one, the result of the first exclusive ORing is exORed with the generating polynomial plus the next bit in the data word,

If a logic zero is encountered the result of the last exclusive ORing plus the next data bit is exclusive ORed with zero. The result of exclusive ORing a number with zero is to do nothing! If we consider the process it involves shifting and exclusive ORing. This very similar to the creation of maximal length codes for PRN generation using shift registers with linear feedback. This is no accident; there are connections to maximal length sequences and error detection.

The remainder bits are for error detection and combined with data bits in some way. The quotient is not used for any purpose. One method, in the previous example, uses decimal numbers to append the error check bits. Another method is to interleave the bits. Interleaving is more effective since the detection bits are scattered throughout the data word, so any noise is equally likely to corrupt data or correction bits. This is the method used for mode S. For the sake of simplicity in this example, detection bits are appended to the data bits:

1 1 0 1 1 1 0 1 0 1 1 0 1 0 1 1

As a demonstration, one bit, the center data bit, is changed as shown below:

1 1 0 1 1 1 0 1 1 1 1 0 1 0 1 1

Divide the corrupted word using the same generating polynomial and compare the remainder to the error check bits:

```
              1 1 1 0 1 0 0 1
1 0 1 0 1)1 1 0 1 1 1 0 1 0 1 1 0        CRC check bits  1 0 1 1
       1 0 1 0 1
         1 1 1 0 1
         1 0 1 0 1
           1 0 0 0 0
           1 0 1 0 1
             0 1 0 1 1
             0 0 0 0 0
               1 0 1 1 1
               1 0 1 0 1
                 0 0 1 0 1
                 0 0 0 0 0
                   0 1 0 10
                   0 0 0 0 0
  Remainder          1 0 1 0
```

This remainder does not match the 1 0 1 1 appended to the data and this error has been detected.

What would happen if noise not only affects the middle data bit but changes the error check bits so the sequence becomes 1 011? The error detection would miss this error and pass the data as valid.

The combination of 12 data bits and 4 check bits has $2^{16} = 65,536$ different combinations of which only one is correct. No CRC error detection can detect all 65,535 incorrect combinations, but some generating polynomials are better than others. We saw how poor the choice of 10 was in the decimal example. The ability of generating polynomials to find errors has been well researched and those with the best characteristics are used in the mode S system.

The last 24 bits of all mode-S selective transmissions are a combination of parity bits and address bits or the AP field. For an interrogation, the combination of interrogator identification and parity is called the PI field.

The generating polynomial for all mode S transmissions is:

$$G(x) = \sum_{I=0}^{24} g_i xI \qquad (5.8)$$

Where $g_i = 0$ for i = 1, 2, 4, 5, 6, 7, 8, 9, and 11 and 1 for all others.

The first 32 bits of a 56 bit reply and the first 88 bits of a 112 bit reply are divided by the generating polynomial G(x). The remainder, R(x) which is 24 bits, assuming leading zeros are counted produces the bit sequence which are the parity bits, b_i.

The sequence of bits in the AP or PI field, the last 24 bits of a mode-S selective transmission is given as:

$$t_{k+1}, t_{k+2}, t_{k+3} \cdots\cdots t_{k+24}$$

where k = 32 for the short reply and 88 for the long reply. For replies and squitters transmitted from the mode-S transponder

$$t_{k+i} = a_i (+) p_i \qquad (5.9)$$

where (+) indicates modulo two addition or the exclusive OR function, a_i are the bits of the mode-S address and p_i are the bits of the parity sequence taken from R(x).

For interrogations

$$t_{k+i} = b_i (+) p_i \qquad (5.10)$$

where b_i is the coefficient of the x^{i-1} coefficient of the polynomial:

$$H(x)A(x) \qquad (5.11)$$

where: (5.12)

$$H(x) = \sum_{i=0}^{24} g_i x^{24-1}$$

Notice that H(x) is the generating polynomial in reverse. These techniques overlay the CRC checking bits with the address bits rather than adding 24 additional bits to the mode-S interrogations and replies.

The effectiveness of mode S CRC checking is only one error in 10^7 is missed. This applies to both up link and down link. Consequently, only one correctly received transmission followed by one reply is required from the mode S transponder. The possibility of the exchange having an error is only 2 in ten million.

5.11 Mode S Replies

During development, there was much discussion of modulation for mode S replies. Conventional wisdom suggests that replies be the same modulation used for interrogations. Pulse amplitude and DPSK were employed for uplink interrogations. Pulse amplitude modulation was used only because mode S had to operate with ATCRBS transponders. Selective interrogations used DPSK and it would appear that DPSK modulation would be the obvious choice for selective replies. As it turned out, DPSK is not used. In order to understand the reason, consider the advantages and disadvantages of pulse amplitude modulation and DPSK.

Pulse amplitude modulation is simple; the transmitter carrier is turned on and off. It was the first modulation used when Morse code was sent with a hand key. There are, however, disadvantages. The first is that pulse amplitude modulation is not spectrum efficient. Suddenly turning a carrier on and off creates wide sidebands and a broad signal. The spectrum is reduced by increasing the time to turn the carrier on and off. This works but some simplicity is lost. Another problem is that when a logic zero is sent, there is no transmitter output power; no signal is the same as a logic zero. This makes the system vulnerable to noise. If signal was present it could help "cover up" noise.

For phase modulation, a carrier is present at all times, which reduces noise. The carrier is turned on at the beginning of the transmission and remains on until the end. Although phase modulation produces sidebands, they are not as broad as those obtained when a carrier is pulsed on and off. It would appear that phase shift modulation is the obvious choice for selective replies, but it was not selected. In spite of the benefits, phase modulation has disadvantages. It is not as easily implemented as pulse amplitude modulation.

The first transponder designed during the Second World War for IFF was a single vacuum tube oscillator using a cavity resonator. Vacuum tubes were developed to fit into "plumbing" of the resonant cavity. These transmitters were large power oscillators that could produce hundreds of watts. Although special tubes were expensive, only one was required for the transponder transmitter. This simple transmitter has problems. First, frequency stability of plumbing for the cavity requires that the system cope with transmitters off by more than a MHz. Secondly, transmitter frequency drifts long term as the transmitter warms up and short term during the pulse. Third, since an oscillator is connected directly to an antenna, its frequency is affected by objects near the antenna. Frequency had to be adjusted when the transponder was mounted in the aircraft, as each installation was different. Moreover, if the antenna is near, say, a landing gear, the frequency of the transponder could change from gear up to gear down. In spite of the problems, a single vacuum tube transponder transmitter was used for many years, and continues in inexpensive transponders to this day.

One solution to frequency pulling is an oscillator followed by an amplifier. The amplifier provides isolation from the antenna and reduces the effect of the antenna. Even more improvement is obtained by several stages of amplifier. The oscillator operates continuously and the pulse is applied by providing power to the amplifiers.

The ultimate in a pulse amplitude modulated transmitter is crystal control for the carrier frequency and modulated amplifiers to feed the antenna. This has the stability of a crystal oscillator, both long and short term, and is virtually immune to antenna impedance. This technique is used for high-performance transponders in modern military and air transport aircraft.

For phase modulation, a simple cavity oscillator is unacceptable as are cavity oscillators with amplifiers. Phase modulation requires a crystal controlled carrier generator. The most advanced transmitter for pulse amplitude modulation is the starting point. With a few exceptions, linear amplifiers are required for amplifying phase modulated signals, which further increases complexity and cost.

When mode S was being developed, the intention was for all aircraft to be mode S equipped in a few years. It was decided that phase modulation for the reply would raise the cost of the transponder beyond the means of small aircraft owners. Therefore, pulse amplitude modulation was specified for mode S replies.

The type chosen is Manchester modulation, which is superior to "pulse/no pulse" modulation for ATCRBS. Manchester modulation uses time slots, as do many pulse systems. Each time slot represents one transmitted bit of information. There is always a pulse in half the time slot as shown in Fig. 5.6. If a logic one is transmitted, the pulse is in the first half of the time slot; if a logic zero is transmitted, the pulse is in the second half.

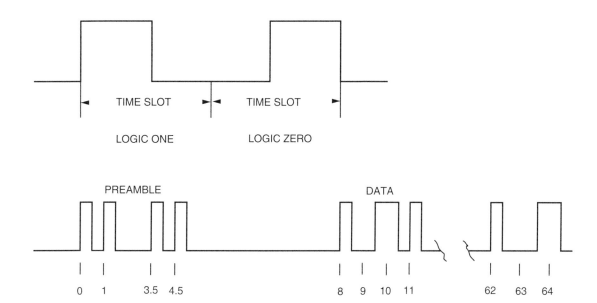

Fig. 5.6 Manchester coding

Replies are 56 data bits for the short reply and 112 data bits for the long reply, or an extended length message, ELM. In addition to data bits, which include CRC check bits, 4 pulses are for the preamble. Be careful of the nomenclature in this description; there are 56 or 112 *data bits* and four additional *pulses*.

The preamble consists of four pulses of the same width as the data pulse but violates the rules of Manchester coding. The first two pulses of the reply could be two ones or zeroes because the timing reference has not been established early in the data transmission. It is, in fact, the job of the preamble to establish the time reference. Between second and third preamble pulses, there is a gap of 1 μs with no pulse. This is a violation of Manchester encoding. Every time slot, each 1 ms for the mode S reply, must have a 0.5 μs pulse in the period. There is a missing pulse. This characteristic sets the preamble apart from the four data bits.

There are advantages of Manchester pulse amplitude modulation over pulse/no-pulse modulation for ATCRBS. First, a pulse is always transmitted in a time slot, regardless of whether the data is logic one or zero. This reduces vulnerability to noise. Secondly, the same energy is in each transmitted message. This aids in controlling gain of a receiver or power supply of the transmitter. Finally, there is a transition from pulse on or pulse off in the center of each time slot. This helps in timing the received data because the transition is a marker for the center of the time slot.

Although not as good as phase modulation, Manchester is far superior to the ATCRBS reply and permits an inexpensive transmitter for airborne transponders. Mode S specifications even provide a vacuum tube transmitter for low altitude use. At the time of this writing, no mode S transponder has a vacuum tube transmitter.

5.12 Diversity

This is an old technique to improve radio communications during difficult situations. The two most common diversity techniques are frequency and spatial diversity. Frequency diversity is primarily for high frequency communications where signal fading is common. When a signal fades due to atmospheric conditions, it is common that at another frequency, the signal has not faded. To reduce fading, two operating frequencies are used and the better signal selected. Space diversity uses two antennas. If a signal fades at 1000 MHz it is not usually due to atmospheric conditions but shadowing caused by changes in aircraft attitude. In this case, another antenna position may improve the signal.

The mode S transponder is also part of the TCAS collision avoidance system, where aircraft interrogate other aircraft. When a transponder is interrogated only from the ground a belly mounted antenna is effective. When the transponder is interrogated from above or below two antennas, top and bottom, are superior.

Two complete receivers are required for diversity. Connecting two antennas to the same receiver would appear to be a simple solution, but go back to the localizer antenna. A narrow beam was created by feeding two broad-beamed antennas with the correct phase angle. This was because signals add as vectors in space. If the outputs of a top and bottom omnidirectional antenna are simply summed, an antenna is created with directions of enhanced response and directions with no response. There is no response, for example, where two signals arrive at the summation exactly out of phase. With completely independent receivers, there is no opportunity for signals to add or subtract; there are independent antenna patterns.

Next is to determine which receiver provides the best signal. Strength could be used, except strong signals are not always good, particularly when corrupted with multipath. Since the mode S transmission has powerful error detection, it does not matter which receiver output is used, so long as the error check is functioning.

The diversity system is used for transmitting, too. Here it makes sense to transmit the reply to an interrogation through the antenna that produces the strongest interrogation. The process of deciding which antenna to use is called voting. A voter circuit applies criteria, including those just discussed and decides which receiver output to use and the antenna to transmit the reply

5.13 ATCRBS Transponder

The typical ATCRBS transponder is shown in Fig. 5.7. It is a vacuum tube transponder which represents the majority of transponders in use. Solid state transponders are found in air transport and larger corporate aircraft.

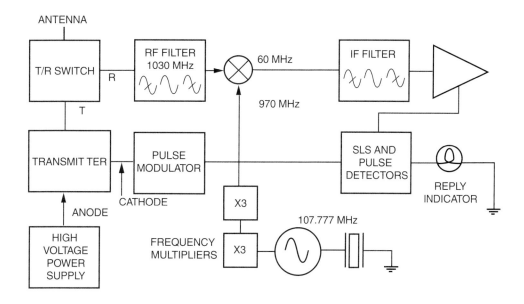

Figure 5.7 ATCRBS transponder

The transponder uses a superheterodyne receiver with single conversion. Historically, a 60 MHz IF was used so the transmitter frequency source could also drive the receiver local oscillator. If sharing is not designed into the transponder, there is no advantage to the 60 MHz IF. Most transponders, however, use 60 MHz for the IF.

The transponder contains a logarithmic receiver. An airborne transponder receives signals from ground interrogators, often by several radar sites at one time. Also, the collision avoidance system, TCAS, interrogates the ATCRBS transponder. Thus, the transponder must receive a large number of interrogations at a variety of signal levels. These interrogations occur close in time or with significant delay between interrogations. It is not be possible to design a receiver with an AGC sufficiently fast to catch each interrogation. To handle the dynamic range the received signals are compressed with a logarithmic IF, or log IF. In this circuit output is proportional to the log of the amplitude of the input signal. If a CW signal is applied, the amplitude of the input is a constant and thus output is a constant. The output has no frequency, only an envelope. If the input is a pulsed RF carrier, the output is a pulse. This output is called detected log video or DLV. An example is shown in Fig. 5.8. The scale factor for this logarithmic IF system is 0.1 volt per decibel. The noise level of this log IF is –90 dBm, with a dynamic range of 80 dB. With no signal input, output is one volt and increases to 9 volts at the maximum input signal of –10 dBm. This log IF is typically used in a transponder.

In addition to handling a wide range of transponder receiver signals, the log IF eases implementation of the transponder. The transponder receiver has a defined sensitivity. For most receivers, and we are referring to any type of receiver, sensitivity is a characteristic that improves performance and sells products. In the case of the transponder, the receiver may not be more sensitive than necessary. Nominal sensitivity of a transponder is –72 dBm at the input connector, which is called the minimum trigger level, or MTL. (There are small variations of this sensitivity but for this discussion assume an MTL of –72 dBm.)

193

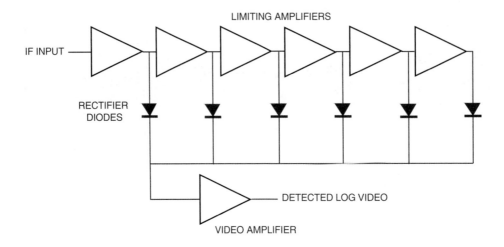

Figure 5.8 Log IF amplifier

Without AGC, DLV pulses from the log IF are proportional to signal strength in dBm. Therefore, to set sensitivity of the transponder, a comparator is supplied, as shown in Fig 5.9. An adjustment allows only input pulses greater than –72 dBm at the antenna input to trigger the comparator.

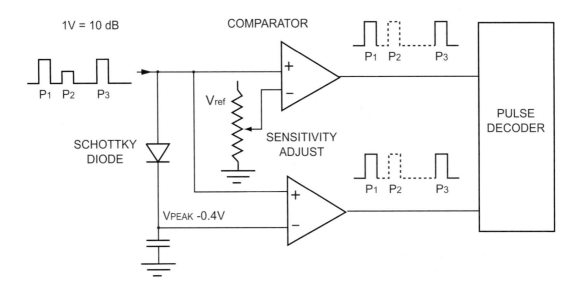

Figure 5.9 Setting transponder sensitivity

The log IF also eases detection of an SLS (side lobe suppression) interrogation. The requirement for a side lobe interrogation is if P1 and P2 are the same amplitude; the transponder must not reply. If P2 is 9 dB below P1, the transponder must reply. Between equal and –9 dB is the "gray area," where the transponder may legally reply or not reply. As a design goal, the crossover between detecting and not detecting a side lobe interrogation is between -4 and –6 dB. For this discussion –4 dB is the criterion.

The scale factor of one volt per ten decibels for this example is convenient. The forward voltage drop of a Schottky diode is about 0.4 volts, the equivalent of a 4 dB difference in

194

signal level. The Schottky diode charges a capacitor, which implies that voltage across the capacitor in Fig. 5.9 is equivalent to an output voltage from a pulse that is 4 dB down from the pulse that charged the capacitor. If P1 charges the capacitor, and capacitor voltage is a reference for a second comparator, only pulses greater than –4 dB from the first pulse cause the comparator to change state. Therefore, we have an SLS detector.

The upper comparator in Fig. 5.9 changes state for any pulse greater than the MTL (minimum triggering level) which, in most cases, is P1 and P3. When the SLS pulse is greater than the MTL it, too, provides an output pulse from the comparator. The fact that P2 provides an output does not matter. It is important to have an output from the lower comparator 2ms after P1. This constitutes a side lobe interrogation.

Generally, a transponder continually receives pulses. Any two that are 8 μs apart constitute a mode A interrogation and two pulses 21 μs apart are a mode C interrogation. This assumes there is no SLS pulse greater than the SLS threshold.

As soon as an interrogation or SLS pair is received, the transponder is "suppressed," meaning it no longer receives pulses. If an interrogation is received, the transponder selects data from the squawk switches or the encoding altimeter and initiates a reply. If an SLS pair is received, the transponder continues not to receive and does not transmit a reply for 25 to 45 μs from the receipt of P2.

There are methods for decoding a valid interrogation. An early approach using a shift register and AND gate as shown in Fig 5.10. Improved methods with gate array logic are used in modern transponders.

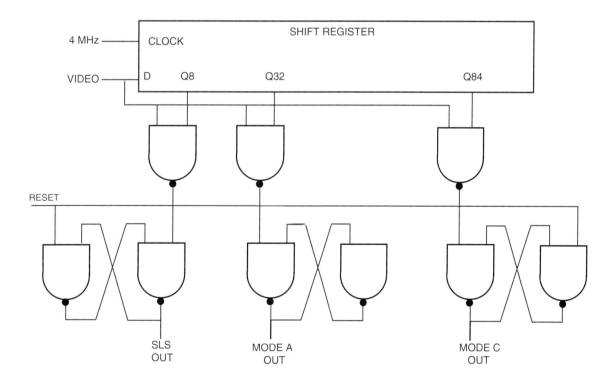

Figure 5.10 Example of decoding interrogations

195

One important parameter is the delay from when an interrogation is received and the reply is transmitted. Called the delay time, it is 3 μs plus or minus 0.5 μs. The reply rate *jitter*, that is, rapid variation in reply delay time cannot exceed 0.1 μs.

If a shift register decodes ATCRBS interrogations, a 10 MHz clock causes a 0.1μs jitter because of clock uncertainty. Other parts of the transponder cause jitter and the clock for decoding must operate at 20 MHz or higher. Programmable logic is capable of providing clock rates at 20 to 50 MHz. Other methods of decoding interrogations include a counter to measure time between receipt of pulses. As in the shift register, the clock must operate greater than 20 MHz.

To generate transmit pulses, again a shift register may be used. All transmitted pulses are multiples of 1.45 μs, equivalent to a 689.7 kHz clock. Only a synchronized 689.7 kHz clock may clock the transmit shift register due to the jitter requirement. This means the clock must be controlled so the first cycle starts within 0.1 μs of receipt of the valid interrogation. One solution is a 40 MHz clock for the decoder shift register and divide that by 58 to derive the 1.45 μs clock for the transmit shift register. In this fashion the entire delay jitter due to digital clocking is only plus or minus 50 ns. Modern microprocessors could decode received signals but would result in the processor being tied to decoding signals. Even with a fast processor, a hardware decoder is preferred, now done with a programmable chip.

The same antenna receives and transmits transponder signals. A transmit/receive switch changes the antenna from receiver to transmitter when a reply is sent. In the discussion of the DME interrogator, a T/R switch was described. For solid state transponders the techniques are the same. The T/R switch for the transponder is slightly easier to design because there is only one transmitting and receiving frequency.

The RF filter in transponders for many years was an interdigital type, having the characteristic of low impedance at its center frequency. These filters are constructed with rods of brass or copper and plated with silver to increase circuit Q. Supported in air, the rods are capable of high Q. Newer, usually solid state, transponders employ microstrip RF filters. Although they eliminate the image frequency for the transponder receiver, these printed filters do not have the extremely high Q of older interdigital filters.

The cavity transmitter also has a high Q cavity. The impedance of the transmitter cavity, like the interdigital filter, is very low off the resonant frequency. There was, essentially, no T/R switch on the vacuum tube cavity transponder. Antenna sharing was done with transmission lines, as shown in Fig. 5.11.

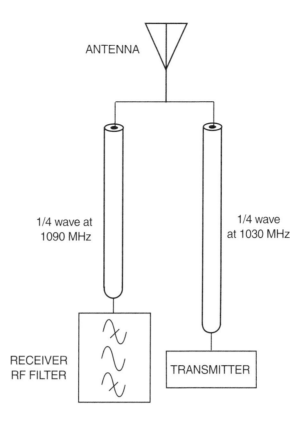

Figure 5.11 Transmission line T/R switch

From the figure, it can be seen that transmitter and receiver are simply tied together. The technique is in the length of transmission line which is, for the transmitter, a quarter wavelength at the receiver frequency, 1030 MHz. The transmission line leading to the receiver is a quarter wavelength at the transmitting frequency, 1090 MHz.

When a short is applied to a transmission line that is a quarter wavelength at a particular frequency, the short is converted to an open circuit at the other end of the line. Consider the cavity transmitter; at the 1030 MHz receiver frequency impedance is low. Since the transmission line is a quarter wavelength, reflected impedance is high. Thus, the transmitter causes no significant loss to the received signal if the two transmission lines are paralleled.

What about transmitter energy? The receiver interdigital filter has a low impedance at 1090 MHz transmitter frequency. The transmission line is a quarter wavelength at the 1090 MHz and, therefore, a high impedance is reflected at the end of the transmission line. This high impedance does not load the transmitter and provides very low loss.

Some energy from the transmitter enters the interdigital filter. Even a small amount could damage the sensitive receiver but the high Q of the interdigital filter reduces the energy to a safe level.

5.14 Mode S Transponder

There are similarities between mode S and ATCRBS transponders, primarily because the mode S transponder replies to ATCRBS interrogations as if it were an ATCRBS transponder. The major difference is the two receivers in the mode S transponder for diversity. (Mode S transponders for small aircraft do not use diversity and will not have two receivers.) Other differences include a transmitter controlled by a quartz crystal or ceramic resonator.

A mode s transponder block diagram is shown in Fig. 5.12. The transponder contains two receivers which share the local oscillator. Output of the receivers feeds a voter circuit which determines which of two received signals is superior. The TR switch routes the transmitter to the desired antenna while protecting the receivers from excessive transmitter power.

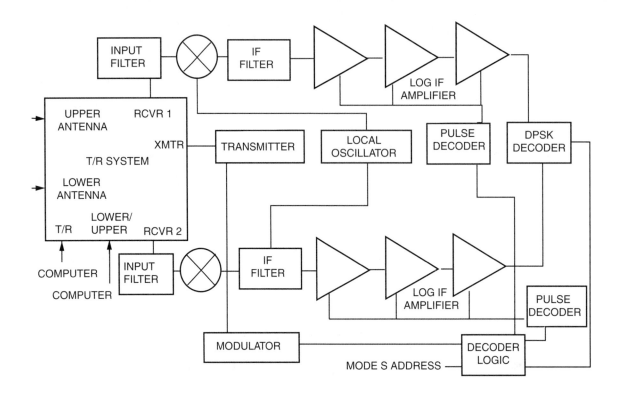

Fig 5.12 Mode S transponder

The transmitter in the figure uses a ceramic resonator oscillator, which is similar to a quartz crystal except for superior frequency stability. The advantage is that a ceramic resonator can operate at 1090 MHz.

A surface acoustic wave, SAW, resonator can also perform at 1090 MHz. The stability of the SAW resonator is better than a ceramic resonator but less than a quartz crystal. The SAW resonator cannot handle the power of a ceramic resonator. This means the oscillator must provide a lower level signal, which requires more amplifiers.

Notice that the local oscillator for the receiver is not shared with the transmitter oscillator. If the transponder uses a 60 MHz IF, the 1090 MHz oscillator for the transmitter can be shared with the receiver as a local oscillator. There are two reasons why this is not done in this design. First, the receiver requires a quartz crystal local oscillator. This is because the receiver works on DPSK which requires a stable, accurate receiver. Secondly, it is important that the transponder not radiate energy at the transmitter frequency to prevent interference. It is difficult at 1000 MHz to prevent signals from escaping. If the receiver local oscillator is not at the transmitter frequency it is easier to reduce interference. Therefore, the transponder in Fig 5.12 has a separate receiver local oscillator at a frequency apart from the transmitter frequency.

The DPSK demodulator uses a delay line of 250 ns. The most effective technique is a SAW delay line or bulk acoustic wave, BAW, delay line. To demodulate DPSK, the IF signal after amplification is delayed by one bit time and multiplied by the undelayed signal, as shown in Fig. 5.13.

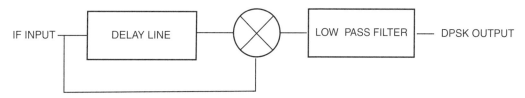

Figure 5.13 DPSK demodulator

When the delayed signal is multiplied by the undelayed signal the current bit is multiplied by the previous bit. Since DPSK is being demodulated, the phase of the previous bit is exactly the same or exactly out of phase with the current bit. If an IF is selected that has an integer number of cycles in 250 ns, the time delay, there is no phase shift by the delay line. One common IF is 60 MHz, which has exactly 15 cycles in 250 ns and qualifies as a suitable IF.

5.15 Collision Avoidance

Midair collisions are rare but when they occur, damage and loss of life are great. Electronic means to prevent them have been sought for many years. Interest in collision avoidance would rise and fall. If there were a mid-air crash there would be a call for a collision avoidance system. After a collision-free period, funding and interest in a system would wane. A June 1956 midair collision of a Lockheed L-049 Super Constellation and a United Airlines Douglas DC-7 over the Grand Canyon was the first of a series. In April 1958 there was a collision of another DC-7 and an Air Force F-100 over Arden, New York. Then, in 1960, there was a collision of two aircraft flying under instrument flight rules on approach to Idlewild (now JFK) airport over New York City. This collision involved a Lockheed Super Constellation and a DC-8 jet. These collisions made clear several problems with flight in the late 1950s. The collisions involved aircraft under positive control. Some collisions were between jet-powered aircraft and propeller aircraft. Some collisions were en route while others were on approach. Both military and civilian aircraft were involved. A need for a midair collision avoidance was apparent.

One of the earliest systems was developed in the 1960s by Bendix and was called airborne collision avoidance system, or ACAS. In this system a parameter called tau, τ, was invented by Dr. John "Smiley" Morell, and was range divided by range rate. Dr. Morell's 1956 publication, "Fundamental Physics of the Aircraft Collision Problem" was one of the first scientific investigations into aircraft midair collisions.

The major problem with ACAS was that to be protected against midair collisions all aircraft had to be equipped with an ACAS system, and ACAS was very expensive.

Another system was called "eliminate range zeros," or ER0S, where the 0 is a zero. There was a quiet period of no significant midairs and this system was forgotten. Then in 1978 a midair collision between a Pacific Southwest Airlines Boeing 727 and a Cessna 172 took 135 lives over San Diego. Shortly thereafter FAA administrator, J. Lynn Helms mandated that a collision avoidance system would be developed and installed in air transport aircraft.

A system emerged based on airborne transponders. Called active BCAS, for Beacon Collision Avoidance System, the "beacon" was the transponder in ATCRBS. A new transponder called mode S was also in development and was intended to complement the collision avoidance system.

BCAS was already under development but like so many previous collision avoidance systems, was making only minor progress. Changes were made to the goals for BCAS, primarily involving the mode S transponder. The thrust was to make mode S provide communications for collision avoidance. The name was changed to TCAS, which stands for Traffic alert and Collision Avoidance System, pronounced "tee-kass".

TCAS determines a collision potential based on air-to-air interrogations and replies of aircraft through their transponders. The system evaluates threats by measuring their range, track, altitude and velocity. (In TCAS, velocity, or speed, is called range rate.) An airplane which is searching for possible collisions is called "own" aircraft, while other aircraft, the potential threats, are called "proximate" aircraft.

5.15.2 Collision Avoidance Concepts

During the development of TCAS, there was much discussion of who would be responsible for collision avoidance. Without TCAS, aircraft under positive control were in the hands of the air traffic controller. For the most part, air traffic controllers are FAA employees. The government enjoys a certain amount of immunity from litigation should a collision occur while aircraft are under air traffic control. There was much discussion of where collision avoidance should take place. One suggestion was to use existing radar data to provide alerts from a ground station. There were two main reasons for not choosing this route. First, several accidents that prompted the development of TCAS were between aircraft under air traffic control. The radar data were available and an air traffic controller could deliver an alert but did not. A ground-based system would simply be a remake of what was already in place. The other reason for not developing a ground-based collision avoidance system was that it would not function out of radar range. This would include oceanic and polar areas, as well as unpopulated areas such as Siberia, northern Canada and so on. The range of an air traffic control radar is about 200 NM. Huge areas of the earth not covered.

Airborne TCAS was the system of choice. There were interesting problems with the development of the airborne TCAS. First, no company wanted the responsibility of developing the software for TCAS. Although there was significant profit potential, the danger of law suits from an accident caused by a software fault was too great. Another problem; since each TCAS unit is a part of a system, it is extremely important that software for each unit is compatible with all other TCAS-equipped aircraft.

The solution to both problems was the development of "pseudo code," which are highly detailed algorithms that dictate how the computer code is written. The FAA contracted with independent organizations to write and test the code. Therefore, each manufacturer used government-mandated code. Any problems due to software were U.S. government problems and would shield manufacturer from debilitating lawsuits.

As it turned out, this concept will never be used again. There were so many problems associated with pseudo code, it caused more trouble than it avoided. First, pseudo code may not suit how a company does its software. The code did not necessarily suit certain processors or operating systems. The code was written in the late 1970s and may not be synergistic with modern microprocessors.

Another problem is that code is standardized for the entire industry. If a problem appears, and they have, changing the code to effect a fix involves changing an official document and distributing it to the industry; a time consuming maneuver. All the while, faulty software is being used.

5.15.3 CAS Logic

The software for determining when to issue an alert and the type of alert is called "collision avoidance system logic", or CAS logic. A key parameter is Dr. Morell's tau, or τ, which is range divided by range rate. Tau is a scalar, not a vector. Range divided by range rate produces time. Range and range rate are relative to data obtained from proximate aircraft using a secondary radar interrogator and transponders. Time is elapsed time from now until the proximate aircraft would collide with own aircraft if conditions remain the same. In practice, one aircraft will turn, level off, climb, etc., to avoid a collision. When tau becomes a low number, say a few seconds, there is little time for maneuvers and danger is imminent. Further, if tau is allowed to become very low, there is no time to take evasive action and the system would fail. An important part of TCAS is to avoid false alarms while producing an ample margin for evasive maneuvers.

The task of the TCAS computer is to track all aircraft that reply within its coverage area and continually calculate and monitor the value of tau. When tau falls below a threshold, typically 40 seconds (but varies for aircraft of different speeds and altitude), an alarm activates. The first warning is a traffic advisory, or TA, which alerts the crew to an uncomfortably close aircraft. The 40 second lead is approximately the time that would elapse before a collision. Once the nearby aircraft has a tau less than 40 seconds, it is called an "intruder". In most cases, the crew can visually spot an aircraft in 40 seconds and evade it. The intent of the threat advisory, TA, is to leave the choice up to the crew. The alarm is a voice announcement; "traffic, traffic, traffic". This was chosen rather than a bell or siren, because so many alarms already exist on the flight deck.

If the flight crew does not maneuver to increase tau, a second alarm threshold is set at about 25 seconds. This is a resolution advisory, or RA, and the evasive maneuver is announced as part of the alarm. As an example, if an aircraft has a tau that slips to 25 seconds, a resolution advisory could be; "climb, climb, climb". In this example, TCAS determined that a climb is the best evasive maneuver. The RA implies there is insufficient time to see the intruder aircraft, formulate an evasive maneuver and inform air traffic control. TCAS determines the evasive maneuver and communicates it to air traffic control and other aircraft via the mode S data link without pilot intervention.

TCAS developers realized that a false alarm is dangerous. A misleading TA (traffic advisory) is an annoyance as the crew searches for non-existent aircraft. The danger comes after a number of false alarms and the crew begins to ignore them. False RAs, resolution advisories, (which issue the wrong evasive maneuver) are extremely dangerous because they are acted on immediately without coordination from air traffic control. Traffic is positioned by controllers for safe separation and arrival and departure sequencing. Changing altitude without air traffic control coordination is a violation of the FARs. The crew is not in violation because it is acting on a TCAS RA, which is proper procedure because an RA is an emergency. The problem is that air traffic control sets up safe separation and, because of a false RA, an aircraft suddenly changes altitude. Instead of avoiding a danger, the maneuver could create one. Much thought has gone into avoiding false TCAS alarms.

One technique is the use of sensitivity levels. An area where aircraft by necessity are in close proximity, where tau can become small and there is no impending collision, is at an airport. Generally, an aircraft that is at low altitude is very limited as to what vertical maneuvers may be taken regardless of the location. This has led to TCAS sensitivity levels, which are a function of altitude.

Altitude(feet)	Sensitivity Level	Tau for TA	Tau for RA
0 – 999 AGL	2	20	None issued
1000 – 2349 AGL	3	25	15
2350 – 4999 MSL	4	30	20
5000 – 9999 MSL	5	40	25
10000 – 19999 MSL	6	45	30
20000 MSL and greater	7	48	35

Table 5-1 Sensitivity Levels

5.15.4 TCAS Hardware

TCAS consists of an airborne interrogator that interrogates aircraft within about 20 to 40 NM. In its simplest form, TCAS does not interrogate with a directional antenna. Interrogations result in replies where range may be determined and not direction. By taking the time derivative, range rate may be determined but it, too, is not a vector and has no direction. This is the reason the time derivative is called range rate and not velocity.

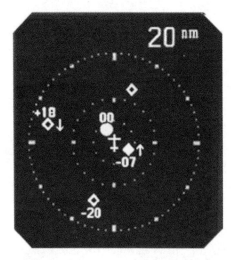

TCAS Display. Own aircraft is at center.
Target at "00" is at same altitude. Target
at "+18" is 1800 feet higher and descending.
"-07" is 700 feet below and climbing.
"-20"is 2000 feet below and level.
Outer ring is 20 nm range.

Aircraft are interrogated with the ATCRBS mode C/mode S all-call. This insures that both mode S and ATCRBS transponders reply. Altitude is required to establish vertical separation because aircraft can pass safely with little separation in altitude, relative to horizontal separation. This is because aircraft cannot change altitude rapidly when compared to closing speeds (which occur horizontally). As an example, two aircraft flying toward each may easily have a closing speed of 1000 knots. Altitude changes are only about 1000 to 2000 feet per minute, which is 10 to 20 knots.

By interrogating with the mode S all call, mode S transponders answer with a mode S reply. This is beneficial for several reasons. First, the transponder has been identified and can help reduce garble. Because airborne TCAS is an interrogator, it suffers the same problems as a ground interrogator, such as garble. The act of replying with mode S tells the TCAS the other aircraft has a mode S transponder and provides the aircraft mode S address. This implies the TCAS interrogator may communicate with the aircraft through the mode S transponder and obtain additional information. Typical data is maximum airspeed of the aircraft and whether the aircraft is TCAS-equipped. All TCAS aircraft in air transport have a mode S transponder, which provides TCAS communications. This information aids TCAS in tracking aircraft and is important for coordinating evasive maneuvers. If an aircraft reports high maximum airspeed, the TCAS computer monitors this aircraft more often than a slower aircraft.

TCAS interrogates proximate aircraft within range and calculates tau for each. The interrogator provides protection from aircraft equipped with either ATCRBS or mode S transponders. Because the TCAS unit is an interrogator, it can suffer loss of replies due to garble as would any other interrogator. From calculated values of tau, the TCAS computer will issue a TA or RA, which includes the voice announcement.

In addition to the voice announcement, the crew receives an indication on the vertical speed indicator, VSI, or instantaneous vertical speed indicator, IVSI It appears on color bands on the indicator's scale. Typically, a red band refers to the range of vertical speeds that are undesired, while a green band indicates the vertical speed to avoid a collision. An example of a TCAS-equipped IVSI is shown in Fig. 5.14.

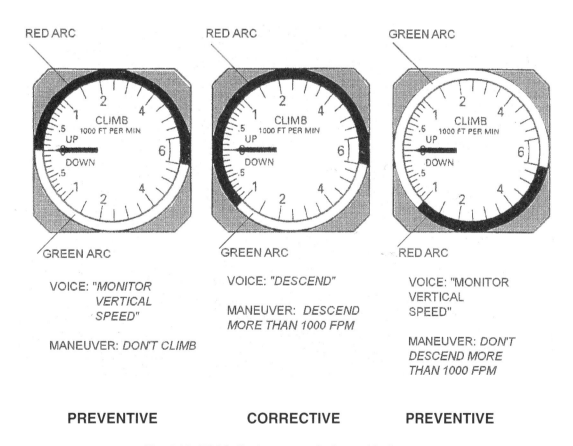

Fig. 5.14 TCAS display on vertical speed indicator

In addition to climb, there are other advisories, such as descend. Advisories are divided into two classifications, preventive and corrective. A preventive advisory prohibits the aircraft from making a maneuver that could lead to a collision. As an example, an aircraft flying straight and level could receive a preventive RA with the voice announcement; "Monitor vertical speed". The VSI shows a green band near zero. This implies the aircraft, flying straight and level, will be safe if it continues straight and level. Another RA would be an aircraft in a climb that announces; "Monitor vertical speed". In this example, assume the same zero vertical speed is indicated by the green band near zero. This means the aircraft must cease climbing and fly level. In this case, the RA, which had the same voice announcement and VSI indication, is not corrective because the aircraft must alter its flight.

RAs in these examples involve climbs and descents, which suggests TCAS provides only vertical maneuvers. At the time of this writing this is true. The system described is TCAS II. As the most common it is required in air transport category aircraft with 30 or more passenger seats. A simpler TCAS for aircraft with fewer than 30 seats but more than 12, is TCAS I. The original plan called for TCAS III, which included horizontal as well as vertical maneuvers. TCAS III was declared obsolete in favor of a system called ADS-B, discussed later in this chapter.

TCAS II in air transport category aircraft includes a display which shows the aircraft tracked by the TCAS unit in a PPI (plan position indicator) display. This requires a directional antenna to obtain angular position. TCAS is like secondary radar in that it operates with secondary radar transponders. The ground interrogator for mode S or ATCRBS employs a large directional antenna mounted on the primary antenna and rotates with it. Because of large size, drag and expense rule out a true directional antenna.

TCAS achieves directionality in a unique way; the characteristics of the SLS (side lobe suppression) pulse. In the discussion of the localizer antenna, it was easier to produce a sharp null than a sharp peak. A directional, steerable antenna is used with a sharp null and slightly directional antenna. Assume P1 of the four-pulse all call interrogation is transmitted from the directional antenna. This could be generated with a sum antenna as discussed with the localizer antenna. SLS pulse P2 is transmitted from the antenna with the sharp null, which is a difference antenna. The remaining pulses of the interrogation are transmitted from the sum antenna.

For a transponder to reply, it may not receive SLS P2 pulse. Only transponders in the sharp null will not receive P2 and reply. Replies are received from transponders in a narrow beam but it was not done with a highly directional antenna, but an antenna with a deep null. The important difference is, it is easy to create deep nulls with simple, small antennas. It is not easy to create sharp peaks with a small antenna.

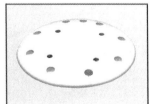

TCAS directional antenna typically mounts on the top and/or bottom of the fuselage

5.15.5 Reducing Garble

TCAS faced a challenge due to garble. It is an interrogator and shares the problems of a ground interrogator, except it is restricted by weight, size and cost. The range of a TCAS interrogator is less than air traffic control radar and, therefore, there is less chance of garble. If two transponders that garble include a mode S transponder this can be recognized because the mode S transponder gives a mode S reply. The fact that one transponder is mode S can be seen because the reply is much longer than ATCRBS and much of the reply is in the clear and recognized. If the interrogation is changed to ATCRBS only all call, the mode S transponder will not reply and the ATCRBS reply will be in the clear. When an ATCRBS and a mode S transponder garble, the two aircraft are not physically close. This is because the mode S transponder delays 128 μs before transmitting a reply and the time delay for an ATCRBS transponder is 3 ms. When an ATCRBS and mode S transponder garble on an all call interrogation, the mode S transponder is about 10 NM closer.

Problems arise when two ATCRBS transponders garble. In this situation there is no method to cause one transponder to not reply and separate the two transponders. On the other hand, if two ATCRBS aircraft garble, a tau can be calculated for both as a single target; if tau is sufficiently large, it does not matter if there are one or more aircraft because there is no chance of collision. TCAS, however, is a three dimensional system Altitude will most likely not be available if two transponders garble. As long as the tau for two aircraft is greater than 40 seconds, altitude is not important. When TCAS must issue a traffic or resolution advisory, altitude is very important.

Although garble is not as serious as experienced with an air traffic control radar ground interrogator, TCAS employs methods for preventing garbled replies. The system is called "whisper-shout". It is based on the fact that not all transponders have the same sensitivity or SLS threshold. Transponders are required to have a specific sensitivity but when the entire system is considered—antenna, antenna placement and transponder transmission line—the difference can be several dB for two legal systems.

One whisper-shout implementation is the transmission of a "pre-pulse" from an omni-directional antenna, which occurs 2 μs before a normal ATCRBS mode C interrogation. The level of the pre-pulse is varied over a series of interrogations, from weak to normal power levels. If the receiving transponder has a sensitive receiver, the pre-pulse is received. The P1 pulse of the mode C interrogation is also transmitted from the omnidirectional antenna with normal power. This appears as a strong P2 SLS pulse and the transponder with the sensitive receiver will suppress and not reply.

The less sensitive transponder, it is assumed, received the normal interrogation and did not receive the pre-pulse and, thus, replied to the interrogation. To get the more sensitive of the two transponders to reply, interrogate at decreasing power until only the more sensitive transponder replies.

Separating garbled ATCRBS transponders is usually an iterative operation where signals are tried repeatedly, while radiated power is reduced or increased until only one of the two transponders replies. This is not a scientific method and results in quite a bit of interrogating. On the other hand, it is only used when two ATCRBS transponders garble.

The name "whisper-shout" comes from this technique, where the weak pre-pulse is a whisper, and the strong P1 is the shout. Remember, the actual SLS P2 pulse is transmitted from the difference antenna, where transponders in the sharp null do not receive P2 and initiate a reply.

As an aid to TCAS, mode S transponders transmit squitter (as in DME). Squitter is not employed in the ATCRBS transponder. About once per second, a mode S transponder transmits an all-call reply. This spontaneous transmission of a mode S "reply" permits the design of a "listen only" collision avoidance system. It can also serve as a broadcast message and is helpful to TCAS II systems if the squittering transponder is involved in garbling.

5.15.6 Coordination

If two closing aircraft are TCAS-equipped, they calculate the same value of tau. Since the range from one aircraft to the other is scalar, both calculate the same range. For the same reason, range rate is the same and, therefore, tau is the same.

If two aircraft have the same model TCAS (from one manufacturer), input data, range and range rate are the same, and they should respond the same way. They issue the TA (threat advisory) and RA (resolution advisory) at exactly the same time. The two aircraft are, essentially, flying into a mirror. A protocol called coordination prevents TCAS from leading the two aircraft into a collision as a result of simultaneous RAs (where both aircraft, for example, are told to "fly up").

Whenever TCAS issues an RA that fact is broadcast via the data communication feature of the mode S transponder. This broadcast, like all mode S transmissions, includes the mode S address of the broadcasting aircraft. The broadcast also identifies the evasive maneuver. For example, if the RA is to climb at 1500 to 2000 feet per minute, this is broadcast. All mode S equipped aircraft receiving the broadcast know an aircraft has issued an RA and what evasive actions are contemplated. If any other aircraft is about to issue an RA, it is cancelled. Most likely, the RA about to be issued would be to climb for reasons discussed. New calculations are made with the latest data, which includes the climb of the subject aircraft. A new RA could be issued which would, most likely, be "don't climb" with the voice announcement "monitor vertical speed". A descend RA could also be a possibility. It is through such coordination that preventive RAs are generated.

5.16 Automatic Dependent Surveillance (ADS)

With the advances of GPS, improvements in accuracy, availability and lower cost, many aircraft are equipped with GPS receivers. Even small aircraft typically have GPS navigation equipment on board. The capability offered by modern GPS systems is a huge advance in radio navigation. The cost of GPS ownership makes the technology one of the best buys in avionics. It would be expected that larger aircraft would have more expensive and sophisticated systems, while smaller aircraft would use systems with less capability. The differences in GPS equipment installed in aircraft have more to do with what is done with the position data rather than the precision of the data. A high-end, expensive GPS navigator has elaborate displays and a number of convenient features but internally, the position data are not significantly better than for an inexpensive unit. With the great popularity of GPS, nearly every aircraft, large or small, has up-to date, accurate latitude, longitude and altitude data on board.

If aircraft with position data simply transmitted current position with a short-range radio datalink to all other aircraft in radio range, as well as ground stations, these data could be used to plot nearby aircraft in a coordinate system. The displayed result would provide situational awareness previously available only from a radar site. Unlike radar, equipment must be installed in the aircraft to have its position displayed.

In addition to position, each equipped aircraft can provide other data such as ground speed, vertical speed, intended course and the aircraft's identity. These data can not only display the current situation but with predictive algorithms, determine the probable future situation.

The system in use that fits this description is Automatic Dependent Surveillance-Broadcast mode or ADS-B. "Automatic" in that no operator intervention is required, such as setting "squawks" for the transponder or frequencies, like other navigation systems. "Dependent" in that the system requires equipment to be installed in aircraft, unlike a primary radar that can detect all targets. The key to successful operation of this system is a reliable and cost-effective data link.

5.16.1 ADS-B DATA LINK

A number of potential data links were considered for ADS-B; VHF data link (VDL mode 4), mode S extended squitter and the universal access transceiver, UAT. Mode S and VDL are existing airborne services and the inclusion of ADS-B would be adding a service to an existing communications system.

The UAT refers to the airborne transceiver, while the ground station is referred to as the Ground Based Transceiver, or GBT.

The extended mode S squitter could provide 112 data bits for each transmission, which occurs about once per second. This would provide an overall data rate of about 112 bits per second. The VDL has a 10.5 kilo symbol per second rate but the VDL channel must be shared with other users. Therefore, if 100 aircraft share a VDL channel, the equivalent data rate would be about 300 bits/second, based on three bit symbols.

A broadcast system where there are, potentially, a significant number of broadcasters, the capacity of a channel comes down to bandwidth. The mode S downlink bandwidth is wide, being on the order of 2 MHz. The channel is already used for the mode S secondary radar system and is also shared with older, less efficient mode A/C transponders. Most larger and newer aircraft have mode S installations and, thus mode S squitter is readily available in these aircraft. The squitter has the capability of accepting the new data transmission requirements, which makes mode S an attractive candidate for the ADS-B data link. The older mode A/C transponders tend to be serious sources of interference. Fortunately, many of the old transponders are being replaced, but there is still significant activity on the 1030/1090 MHz pair.

The VDL is not widely used at the time of this writing and the equipment promises to be expensive. VDL is the vehicle that will modernize VHF communications and its full implementation may be a number of years in the future. However, the bandwidth of the communications channels is 25 kHz and, for a broadcast system, this is not sufficient.

The UAT is a new system designed specifically for high speed data transmission for aviation. The UAT was field tested and found to be superior to other candidate systems in high density airspace. Mode S squitter is considered a temporary fix intended for air transport and commercial aircraft, where a mode S transponder is required by law.

When using the mode S squitter data link for ADS-B, the mode S transponder uses downlink format 17, DF-17. The total ADS-B message uses the long, 112 bit message, where 56 bits are for "Position, Velocity, Time", PVT, and intent. The remaining 56 bits are 5 for DF-17 identification, 3 for capability, CA; 24 for the standard ICAO aircraft identity; and 24 for CRC parity and interrogator ID.

The Federal Radionavigation Plan has suggested for a number of years that TACAN and DME be replaced with satellite navigation and the ground stations be discontinued. The frequencies used by the TACAN system will become available for other uses. There is nearly 200 MHz of bandwidth in the entire TACAN band and each TACAN channel includes an uplink and downlink channel, each 1 MHz wide.

A number of TACAN channels are for military use only and have already been discontinued. This affords the opportunity to reassign a TACAN frequency to airborne communications without disrupting civilian users.

The TACAN portion of the L band for both civil and military applications uses primarily pulse transmission. This is a shared band and not for the exclusive use of civilian aviation. The military does operate a pulse-like communications system, the Joint Tactical Information Distribution System or JTIDS, in the same frequency range as TACAN. JTIDS operates from 969 MHz to 1206 MHz with airborne output power as high as 200W and, in some cases, up to 1000W. Frequency hopping spread spectrum is used with 3 MHz channels with TDMA and encryption. Reassigning TACAN frequencies for communications links must take in to account compatibility with existing services in the L band.

In order to minimize interference with existing pulse services in the L band, the UAT channel frequency was set at 978 MHz after consideration of several potential frequencies. This frequency is the reply frequency for the TACAN/DME channel paired with 108.00 MHz, which is a test frequency. Therefore, there is no potential interference from active TACAN or DME ground stations.

Even though the UAT operating frequency has been chosen to minimize mutual interference to existing L band services, there must be a certain level of immunity afforded by the UAT system. The receiver should be capable of successfully receiving 99% of transmitted long UAT ADS-B messages for a signal level between -90 dBm and -10 dBm when subjected to DME X or Y channel pulse pairs at -36 dBm on any valid DME channel between the frequency of 980 MHz and 1213 MHz at a rate of 3600 pulse pairs per second.

The receiver should also be capable of receiving a 90% long ADS-B message success rate with a DME interfering signal at the first adjacent channel at 979 MHz. This test requires only the X channel be tested, as 979 MHz is an X channel. The interfering level is -70 dBm.

There are two basic message types handled by the UAT, the ADS-B message and the ground uplink message. The ADS-B message transmits the aircraft state vector, latitude, longitude and altitude, and associated information. The ground uplink message contains traffic, weather and other information.

The ADS-B message broadcasts the position of aircraft for surveillance and collision avoidance. The Traffic Information System Broadcast, or TIS-B, is intended to broadcast traffic information for non ADS-B equipped aircraft. This implies that the state vector for the aircraft identified by TIS-B has been determined from sources other than ADS-B, such as ground radar. It can also be used as a gateway for multiple ADS-B data links. For ADS-B equipped aircraft, TIS-B can provide traffic information concerning non-ADS-B equipped aircraft.

Another information service provided by the GBT is Flight Information Service Broadcast, FIS-B. This will provide non-traffic control information, such as weather radar images, notice to airmen, restricted use airspace and so on.

In addition to the broadcast modes described, there is an addressed mode of ADS-B called ADS-A, which is also known as ADS-Contract or ADS-C. The contract term is primarily used in Europe. ADS-B can also be employed in airport vehicles and share state vector information with other vehicles and aircraft. Also, obstacles such as tall structures can be fitted with ADS-B broadcast transmitters. Obstacles can be mobile but their velocity must be very slow, such as tall construction cranes.

The UAT employs continuous-phase frequency shift keying, FSK, with a frequency deviation of 625 kHz. A binary one represents a shift up from the nominal carrier frequency of 312.5 kHz while a binary zero represents a shift down from the nominal carrier frequency by the same amount. The data rate is 1.041667 Mbps or a time slot width of 960 ns. To minimize the amount of energy in adjacent channels the input data stream is filtered before modulation. The spectrum of the UAT is -18 dB, minimum, 1 MHz from the nominal carrier frequency.

5.16.2 ADS-B Message Structures

The basic ADS-B message, also called the "short" ADS-B message or "payload type code zero," consists of a header and the aircraft's state vector. Ten "long" ADS-B messages, "payload type code" 1 through 10 are defined at the time of this writing. Header type codes 11 through 31, also long ADS-B messages, are reserved for future use. Aircraft state vectors are broadcast at a 1 Hz rate and may be short ADS-B messages or as a part of the long ADS-B message.

The UAT is a time division multiple access, TDMA, system. The basic UAT frame is a length of 1 second and transmitted at a rate of one frame per second. Each frame has 3200 message start opportunities, MSO. Each message frame starts with MSO zero, which is concurrent with the exact time of a UTC second. Notice that the timing is synchronized to UTC and not GPS time. The actual synchronization in an aircraft is obtained from the GPS receiver and the GPS/UTC differential information from the GPS almanac is used determine UTC from GPS time.

The UAT uses both time slotted and random message start opportunities, MSO. The system is synchronized to UTC with sufficient accuracy such that a certain amount of medium-precision ranging with an accuracy of about 0.2 NM, can be performed using the receipt time of messages from other transceivers.

There are two basic types of messages on the UAT channel; the ADS-B message and the ground uplink message. The uplink message is used for the broadcast services TIS and FIS. The UAT system will also allow for future messages. All messages have a payload and an overhead component, which is mostly the forward error correcting parity bits. The 1.0000 second UAT frame is synchronized with the start of the UTC second. The UAT frame has a MSO every 250 µs.

Fig. 5.15 ADS-B Message

Fig. 5.15 shows the one second UAT frame. The first 6 ms is a silent guard time, which allows for the transit time of UAT transmissions plus errors in transceiver clocks. Of the 3952 MSOs in the UAT frame, the first 704 MSOs are reserved for the ground segment transmissions. There is a guard time, or silent period, between the ground segment and the ADS-B segment consisting of 48 MSOs or 12 ms, again for different transit delays and timing errors between the various transceivers.

Following the guard time, the ADS-B segment of the UAT frame is 800 ms in length and consists of 3200 MSOs. Each ADS-B equipped aircraft makes one transmission during this time on a pseudorandom schedule. Finally, another 6 ms guard time is provided at the end of the 1 second ADS-B frame. In addition to the benefits from the initial 6 ms guard time, the trailing guard time allows for completing the transmission of ADS-B messages initiated in later MSOs.

To prevent interference from ADS-B transmissions becoming synchronized, ADS-B transceivers transmit at pseudorandom intervals in a fashion that is similar to DME. There is a basic 1 second transmission rate, plus or minus a random offset.

Each ADS-B message consists of 4 MSOs for ramp up and ramp down, which is a time to allow the transmitter and receiver to stabilize. An additional 36 MSOs are used for synchronizing. The ADS-B message synchronizing word, separated into groups of 4 bits for clarity only is:

1110 1010 1100 1101 1101 1010 0100 1110 0010

transmitted from left to right.

This is followed by an 8 bit length/ident word that identifies the length and nature of the message. Two message lengths are available, 128 or 256 bits.

The synchronizing word for the ground uplink message is:

0001 0101 0011 0010 0010 0101 1011 0001 1101

Notice this synchronizing word is the inverse; zeros changed to ones and vice versa, of the ADS-B synchronizing word.

After the 36 bit synchronizing sequence is the UAT payload, or data. For the basic message, the payload consists of 144 bits followed by a 96 bit Reed-Solomon 256-ary forward error correction, FEC, code. For long message, the payload consists of 272 data bits followed by 112 FEC bits.

The FEC for the basic ADS-B message is capable of correcting up to 6 symbol errors per data block. For the long ADS-B message up to 7 errors can be corrected.

TIS-B transmissions from the GBT appear nearly identical to ADS-B messages and are transmitted during the ADS-B segment of the UAT frame.

5.16.3 Ground Uplink Messages

Ground uplink messages are for transmitting flight information such as weather advisories, weather graphics and other flight deck information. Each uplink message can provide 432 bytes of information.

Most aircraft will receive uplink messages from more than one ground station and the uplink payload section of the GBT frame is divided into 32 ground broadcast time slots. Ground stations are assigned to one or more time slots and can be reused when ground stations are separated by sufficient distance to eliminate interference. This protocol is similar to conventional frequency reuse strategies.

A ground station is assigned a 22 MSO time slot or 5.5 ms of which slightly more than 4 milliseconds are required to transmit the uplink message. The gap time between ground station messages prevents interference due to different propagations times and clock errors. Ground station MSOs are multiples of 22, beginning with 0; 0, 22, 44, 66,..........682.

By using the ranging capability of the GBT and knowing the location of the ground stations, an airborne transceiver can determine position by ranging on multiple ground station transmissions. In a similar manner, multiple ground stations can determine an aircraft's position.

A GBT uplink message starts with a UAT specific header, which is an 8 byte field that contains the location of the GBT, the time slot used for the transmission, and system flags indicating validity of the data.

The station latitude based on WGS-84 requires 23 bits, the longitude, 24. The header contains 4 bits for flags, 5 bits for slot number, 4 bits for TIS-B site identification and 4 reserved bits for future applications.

Following the header is the information frame, which consists of 424 bytes. Byte 1 of the information frame is the length of the information to follow. The length is in bytes and partial bytes are filled with zeros. The second byte consists of 4 reserved bits and the frame type identifier.

5.16.4 ADS-B Payload

Each ADS-B payload is identified by a 5 bit code which represents the first 5 bits of the ADS-B message header. Also in the ADS-B header is the 24 bit ICAO aircraft identity, the same as that used for the mode S transponder, and an address qualifier. The qualifier indicates whether the address is an ICAO aircraft address, a surface vehicle or an obstacle.

The remaining data of the ADS-B message includes:

latitude,	WGS-84 23 bits
longitude,	WGS-84 24 bits
altitude,	12 bits
altitude type,	1 bit (MSL or barometric), -1000 feet to 101,338 feet
horizontal velocity,	two components; north and east, 11 bits each
vertical velocity,	9 bits

5.16.5 Traffic Information Service Broadcast (TIS-B)

Traffic information Service Broadcast mode, TIS-B, is usually broadcast from a GBT in the ADS-B time slot. It provides state vector information on non-ADS-B equipped aircraft, which has been determined from other sources. Although the TIS-B message is broadcast in the ADS-B segment and can be handled in the same fashion as ADS-B messages from aircraft, it is important that the message be identified as ground information. This prevents airborne equipment from ranging on a ground station as if it were an airborne unit.

5.16.6 Classes of ADS-B Installation

The UAT transmitter operates with a power output in one of three categories; low, medium and high power variants, as shown below.

Transmitter Class	Minimum Power	Maximum Power	Air-to-Air Range
Low	7 watts	18 watts	20 NM
Medium	16 watts	40 watts	30 NM
High	100 watts	250 watts	120 NM

Table 5-2 UAT Transmitter Power and Intended Range

The UAT system is designed to operate with a maximum frequency tolerance of +/- 1 PPM and a Doppler shift due to 1200 knots, or that which could be experienced with two aircraft approaching head on.

Exercise:

What is the Doppler shift at 978 MHz for a closing velocity of 1200 knots. Compare the result with 1 PPM.

1200 kts = (1200 NM X 1852 meters)/3600 seconds = 1852 m / 3 s = 617.3 m/s

Wavelength of 978 MHz = 3E8/978E6 = 0.307 m

Doppler shift = velocity/wavelength = 617.3 (m/s) / 0.307 m = 2.012 kHz

One part per million is 978 Hz

ADS-B installations are divided into two fundamental classes, A and B, where class A aircraft can transmit and receive, while class B aircraft, ground vehicles and obstacles can only transmit. The A and B classes are further divided into capability sub classes.

Similar to the requirements of the TCAS system, space diversity is used for ADS-B. True space diversity requires two independent receivers and a transmitter capable of transmitting independently on either of two antennas. An alternative to true diversity, and not as effective, is the use of two antennas with a single receiver which alternates receiving between the two antennas. Typically, the antennas are mounted top and bottom of the aircraft. When a single antenna is used, it is mounted on the bottom. All signals are vertically polarized.

The capabilities, transmitter power and antenna installations are discussed below. The high, medium and low power classifications refer to the power ranges previously discussed and as shown in table 5-2.

The receiver performance is the same for all classes. The receiver is required to have a 90% message success rate for long ADS-B messages with an input signal at the receiving antenna of -93 dBm. Also, the receiver must have a minimum of a 90% message success rate with a signal level of -91 dBm for uplink messages.

The performance of the UAT is predicated on an antenna system with an omnidirectional pattern with minimal nulls due to aircraft installation, and with a gain of 0 dBi, gain over isotropic. Since the specified signal level is at the antenna, losses due to the transmission line reduce receiver sensitivity and increases receiver noise figure and must be accounted for in receiver design. Like any L band system, low loss transmission lines are required.

Class A0.
This class is used as an aid to visual spotting of proximate aircraft and is intended to be used in aircraft that fly only below 18,000 feet. The system uses a low power transmitter and a single antenna.

Class A1L and A1H: A1(low altitude) A1(high altitude)

This class is for conflict avoidance and uses diversity with a single receiver. The transmitter alternates between antennas every 2 seconds, while the receiver alternates every second. A low power transmitter is used in aircraft that fly only below 18,000 feet, while a medium power transmitter is used for aircraft that fly above 18,000 feet.

Class A2

This class is used for separation and sequencing of aircraft and on aircraft that are capable of any altitude. A medium power transmitter is used with a true diversity, dual receiver. The transmitter alternates antennas every two seconds.

Class A3

This class is identical to class A2 except the use of a high power transmitter.

Class B0

This class is a transmit-only single antenna installation intended for state vector reporting only for low altitude aircraft; below 18,000 feet

Class B1

This is a transmit-only, single antenna installation intended for state vector reporting for aircraft capable of flying above 18,000 feet. This class uses a medium power transmitter, with alternating top and bottom antennas, alternating every two seconds.

Class B2

This class is for ground vehicles with a single top mounted antenna and a 1 watt transmitter.

Class B3

This class is for obstacles with a 1 watt, minimum, transmitter.

Exercise

Assume two airborne UATs operate in the medium power range with the minimum power. Each airborne installation uses a typical one-quarter wavelength vertically polarized antenna. What is the theoretical air-to-air range based on free space propagation?

Solution

Let G be the gain of the antenna, used both for transmitting and receiving.
R is the radial distance between units in meters.
λ is the wavelength.
P_T is transmitter power.
P_R is minimum receiver power.

The minimum power for the medium power range is 16 watts or +42 dBm. The gain over an isotropic radiator for a 1/4 wavelength radiator is 2.1 dB or a gain of 2.1 dBi.

The receiver input power is -91 dBm or 0.794 pW

The capture area for the same ¼ wavelength antenna is $A = G \lambda^2 / 4 \pi$

The free space loss is:

$$L = (4 \pi R / \lambda)2$$

The signal at the receiver can be given by:

$$P_R = P_T G^2 (\lambda / 4 \pi R)^2$$

Solving for R:

$R = (P_T / P_R)^{1/2} (G \lambda / 4 \pi) = (16 / 0.794E{-}12)^{1/2} (1.622 X 0.307 / 12.57) = 178$
km = 96 nm

Exercise

The operation range for the medium power ADS-B is 30 NM which implies from the calculation of the previous example that 16 watts is more than sufficient power. This additional power provides a margin or extra power for reliable operation. How much is the margin for the 16 watt transmitter?

Solution

Power density for a radio system decreases with R^2. Since this system provides sufficient power to operate at 96 NM and only 30 NM is required, the excess power is:

$$10 \log [(96 / 30)^2] = 10 \, dB$$

This system has a generous 10 dB margin.

However, since the ADS-B system may operate with antennas that have no gain over isotropic, 0 dBi, one or both systems could have 2.1 dB less gain. If both have 0 dBi radiators,,,,, the margin reduces to 6 dB. The margin is 8 dB if only one has a 0 dBi radiator.

5.16.7 System Implementation

GBTs will have to be installed in a seamless network in order for the ADS-B system to be effective. The first is physical layer coverage. Simply, the GBT must cover a service volume with signals in space that will function with the UATs. Secondly is product coverage. This means the TIS and FIS information is relative and valid for the service volume. Ground station coverage will be laid out in a fashion similar to a cellular telephone system relative to frequency and time slot reuse. Ground stations are nominally 90 NM apart using a 7 cell reuse pattern and a desired to undesired signal ratio of 10 dB. For critical coverage areas, sectorized antennas may be used, also similar to cellular telephone.

Sources of data for TIS-B and FIS-B will come from ADS-B broadcasts and other sources requiring data links, either wired or wireless.

Because the ADS-B system is linked to UTC, it is quite possible that other interfering sources such as JTIDS could also be linked to UTC and cause synchronous interference. To prevent this, ground stations change MSO every 32 seconds. The ground station starts at exactly 0000 UTC with its assigned slot number and will increment by one slot every 32 seconds.

A diagram of an ADS-B system is shown in Fig. 5.16. A GPS receiver determines present position. This receiver could also be a part of the aircraft's navigation system. Present position is broadcast by data link at a rate and time determined by the ADS-B unit. The transmission does not rely on an interrogation or specific time slot.

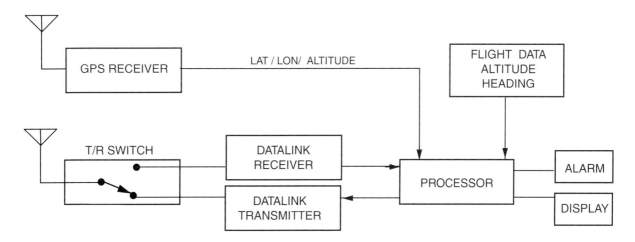

Figure 5.16 ADS-B (Automatic Dependent Surveillance - Broadcast)

The ADS-B processor obtains own aircraft's present position from the GPS receiver. The processor also receives the SV position from nearby aircraft, much of which is based on the same GPS data as own aircraft. Having these positions, simple geometry calculates range and distance from each proximate aircraft. The terms are borrowed from TCAS for this description because ADS-B could eventually become the replacement for TCAS.

Example:
Calculate the distance from a proximate aircraft when own aircraft position is N29° 46.18', W81 38.92', 10 000 feet. The proximate aircraft is N 29 40.84', W 81 32.74', 21 000 feet .

Solution: This is similar to the problem involving two LORAN-C stations. In this case, however, there are three dimensions. There is a problem of spherical geometry with two spheres having two radii differ by the difference in altitude. The radii differ by 1.8 NM as compared to the sea level earth radius of 3444 NM. We find the great circle distance between the two aircraft as if they were at sea level, then consider that as one of the sides of a linear triangle with the difference in altitude as one side.

The map distance can be found by:

$$cos (c) = cos (a) cos (b)$$

where a is the angular difference of latitude and b is angular distance of longitude and c is the radial difference along a great circle. In this case a = 5.34', b = 6.18'. Therefore:

$$cos (c) = cos (0.089°) cos (0.108°) = 0.999997$$

$$c = 0.136125° = 2.3578E-3 \ rad$$

The great circle distance is:

$$R_c = 3444\ NM \times 2.3578E\text{-}3\ rad = 8.18\ NM$$

Including the altitude, the distance is: $D^2 = (8.18\ NM)^2 + (1.8\ NM)^2$

$$D = 8.376\ NM$$

Geometric altitude was used in this example. Aircraft flying at lower altitudes use MSL altitude by manually correcting barometric altitude. Human error in setting the correct baro-set can cause altitude errors when using MSL. For this reason high altitude flight uses pressure altitude. Aircraft flying above 18,000 feet use pressure altitude which deviates from geometrical or MSL altitude depending on the ambient air pressure. What is important is that all aircraft fly at the same altitude and the actual AGL, MSL or geometrical altitude is not important. Therefore, for collision avoidance barometric altitude is an important parameter.

The ADS-B processor calculates ranges to proximate aircraft as a scalar and vector. The calculations are relative to an X, Y and Z coordinate system. The magnitude of range is calculated and the time derivative of that magnitude. Therefore, a TCAS-like algorithm determines when TAs and RAs are issued.

What about coordination? ADS-B does not have two-way communications and coordination requires a broadcast. However, TCAS II was limited to vertical evasive maneuvers. Since ADS-B is inherently three dimensional, evasive maneuvers can be in three dimensions. Certain "rules of the air" can determine which aircraft has the right of way and in the direction for evasive maneuvers. Using these rules, maneuvers in three dimensions may be made without coordination.

5.17 Lightning Detection

Weather was the prime reason for avionics in the first place! There is one common type of weather, however, that few aircraft, regardless of strength or size, can safely fly through, and that is the thunderstorm. Avionics can guide aircraft through bad weather, but in the case of thunderstorms, it keeps them out.

Localized storms are easily circumnavigated. They are often spawned on hot, humid afternoons or associated with weather fronts and hurricanes. What makes thunderstorms dangerous is their speed of development and strong up and down drafts. Many landing accidents have been caused by wind shear which accompanies a fast-moving storm cell. The storm may also produce hail large enough to damage aircraft windows and structure. Although short lived, thunderstorms can cause loss of control, airframe failure and loss of life. Flying over a storm is not a good idea, either. Thunderheads can reach over 50,000 feet, higher than most aircraft fly. The only safe procedure for thunderstorms is to avoid them.

Fortunately, many thunderstorms are visible. Aircraft at cruising altitude can see high cloud tops at a great distance and plan a wide berth. High winds and hail can extend more than 10 NM outward from the clouds. Most dangerous is the embedded thunderstorm, concealed within an area of clouds.

Lightning strikes from thunderstorms cause loud static in low frequency navigation equipment, especially ADF. Many pilots believe their ADF needle tends to point toward lightning strokes and, therefore, is a type of storm indicator. Although ADF is very responsive to such electrical activity, the large number of strokes from a storm can cause the needle to swing aimlessly over a wide arc. Many ADF receivers have electromechanically operated indicators which cannot respond with speed and accuracy. Safety experts strongly recommend not using an ADF in this fashion.

The large amount of radio frequency energy from thunderstorms, however, is the basis of a lightning detection device called the StormScope. With an electronic display and no mechanical indicators, the instrument overcomes the limitations of ADF. StormScope places a dot or lightning symbol on an electronic display for every strike received. The dots are removed

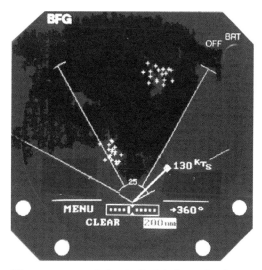

Stormscope detects lightning strokes in thunderstorm. Clusters are seen at 11 and 1 O'clock. Max. range of display is 200 nm. Display can also be set for full-circle viewing (360 degrees).

after a certain number of minutes to keep the display up to date and uncluttered. A large number of dots which build rapidly indicate a dangerous storm.

The dots appear on a polar coordinate system, usually with the aircraft at the center. The direction of the lightning stroke is seen relative to the nose of the airplane. Determining distance to the stroke, however, requires an assumption that all lightning strikes radiate the same amount of electromagnetic energy. As it turned out, this was a good assumption by the designer; the amount of received signal strength can be a measure of distance. Otherwise, if there were weak and strong strokes, a weak stroke at close range could not be distinguished from a strong stroke at greater distance. (When a storm grows more powerful, it doesn't produce stronger lightning strokes, but discharges them more frequently.)

The lightning detection system is much like ADF. Maximum RF energy of lightning discharges occurs around 50 kHz, which is the receive frequency of the StormScope. A crossed-coil antenna, like the one for ADF, receives the electromagnetic field. As in ADF, an electric field (sense) antenna removes the direction-finding ambiguity.

The lightning detection receiver is shown in Fig. 5.17. Because it operates at a frequency much lower than ADF and only one frequency is involved, the crossed-coil signals and electric field antenna signal are amplified in three separate amplifiers. It is not difficult to maintain the same phase shift in the three amplifiers at 50 kHz. The crossed-coil signals are multiplied by the electric field antenna and low pass filtered. This results in two signals proportional to X and Y components of the magnetic field intensity. X and Y components are complete with the sign.

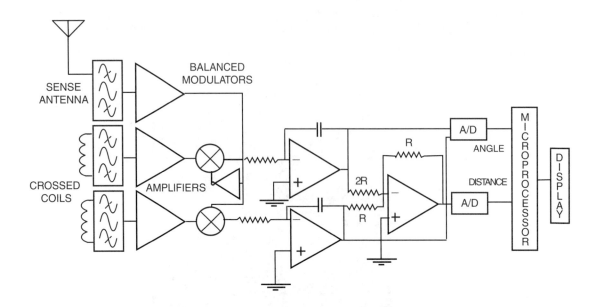

Fig. 5.17. Lightning detection system.

The electric and magnetic field intensity of a propagating electromagnetic wave is inversely proportional to the distance. Do not confuse this with the so-called "inverse square" law which relates to signal power. Since signal power is proportional to the electric or magnetic field squared, field intensities are inversely proportional to the distance, not the distance squared.

Every time a lightning strike is received, a dot is placed at X and Y coordinates of the strike and remains displayed for a fixed period. Depending on the model, the display is a CRT or LCD. Although Cartesian coordinates place the dots, it is a polar display with the aircraft at the origin.

Because the display holds new dots before eliminating older ones, there is memory storage. Each data point, a dot, is time-stamped so the computer knows when to remove it. Each data point has an X coordinate, a Y coordinate and time of arrival.

The display places the aircraft at the center, with heading at the 12 o'clock position. If the aircraft turns, the dots move to maintain their correct position relative to the nose. This is based on heading information from the directional gyro or navigation computer and performing vector addition. This is known as a stabilized display. Low-cost models, however, have no stabilization and require the pilot to manually clear the display each time there is a heading change. Otherwise, the dots will not be in the correct position relative to the aircraft nose.

5.18 Weather Radar

While lightning is a good indicator of a thunderstorm, some storms have more lightning activity than others. Generally, the most intense area has maximum lightning activity. However, there are exceptions. (Being struck by lightning in an aircraft is one of the lesser dangers of a thunderstorm.)

218

RED   BLUE   YELLOW

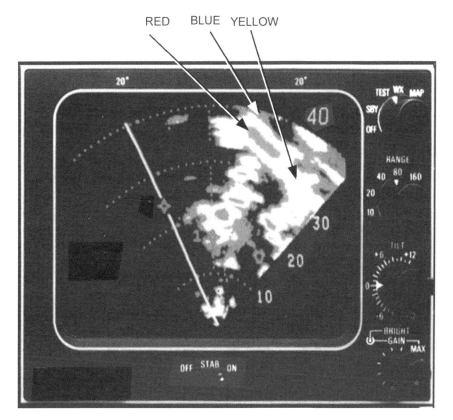

Weather radar for General Aviation. This model shows rate of precipitation in three colors; red for heaviest rain, yellow for intermediate, blue for light. Aircraft, at bottom of display, has plotted a course to the left to circumnavigate the storm.

Turbulence and wind shear (rapid changes in wind direction) are the hazards. One method of detecting the precipitation that accompanies these hazards is radar. It is interesting that radio waves were originally used for blind flight because they penetrate weather; for radar they are valuable because they reflect from weather.

The principles behind weather radar are the same as in air traffic radar; receiving back scattered energy from a target. In this case, the targets are water drops. Some energy is scattered by drops while some continues on to be scattered by other drops. If wavelength is too long, excessive energy passes through the cloud and it will not be visible. If wavelength is too short, all energy back scatters from the outer edge of the cloud and no information arrives from its interior.

One scenario is to imagine a cloud illuminated with visible light. If the cloud is thin, it might be possible to see through it. If it is fair weather, puffy cumulus, you may hardly see through at all. This is an example of illuminating with light, which has very short wavelength. What happens if wavelength is long relative to water drops? Consider the standard AM broadcast band from 550 kHz to 1700 kHz, representing wavelengths from 545-176 meters. At night, when signals from distant stations are carried by sky waves there is no reduction of signal strength on cloudy nights.

Most weather radar operates at a frequency of 9375 MHz in the X band. It suffers all the problems associated with primary radar, particularly the received signal power. Again, the same solutions may be applied, such as high radiated power and high-gain antennas.

When the radar equation was derived earlier in this chapter it was found that the received signal backscattered from the target was inversely proportional to range to the fourth power. This implied that the received signal would be quite small and decrease rapidly with increasing distance. The situation is different in the weather radar. Energy is still backscattered but it is from a very large number of scatterers. Consider a narrow cone-shaped beam, which is reasonably close to the typical weather radar antenna. For one water drop or one ice crystal the scattered energy does decrease with $1/R^4$ as if it were a much larger target such as an aircraft. However, the backscattered energy is proportional to the number of water drops or ice crystals a constant distance from the radar antenna. The constant distance is important because it is signal power that we are interested in and the total energy at a specific time adds to the power. The instantaneous power is not affected by energy arriving at other times.

Let us assume water drops or ice crystals within the antenna beam are all the same size and uniformly spaced, which are reasonable assumptions. Let us further assume that the cloud formation fills the entire beam of the antenna, which is also reasonable. The number of scatterers is proportional to the area of the radar antenna beam falling on the cloud/weather formation. At the moment, we do not need to know the antenna beam solid angle, which is a function of the antenna gain because the area intercepted by the antenna beam is proportional to R^2. Therefore the cross sectional area of the weather formation illuminated by the antenna beam is proportional to the square of the distance. The energy backscattered from each drop or ice crystal decreases with $1/R^4$ while the number of scatterers increases with R^2. Therefore, when the target fills the antenna beam the signal received by the radar is proportional to $1/R^2$ and we can write an equation expressing this as:

$$Pr(R) = (K\ Z) / R^2, \qquad\qquad (5.14)$$

Where $Pr(R)$ is the received signal from a cloud formation of water or ice crystals. K is a constant of the radar which includes the transmitter power, antenna gain and other parameters. The antenna beam solid angle was not considered previously but is now accounted for in the factor K. R is the distance from the transmitter to the weather formation and Z, often called the Z factor, takes into consideration the number, size and density of the water drops or ice crystals.

It is common to use the decibel form of the Z factor, which is

$$DBZ = 10 \log Z. \qquad\qquad (5.15)$$

As with any decibel representation it is necessary to have a 0 dB reference. The value of 0 dBZ has been selected so that typical weather radar returns that would be of interest to weather prediction span from about -40 dBZ, which represents clouds not producing precipitation to +70 dBZ, which represents a severe hailstorm. Other example dBZ values would include +20 to +50, light to heavy rain and +60 dBZ, flooding rains. Airborne weather radars for navigation safety purposes, rather than weather prediction, do not use the full dynamic range of weather phenomenon. Only clouds producing rain are of any interest to airborne navigation. Typically, 5 levels of rain intensity are displayed in accordance with the following table:

Z level	dBZ	Rain Rate (mm/hr)
1	10 dBZ	0.152 to 0.762
2	20 dBZ	0.762 to 3.81
3	30 dBZ	3.81 to 12.7
4	40 dBZ	12.7 to 50.6
5	50 dBZ	50.6 to 203.2

Not only do the rain drops cause back scattering of the radar signal, they also cause attenuation of those signals. As an example, in a large rain formation the outer periphery will produce a strong return. Rain well within the formation, even at possibly a greater rate than on the outer bands will produce a much weaker return. This is because the radar illumination signal is first attenuated before it reaches the inner rain and the scattered energy is attenuated on its way out.

Rain is the real culprit in this problem. Ice crystals and hail produce very little attenuation as compared to rain. The shorter wavelength weather radars, which have an advantage in producing the strongest back scatter, now suffer the most attenuation through the rain. The amount of attenuation for an X band radar ranges from about 0.01 dB/km for a rain rate of 1 mm/hr to about 3.25 dB/km for a rain rate of 100 mm/hr.

Correction for rain attenuation is a matter of using the rain rate determined by the measured Z factor to correct for the attenuation of the return signals received from a slightly greater range in an iterative process. If the total attenuation of the outer bands of a formation completely obliterates returns from the interior by reducing the signal to noise level, some assumptions may be made about the rain rate in the interior and the display shows an estimation. This must be done with great care. If a weather radar shows a formation that can be flown through but, in fact, has an embedded area of extreme rain, a flight crew can be misled to believe there is safe passage through the weather. The use of sophisticated algorithms and Doppler information can minimize this type of false display.

One type of interference that detracts from the performance of airborne weather radars is ground clutter. If a radar antenna were perfect it would project a fine conical beam of about 1 degree or so, which would be horizontal. However, all antennas have a certain amount of side lobes. These lobes can extend several degrees from the main lobe and some are projected towards the ground.

In a well designed antenna the gain from a side lobe is considerably less than from the main lobe, as much as 50 dB or more. However, the return signals are very strong for several reasons. First, the equivalent "Z factor" of the ground, water, roadways, buildings, etc., is much greater than rain. Secondly, the range to the ground is often much less than from the nearest weather.

There are several methods of eliminating ground clutter. The first is to improve antenna designs to reduce side lobes in the ground direction. Asymmetrical reflector antennas are often used, but the phased array antenna is inherently superior in side lobe reduction. Another technique in the reduction of ground clutter is analysis of the Doppler shift of the return signal. Knowing the aircraft altitude, AGL, and the ground speed, the expected Doppler shift of returns from the ground at specific ranges may be calculated. Therefore, returns with Doppler shifts in this range may be eliminated as ground clutter.

However, there are times when a radar map of the ground is useful in navigation. If the antenna is tilted down so the radar is directed toward the ground, a radar map of the ground may be obtained. Because the reflection constants from various features on the ground are different, contours may be displayed. Water, as an example, is different than earth and the typical weather radar can show outlines of rivers and lakes quite accurately. Cities, agriculture fields and forested areas are easily discernible. This ground mapping mode is found in many weather radars.

There are several types of weather radar; broad band and narrow band (turbulence). A block diagram of broad band radar is shown in Fig. 5.18. The transmitter is usually a magnetron, an old vacuum tube oscillator. The "magne-" in magnetron stems from the strong magnetic field which causes electron beams to traverse circular paths. The magnetron has resonant cavities that determine oscillation frequency.

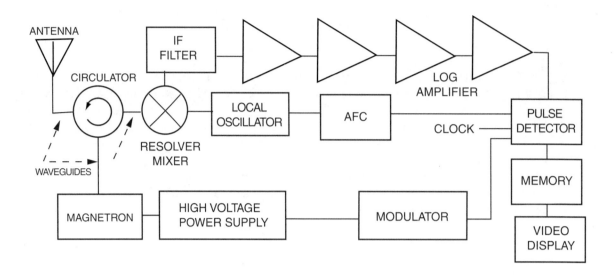

Fig. 5.18   Weather radar

Great care is taken to insure mechanical stability of the cavities, but even with the most stable metal alloys there is frequency drift. Other problems include changing frequency during the pulse. The drift due to mechanical expansion and contraction with temperature is an example of poor long-term stability, while frequency change during the pulse is of lack of short-term stability. In spite of the problems many weather radars still use magnetrons. They're applied where frequency instability is not serious and high power is important (as in a microwave oven, one of the remaining applications for the magnetron).

The transmitter (magnetron) feeds the antenna through a T/R switch which allows transmitter and receiver to share the antenna. Airborne weather radar antennas come in a variety of diameters ranging from nearly a meter for air transport, to the size of a large dinner plate for small aircraft.

There are two types of weather radar antennas, mechanically scanned and phased array. A mechanically scanned antenna is usually a parabolic dish with a waveguide feed. Although it dates back to the birth of radar, it performs admirably. The major disadvantage is that it must be physically rotated to scan ahead of the aircraft. It is driven with a motor and control system so the position of the antenna is known. It is impractical to place a parabolic dish in the aircraft slip stream because of enormous drag. It is placed behind a radome, an aerodynamically low drag cover in the nose. The radome is transparent to X band radiation from the transmitter.

Since the antenna rotates plus and minus about 40 degrees from the center, the area behind the radome must be sufficiently large. It is not a problem for large aircraft, which house the antenna in a radome in the tip of the nose, as well as the glide slope and, in some cases, MLS antenna. Because single-engine aircraft cannot position a radome in the nose (where the propellor is located), the radar antenna is slung under a wing or recessed into the leading edge.

There are two types of phased array antennas, fixed and steerable. The fixed phased array is mechanically scanned in the same fashion as the parabolic dish. It offers a smaller antenna in the form of a flat plate and does not require a feed horn in front of the antenna. The phased array antenna also produces fewer side lobes. The steerable phased array antenna is electronically steered and is considerably more complex and expensive However, there are no moving parts and the antenna can be located in difficult areas.

The received signal is routed through the T/R switch to the receiver. Usually there is a limiter between the T/R switch and receiver front end. This is because transmitter power is so high that even small leakage in the T/R switch could damage sensitive receiver front end components.

The receiver is a conventional superheterodyne. The local oscillator is typically a Gunn diode or transistor oscillator. Usually free-running, the oscillator uses a cavity for the frequency controlling element. Extreme frequency stability is not an issue for two reasons. First, the transmitter is not stable, and secondly, automatic frequency control is supplied so the receive local oscillator tracks the transmitter. The weather radar receiver is usually a double-conversion superheterodyne with a first IF at about 2 GHz. It is a pulse amplitude receiver (unlike the turbulence mode radar discussed later).

The receiver IF must handle a wide range of signal amplitudes and cannot use AGC. A logarithmic IF might appear to be the best choice but there is a clever scheme to reduce the dynamic range of the receiver without a log IF. Since the receiver works on returns from the onboard transmitter, the first signals received after transmission are the strongest, and continually decrease. Signals received 12.35 µs after transmission are from targets 1 NM away. Signals from targets with the same radar cross section at 2 NM are 6 dB less. Signals from 4 NM are another 12 dB less and so on. The gain of the receiver is steadily increased during the time to accommodate the reduction in signal strength due to increasing path loss. This technique is called sensitivity time control, or STC.

If sensitivity of the receiver is compensated for distance, the strength of the return is a function of the radar cross section of the weather. The variation in cross section is a function of the type of weather. The variation between light haze and a serious thunderstorm is more than 60 dB. A meteorological weather radar used in forecasting accommodates the entire dynamic range of cross sections. The airborne weather radar is concerned only with severe weather and will not use the entire 60 dB of dynamic range, but about 30 dB of the range.

Received signals, which are not individual targets but areas, are amplitude demodulated and converted to digital. These areas are stored for display. The amplitude of the return signal sets the intensity for a monochrome display or selects the appropriate color for a color display.

Determining where received signals are displayed depends on the position of the antenna when the return is received. The position is determined by a synchro connected to the antenna. Antenna position, range and signal intensity are combined to provide a set of pixels compatible with the display type.

Many weather radars stabilize the horizontal orientation of the antenna so it scans towards the horizon, even while the aircraft climbs or descends. The information for horizontal position is available from the vertical gyro.

5.18.1 Turbulence Mode Weather Radar

Weather radar displays levels of brightness or color to represent rain rate, which is a key to the severity of the weather. However, the most dangerous threat in a thunderstorm is turbulence. Heavy rain is not comfortable to fly through and hail can break parts of an airplane, but turbulence causes control and structural failure. A system that provides a warning is the Turbulence Mode or Doppler Radar. In addition to the time delay and amplitude of a signal returning from a rain drop, which mainly falls vertically, it can measure Doppler shift. This happens when turbulence drives the rain horizontally; if the drop moves toward the airplane, for example, the frequency of the reflected signal rises due to Doppler shift—or lowering in frequency if the drop moves away. Turbulence, therefore, spreads the signal spectrum. A magnetron transmitter, however, has too much random frequency shift to allow the fine frequency measurements required for turbulence detection. A crystal controlled transmitter is essential for this application.

One advantage of the magnetron is its ability to simply generate enormous amounts of transmitter power. Since quartz crystals are not available at X band, a crystal oscillator at a significantly lower frequency must generate the X band carrier frequency. The lower frequency is multiplied until it reaches the desired 9375 MHz carrier frequency. The multiplied signal is amplified to the desired power level.

This raises the next problem. There are no X band power transistors that produce the power of a magnetron. Even multiple transistors in parallel and push-pull cannot approach it. This calls for a method which uses less transmitter power for turbulence mode radar.

Bandwidth of the magnetron radar is on the order of several MHz. This is because the pulse is narrow, making bandwidth of the transmitted signal relatively broad. In addition, receiver bandwidth must be sufficient to follow the drift of the radar transmitter. Crystal control insures that the signal does not drift in frequency. We can investigate reducing bandwidth of the transmitted signal with a broader pulse.

The typical pulse width for a magnetron type transmitter is 1 μs. The resolution of radar with a 1 μs pulse is about 1/8th of a nautical mile. This is reasonable for presenting weather information that is relatively close. The energy per pulse is directly proportional to the width of the pulse. To accommodate lower transmitter power, width of the pulse could be increased proportionately. For example, for a magnetron of 1500 watts output there is the same energy per pulse from a 100 watt transmitter if pulse width is increased from 1 μs to 15 μs.

The bandwidth of the pulse has decreased by a factor of 15 and thus receiver bandwidth can be decreased by a like factor. Since noise level of a receiver is a function of bandwidth, the 15 fold reduction in bandwidth becomes a 15 fold reduction in noise power, which implies the receiver becomes more sensitive.

On the down side, the resolution from the 15 ms pulse is 1.2 NM which is not suitable for close in weather. A resolution of 1.2 NM is fine at 50 NM or farther. To keep everything in perspective; the 1 ms pulse produces reasonable resolution for nearby weather but results in a broad spectrum, low energy and the need for a broad bandwidth receiver. However, this is required for close-in weather where return signals are strong. For distant weather, we can use the broad pulse and survive the loss of resolution. Why not provide two or even three transmit pulse widths and matched receiver bandwidths? The transmitter could scan for close weather with narrow pulses, mid range weather with a mid pulse width and distant weather with a broad pulse. This technique proves effective for solid state radar.

Example: How much Doppler shift would be produced from turbulence at 125 kts?
Solution: For velocities significantly less than c, the equation below gives the Doppler shift (even though 125 kt turbulence is severe, it is well below 3E8 m/s!)

$$\Delta f = 2v/\lambda = 2vf/c$$

where Df is the Doppler frequency shift, v is the velocity of the scatterer, and l is the wavelength of the radar. First we must convert 125 kts to meters per second which is,
$$v = 125 \ kts \ X \ 1852 \ m \ / \ 3600 \ s = 64.3 \ m/s$$

Calculating Δf, we obtain,

Δf =2 X 64.3 X 9.375E9 / 3E8 = 4.0 kHz

It can be seen that a stable transmitter is required to measure a 4 kHz Doppler shift.

The Doppler shift has two components. First, there is a steady shift due to relative motion between the aircraft and weather. The second is a random shift due to the random motion of turbulence. The return signals are demodulated with a frequency demodulator. The DC term, which is the constant Doppler, is eliminated with a high pass filter. Thus, only the noise component of the Doppler shift passes through the filter. The peak to peak value of this noise signal is directly proportional to turbulence.

5.18.2 Weather Picture

Next, compare information from the lightning detection system and weather radar. The lightning detector indicates lightning activity. Generally, the more severe the storm the more intense the lightning. Like any phenomenon there are exceptions. There are severe storms without lightning and vice versa. But experienced pilots often report an excellent correlation between the display and hazardous areas. One minor shortcoming of lightning detection systems is that they tend to show activity closer to the aircraft than the actual distance (called "radial spread"). This, however, is not a serious error because it produces a warning earlier than is necessary. Another advantage of the lightning detector is an ability to report weather over 360 degrees, so the pilot gets a picture of what is developing off to the sides and rear of the aircraft. Further, the pilot may preview the weather on the ground, before taking off. The low, 50 kHz signal from lightning strokes easily follows the curve of the earth.

Although lightning detectors are well proven for helping a pilot avoid thunderstorm turbulence, they cannot match weather radar for clearly outlining areas of heavy precipitation. On the other hand, weather radar is subject to "attenuation," where heavy rain can block radar energy. On the screen it may appear as no precipitation and has led the unwary pilot into a trap. Weather radar cannot detect clear air turbulence, CAT, or turbulence without precipitation. Although CAT usually refers to turbulence without storm activity, thunderstorms can generate turbulence many miles from the storm center. When the scatterers are present, weather radar provides a well-defined image of the storm.

Neither system is perfect. Thus the question becomes which system to use. The answer, where possible, is both. By combining information from the two, the combination provides the best picture of weather hazards.

Another enhancement provides weather information from ground-based weather sources using a ground to air data link. Radar equipment on the ground, with very high power and large antenna arrays, is far superior to airborne units. In addition to detecting severe weather, ground based weather networks provide information for the immediate vicinity, the destination airport and all points between. The picture generated by the National Weather Service, NWS, a division of the National Oceanographic and Atmospheric Administration, NOAA, is based on a network of sensors, including satellite observations at all parts of the spectrum. At the time of this writing, data links are beginning to upload this information to a cockpit display. Superb weather data is already available and a standardized data link is the "missing link".

Chapter 5 Review Questions

5.1   What is primary radar? How does it differ from secondary radar?

5.2   From which World War II system did the current ATCRBS evolve?

5.3   What is radar cross section, RCS?

5.4   What is a "radar mile"?

5.5   What advantages does a secondary radar provide?

5.6   What is does the SLS pulse provide?

5.7   What type of data entry is available on the transponder?

5.8   How many data bits are there in the transponder reply?

5.9   How many different "squawks" does a transponder provide?

5.10   Which type of altitude does the transponder transmit?

5.11   When a pilot is asked to "squawk and ident", what happens to the reply?

5.12   What is an encoding altimeter? What is a blind encoding altimeter?

5.13   What problems of the ATCRBS system does the mode S system improve?

5.14   What are the types of mode S interrogations?

5.15   What type of modulation is applied to P6?

5.16   What type of modulation is used for a mode S reply?

5.17   An ATCRBS transponder is replying with 1200 and no ident with a peak power of 230 watts. The transponder is interrogated with a test set at the test rate of 135 interrogations per second. What is the average power of the transponder?

5.18   What is the average power of a mode S transponder selectively interrogated at 50 interrogations per second, if peak power is 250 watts? The transponder is replying with the short message.

5.19   How would a mode S transponder reply to an ATCRBS mode C interrogation?

5.20   What is the reply delay for an ATCRBS transponder? For the mode S transponder?

5.21   From what points is the reply delay measured for an ATCRBS transponder?

5.22   From what points is the reply delay measured for a mode S transponder for an all-call? For a selective interrogation?

5.23   What error detection is used with the mode S transponder?

5.24   What is the maximum number of different mode S addresses?

5.25   Why is space diversity used with the mode S transponder?

5.26   Does the ATCRBS transponder receiver have AGC? How does the receiver handle a wide range of signal strengths?

5.27   What is "tau" in collision avoidance systems?

5.28   What is a traffic advisory (TA)? When is it issued? How is the crew alerted to the advisory?

5.29   What is a resolution advisory (RA)? When is it issued? Where is advisory information presented?

5.30   What is coordination in TCAS?

5.31   What is the basic principle of ADS-B?

5.32   What considerations must be taken when choosing an operating frequency for weather radar?

5.33   How does weather radar differ in performance from the lightning detection system?

5.34   How does turbulence weather radar achieve the same range as higher powered radar?

Chapter 6

Airborne Communications Systems

6.1 Introduction

The first communications installed in aircraft were one-way systems, where pilots received bulletins and information relating to air traffic and weather. Air-to-ground communications often involved turning on landing lights and wagging wings. There were debates over whether HF or VHF communications were superior for airborne communications up to World War II. During the war, both types were employed and the advantages of VHF became clear. One disadvantage was the complexity of the radio transmitters. However, advances in electronics paved the way for VHF communications in aircraft.

AM, full carrier, double sideband modulation was adopted for VHF airborne radios for two reasons. When communications were contemplated well before the war, only AM was available. FM was not yet invented. Even after FM appeared, it took a long time before circuits and components became available. Even though AM and FM were in operation, AM was chosen for airborne use because it was a proven system.

6.2 VHF AM Communications

The first band for airborne communications was from 118 MHz to 132 MHz, with 200 kHz channels. The number of channels was doubled by assigning frequencies every 100 kHz in 1958. In 1959 an additional 4 MHz was added to the top end and, in 1964, channels were doubled by decreasing width to 50 kHz. In 1974, the number was doubled again by reducing channel width to 25 kHz. In 1979 another 40 channels were added by increasing the band 1 MHz at the top end, increasing the total span from 118 MHz to 137 MHz.

The original VHF band had 70 frequencies and extremely wide channels to accommodate frequency drift and poor dial calibration of mechanically-tuned receivers. VHF transmitters were always crystal-controlled but many receivers were tuned with a variable capacitor. Even the broad 200 kHz channel required a high quality, expensive tuning capacitor and dial. When channels were narrowed to 100 kHz, the end of the mechanically-tuned receiver was at hand. The move to 50 kHz and finally 25 kHz required a crystal controlled receiver.

The VHF communications band with 25 kHz spacing produces 760 channels, which is insufficient in some locations around the world because of interference. In the late 1990s, the number of channels was tripled to 2280 by reducing bandwidth from 25 kHz to 8.333 kHz.

This plan met with opposition and the tripling of channels is being implemented in Europe and not in the United States. The solution to communications capacity is not a further reduction in channel width but a system more elegant than full carrier double sideband AM. This type of voice communication is not the most efficient use of spectrum.

Alternative modulation or encoding methods were proposed when the last increase of channels was discussed. The methods employed thus far to increase channels from the original 70 to 2280, a thirty two-fold increase, involved the same modulation, DSB AM. One proposal was single sideband, SSB, a modulation which takes half the bandwidth. The frequency range of voice communications is from 300 Hz to 3.00 kHz or a total spectrum of 2.7 kHz. A DSB AM signal has a spectral width of 6 kHz while an SSB signal has a width of 2.7 kHz, which is only 45% of the bandwidth of DSB AM. Theoretically, about eight SSB voice signals could be placed in the space of one 25 kHz channel. In practice, however, this expansion would strain the state of the art and require an expensive communications transceiver.

Aircraft communications have had difficulty obtaining sufficient channels. The entire VHF communications band is 19 MHz wide. Land mobile radio, with many more users, has had problems with lack of channels but nowhere as severe as aviation. The reason is not the number of users but that each user transmits and receives over a very long range. A typical land mobile station has a range from one automobile to another of, perhaps, 7 NM, depending on terrain and frequency. The range from a mobile unit to a base station using a 35-meter tower could be 18 NM. If the base station has a tower on a mountaintop, range could extend to 50 NM. With this distance, frequencies can be reused every 50 to 100 NM.

This is not the case with airborne transmitters. Air to ground radio range is given by the formula:

$$R = 1.225 \ H^{1/2} \qquad\qquad (6.1)$$

Where R is the radio line of sight in nautical miles and H is the altitude in feet.

Consider the range of a transmitter in a small general aviation aircraft at 10,000 feet:

$$R = 1.225 \ (1E4)^{1/2} = 123 \ NM$$

The range of an air transport aircraft at 40,000 feet is twice that of GA aircraft, or 246 NM. Aircraft frequencies, therefore, can be reused only when separated by hundreds of miles. It is also apparent how frequencies became scarce in Europe where countries may be only a few hundred miles across.

In addition to voice, there is a need for data transmission. Much of what is carried on voice is more efficiently communicated with a data transceiver. The need for both voice and data, an inexpensive transceiver and more effective use of the spectrum prompted a proposal for a digital communications radio. This system uses time division multiple access or TDMA. At the time of this writing, TDMA has not been fully described or internationally accepted but required documents are nearing completion. VHF radio of the future will be a TDMA digital system this subject is covered later in this chapter.

Amplitude modulation, unless otherwise specified, represents a DSB (double sideband) signal with a full carrier. The carrier frequency is the center of the channel and designates it. As an example, if a communications channel is 131.575 MHz, the carrier frequency is 131.575 MHz and upper and lower sidebands extend above and below the carrier. For speech with a maximum of 3 kHz bandwidth, the frequency range covered by 131.575 MHz is from 131.572 MHz to 131.578 MHz, as shown in Fig. 6.1. The channel, called 131.575 MHz, extends from 12.5 kHz below the nominal channel center to 12.5 kHz above. Why would a signal that extends from the nominal channel frequency up and down by 3 kHz be allocated a channel that extends plus and minus 12.5 kHz? The extra 8.5 kHz, plus and minus, is taken up by errors in the carrier frequency and a guard band.

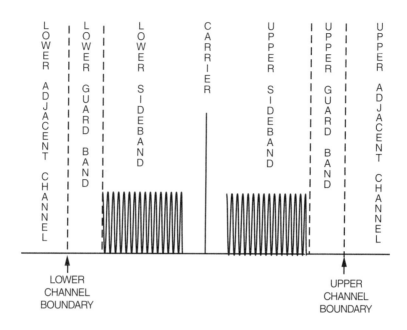

Figure 6.1 Communications channel

As an example, a DSB AM aircraft transmitter has a required frequency tolerance of 10 parts per million, or 10 PPM. The maximum frequency error of the carrier is 1.32 kHz. The transmitter could have an output spectrum as low as 131.575 MHz minus 3 kHz because of the lower sideband, minus 1.32 kHz due to frequency tolerance. The same is true on the upper side of the carrier. The DSB AM signal can cover from minus 4.32 kHz to plus 4.32 kHz. This leaves 8.18 kHz from the signal to the channel boundaries. The additional, unused, spectrum is the guard band. Before frequency tolerance was tightened to 10 PPM, the guard band was considerably less.

6.3 VHF Communications Hardware

The earliest VHF communications consisted of separate transmitter and receiver. This is no longer the case. Because many circuits can be shared, transmitter and receiver are combined into a transceiver. There are advantages to a transceiver over separate transmitters and receivers. First, a communications receiver is no good without a transmitter and vice versa. There are few applications where only a receiver is required for picking up some sort of broadcast. One example is the automatic terminal information service, or ATIS.

There are other advantages to transceiver circuit sharing. For a DSB AM transceiver, the frequency synthesizer, power supply and some audio circuits are shared. It may not sound like a lot of sharing, but the synthesizer and power supply are significant parts of the radio. In the area of mechanical items, cases, chassis and connectors are shared. These items are expensive and savings are significant.

6.3.1 VHF Communications Receiver

Fig 6.2 shows a block diagram of the VHF transceiver. The receiver portion is a conventional superheterodyne. Single conversion is shown, but multiple conversion may be used. Older receivers are more likely to have multiple conversion in order to implement a sharp

229

skirted IF filter at a lower frequency. Modern monolithic crystal filters provide suitable performance at a higher frequency, allowing a single conversion receiver to be practical.

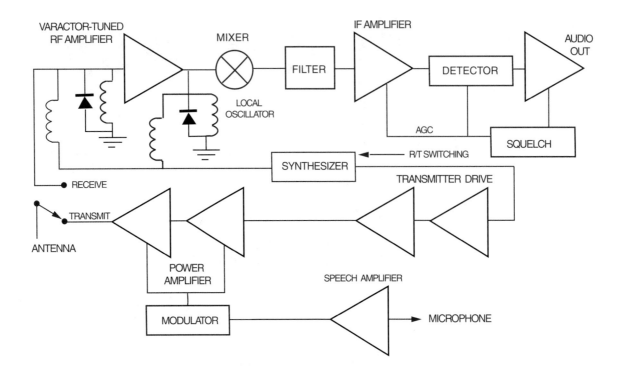

Figure 6.2 AM transceiver

The receiver has a varactor-tuned RF filter. It is possible to provide a fixed-tuned RF filter but since frequency range is from 118 MHz to 137 MHz, the image of the lowest input frequency would have to be greater than 137 MHz. This would require a minimum IF of 9.5 MHz.

Before assuming that a fixed-tuned filter is acceptable, be aware that image rejection for a communications receiver should be greater than 60 dB. The rejection of the RF filter must be 60 dB or more just above the 137 MHz band edge. This type of filter is not practical. A filter with 60 dB rejection 20 MHz above the band edge might be practical, but this requires a minimum IF of 19.5 MHz. Most VHF communications receivers use the highest IF practical with a varactor-tuned front end filter.

The choice of an IF depends on the ability of the RF filter to reject an image. An IF of 21.4 MHz is reasonable. The local oscillator operates at the channel frequency plus the IF. For the example at hand, the local oscillator operates from 118.00 MHz plus 21.4 MHz or 139.4 MHz to 136.975 MHz plus 21.4 MHz or 158.375 MHz. It is preferable to use a local oscillator frequency above the RF frequency to reduce spurious responses. This is called high side injection.

The RF filter is followed by an RF amplifier which feeds the mixer, where RF is converted to the IF. Immediately following the mixer is the IF filter. Generally, an active mixer such as a dual gate MOSFET or transistor is used to obtain some of the gain required by the receiver. In recent years, diode type mixers are found in radio receivers. The passive diode mixer offers a higher dynamic range and reduces spurious responses of the receiver. The rising number of users also contributes to the possibility of spurious signals generated in the receiver. Thus, a modern receiver not only has more channels and a tighter frequency tolerance but higher dynamic range.

Power Measurement in dBm

A misunderstood area of electrical measurement is the decibel. Gains and losses could be specified as a pure ratio but this is cumbersome because the range can be great. A technique for handling large ratios is the logarithmic form. The gain of a circuit using a logarithmic form, the Bel, named after Alexander Graham Bell, is defined as:

$$B = \log (P_{out} / P_{in}) \qquad (6.2)$$

The relationship between two powers in Bels is the log of the ratio. For electronics, the Bel is not a convenient unit; typical gains and losses involve numbers that are too small. Therefore, the common unit is the decibel, dB, which is one tenth of a Bel. The equation for power ratio :

$$dB = 10 \log (P_{out} / P_{in}) \qquad (6.3)$$

For example: A public address, PA, amplifier takes an input signal from a microphone which is 50 mv and amplifies it to 50 watts to drive speakers in an auditorium . How much gain does this amplifier have? The input impedance is 2200 ohms.

First, input power is calculated, which is $(0.05)^2/2200 = 1.14E\text{-}6$ watts. Take the ratio. $(P_{out} / P_{in}) = 50/1.14E\text{-}6 = 44.0E6$. The gain, decibels is $10 \log(44.0E6) = 76$ dB. Notice that this calculation involves small numbers, the power from the microphone; a normal number, 50 watts, and a large number, the gain of 44 million of the amplifier.

The decibel compares two powers; i.e. the ratio is dimensionless. This is necessary to take the logarithm. If the denominator of the ratio is made a fixed reference power, only one power could be represented in a decibel form:

$$dBw = 10 \log (P / 1 \text{ watt}) \qquad (6.4)$$

The equation is for dBw, where w indicates that the decibel number represents a power relative to one watt. Notice that the equation is still a ratio of two powers, but one is a reference. Returning to the PA amplifier example, convert the output power of 50 watts to dBw:

$$dBw = 10 \log (50) = 17 \text{ dBw} \qquad (6.5)$$

One watt is not the only reference that may be used in the decibel equation. Another common one is one milliwatt, which is used in radio receivers and other systems where low power may be encountered. When the reference is one milliwatt, the dB relationship is written as dBm. If the reference were one kilowatt, decibel power would be dBk. This is used for high power transmitters. Let us go back to the public address system and express power from the microphone in dBm:

$$dBm = 10 \log (1.14E\text{-}6 / 1E\text{-}3) = \text{-}29 \text{ dBm}$$

In this example the answer has a negative sign. It indicates that power is less than the reference power. To convert from dBw to dBm; +30 dBm is 0 dBw. Notice that one watt in dBm included the plus sign. This is a good habit as both plus and minus dBm are encountered. *(Continued)*

In the public address system example, output power, +17 dBw is +47 dBm. The difference between input and output power is +47 dBm – (- 29 dBm) = 76 dB. Note that dBm is subtracted from dBm and obtained dB. This is because subtracting logarithms produces the logarithm of the division of two numbers. Since dBm represents a power, the result is the logarithm of the division of two powers, which is the original definition. Also, notice that the result is the gain of the PA amplifier that had been previously calculated.

The advantage of decibel notation may not be evident from the PA example. This is because the microphone was specified in volts and the speakers in watts. If the microphone and speakers were in dBm, finding gain is a matter of subtracting input power in dBm from output power in dBm, arriving at gain in dB. If all measurements are made in dBm and signal generators calibrated in dBm, gains and power levels are easily calculated. This is the technique in virtually all RF measurements.

There are common decibel relationships to calculate dBm for other decibel based measurements without a calculator. Decibels allow gains and powers to be calculated with simple addition rather than division and multiplication. The input power of a system is added to all system gains, system losses are subtracted; and the result is output power. The same calculation without decibel notation requires multiplying by all gains and dividing by losses to obtain output power.

Some common decibel relationships may remembered as tools for calculating decibel figures by simple calculation. The first is 3 dB, which represents a doubling of power. Second is 1 volt in a 50W system; (every thing in RF measurement is relative to 50W), is +13 dBm. The third is 1 dB is a 25 percent increase in power, (actually 25.8 %). Next, these tools are used to calculate powers in dBm.

1. How much power is –97 dBm?
Solution: If power were –100 dBm, the power would be 100 dB below one milliwatt or 1E-13 watts or 0.1 picowatts. Since power is –97 dBm, or 3 dB higher, the answer is 0.2 pW.
2. How much voltage is present in a –47 dBm signal in a 50W system?
Solution: +13 dBm is one volt. – 47 dBm is 60 dB less or one millionth the power of one volt. Since power is voltage squared, the voltage is one thousandth, or one millivolt.
3 .How much power is represented by –15 dBm?
Solution: If power is reduced by one half, five times, it is 1 milliwatt divided by 2^5 = 32, or 31 microwatts.
4. If the power of a signal is reduced by 20 dB, by how much would voltage be reduced?
Solution: This is a trick question that has fooled many a student. The answer is 20 dB. If a signal is attenuated by X dB, power, voltage and current are all reduced by X dB. The confusion comes from the following definition of a decibel.

$$dB = 10 \log (P_{out} / P_{in}) = 20 \log (V_{out} / V_{in}) \qquad (6.6)$$

where V_{out} is the output voltage and V_{in} is input voltage. For this relationship to be correct, input and output impedances must be the same which, in the RF world, is usually true.

What students remember from this relationship is that when power is increased by a factor of two, the decibel notation increases by 3 dB. When voltage is doubled, decibel notation increases by 6 dB. From this the student assumes that a 3 dB increase in power is the same as a 6 dB increase in voltage, which is wrong. When voltage is doubled, the power is quadrupled, which is doubled twice, or 6 dB.

An AM detector follows the IF amplifier. The DC component of AM detection is for AGC action. The AGC adjusts the gain of the receiver to stabilize audio output from the receiver. In most superheterodyne receivers the majority of gain is obtained in the IF amplifier. It is also in the IF where most gain reduction is obtained. Therefore, the AGC system controls gain of the IF amplifier. In many cases it is desirable to achieve gain reduction in the RF amplifier as well. This is because the amount of gain cutback required is so great, the IF amplifier cannot supply it all. When RF amplifier gain is adjusted, as well as the IF, it is desired to not cut back RF gain until the signal reaches a relatively high level. If RF gain is cut back for weak signals, just above the AGC threshold, the receiver's noise figure is affected and the signal becomes noisy. Therefore, the cutback of the RF amplifier does not occur until the receiver has a significant signal level, perhaps -80 dBM.

.

The effectiveness of an AGC system is given by the figure of merit. To determine this parameter, an amplitude modulated signal is applied to the receiver and the signal level is varied from the AGC threshold, to the point where the AGC no longer functions or causes distortion. The variation in audio output throughout the range of the AGC is the figure of merit. If, as an example, the audio output of a receiver is set to 0 dBm for a weak signal and the output increases to +2 dBm with a very strong signal the figure of merit is 2 dB.

Example: How much AGC action is required if a communications receiver operates with a strong signal from an air transport category aircraft using a 50 watt transmitter at a distance of 50 meters and a weak signal from a 5 watt transmitter at a distance of 100 NM?

Solution: Find the difference in signal strength due to distance in dB and the difference in transmitter power in dB and add the two. This gives the variation in levels of the two signals.

Do the transmitter powers first, as that is the easiest . A = 10 log (5/50) = - 10 dB. In other words, the 5 watt transmitter is 10 dB less than the 50 watt transmitter.

The loss due to distance is inversely proportional to the distance squared or $10 \log (D_1/D_2)^2 = 20 \log (D_1/D_2) = 20 \log (50 / (100 X 1852)) = -71 dB$. In order to have the two signals produce the same output from the communications receiver, the AGC must have 81 dB of range.

The receiver includes a squelch circuit which removes audio from the speaker when no signal is received. This prevents noise of the receiver from being heard in headphones or speaker. There are two general methods for squelch. The first and oldest is to sense AGC voltage and, once AGC action begins, enable the audio output. Although this has been in use for years, there are disadvantages. First, AGC action must take place before receiver audio is enabled. In many receivers there are useful signals below the AGC threshold that provide AGC action on noise, so the squelch may open on noise.

Squelch circuits in FM receivers are very effective and do not use AGC voltage because FM receivers do not have AGC. FM squelch uses a characteristic of FM receivers called quieting. When not receiving signals, there is considerable background noise. Once a carrier is received and, assume the carrier is not modulated, the level of background noise decreases. In a good FM receiver, a very weak signal can produce a significant drop in noise level. If the received carrier contains frequency modulation, the noise is reduced but audio output will now contain audio modulation. In the case of voice FM radio, the modulation spectrum extends from about 300 Hz to 3 kHz. The noise spectrum extends above and below the modulation frequency range and thus the squelch can use the noise level above the 3 kHz modulation range.

Audio output from the FM detector is high pass filtered to eliminate speech energy and noise voltage is rectified, as shown in Fig. 6.3. DC from rectification of noise voltage activates the squelch.

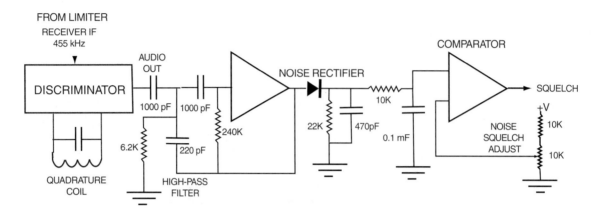

Figure 6.3   Squelch circuit

When an AM signal is received by an FM receiver, the AM carrier is just as effective in producing squelch action as an FM signal. An FM IF is provided in the communications receiver for its squelch capability. With the advent of inexpensive FM IF subsystem integrated circuits, adding an FM IF for squelch action is cost effective.

The noise-activated squelch is effective primarily for weak signals, whereas the AGC activated squelch is effective for stronger signals. Noise-activated squelch has a drawback if two signals are present, desired and undesired. If they are more than 3kHz apart, in an AM receiver a beat is generated at a frequency equal to the difference in the two signals. This beat frequency, higher than 3 kHz, passes through the high pass filter and causes the beat to be rectified and squelch the receiver. The best squelch system uses a combination of noise and AGC squelch.

234

Microvolts: Two Types.

The virtues of dBm were praised earlier because of ease of calculation. There is another benefit of dBm; it replaces a confusing method for specifying receiver sensitivities in microvolts. It sounds harmless, just a simple microvolt, but dangers lurk here. A bit of history will explain. When signal generators were first manufactured, the fledgling radio industry had not standardized on an impedance for measurement, which now is 50 ohms. Radio receivers also were not standardized and often not even resistive. Many radio receivers, which were in the LF and MF range, matched an antenna that was mostly capacitive. In order to test a radio receiver a dummy antenna was connected between the signal generator and receiver under test. The output impedance of early signal generators was not 50 ohms. They were typically low and varied over frequency. This made it difficult to gain correlation between signal generators— and dummy antennas only matched one brand of signal generator to a radio receiver. Because of the dummy antenna, voltage from the signal generator and voltage at the receiver were not the same. It was not known how much the dummy antenna decreased the signal to the load, so signal generator output voltage was specified with an open circuit.

The radio industry realized the problems with signal generators and made them all with an output impedance of 50 ohms. Many newer radio receivers, particularly for higher frequencies, were designed with 50 ohm inputs that matched the signal generators. High frequency and VHF antennas have impedances around 50 ohms and the movement to the standardized impedance made a lot of sense.

Since a 50 ohm signal generator is designed for a 50 ohm load, some were calibrated with the terminated voltage, that is, the voltage across the load. An unpleasant situation developed. Some signal generators were calibrated with open circuit voltage, while others with the terminated voltage. The open circuit voltage was twice the terminated voltage when the 50-ohm generator terminated in 50 ohms. To counter this difficulty, two types of voltages were specified. Since receiver sensitivities are usually measured in microvolts these became two types: "hard microvolts" and "easy microvolts".

Hard microvolts was the calibration of a signal generator in open circuit voltage. This is because voltage across the load is only half that marked on the signal generator and meeting a certain specification was "harder" than when using the actual voltage across the load. If a radio was to receive signals at 1 microvolt hard, the signal generator was set to 1 μv but voltage across the load was 0.5 μv. If the radio was to receive 1 μv easy, the signal generator calibrated in easy microvolts would be set to 1 μv and the receiver would see 1 μv, which is twice the voltage the receiver would see if the requirement were hard microvolts.

All aviation specifications still in microvolts are hard microvolts. When a signal generator is calibrated in easy microvolts, the output level can be corrected by adding a 6 dB attenuator to the output or making a correction when setting the level. There is no such thing as hard and easy dBm. This is one reason microvolts have been removed from new avionics specifications.

6.3.2 VHF Communications Transmitter

AM transmitters, that is, simple DSB (double sideband) AM, typically modulate the supply voltage to an amplifier that is driven into saturation. If the amplifier has sufficient drive to go into saturation, the output power is a function of the amplifier supply voltage.

In the case of high power, with about 5- to 50-watt transistor amplifiers, considerable power feeds through from the drive that appears at the output. It is not possible to obtain a high percentage of modulation with a fixed drive level to assure that the amplifier will remain in saturation. Therefore, the power supply of the driving amplifier is also modulated. Typically, two or three stages of amplifiers are modulated to provide the required 90% modulation.

A common form of amplitude modulator is the series modulator, shown in Fig. 6.4. The modulator is in series with the power amplifier and power supply. If there were no modulation, that is, just a carrier, nominal power amplifier voltage is one half the supply voltage. To provide a modulation peak, the voltage to the power amplifier is increased to nearly the power supply voltage. For the modulation minimum, voltage is decreased to, theoretically, zero, but in practice to about 5 volts. The modulation minimum is achieved by reducing drive power, as well.

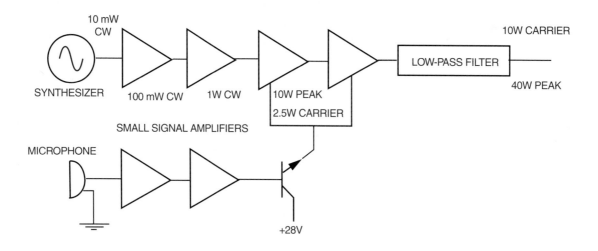

Figure 6.4   Series modulated AM transmitter

Let's recall a few facts about amplitude modulation to appreciate its requirements. Assume a General Aviation transceiver with a carrier power of 10 watts. The instantaneous power on modulation peaks, if 100% modulated, is 40 watts. This means the power amplifier must provide a 40-watt output.

The *average* power of an AM signal is equal to the carrier power, P_c. Notice the word *average* is emphasized. For every positive peak of an AM signal there is a similar negative peak. Transmitter power is higher than carrier power as much as it is lower.

Let η be the efficiency of the transmitter power amplifier. Therefore, power input to the amplifier is:

$$P = P_c / \eta$$

Total input power for a 10-watt AM transmitter with an efficiency of 50% is

$$P = 10/0.5 = 20 \text{ watts.} \qquad (6.7)$$

236

For a transmitter using a series modulator the nominal power supply voltage one half the supply voltage, V_s. Therefore, input power to the power amplifier is $(V_s I_s)/2$, where I_s is the average supply current. Input power to the series modulator is $V_s I_s$ which is twice the power supplied to the amplifier. When no modulation is applied, a 10-watt transmitter requires 20 watts to the input of the power amplifier and 40 watts into the series modulator. What happens to the extra 30 watts? Ten watts are dissipated as heat in the power amplifier while twice that, 20 watts, is dissipated in the series modulator. Three times the power delivered to the antenna is dissipated as heat in the transceiver for an efficiency of 25%. This technique is very inefficient.

Conditions improve when modulation is applied. Since an additional 50% of carrier power is added to the total, RMS, transmitter power when a transmitter is modulated with a single tone, 15 watts are fed to the antenna. This leaves 25 watts to be dissipated as heat in the transceiver. The efficiency is now $15/40 = 37.5\%$, which is an improvement.

An alternate to the series modulator is the transformer-coupled modulator. In this scheme a high powered amplifier drives the primary of a transformer as shown in Fig. 6.5. The input power to the RF amplifier passes through the secondary of the transformer and to the power amplifier. The AC voltage from the transformer, coupled from the audio amplifier, causes the supply voltage of the RF power amplifier to go from the nominal input power supply voltage to twice that voltage and down to near zero. This changes the voltage to the amplifier to provide amplitude modulation.

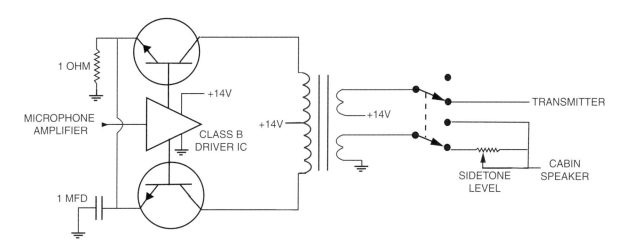

Figure 6.5 Transformer coupled AM modulator

DC power to the amplifier passes through the transformer secondary. Because the transformer is, theoretically zero impedance to DC, there is no power loss. On the other hand, consider the inefficiency of the audio amplifier. Typical efficiency for voice is about 70%. To calculate efficiency of the entire system we need to know how much power is required of the audio amplifier. A fully modulated AM carrier, that is 100%, by a single tone adds 50% of the carrier power in the sidebands. This is close to the case for voice modulation. Therefore, power in both sidebands, provided by the 10-watt transmitter, is 5 watts. The efficiency of the power amplifier is 50% so it is safe to assume that an additional input of about 10 watts is required to the power amplifier. This comes from the audio amplifier, which is 70% efficient and, thus, $10/0.7 = 14.3$ watts are required. Power from the power supply is $20+14.3 = 34.3$ watts. When a transmitter is modulated with a single tone at 100%, 34.3 watts are supplied to the power amplifier and modulator and 15 watts, carrier plus sidebands, are fed to the antenna. The efficiency is $15/34.3 = 43.7\%$ which is significantly better than the series modulator. When the transmitter has no modulation, the audio amplifier consumes little power and efficiency becomes that of the RF power amplifier, 50%.

6.3.3 Frequency Synthesizer

A VHF transceiver frequency synthesizer uses the dual modulus techniques outlined in earlier chapters. There is one significant difference. The communications transceiver must provide two output frequencies; one for the local oscillator and a second for the transmitter carrier.

Except for old transceivers using crystal banks, the synthesizer is a phase locked loop. There are two methods of providing the frequencies. The first is to rechannel the synthesizer from the receiver local oscillator's frequency to the transmitter carrier frequency when the push-to-talk switch is pressed. The amount of frequency the synthesizer must change is exactly the IF. The advantage is simplicity. On the negative side are lock up time and the need to increase the bandwidth of the synthesizer.

Assume a communications transceiver has an IF of 21.4 MHz, which is a standard for a VHF receiver. For low spurious response, high side injection is used for the local oscillator. The frequency range of the local oscillator is 139.4 MHz to 158.375 MHz. If the synthesizer is designed only for a receiver this would be the entire frequency range, which is a 1.14 high to low frequency ratio.

If the same synthesizer generates transmitter carrier frequencies, the entire range is from 118.00 to 158.375 MHz or a 1.34 to one ratio. This increased ratio makes the synthesizer more difficult to design.

The other problem is lock up time. When the synthesizer changes from one frequency to another 21.4 MHz away, a finite time is required to slew to the new frequency and settle. Depending on the design of the phase locked loop, this can take considerable time, perhaps hundreds of milliseconds. During this period the transmitter may not provide an output, as the frequency of the output is changing. If the synthesizer does not change frequency quickly enough, the first word of the communication may be lost. The higher frequency ratio and lockup time can be overcome, but at the expense of additional circuits and careful design.

An alternative is not to change frequency but have it remain on the local oscillator and heterodyne a crystal oscillator at the receiver IF, then extract the transmitter frequency. The advantage is that the synthesizer does not have to change frequency. There are no problems with lock up time. On the other hand, a tuned circuit must follow the mixer to select the transmitter frequency. Typically, this filter, like the receiver RF filter, is varactor-tuned. Since the transmitter filter covers the same frequency as the RF filter, the same design with the same tuning voltages may be used.

6.3.4 NAVCOM Transceiver

It is common to put a navigation receiver and communications transceiver in the same box. There are significant advantages and disadvantages. On the good side, sharing is possible, which is the reason for transceivers rather than separate transmitter and receiver.

The first shared item is the case and mounting hardware. Cases, mounting hardware and connectors are expensive. The power supply is also shared. Most modern equipment involves a microprocessor and this can be shared. A combined unit also reduces the instrument panel area. Audio amplifiers may be shared. Although there are separate receivers, they drive one loudspeaker.

Now for the down side; if one unit fails, NAV or COMM, and is removed to be repaired, the other side is also out. New technology will eventually obsolete NAV and COMM, but probably not at the same time. This means that half the unit may be obsolete for a while.

Navcomm transceiver, panel-mount. VHF Communications are on left side; navigation (VOR/localizer) on right.

Designing the two units to fit the same case is a challenge because signals from one tend to be spurious signals for the other. Sharing the microprocessor is not as attractive as it once was because the component has become very inexpensive.

6.3.5 Antennas

The radiated signal for VHF communications is vertically polarized, which means the electric field of the electromagnetic field is vertical. This is the usual polarization for terrestrial communications in transportation vehicles such as automobiles, trucks, ships and trains. It is easy to design omnidirectional antennas that are vertically polarized.

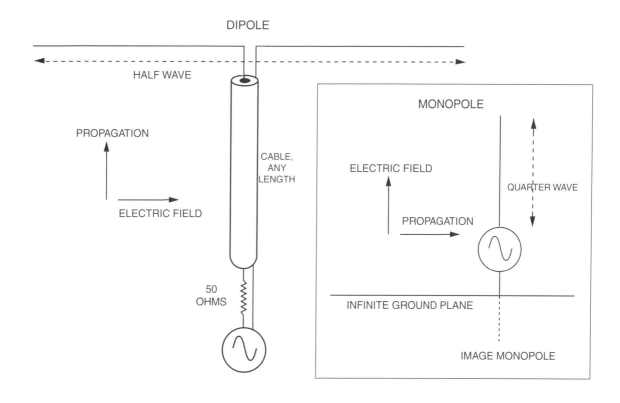

Figure 6.6   Dipole antenna

The simplest, yet effective, antenna for vertical polarization is a ¼ wave antenna over an "infinite" ground plane. To understand it, consider first the dipole antenna. The dipole consists of two conductors that are $\lambda/4$ each, as shown in Fig. 6.6. The generator varies the voltage between the two, which sets up an electric field, and energy radiates from the dipole.

239

Most energy travels outward, perpendicular to the axis of the conductors. The electric field is parallel to the axis of the dipole.

The conductors can be virtually any length. If each is a quarter of a wavelength, for a total of one-half wavelength, impedance of the antenna is resistive. It's about 50 to 70 ohms and pure resistance. Supplying energy to the antenna is a matter of connecting the antenna; take one half of the λ/2 dipole and mount it on a perfectly-conducting, infinitely large ground plane. Feed energy to the half dipole, or monopole, using a voltage generator connected between the ground plane and monopole.

The perfectly conducting ground plane acts as a radio mirror. Look at a monopole in an optical mirror and a dipole is perceived because of the reflection. Although the explanation is beyond the scope of this text, the same happens to the radio image; the antenna appears as a dipole. The antenna has a resonance where impedance is purely resistive, just as the dipole.

The monopole antenna radiates as a half dipole. Remember, the ground plane is infinite. On the back side of the ground plane there is no electric field and, therefore, no radiation.

Example: What is the length of a λ/4 antenna for aircraft?

Solution: Use the center of the communications band at 127.5 MHz. A full wavelength is λ = c/f = 3E8/127.5E6 = 2.35 meters. A quarter wavelength is 2.35/4 = 0.59 meters.

In an installation on a vehicle, the ground plane is far from infinite. As long as the ground plane is at least one half to one wavelength, the monopole antenna is nearly resonant and there will be some radiation from the back side of the ground plane. The communications antenna on an aircraft may be mounted at the top or bottom. Bottom mounting is more difficult on small aircraft because of the small clearance between the bottom of the fuselage and the ground. Mounting the antenna on the top of the fuselage is preferred for small aircraft. Air to ground communication is not severely compromised because the small ground plane of the aircraft allows significant radiation from the back side of the ground plane.

Advanced problem: An unpressurized GA aircraft flying at 10,000 feet is communicating with a ground station on a frequency of 120 MHz. The receiver on the ground can receive signals as weak as –89 dBm. The antennas at both ends are λ/4 monopoles. How much transmitter power is required to maintain this communications link?

Solution: The answer lies in calculating the link power budget. The ability to communicate 123 NM, the radio line of sight, lies in transmitter power, antenna gains of transmitting and receiving antennas and distance between transmitter and receiver. Add these as decibel figures to arrive at the link power budget. This can be written as:

Received power = transmitted power + transmitter antenna gain + receiver antenna gain + path loss

The received signal is proportional to transmitter power. The more powerful the transmitter, the stronger the signal. The transmitter antenna gain is also clear. The more gain an antenna has, the more it directs transmitter power to the receiver, the greater the received signal. The same holds for receiver antenna gain. The path loss may need some explaining.

When energy radiates from an antenna it spreads over an increasingly large area. The strength of the received signal is a function of distance from the radiator. This reduction in signal strength is called path loss, given by:

240

$$L = 10 \ log[(1/4\pi)(\lambda/R)^2]$$

where R is the distance between transmitter and receiver. In this example, R is 123 NM or 228 E3 meters. The path loss is:

$$L = 10 \ log \ [(\ 1/4 \ \pi \ )(2.5/228E3)^2] = -110 \ dB$$

The gain of the two monopole antennas is the same as that of a dipole which is +2.1 dB. Solving for transmitter power:

$$P_t = P_r - G_t - G_r + L = P_r - 2G_r - L = -89dBm - 2X2.1dB + 110dB = 16.8 \ dBm$$

It seems surprising that transmitter power of only 48 mw can communicate 123 NM. This is particularly so when it is considered that most GA transceivers have a power output of about 5 watts, while large aircraft have output power between 10 and 25 watts.

Consider the 5 watts in a GA transceiver. This is 100 times greater than the calculated power of 48 mw. This excess is 20 dB more than necessary. The 48 mw transmitter provided the minimum required signal. If the signal degrades a small amount, it could become unintelligible. The system has no margin. With a 5 watt transmitter, the system has a 20 dB margin.

Just how much is required? The losses between transmitter and receiver included gain of the antennas and free space loss. Not considered is the loss in the transmission line between transmitter and its antenna or receiver and its antenna. In the aircraft, the length of transmission line between transceiver and antenna may only be a few meters. At VHF, this loss is a fraction of a dB. At the ground station, the antenna is on a roof or a tower and the transmission line is as much as 100 meters. For long cable runs, low loss cable is used but losses could be one or two dB. Transmission lines have chipped away up to 3 dB from the signal margin.

We used 2.1 dB of gain for a dipole antenna. The ground station antenna is easily as good as a dipole, but the antenna on the aircraft will probably have a gain less than a dipole. Remember, the $\lambda/4$ monopole has the same gain as a dipole only when mounted on an infinite ground plane. The aircraft provides a ground plane that is a compromise and the gain of the monopole is, typically, less than that of a dipole. What happens is that the gain of the antenna is greater in certain directions. Depending on the relationship between the aircraft and ground station, antenna gain could be less or greater than a dipole. Projections on the aircraft such as rudder and stabilizer can cause shadowing and nulls in the antenna pattern.

When the aircraft banks, it is possible that the antenna turns away from the ground station, which introduces additional loss of 3 dB or more. It should be evident that a 20 dB margin can be chipped away by normal conditions.

6.4 High Frequency Communications
VHF is limited to line of sight , which restricts range to about 150 NM. For longer distances, over oceans and in remote areas, high frequency, HF, is used. The longer wavelengths of HF are refracted by the ionosphere which propagates signals high in the atmosphere and returns them to earth a long distance away.

Ionospheric propagation is variable, changing from night to day and season to season, and is different at locations around the globe. Finally, there is an 11 year sunspot cycle. Because of these variations, frequencies are chosen to propagate to the area of interest. The range from 2.8 MHz to 22 MHz is used for aircraft, although many communications transceivers cover to 29.9999 MHz. This is because some airborne equipment has adapted existing designs, particular military transceivers, that cover additional frequencies. The extended range also permits future expansion. This band is shared with many radio services, with small segments for aviation spread throughout.

HF Transceiver Control Display Unit (Collins)

The typical HF transceiver covers 3.000-29.9999 MHz in 100 Hz increments. The 100 Hz resolution of the typical transceiver does not imply that channels are a mere 100 Hz wide. The VHF communications transceiver has 25 kHz resolution and each possible frequency is a channel. In the case of the SSB (single sideband) transceiver, channels are in even kHz increments but channels are 4 kHz wide. Typical transmitter power output is 100 watts peak envelope power, PEP. Receiver sensitivity is on the order of –107 dBm.

SSB is used for HF communications because of its spectral efficiency. With worldwide coverage and bandwidth, the number of users sharing the band is huge. Only highly efficient modulation may be used. In the case of single sideband for voice, bandwidth is on the order of 2.4 kHz. To insure a narrow spectrum, audio frequency range of the transceiver is from 300 Hz to 2.7 kHz.

6.4.1 Generating Single Sideband
Producing SSB is more involved than generating normal AM. There are two methods; phasing and filter. The phasing method has not been popular because of difficulties with sensitive circuits. New technologies such as digital signal processing, DSP, may overcome these difficulties and the phasing method could find increased use. At this time, however, the filter method is the only choice for aircraft transceivers.

Figure 6.7 is a block diagram of an HF SSB transceiver. The advantages of sharing are even greater in the transceiver design, so much so that SSB for aviation has always used a transceiver. It is more difficult to design a separate transmitter and receiver.

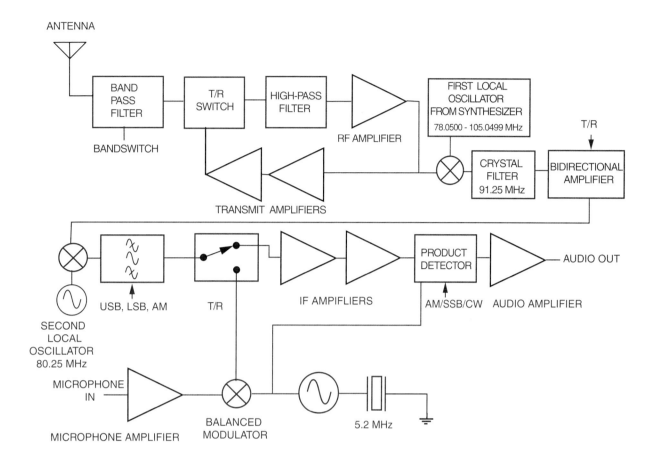

Figure 6.7 Block diagram of HF SSB transceiver

The transceiver in the block diagram is an example of up-conversion. We met this technique in ADF receivers in a previous chapter. As in ADF, earlier designs used conventional superheterodyne techniques but modern designs use up-conversion.

The choice of IF for an HF SSB transceiver must be greater than 30 MHz. Typically, the IF is between 50 and 100 MHz. At these frequencies, crystal filters are available but not sufficiently narrow to provide channel selectivity of about 3 kHz. The transceiver must be dual conversion with a second IF sufficiently low to allow an IF filter with ample selectivity. The example shows a 75.050 MHz first IF and 5.2 MHz second IF. This reference to the IF relates to a "virtual carrier frequency"—where the carrier would be if there were a carrier.

A major difference between AM and SSB is the transmitted signal. SSB is generated at low power and amplified, fully modulated, to the power output level. It is easier to generate SSB at a lower frequency, as well as lower power and translate to the operating frequency. The process is similar to a superheterodyne receiver in reverse. Instead of reducing the frequency of a received signal to an IF, where it can be amplified and processed, the SSB transmitter generates the signal at a lower frequency where it can be easily processed, then amplified and translated to the operating frequency.

The SSB signal is generated with a 5.2 MHz carrier and a doubly balanced modulator. The output of the doubly balanced modulator is a double sideband, suppressed carrier signal which is converted to SSB with an IF filter. The transceiver uses one of two filters which removes one of the two sidebands; the result is single sideband.

The SSB signal is translated to the operating frequency by heterodyning the first IF, or 5.2 MHz, to the second IF of 75.05 MHz by an 80.25 MHz local oscillator. Why such unusual frequencies for the IFs in this transceiver? They are chosen to minimize spurious responses and facilitate the internal signals. As an example, 80.25 MHz is (321/40) X 10 MHz, and 5.2 MHz is (52/100) X 10 MHz, which implies that both local oscillators may be generated from a 10.00000 MHz precision frequency reference.

The 75.05 MHz output is translated to the operating frequency by heterodyning the 75.05 MHz IF with a 78.050 MHz to 105.0499 MHz local oscillator. When an SSB signal is frequency translated by high side injection the sideband is inverted. This is because the equation for the output frequency of such a frequency conversion is:

$$F_{out} = F_{lo} - F_{in} \qquad\qquad (6.8)$$

Where F_{out} is the output frequency, F_{in} the input frequency and F_{lo} the local oscillator frequency. The negative sign in front of the input frequency shows that the spectrum of the input will be inverted. Since high side injection is usually employed in receivers to reduce spurious responses, when an SSB transmitter shares receiver circuits, sideband inversion occurs. In this example, there are two conversions and each involves an inversion. The sideband at the operating frequency is not inverted. If low side injection is chosen for the first conversion, using 69.85 MHz, there would be an odd number, i.e. one frequency inverting conversions and the output would be the opposite sideband from the actual SSB generation. The solution is to generate the opposite sideband from what is required at the output. The phenomenon is mentioned here because it often confuses repair technicians. The technician selects one sideband from the front panel and, while troubleshooting, is confused by the fact that, at some point internally, the opposite sideband is observed.

HF ANTENNA

HF antenna may be enclosed in the leading edge of the rudder fin, behind a fiberglass cap.

6.4.2 Frequency Synthesizer

The frequency synthesizer for the example HF transceiver provides an output from 78.050 MHz to 105.0499 MHz in 100 Hz steps for a total of 270,000 frequencies. The synthesizer for an HF transceiver is one of the more complex synthesizers found in avionics. Generally, it requires two phase locked loops; one with a wide frequency range and a second with a narrow frequency range. A technology called direct digital synthesis or DDS, could simplify synthesizer design but existing airborne HF transceivers use the dual loop technique.

The most important rule in the design of a synthesizer for an HF transceiver is not to generate spurious signals that could interfere with the receiver. This requires that phase locked loops operate at or above 30 MHz, which places the synthesizer phase locked loop out of the input frequency range. The range below 3 MHz is not desirable because harmonics of a VCO (voltage controlled oscillator) could appear in the receiver. Also, the image range, 153.01 MHz to 180.0099 MHz, should be avoided. The IF of 75.005 should be avoided as well; 37.5025 MHz is one half the IF. In spite of the restrictions, there are sufficient bands to provide two phase locked loops.

Before discussing local oscillator phase locked loops, it is helpful to understand why the local oscillator requires more than one loop. If the local oscillator is designed with only one loop, the reference frequency has to be 100 Hz because this is the frequency resolution. The frequency division of the programmable divider spans from a low of 780 500 to 1 050 499. These large frequency divisions which are a loss in a phase locked loop are compensated for with large loop gains if the loop is to lock up. With a reference frequency of 100 Hz, it is extremely difficult to provide a phase locked loop with quick lock up time and low noise. Using two loops allows much smaller loop gains and quicker lock up because of higher reference frequencies.

Generating the local oscillator involves two phase locked loops, where one VCO is mixed with the other and the sum or difference frequency is used for the local oscillator. In theory this works but there are problems generating spurious signals on the local oscillator which translate to spurious responses of the receiver. The alternate method is to arrange the phase locked loops so one provides the local oscillator directly.

In the synthesizer shown in Fig 6.8, a phase locked loop using a 500 kHz reference covers 90.0 MHz to 116.5 MHz in 500 kHz steps. This corresponds to operating frequencies 3.0XXX to 29.5XXX in steps of 0.5 MHz. This is called the coarse loop. A VCO, which is the local oscillator, is mixed with the coarse loop output and the difference spans 11.9500 MHz to 11.4501 MHz. This frequency spans in reverse, that is, decreasing difference frequency indicates an increase in local oscillator frequency. This is fed to a phase detector, also fed from a phase locked loop called the fine loop. This loop is derived from a phase locked loop operating in the range 191.2000 MHz to 183.2016 MHz. The fine loop has a reference frequency of 1.6 kHz and a range of 8 MHz. The output is divided by 16 and results in 100 Hz resolution and 0.5 MHz range. The 1.6 kHz reference frequency allows quick lock up time and the narrow frequency range of only 4% permits a low noise oscillator. Since the output of the VCO is divided by 16 there is an additional reduction of a factor of 16 of the VCO phase noise.

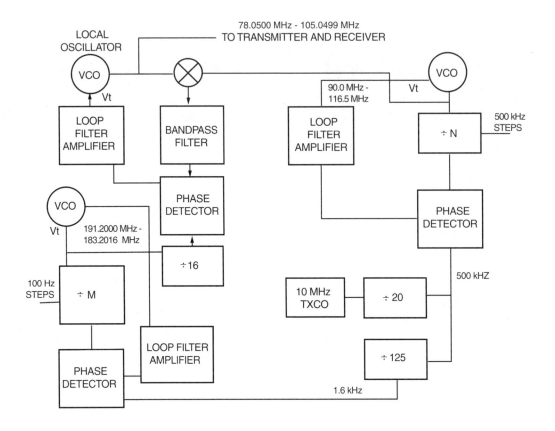

Figure 6.8 Frequency synthesizer for an HF transceiver

The output of the phase detector is fed to a loop filter and amplifier and drives the local oscillator VCO. The condition for phase lock is the coarse loop and VCO are different in frequency by an amount equal to the fine loop output. Another way of expressing this:

$$F_{vco} = F_{coarse} - F_{fine} \qquad (6.9)$$

Example: Find the F_{fine} and F_{coarse} frequencies for a carrier frequency of 12.3456 MHz.

Solution: The local oscillator frequency for a dialed frequency of 12.3456 MHz is 75.050 MHz + 12.3456 = 87.3956 MHz. The coarse frequency synthesizer can be found by truncating the operating frequency to the nearest multiple of 0.5 MHz, which is 12.0 MHz. The coarse loop frequency is 12.0 MHz + 87 MHz = 99.0 MHz. The difference frequency between the coarse loop synthesizer and local oscillator is 99.0000 – 87.3956 = 11.6044 MHz. This requires the fine loop to generate a frequency of 185.6704 MHz.

Fixed reference frequencies generate phase locked loop references, fixed frequency local oscillators and carrier generator. The entire transceiver is controlled by a single precision 10.000 000 MHz, temperature compensated crystal oscillator, TCXO. Using eight significant figures is deliberate when specifying this oscillator because precision is better than one part per million, PPM, over the operating temperature range. Maximum error of this oscillator is 10 Hz. For accuracy of the virtual carrier frequency of the transceiver, for transmit and receive to have the same relative frequency accuracy for all operating frequencies, all internal frequencies must be derived from the TCXO.

The following table shows the mathematical relationship between the 10.000 MHz TCXO and critical internal frequencies.

Frequency	Relationship
5.2000 MHz carrier	13/25
0.5 MHz coarse synth. ref.	1/20
1.6 kHz fine synth. ref.	1/625
80.25 MHz second LO	321/40

To understand how ratios in this table relate to the generation of frequencies, consider the first example; the 5.2 MHz carrier. This is generated by dividing the 10 MHz master reference by 25 to obtain 400 kHz. The 5.2 MHz VCO is divided by 13, which also produces 400 kHz. The two are inputs to a phase detector and the 5.2 MHz VCO is locked to exactly 5.200 000 MHz.

The coarse synthesizer, which provides frequencies multiples of 0.5 MHz or (500 kHz)N, the synthesizer reference, is derived by dividing the 10 MHz master oscillator by 20. The same techniques are used for the other two frequencies.

Why maintain such tight frequency tolerance for the HF transceiver? First, the width of the SSB signal is very narrow, only about 2.4 kHz. SSB is spectrum-efficient but to take advantage of it, the channel should not be wider than necessary.

6.4.3 Demodulation

The original VHF-AM communications channels were 100 kHz wide. Excess width was due to the lack of frequency stability in transmitter and receiver. AM has an advantage over SSB in that it tolerates considerable mistuning, another way of saying frequency error, and still be intelligible. SSB tolerates little mistuning; an error of 100 Hz causes difficulty in understanding voice communications.

Early SSB transceivers had a control called a "clarifier" to vary the receive frequency. The received virtual carrier frequency should be precisely the same as the transmitted virtual carrier frequency because the same frequency sources generate transmitter output, receiver local oscillators and carrier oscillator. By definition, SSB transmits and receives on *exactly* the same frequency. This is a significant advantage, but also a disadvantage.

There is no carrier, no pilot signal or other reference transmitted with the SSB. There is no automatic method of tuning the SSB receiver. Pilot carriers and other techniques are used for some SSB communications systems that can tune automatically. The only tuning aid for the airborne SSB transceiver is the operator's ears! If a transceiver has a clarifier control, the operator turns it until the voice is clear. Generally, clearest tuning occurs with a frequency error of less than 50 Hz.

The clarifier control must affect only the receiver. If it controlled both receiver and transmitter, an operator would adjust the clarifier so the incoming signal sounds clear, which could still have an error. If the clarifier adjusts the transmitter as well, the other end of the communications link would adjust its clarifier to compensate for the change in transmitter frequency. As an example, assume the first transceiver is adjusted to increase carrier frequency by 50 Hz to improve clarity of the voice. The other transceiver is adjusted up 50 Hz to return clarity to where it was previously . Every time one user receives, the clarifier is adjusted. What happens is, the two stations constantly change; a process called leap frogging. If a clarifier only controls the receiver, this does not happen.

Ideally, the virtual carrier frequency should be within about 25 Hz and no clarifier used. It is the difference in frequency between the two transceivers, and each transceiver can contribute to the overall frequency error. ICAO recommendations for frequency tolerance are a maximum frequency error of 20 Hz for airborne transceivers and 10 Hz for ground stations. For our example, the master oscillator could control the frequency of transmitter and receiver to 1 PPM which represents +/- 30 Hz carrier error at the highest frequency of 29.9999 MHz. Thus, two transceivers with a 1 PPM maximum frequency error can have a frequency difference error of 60 Hz, slightly higher than the optimum 50 Hz maximum. The lack of clarity due to a frequency difference of 60 Hz is not severe. This is unlikely where one transceiver is at the positive extreme of its frequency accuracy while the other is at the negative extreme. Finally, most airborne HF communications frequencies are significantly below 30 MHz, commonly in the 5 MHz region.. The frequency error here is only 5 Hz.

Clarifier controls, when provided, correct frequency errors of older HF transceivers. Even this is not usually necessary because HF communications take place from air to ground and seldom air to air. Ground stations typically have little frequency error.

6.4.4 HF Receiver

The receiver portion of the transceiver is a double conversion superheterodyne with the same IF and frequency conversions. The demodulator for SSB reinserts the carrier. When the SSB signal is generated, the 5.2 MHz virtual carrier is very important even though it is not present. The 5.2 MHz was the reference frequency on which the SSB signal is based, but this carrier frequency is not transmitted. To restore the original modulation, the reference frequency must be used. Since the carrier is not transmitted, the receiver must provide it. This is called carrier reinsertion and achieved by multiplying the SSB signal from the second IF by a 5.2 MHz carrier. This is the same process to generate the DSB that was stripped of one sideband to make SSB, except audio was multiplied by the 5.2 MHz carrier. In the receiver, SSB is multiplied by the 5.2 MHz carrier to produce demodulated audio.

6.4.5 HF Antennas

It was mentioned that a λ/2 dipole antenna or a λ/4 monopole were resonant, meaning they have a resistive impedance. To get maximum power to these antennas a generator with the same resistance is connected through a transmission line of the same impedance.

A resonant antenna for HF in an aircraft is not possible because of length. A quarter wavelength at 3.0 MHz, the longest, is 25 meters. Large aircraft can string a wire this length; in fact, when HF first appeared on aircraft, trailing wire antennas were used. Length was adjusted for antenna resonance. Wire antennas are dangerous because they can break and tangle with parts of aircraft, especially at jet aircraft speeds. Long wires also create drag.

Most HF antennas are constructed by insulating a part of the aircraft empennage (tail) from the rest of the aircraft and providing power to that part. A common area is the leading edge of the vertical stabilizer. In a large aircraft, the radiator can be as long as 10 meters. This is resonant at about 7.5 MHz. At other frequencies, however, the antenna would be reactive.

At frequencies below resonance, the antenna generally has capacitive reactance in its impedance. For frequencies above resonance, the antenna has inductive reactance in the impedance. When a reactive component appears in the impedance it must be tuned out or removed with a conjugate match to provide maximum power to the load. If an antenna has a capacitive component, an equal inductive reactance is placed in series so the two equal zero. The resulting impedance is purely resistive.

The λ/4 monopole and λ/2 dipole antennas have an impedance of 50 to 60 ohms,

248

resistive. When reactance of the non-resonant antenna is tuned out, the remaining resistive component is not necessarily 50 or 60 ohms. A short antenna, that is, short relative to resonant, usually has a much lower resistive component while the longer antenna has somewhat higher impedance.

To use an HF antenna aboard an aircraft, reactance must be tuned out and impedance converted to a standard such as 50 ohms. The device for this is an antenna tuner, an impedance-converting device that matches impedance between a non-resonant antenna and 50 ohms. The constant impedance side of the antenna tuner theoretically does not have to be 50 ohms, as long as the antenna tuner matches the transmitter. Since all transmitters are 50 ohms, antenna tuner output impedance is 50 ohms.

A block diagram of an antenna tuner is shown in Fig. 6.9. RF from the SSB transceiver is fed to an autotransformer, which converts the 50 ohm impedance of the transmitter to a lower or higher value. Inductors and capacitors in series with the non-resonant antenna tune out the reactance.

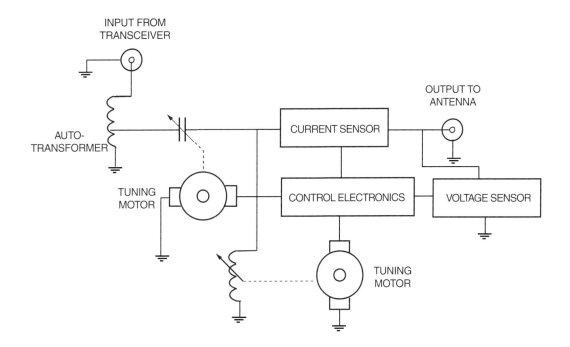

Figure 6.9 Antenna tuner for airborne HF transceiver

Before the antenna can be tuned, there must be indicators to show the antenna is matched. This could produce a perfect 1:1 VSWR (voltage standing wave ratio) measured at the input. The problem with input VSWR is that a low VSWR exists when the antenna is free of reactance and is 50 ohms. The antenna tuner provides two adjustments, amplitude and phase. When the antenna resonates, voltage and current are in phase, regardless of impedance. When impedance is 50 ohms, the ratio of voltage to current is 50. If there is a voltage to current phase detector at the output of the autotransformer, we could adjust the series capacitors and inductors and detect resonance. With a voltage to current ratio detector, the autotransformer can be adjusted for correct impedance.

The tuner consists of variable inductors and capacitors which, historically, have been motor-driven. Capacitors have been parallel plate types adjusted by a rotating shaft. Variable inductors have been mechanical as well. The usual variable inductor has a contact rolling on a shaft along turns of wire.

249

Because of the voltages and currents, it is not possible to use varactor diodes for the variable capacitor, or a voltage variable inductor (a rare item) Motor-driven variable inductors and capacitors have been used in antenna tuners for many years.

There are problems with the roller inductor and variable capacitor. The capacitor is exposed to ambient air; when air pressure is reduced, less voltage can break down the capacitor. There are two solutions. First, place the capacitor in a pressurized container so air pressure is not lowered. The second is to evacuate air from around the capacitor. The latter is called a vacuum variable capacitor and used for high power antenna tuners and transmitters. Total evacuation of air from capacitor plates increases the breakdown voltage and permits the use of smaller capacitors. These capacitors are found in airborne, as well as ground, applications. Electrical breakdown is not only a problem of capacitors. High voltage breakdown can occur anywhere in the antenna tuner. Many tuners, therefore, are enclosed in a pressurized housing.

Because the pressurized antenna tuner is large and heavy, there have been efforts to reduce size and weight. A variable capacitor is made with fixed value capacitors and switching them in parallel with a relay, as shown in Fig. 6.10. This example shows 6 capacitors, which provides a range from 2 pF to 126 pF in 2 pF steps. Capacitors are switched with electromechanical relays. To prevent breakdown, the relays are vacuum-sealed. Ceramic capacitors, which do not use ambient air as a dielectric, are not affected by air pressure.

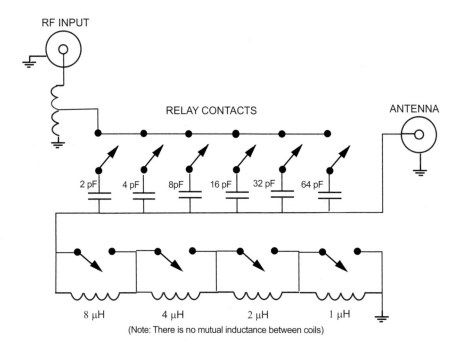

Fig. 6.10 Antenna tuner for HF transceiver using switched capacitors and inductors

How much voltage might cause breakdown? To understand the peak voltage level determine instantaneous peak voltage across 50 ohms for the typical 100 watts PEP (peak envelope power).

Example: PEP refers to peak RMS power. Peak RMS voltage is E = (50 PEP)$^{1/2}$ = (50 X 100)$^{1/2}$ = 70.7 volts. The instantaneous peak is the RMS voltage multiplied by 1.414 or 100 volts. How is it possible that only 100 volts causes breakdown problems? What was calculated was the resistive part of the current from a 100-watt transmitter. Capacitors and inductors in the antenna tuner remove reactive currents and voltages. To determine how much voltage is across the reactive elements of the antenna tuner, assume a carrier of 3.3 MHz. The antenna tuner places a 22 μHy inductor in series with the antenna to achieve resonance. Also assume the radiation resistance of the antenna is 10 ohms. Now, calculate peak current to the antenna by the relationship P = I^{2}R. The instantaneous peak power is 200 watts and I is (200/10)$^{1/2}$ = 4.47 amps.

Voltage across the 22 μHy inductor is:
I X$_C$ = I (2 πf L) = (4.47 X 2 X 3.14159 X 22E-6) = 2040 volts.

There are situations where the antenna is not fully tuned to resonance, where peak voltages exceed this value. This brings up the subject of how and when the antenna is tuned.

The antenna is tuned only if the transceiver changes frequency. The SSB transceiver is protected from damage by continuously monitoring the standing wave ratio of the power amplifier output. When the antenna tuner is removed from the aircraft for maintenance and replaced, unless the tuning elements are returned to exactly the same values, their settings will be wrong. The same is true for modifications to the antenna. Also, there is the possibility that the tuner became "glitched" and mistuned the antenna. When excessive VSWR is detected at the transmitter output, the antenna tuner prevents transmission and retunes the antenna.

Unless the operator speaks into the microphone, there is no output power from the SSB transceiver. To tune the antenna, a small amount of power is applied to start the tuning process. Only enough power to activate the sensors is used. The reason is, a radiated signal can cause interference so power is kept to a minimum. Secondly, when the antenna is not tuned to resonance, high voltages can be generated across inductors and capacitors which resonate the antenna.

6.4.6 Naming Communications Channels

In VHF, a channel is designated by its center frequency. As an example, VHF communications channel 118.1 is a 25 kHz band of frequencies centered around 118.1 MHz. The nominal carrier frequency is 118.1 MHz. If the same channel is used for an FM system the carrier is also 118.1 MHz, and the resulting sidebands are symmetrical around the carrier frequency.

The relationship between carrier frequency and communications channel is not always applicable. Broadcast television has a carrier towards the lower end of the assigned channel. Channel 2 in the U.S. is a 6 MHz band from 60 MHz to 66 MHz. The television carrier is 61.25 MHz. There is a second carrier for audio, at 65.75 MHz. With an asymmetrical signal, it would be confusing if the television channel were called 61.25 MHz. Saying "Channel 2" is simpler.

Single sideband has a similar problem. There is no carrier. There is, however, a carrier *frequency* where the carrier would be if transmitted. It is at the low end of the channel if the USB (upper sideband) is used and at the high end of the channel for the LSB (lower sideband). HF channels are specified with a frequency called the virtual carrier frequency and a sideband.

Digital radios require an RF frequency and specific digital encoding. For the case of TDMA, the channel specifies an RF frequency and a time slot. For CDMA, an RF center frequency and PRN code are required.

Whatever the nomenclature, communications channels must be standardized. This caused confusion when 8.33 kHz channels were implemented. The conventional nomenclature is to specify carrier frequency for VHF communications. As an example, the early 25 kHz channel, 118.1 MHz is now split into three channels; 118.0916666, 118.100000, and 118.1083333. Frequencies are often communicated to the pilot by voice so an assignment could be "one one eight point zero nine one six six six." The "sixes" go on forever and we could round them off to seven, skip the first, and transmit the frequency as "zero eight point zero nine one seven". The next channel is 118.1 which is the original channel before splitting. The next channel is 118.1083 after rounding off.

So far, so good. We added only one digit to increase the channels by a factor of three. Consider the next 25 kHz channel and its new 8.33 kHz channels. The old 25 kHz channel is 118.125. The channel below is 118.1166666, which can be rounded off to 118.1167 and the channel above the old channel is 118.13333, which can be rounded off to 118.1333.

With the old 25 kHz channels, assigned frequencies ended in 00, 25, 50 and 75 kHz. With 8.33 kHz channels, the frequencies, after rounding off, end in 00.0 kHz, 08.3 kHz, 16.7 kHz, 25.0 kHz, 33.3 kHz, 41.7 kHz and so on. This not only adds one additional digit to the frequency nomenclature, but there are 12 different sets of least significant digits. This could lead to difficulties in frequency displays and communicating frequencies via voice. There is a proposal to name frequencies that end in multiples of 5 kHz, as shown below.

Actual Frequency	Channel Name (8.33 kHz environment)	Channel Name (25 kHz environment)
118.000000	118.005	118.000
118.008333	118.010	
118.016667	118.015	
118.025000	118.030	118.020*
118.033333	118.035	
118.041667	118.040	
118.050000	118.055	118.050
118.058333	118.060	
118.066667	118.065	
118.075000	118.080	118.070*
118.083333	118.085	
118.091667	118.090	
118.100000	118.105	118.100

*At the time of this writing these channel names were being considered for change to 118.025 and 118.075.

A look at the table shows only slight resemblance of the channel name to the operating frequency. Channel frequencies are equally spaced, whereas channel names are not. The same frequency has two different channel names, depending on the operating environment. At the time of this writing, these channel names are proposed, but not yet in place.

As digital communications loom near we must consider the impact of digital channels. Each 25 kHz channel will have four digital, TDMA, time slots. These have been usually designated as digital "channels" A, B, C or D. To summarize, each 25 kHz channel may have one conventional 25 kHz channel, three 8.333 "splits" and four digital "channels". At the time of this writing there is a creditable proposal to name the VHF communications channels according to the table below.

Frequency (MHz)	Mode	Slot	Channel Name
118.0000	AM, 25 kHz	NA	118,000
118.0000	TDMA	A	118.001
118.0000	TDMA	B	118.002
118.0000	TDMA	C	118.003
118.0000	TDMA	D	118.004
118.0000	AM, 8.33 kHz	NA	118.005
118.0083	AM, 8.33 kHz	NA	118.010
118.0167	AM, 8.33 kHz	NA	118.015
118.0250	TDMA	A	118.021
118.0250	TDMA	B	118.022
118.0250	TDMA	C	118.023
118.0250	TDMA	D	118.024
118.0250	AM, 25 kHz	NA	118.025
118.0250	AM, 8.33 kHz	NA	118.030
118.0333	AM, 8.33 kHz	NA	118.035
118.0417	AM, 8.33 kHz	NA	118.040
118.0500	AM, 25 kHz	NA	118.050
118.0500	TDMA	A	118.051
118.0500	TDMA	B	118.052
118.0500	TDMA	C	118.053
118.0500	TDMA	D	118.054
118.0500	AM, 8.33 kHz	NA	118.055
118.0583	AM, 8.33 kHz	NA	118.060
118.0667	AM, 8.33 kHz	NA	118.065

The "official" channel nomenclature has not been selected at the time of this writing. It is clear that a standardized channel nomenclature is necessary and the problems associated with creating an international standard. It is of paramount importance than during the period of transition which all three environments are co-existing that a standard nomenclature be adopted.

6.5 ACARS

A system of 2400 baud digital communications provides private communications between aircraft and ground stations. It is the Aircraft Communications and Reporting System, or ACARS. The designation "private" means that communications do not relate directly to air traffic control (which is operated by FAA or government facilities). In the airline industry ACARS handles what is called "company communications," relating to such operational information from airline operational centers, AOC, as time of pushback from the gate, wheels off (the runway), wheels on (touchdown), arrival time at the gate, number of passengers, wheel chairs required and other organizational matters. Much of the ACARS communications channels are provided by private communications suppliers such as ARINC.

Some data are quite sophisticated such as engine parameters that would alert the ground maintenance that a fault needs investigation when the aircraft arrives. Much ACARS data is automatically sent and does not require pilot action.

ACARS operates on VHF for domestic flight and the HF band for continental and oceanic coverage. The technique for VHF is audio frequency FSK (frequency shift keying). Audio tones shift between mark and space and are applied to the VHF communications transceiver. Messages are arranged in a short "packet", which includes recipient address and source. Transmissions are more or less random and uplink and downlink share the same frequency.

Error detection is applied by sending a CRC checksum with each packet. If a packet is arrives with errors, a repeat transmission is requested. Communications are bidirectional but, because each message contains an address, it is received only by the selected aircraft. The receiver assembles complete messages from individual packets.

6.6 SELCAL

Because of high activity on aviation frequencies for both HF and VHF, many aircraft may communicate on a particular channel. This means pilots would overhear traffic between other aircraft and ground stations, which can become distracting. A method known as SELCAL, for "selective call", silences the receiver until it is addressed. SELCAL requires two tone pairs sent in succession. There are 16 tones spanning 312.6 Hz to 1479.1 Hz. The selective calling sequence requires two tones in the group be sent for 1 second, with a gap of 0.2 seconds followed by a second pair of tones for another 1 second. The tone frequencies are related by the ratio 1.10917 between frequencies. The lowest is 312.6 Hz and the next higher is 312.6X1.10917 = 346.7. The ratio 1.10917 insures that harmonics are not the same as any tone.

Selective calling on HF has difficulty achieving error-free SELCAL operation. It's due to frequency translation arising from errors in the virtual carrier frequency of the transceiver. A voice transmission with a frequency error of 50 Hz is reasonably well understood by the pilot. As an example, if a +34 Hz translation error exists, quite acceptable for voice reception, the lowest tone would be received as 346.6 Hz, and decoded as the next higher tone.

There are viable solutions to the frequency translation problem. The first and simplest is higher-frequency tones for HF SELCAL. The frequency difference between the two highest tones is 146 Hz. Since the frequency error should never be so great as to cause an error in decoding a high tone, the frequency of the highest transmitted tone can be measured and used to correct the lower of the two tones for frequency translation errors.

6.7 Search and Rescue Beacons

In 1972, an aircraft crash near Portage, Alaska, took the lives of two U. S. Congressmen and became the catalyst for public law 91-596 mandating emergency locator transmitters, ELTs, on general aviation aircraft. Soon after, FAR 91.25 was amended to require ELTs on U. S. registered aircraft. A TSO (C91) was already in existence since 1971 covering ELTs. In the case of aircraft crashes, data show that initial survivors have less than a 10% survival rate if rescued after 2 days, whereas survival rate is 60% if rescued in less than 8 hours.

The original ELT transmits on the international aviation distress frequency of 121.5 MHz. This frequency can also be used by aircraft in distress using their normal VHF communications transceiver. It is a recommended practice to monitor the emergency frequency in case an aircraft needs assistance. With the ELT transmitting on the common emergency frequency and aircraft and ground facilities monitoring that frequency, the chance of an ELT being received is high. That would be true if a crash occurred near populated areas, but if the incident were in the middle of an ocean or unpopulated land mass, this probability decreases.

The 121.5 MHz ELT transmits an amplitude modulated carrier with an audible tone, that is swept in frequency. This modulation contains no data and is nothing more than an aural alert. An inefficient amplitude modulation was selected in order to be compatible with conventional airborne VHF communications transceivers, allowing the ELT transmission to be widely received. Many ELTs have voice communications capability and some have the ability to receive, and thus two-way communications are available. Although two way communications appear to be an important enhancement, this feature has limited use. The short range of the ELT and that survivors are often incapable of reaching the ELT, limits the usefulness of the feature.

ELTs also transmit on 243 MHz, a military distress frequency which is the second harmonic of the primary 121.5 MHz frequency. 243 MHz is not available on civil aircraft VHF communications transceivers, which eliminates potential interference from aircraft using the emergency frequency. The same modulation is used for 243 MHz, except that voice communication is not available.

The ELT was an important step in facilitating search and rescue, but the system had many problems beginning with false alarms. ELTs have impact switches and, in many cases, these could be triggered by hard landings. Also, the ELT had a test switch which, when pressed, caused the ELT to transmit a normal distress signal. ELT testing was mandated to take place in the first five minutes of each hour, but that did not always happen. Since there are no data transmitted from an ELT, in order to find one that falsely triggered, a search and rescue mission would be initiated. About the only information known from receiving an activated ELT is that it is within radio range. If a false alarm were triggered at a large airport with a control tower, the tower would immediately detect the false alarm and the situation could be corrected. At a small, uncontrolled field this may not happen. An improved distress beacon system would transmit an identification. Each beacon would be registered and entered into a data base which includes the owner of the beacon and pertinent contact information. Any aircraft that falsely triggered a rescue beacon could be located quickly.

The false alarm rate for the 121.5 MHz ELT was 98%, or only one of every 50 activations was a legitimate distress situation.

An improved beacon system would transmit on an internationally-coordinated frequency reserved for beacons only. No other transmissions would be permitted on the frequency. Furthermore, the frequency should not be accessible by airborne transceivers, thus making it even more difficult to cause harmful interference.

In 1979 the United States, France, Canada and the former USSR signed a memorandum of understanding to develop a satellite system to detect and locate distress radio beacons. A demonstration system was developed and declared operational by the four countries in 1985. It was called the COSPAS/SARSAT system; *Cosmicheskaya Sistyema Poiska Avariynich Sudvov* (Space System for the Search of Vessels in Distress) in Russian, and Search and Rescue Satellite Aided Tracking, in English. In 1988 the four participants signed the International COSPAS/SARSAT Program Agreement which provides for continuous service for all nations. As of the time of this writing, 36 nations are participants.

The COSPAS/SARSAT system presently uses beacons that can be mounted on aircraft, boats and even carried by a person. Each beacon transmits a unique identification and is required by law that each owner register the beacon and provide important information such as owner's name, type and registration number of the aircraft and contact information, such as a telephone number. In the United States, these data are registered with the National Oceanographic and Atmospheric Administration, NOAA.

Since 1982 a total of 20,300 persons were rescued with the aid of COSPAS/SARSAT in combined maritime, aviation and personal incidents. Although accurate data from the early years of the system are not available it is estimated that about 2000 persons were rescued in aviation incidents with the aid of COSPAS/SARSAT. The majority of rescues involved water-craft. Just as important, the false alarm rate went from 1 legitimate alarm in 50 activations to 1 in 17 but, because the identity of the beacon was known and the registration included contact information, most false alarms were resolved without launching a rescue effort.

The initial COSPAS/SARSAT system operated with existing ELTs. (The actual operation of these legacy beacons will be described later.) The COSPAS/SARSAT location system uses satellites called LEOSARs for low earth orbiting search and rescue satellites. LEOSARs are either polar orbiting or near polar orbiting and measure the Doppler shift of the 121.5 MHz ELT carrier frequency. The technique is very similar to the old Navy Transit satellite navigation system, a precursor to GPS, discussed in Chapter 4. The original COSPAS/SARSAT system operates like Transit in reverse. Transit radiated a carrier frequency and users measured the Doppler shift to determine their position. COSPAS/SARSAT receives a carrier *from* a user and determines the user's position.

A major problem of the early LEOSAR system was the same as that for Transit; although the system could provide global coverage, it was not continuous. It may take several hours for a LEOSAR to pass within range of the rescue beacon. Secondly, COSPAS/SARSAT, like Transit, determined the minimum Doppler shift, which occurs when the transmitter is exactly east or west of the satellite, assuming a polar orbit. Removing the ambiguity requires either a second fix or other supporting information. In spite of these limitations, in 1982, shortly after implementation, the LEOSAR system aided in the rescue of 3 people from a downed light aircraft in Canada.

The choice of the 121.5 MHz ELT for the initial phase of COSPAS/SARSAT was to take advantage of the large number of ELTs installed on aircraft. Unfortunately, the choice of the 121.5 MHz signal also resulted in inheriting problems of the ELT system, most notably the large number of false alarms. To be successful with watercraft, ELTs would have to be installed in ships. However, the operating frequency, 121.5 MHz, is the aviation VHF voice distress frequency and not originally authorized for maritime use.

In 1996, experiments began on an improved beacon. First and foremost, it would operate with geostationary search and rescue satellites, GEOSARs, so detection of an activated beacon is nearly instantaneous. Only three satellites are needed to provide global coverage up to about 70 degrees of latitude. Polar coverage can be handled by the LEOSARs. Because these satellites have polar or near polar orbits, all LEOSARs converge on the poles and provide nearly continuous coverage at the poles, filling in the gaps left by the GEOSARs.

Geostationary satellites experience no Doppler shift relative to fixed transmitters; meaning fixed, relative to the surface of the earth. Although the GEOSAR can detect an activated rescue beacon nearly instantaneously, it cannot determine position from just a carrier. Therefore, LEOSARs are still required to locate activated ELTs.

A new beacon operating at a frequency of 406.025 MHz was developed. The carrier frequency is reserved for radiolocation beacons for search and rescue and reduces the incidence of false alarms. The new 406 MHz beacon transmits identifying information to LEOSARs and GEOSARs. Every 406 MHz beacon is assigned a unique identification code, which aids in search and rescue, as most aircraft and ships file a flight plan or course, and there would be some initial information to aid in rescue, even before a LEOSAR could determine a fix.

The fact that the rescue beacon can transmit data immediately suggests that if the position of an aircraft or ship is known, these data could be transmitted. The obvious connection is to the GPS system. Out of this connection, the Emergency Position-Indicating Radio Beacon, or EPIRB, pronounced "e-purb," was born. When an EPIRB is activated, a GEOSAR detects it immediately if the beacon is below 70 degrees of latitude. If the beacon is in the polar region it is a matter of a few minutes before one LEOSAR detects the activation. The term EPIRB is used for maritime operations; the aviation version is the 406 MHz ELT with position information.

6.7.1 COSPAS/SARSAT System

The COSPAS/SARSAT system consists of three segments; beacon, space segment and ground segment. The beacon is responsible for transmitting the distress message to a satellite, which is the space segment. The satellite then must return the information to a ground station, which determines where the data should be relayed to initiate a search and rescue effort. The ground receiving station, called a local user terminal, LUT, with a network to search and rescue entities is the ground segment. LUTs intended to operate with LEOSARs are called LEOLUTs and those intended to operate with GEOSARs are called GEOLUTs. There are 43 LUTs throughout the world, including three in the continental United States, and one, each in Alaska, Hawaii and Guam.

The LEOSAR satellite system relays the 121.5 MHz signals on 1544.5 MHz to the ground segment for processing. GEOSAR satellites are not dedicated search and rescue satellites but perform other services, as well. Some data processing is done aboard the GEOSAR and the downlink frequency varies, depending on the satellite provider. One of the GEOSAR providers is the NOAA geostationary operational environmental satellite, GOES, weather observation satellite. The U. S. mission control center is in Suitland, Md., near Washington D. C. and is operated by the National Oceanic and Atmospheric Administration, NOAA.

Beginning February 2009, the COSPAS/SARSAT system will discontinue processing 121.5 MHz ELT signals. Therefore, 121.5 MHz distress signals can only be processed via nearby aircraft and local receiving stations.

6.7.2 The 406 MHz Signal

The 406 MHz ELT/EPIRB signal is a 406.025 MHz carrier, phase modulated with plus and minus 1.1 radians. The data are binary Manchester encoded to insure a net zero phase angle, which aids in Doppler frequency measurement.

The 406 MHz ELT/EPIRB messages are shown in Fig. 6.11. The message begins with a 160 ms unmodulated carrier, allowing the ELT/EPIRB transmitter to stabilize and the receiver to lock on to the carrier phase reference. The unmodulated carrier is followed by 15 synch bits, a string of logic ones, for bit synchronizing. Following bit synchronizing is the frame synchronizing word of 9 bits. For normal distress beacon operation this pattern is 0 0010 1111. A beacon radiating a test message, the frame synchronizing word is 0 1101 0000. Notice the test word has the last 8 bits inverted from the normal frame synchronizing word. The inclusion of a test message allows the beacon to be tested at any time without causing a false alarm.

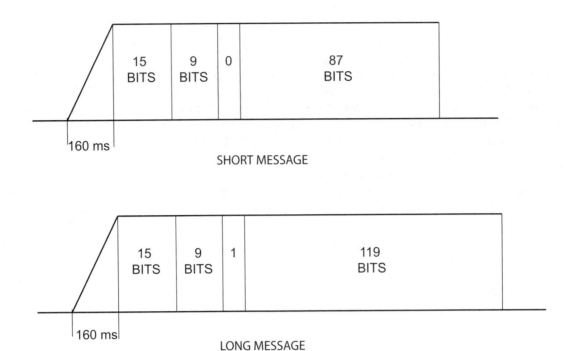

SHORT MESSAGE

LONG MESSAGE

Fig. 6.11 The 406 MHz message structure

Following the frame synchronizing word is a single bit, which a logic zero signifies a short message to follow, or a long message indicated by a logic 1. The standard location protocol for ELTs with the 24 bit ICAO address is a long message.

Bit(s)	Purpose
1-24	Bit and Frame synchronizing
25	1 Format Flag (indicates long message)
26	0 Protocol Flag
27-36	Country Code
37-40	1101 identifies the message as a Standard Location Protocol
41-64	24-bit ICAO aircraft address
65-85	Position data to 15 minute resolution
86-106	21-bit BCH error correction code
107-110	1101 Supplementary Data (fixed)
111	Position data source, 1 = internal 0 = external
112	121.5 MHz radiolocation device 1 = device installed; 0 = no device
113-132	Position offset

The following ten bits, 27 through 36 is the country code. Each country has one or more codes in the form of a three digit decimal number. The decimal value is encoded into a 10 bit binary number. Countries use more than one "country" code for possessions that are a significant distance from the main entity. The United States, as an example, has separate codes for continental US, Alaska, Hawaii and Guam, in addition to other possessions.

Bits 41 through 64 is the 24 Bit ICAO aircraft address. This is the same standard aircraft address used by the mode S transponder and ADS-B, and encoded in the same manner.

Bits 65 through 85 is the position data to 15 minute resolution.

The position data consists of latitude to four second increments for the standard ELT

258

message protocol. Position data are provided as four words; a latitude data word and a latitude offset, a longitude data word and longitude offset. Coarse latitude or longitude is in the 15 minute resolution data, refined by adding or subtracting an "offset" to 4 minute resolution.

The latitude data word occupies bits 65 through 74. Bit 65 is set to 0 for north latitude and 1 for south latitude. Bits 66 through 74 is the latitude in increments of 15 minutes or 0.25 degrees. The latitude ranges from zero to 90 degrees, which requires 360 different numbers and thus requires 9 bits.

Bits 75 through 85 is the longitude in increments of 15 minutes or 0.25 degrees. Bit 75 is set to 0 for east longitude and 1 for west longitude. In the case of longitude, the range is from zero to 180 degrees and, therefore, 10 bits are required for transmission.

Bits 86 to 106 is the Bose, Chaudhuri, Hocquenghem, BCH error correction code for the 15 minute resolution data. Position data with 15 minute resolution plus BCH error correction bits is called the protected data field number 1, PDF-1

Bits 107 through 110 is fixed at 1101 but may be used in the future for supplementary data.

Bit 111 indicates the position data source; 1 indicates an internal data source and 0 an external data source.

Latitude offset is encoded in bits 113 through 122. Bit 113 is the latitude sign, which indicates whether the offset should be added or subtracted from the "latitude to 15 minute resolution" word. Bits 114 through 118 is the latitude offset in 1 minute increments. The minute offset spans from 0 to 30 minutes, which requires 5 bits.

Bits 119 to 122 is the remainder of the latitude offset data word in 4 second increments. A range from zero to 56 seconds is required to "fill in the gaps" between the 1 minute increments. Fifteen different values are required to provide the 0 to 56 minute range in 4 minute increments and, therefore, 4 bits are required.

The same scheme is used for the longitude offset. Bit 123 is the sign of the offset, 124 to 128 is the offset in 1 minute increments and 129 to 132 is the offset least significant bits in 4 second increments.

Bits 107 to 144 are combined as the PDF-2 for the purpose of generating the BCH error correcting code which occupies the final bits of the message 133 to 144.

Maritime EPIRBS use a different location protocol, which uses the short message. Vessel number is used instead of aircraft ID. In addition, a registered serial number can be used for an EPIRB.

The table below shows the comparison of the 121.5 MHz beacon and 406 MHz ELT/EPIRB.

	ELT	**EPIRB**
Carrier Frequency	121.5 MHz	406.025 MHz
Transmit Power	50-100 mw	5W +/- 2dB
Transmission Life	48 hours	24 hours
Modulation	AM	Phase modulation
Modulation depth/phase	> 85%	+/- 1.1 radians
Modulation type	swept tone	bi-phase
Data rate	none	400 bps
Digital message (bits)	none	112 short; 144 long
Message repetition interval	continuous	50 seconds

There are significant differences between the two technologies, evident from this table. First is the 5 to ten-fold increase in transmitter power. The original ELT would be received by airborne receivers or ground stations and the range would be limited due to line of sight. When LEOSARs were employed to enhance the detection of an ELT, the 1000 km altitude orbit required the ELT to be received at a maximum distance of about 2500 km. This distance would be at the limits of the LEOSAR's footprint but is a clear unobstructed path.

The 406 MHz ELT/EPIRB must span a 35,786 km or longer path to a geostationary satellite. This longer distance coupled with the greater free space loss of the shorter, 406 MHz wavelength are the reasons for the much higher 5 watt transmitter power.

The 50 second repetition interval is an average. The interval varies from 47.5 seconds to 52.5 sec randomly distributed, which prevents multiple ELT/EPIRBs from becoming synchronized and mutually interfere. The COSPAS/SARSAT system can handle up to 99 activated distress beacons.

The immediate problem that comes to mind with a much higher transmitter power is the need for a much larger battery to provide the same operational time. However, with the digital 406 MHz ELT/EPIRB, the digital message lasts either 112 bits or 144 bits, which calculates to 280 ms or 360 ms respectively. The 160 ms unmodulated carrier is transmitted before the beginning of the message brings the total transmission time to 440 ms or 520 ms. The messages are repeated nominally 50 seconds, which is an average transmitter output power for the short message of:

$$P_{avg} = P_{xmt} \text{ X Tmessage X D} = 5 \text{ X } 0.44 \text{ X } 0.02 = 4.4 \text{ mW}$$

For the long message the average transmitter power is 5.5 mw.

Even though the ELT/EPIRB is required to produce 5 watts of output power, the low duty cycle reduces overall energy drain. In addition, since the 406 MHz ELT/EPIRB should produce a much shorter rescue time, the total time the rescue beacon needs to transmit should be much shorter. Finally, the low duty cycle permits multiple 406 MHz ELT/EPIRBs to transmit without interference. If two or more ELTs were transmitting there would be interference between the ELT transmitters, reducing the effectiveness of the system.

6.7.2 Rescue Beacon Installations

1. Automatic, fixed, (AF). Rescue beacon is permanently fixed to the aircraft and activates on impact. An antenna mounted to the fuselage of the aircraft provides maximum range. In the case of composite, fabric or aircraft with a large number of windows, an antenna mounted to the rescue beacon could provide adequate signal.

2. Automatic, portable, (AP). The rescue beacon is fixed to the aircraft but can be readily removed and used after a crash This unit must have provision for a portable antenna so the transmitter may be used after removal from the aircraft.

3. Survival (S). This type does not activate on impact and can be easily removed from the aircraft, typically for use on a life raft. This rescue beacon alone does not satisfy the U. S. Federal regulations for rescue beacon carriage. It must be used with an automatic beacon. The purpose of the survival beacon is for aircraft conducting over-water operations where an aircraft may sink after ditching, leaving survivors in a life raft or other flotation device with no beacon.

4. Automatic, deployable (AD). The most sophisticated beacon installation, it automatically ejects from the aircraft after a crash and deploys. The beacon must float with its antenna out of the water for operation in water or is ejected a sufficient distance from the aircraft so that it will not be destroyed if the wreckage burns.

6.7.3 Beacon Testing

The 406.025 MHz EPIRB has a self test capability but the 121.5 MHZ ELT needs to be tested periodically to insure reliable operation. The ideal test is to transmit and verify the signal can be received and is sufficiently strong. The FARs permit this type of test only during the first 5 minutes of each hour and the test is not to last more than 5 seconds. Typically, an aircraft owner would receive the 121.5 MHz signal on the aircraft's VHF communications radio or ask the local tower to listen for the transmission. Even a severely weakened ELT signal will appear strong on the communications transceiver aboard the same aircraft. Receiving the emergency signal at a nearby tower is a slightly better test but gives no indication of battery life. This test procedure also was a source of false alarms for those who tested outside the 5 minute window.

6.8 Digital Communications and Networking

Aviation communications has come a long way since the first one-way ground to air communications used at the Cleveland Municipal Airport's first radio-equipped control tower. For more than 70 years air/ground/air communications remained analog, half duplex, voice. Half duplex means the communications are two-way but only one user can transmit at a time. Typically, users share a radio channel and indicate the end of a transmission with the word "over". Simplex is the one way, broadcast type communications used at the first radio-equipped tower. Simplex finds many uses today such as weather advisories and the automatic terminal information system, ATIS, used at larger airports. Full duplex is similar to a telephone, where both parties can transmit at the same time.

The future of aviation communications is digital networking. The purpose of a network is to pass messages between users connected to the network. There are a number of hierarchies where some users have specific control functions. There could also be networks within a network and so on. Some characteristics that define a good network are speed, capacity, freedom from error, security and flexibility.

There are two basic ways to route a message from a source to destination through a network; circuit switching and message switching. Circuit switching has been the method for telephone communications for many years. The telephone network is, in fact called the "public switched telephone network," or PSTN. In the earliest days of telephone service the user asked an operator for a party and the operator plugged patch cords into a panel, physically connecting the caller's telephone line to the called party's line. The operator would ring the called party's line to indicate a call is present, which is called signaling. Although telephone service advanced immensely since the days of operator-handled calls, signaling remains an important part of the modern PSTN. Later, automatic electromechanical switches were used with rotary dials and automatic signalling. The current system uses a dual tone multiple frequency, DTMF, switch scheme but the telephone system remains a switched network. Although this example suggests an analog network, a switched circuit network can handle digital signals.

The second method of routing messages is the message switching network. In this network, a data block, which contains a header, the data and a checksum is transmitted. The header contains information relative to the source and destination of the data and the checksum is for error detection. The message is routed through whatever communications channel is available to the destination. The big difference between message switching and circuit switching is if a communications channel is not immediately available, the message is temporarily stored and forwarded when the channel is available.

A variant of message switching is packet switching. In this case, the message is divided into small packets with a specified maximum length, then handled as in message switching. In packet switching, the message may not arrive sequentially. Because packets may take different routes, the entire message is not available until the last packet has been received. It is necessary to store and reassemble the message.

Message and packet switching are very efficient modes of communications; channels are shared by all users. In the PSTN, once a connection has been established, that communications channel is dedicated to specific users only. This is not totally true in modern telephonic systems where digital techniques are used. It only appears to the users that a dedicated circuit is being supplied while, in fact, data is inserted. The fact that the user has no indication the channel is shared is called transparent. Therefore, users perceive a dedicated circuit while the channel is being shared.

One advantage of the switched network is there is no delay other than the propagation delay of the channel. If message or packet switching were used for telephone communications there would be variable delays when a communications channel is not immediately available. This is not acceptable for voice communications but for other applications, such as e-mail, this can be tolerated.

6.8.1 Network Topology

A number of network topologies are used in aviation communications. One is the point to point store and forward network. A terminal is interfaced only to the two adjacent terminals. The system operates in full duplex and there is never a problem with contention, where more than two users attempt to use the channel simultaneously.

Another topology for packet switching is multiple access broadcast. In this example a single communications channel is available to all users on the network. An example is a ground station serving aircraft. All aircraft receive the ground station and accept only messages or packets destined for that aircraft. The airborne terminals access the ground station as needed. Some form of "hand shaking" is required to prevent contention from the airborne terminals. In some applications there are advantages if all users can receive the up link traffic. Wired equivalents to the multiple access broadcast network are used extensively for on board aircraft communications, which will be discussed in the next chapter.

A third network topology is the multi-hop store and forward multiple access broadcast. A typical multi-hop radio-based system uses gateway stations, repeaters and ground-based terminals. This type of system finds application in connecting a large number of mobile subscribers where subscribers routinely travel distances that take the user out of range of a gateway or repeater. The mobile station is then acquired by another gateway, which then reinserts the subscriber into the network. The cellular telephone network is similar in that cell sites are interconnected and, when a subscriber has a superior signal in another cell, that cell picks up the subscriber and maintains a continuous network connection. This model is very suitable for air/ground/air communications.

Most network architecture is a linear hierarchical model, where messages pass through various "layers" between end users. There have been a number of hierarchies but the International Organization for Standardization (ISO) in its open systems interconnect, OSI, model is the most common at this time.

An "interface" is the boundary between layers and the rules for crossing the interface are called protocols. The OSI model has seven layers which are:

1. Physical
2. Data link
3. Network
4. Transport
5. Session
6. Presentation
7. Application

The OSI model allows for sublayers within the seven layers.

6.8.1.1 Layer 1, Physical

The physical layer is the actual communications medium, such as wire, radio, fiber optics and so on. The physical layer also includes the mechanism for connecting to the communications medium. This would be a radio transceiver for radio links, line drivers and receivers for twisted pair, and laser diodes and photo diodes for fiber optics. Definitions of signals on the communications medium, such as data rates, half or full duplex, voltage levels, light intensity etc., are part of the physical layer.

The interface between the basic communications medium and the next layer in the OSI model is the "data circuit terminating equipment" or DCE. This element usually interconnects to the "data terminal equipment" or DTE. In the common example of a personal computer connected to the Internet, the modem, either cable, DSL or dial-up telephone, is the DCE ,while the subscriber's computer is the DTE.

An OSI network completely defines every interface. As an example, most computers connect a low speed modem with an RS-232 interface. This specification defines the signals, protocols and even the connector and its pin assignments, for the interface between the DTE and DCE. Open systems interconnect means the interconnect can be made both mechanically and electrically. The mechanical part of an interface specification causes problems when commercial off the shelf equipment is used in aircraft. Many of the connectors were not made to withstand the aircraft environment. This leads to "ruggedized" variants for aircraft use.

6.8.1.2 Layer 2, Data Link

The data link layer provides for error-free transmission of messages connected to the network. There is an upper sublayer which provides synchronization, error detection and correction, and link management. A lower sublayer deals with multiple access and is only present when the physical layer supports multiple access. The upper sublayer is always present.

There are two basic divisions of data link layer protocols; asynchronous and synchro-

263

nous. In simple terms, asynchronous means data may be transmitted at any time and the receiver is capable of determining when the message begins and ends. Synchronous means the message can only occupy a specific time slot.

In asynchronous data when no data are transmitted, the communication is said to be in an "idle" condition. A start bit indicates the channel is to transmit data and the prescribed number of data bits are transmitted. The data is ended with a stop bit, or returning to the idle state for a minimum period of time. The number of data bits transmitted is very small, usually less than 8. Therefore, only one character is transmitted between start and stop bits. The major disadvantage of an asynchronous data link is the overhead of the start and stop bits. The major advantage is no synchronizing system is needed. This is particularly important in moving platforms such as aircraft, where Doppler shift can cause difficulty in maintaining synchronization.

Synchronous protocols allow transmission of much larger data words between synchronizing bits. A frame is a block of characters which is transmitted without overhead bits for synchronism. The synchronous protocols provide delineation of the data block, error detection, link management and recovery from a link failure. Link management detects the presence of data on the link noted by a link going from idle to active. There are two types of data link protocols; bit-oriented and character-oriented.

Character-oriented data link protocols define messages, blocks frames etc. There are a number of character-oriented data link protocols and several are published international standards. In keeping with the OSI model, all protocols must be internationally standardized. In addition to protocols, a character set is defined. One such character set is the common ASCII, American Standard Code for Information Interchange. The ASCII character set includes alphanumerics and control characters. A data link protocol defines the synchronizing character, the number of data bits, any error detection bits and an end of transmission, EOT, character. Other delimiters are end of text, ETX, and ETB, end of block. Also provided are hand shaking characters such as ACK, acknowledge, and NAK, not acknowledged.

Character-oriented data link protocols were developed at a time when most digital communications were between user terminals and a mainframe computer. The character-oriented protocol lacks flexibility and tends to be inefficient. Bit-oriented data link protocols have been developed to overcome many of these inefficiencies. One bit-oriented protocol, the ISO's High Level Data Link Control, HDLC, is used in aviation applications.

The basic transmission unit in bit-oriented protocols is the frame, which consists of a flag sequence which is the delimiter for the frame, followed by the address, a control sequence, the data, a checksum and a trailing flag sequence.

The control field defines the purpose of the frame. There are three types of frames, information or I type, supervisory or S frame, and unnumbered or U type.

A number is included in the control field, which numbers successive frames. This is used for determining that all the packets of a sequence have been received and for the purpose of reassembling data.

Error detection in both character-oriented and bit-oriented data link protocols is via cyclic redundancy check, CRC. Vertical and longitudinal redundancy is also available but these techniques suffer from poor performance.

Cyclic redundancy was discussed in detail in chapter 5. Three standards for OSI networks are CRC-12, CRC-16, CRC-CCITT. These standards designate the generator polynomial. CRC-12 is a 12 bit polynomial while CRC-16 and CRC-CCITT are 16 bit polynomials. The generator polynomials are:

CRC-12 =	1 1000 0000 1111
CRC-16 =	1 1000 0000 0000 0101
CRC-CCITT =	1 0001 0000 0010 0001

6.8.1.2.1 Link Layer: Multiple Access

Multiple access protocols are required when multiple users share the physical layer. There are a number of methods to share a communications medium. One is very familiar; frequency division multiplex, FDM. Essentially, FDM separates voice communications on the existing VHF communications band. The frequency range for communications is divided into 720 channels of 25 kHz each. However, most channels have multiple users, which share the same channel by using radio procedures. Sharing a VHF channel is, to a certain extent, time division multiplex. Selecting the correct channel and accessing it in a manner that does not interfere with other users is a role of the link layer. The digital replacement for the existing VHF voice communications, discussed later in this chapter, is also a combination of FDM and TDM except that it is completely digital.

One method of TDMA that reduces contention is carrier sense multiple access, CSMA. Before transmitting a packet, the data terminal determines that the channel is idle or no carrier is detected. Of course, the lack of a carrier at the time a packet is to be transmitted does not insure that two stations will not attempt to transmit simultaneously. Therefore, a method of conflict resolution is required.

Code division multiple access, CDMA, is a spread spectrum system where signals occupy the same spectrum by modulating the signal with a spreading function. This technique is used in the GPS navigation system as explained in detail in chapter 4.

One method for reducing contention is to control channel access from a central location. Many of these systems involve polling subscribers, asking if a terminal has something to transmit. This technique becomes very inefficient if many terminals have little data to transmit, while a small number of terminals have significant data. The system is tied up polling low activity terminals when high activity terminals are bottlenecked. Special polling schemes are used to adapt to this situation.

6.8.1.3 Layer 3, Network

The network layer provides a transparent path from source to destination. It isolates source and destination from any concerns of network issues such as routing, conflict resolution, error detection, synchronizing and switching. The network layer interfaces with the datalink layer, which provides the network layer with an error-free communications link.

The network layer performs routing. Routers minimize congestion, deciding which link transmits a packet, and maximizing network throughput.

In directory routing, a look-up table is used by the node to determine the most effective route to the destination. Most effective would include the least number of hops to reach the destination, which minimizes time to delivery and reduces the probability of errors.

Hierarchical routing is used for large networks. The network is partitioned into regions; and addresses contain a region and node number. Adaptive routing allows for routing procedures to change as the network changes. Network changes involve deletion and addition of users, changes of mode of operation of users, etc. An airborne network would experience significant changes as terminals appear and disappear as flights begin and end. Also, aircraft will move from one ground station to another and so on.

Centralized routing designates one node as the routing control center which generates routing tables. This relieves the remaining nodes from having to determining routing. However, if the network changes often, considerable overhead results due to the communications required to generate new routing tables.

6.8.1.4 Transport Layer, Session Layer, and Presentation Layer

These layers are specific to the application and will be discussed in the sections where the application is discussed. In many situations some layers are virtually nonexistent. The ISO 7 layer system has been crafted to describe all possible data networks.

6.9 VHF Digital Communications

The state of affairs for airborne communications in the mid 1990s was one of serious deficiencies. The system was mostly voice using double sideband amplitude modulation operating on 25 kHz channels. Data transmission was over ACARS, which is an inefficient character-oriented system that was not compatible with the Aeronautical Telecommunications Network, ATN. When 8.33 kHz channels were implemented to solve problems for Europe, it was the consensus that this was not a permanent solution to the problem.

There was recognition of a number of other issues such as the "stuck mike" problem. This occurs when a microphone button is either stuck or the microphone is jammed in the holder or sat upon, and the transmitter is continually on the air. With the AM system this causes considerable interference. If, as an example, there are 50 aircraft sharing one channel at a large airport, only one user with a problem can bring the entire channel down. A backup channel is unlikely because of the shortage of channels. Another problem is that of "phantom controllers". This refers to a clandestine ground station transmitting bogus air traffic information to unsuspecting aircraft.

A digital system can be encoded to include a unique identifier so that every transmission source is positively identified. A stuck mike or phantom controller would be identified and corrective action can be taken. Although applicable to not only digital but analog communications, various protocols such as maximum transmission time can be designed into the radio to solve existing problems.

Much communication now handled by voice can be designated as digital transmission. Clearances and flight plans may be communicated by data link rather than voice. Other information, not normally available in the current system because lack of appropriate communications, can be provided. One example is a cockpit display of controller-pilot data.

Digital communications systems should have the ability to direct data to a specific user without other users receiving the data. This is similar to SELCAL previously described.

The new digital communications system should include the ability to have broadcast services as well as point to point. These broadcast services should be capable of targeting individual users and small groups or "call groups".

The new digital communications system should transmit digitized voice in party line style. This is similar to the current voice system and has the advantage that flight crew can hear conversations between controllers and other aircraft. This improves the situational awareness of the crew. It's also an example of a call group, where a certain set of users are linked while other users on the RF channel may not be included. The free-flight concept relies on more machine-to-machine communications but not so much in the terminal area where voice communications may be used for the foreseeable future. The new digital system must provide a flexible voice communications capability.

The future airborne communications system, with the exception of voice, will be computers talking to computers in a vast network. Airborne computers desiring en route weather will request the data from the ATN, which will retrieve it from weather stations and forward the information to the aircraft. Free flight will request data from aircraft relative to present position and intent. In the age of the Internet, most people are aware of what can be done with networked computers.

6.9.1 Aeronautical Telecommunications Network

Computers do not directly talk to other computers; data are channeled through a network. A network, such as the ATN, is arranged in various layers in a hierarchical structure, which insure orderly flow of data.

The ATN is based on the International Standards Organization (ISO) seven layer open system interconnect, OSI, protocols with some modifications. ICAO, RTCA and other aviation organizations maintain the modified standards. The network has a very large addressing capability and 16 levels of message priorities.

Most networks are actually a network of networks. An aircraft can have an on board network to gather data which, in turn, connects to a ground network through a data link. The system proposed and currently under development is VHF Data Link or VDL. The VDL is designed to be compatible with the ISO OSI model.

The VDL provides the lowest layer of the ATN hierarchy; layer 1 or the physical layer. This layer, as all but the top layer, responds to requests from the next higher layer, or layer 2, in this example. Layer 1, the RF part of the communications system, provides the RF carrier and applies modulation to the carrier. The layer also provides the carrier frequency, as the system can use a number of RF channels. The usual signal integrity monitoring such as carrier strength and other parameters are included in the physical layer. When multiple users are involved, the VDL insures orderly sharing of the channels, which is layer 2. The VDL is a remote terminal and, as all terminals, must have an address to operate on the network. The address for the VDL is the standard 24 bit ICAO address used for the mode-S transponder and ADS-B. Remember, the mode-S transponder has data link capability and it, too, can be connected to the ATN.

There will be a period of transition from all analog to a mixed period and finally an all digital network. During the transition, VHF communications radios must support both digital and analog communications. These multimode radios are called VHF data radio or VDR. These VDRs will support VDL, amplitude modulation voice and ACARS using a 2400 bit per second AM minimum shift keying, MSK, modulation.

The VDL or VDR is controlled by a communications management unit, CMU. The VDL/VDR has no controls, display or indicators. The VDL/VDR is similar to a computer modem where the only indicators are a power light and maybe a "connect" indicator. The VDL/VDR would have neither as it would be remote mounted and not even visible to the crew.

The VDL/VDR will provide a range of messages such as Air Traffic Service, ATS, which includes air traffic control, ATC, and flight information services, FIS. Weather information such as pilot reports, PIREPS, and significant meteorological reports, SIGMETS, may be transmitted. VDL/VDR will be used for ATC handoffs, clearance delivery and clearances. VDL/VDR can also be used for ADS-B, described earlier.

For aircraft operational control, AOC, messages include weather, flight plan, weight and balance, pilot/dispatcher, flight progress, flight following, maintenance, gate assignment, in flight emergencies, airframe/avionics/engine monitoring, departure delay information and checklists.

Layer 1 determines the channel assignment by choosing a channel frequency. A communications management unit, CMU, will interface with the physical layer using ARINC 429, 629, RS-232 or Mil STD 1553 for military applications.

6.9.2 VDL Modes

There are four modes for VDL. Eight level DPSK or 8DPSK, using TDMA is used for modes 2, 3 and 4 and MSK-AM, carrier sense multiple access, CSMA, for mode 1. Until ACARS is replaced with a digital data link, the old ACARS protocol must be supported. The data rate is 2400 bits/second, b/s, and CSMA is simply listening on a channel; if no activity is detected a transmission is made.

Mode 2 of the VDL is a data only mode. The basic data rate is 31.5 kb/s and modulation is 8DPSK. Eight states of phase shift permits 3 bits per symbol and thus the symbol rate is 10.5 k symbols/second. Channel access is via bit-oriented non-adaptive, p-persistent CSMA. The VDL mode 2 data subsystem is a subnetwork of the ATN. Data communications are reservation based to provide contention-free data service.

Mode 3 media access control, MAC, supports simultaneous voice and data. Modulation is 8DPSK at a bit rate of 31.5 kb/s. Channel access is TDMA using 30 ms slots with 4 slots per frame. This is the equivalent of providing four "channels". Since the VDL occupies the same 25 kHz as a conventional double sideband AM radio, four voice channels can occupy the same space as only one voice channel in the AM system.

Mode 4 is a frequency modulated Gaussian minimum shift keying or FM/GMSK. The data rate is 19.2 kb/s. The channel access is scheduled TDMA, STDMA, with 6.67 ms slots and 9000 slots per frame. Up to 128 users can transmit a full 19.2 kb/s data rate. STDMA is TDMA where time slots are assigned to users. Dynamic slot allocation permits more than 128 users if lower data rates can be tolerated.

The VDL uses an aviation VHF link control, AVLC, protocol for layer 2. This protocol is a connection-oriented protocol derived from the standard ISO high-level data link protocol, or HDLC. The AVLC protocol is characterized by the establishment of a link between parties before the exchange of messages. The link remains connected even though no messages are passing between users and is kept linked until the aircraft leaves a coverage area, whereupon it is handed over to another ground station. When a ground station is lost the datalink layer automatically seeks an available ground station called a link handoff. This provides a totally seamless transition. This connection oriented data transfer protocol increases reliability from the automatic retransmission of data

The VDL datalink uses a modified ISO 8201 protocol for layer 3, which is optimized for delivery of messages over a mobile network. The ISO 8201 is similar to the CCITT X.25 protocol for packet transmission. The ATN implements the ISO/OSI connectionless, broadcast, network protocol, CLNP, in the network layer.

6.9.3 D8PSK

Consider, first, phase shift keying, PSK, and how it's used with differential modulation. Phase shift keying changes the phase of a carrier in discrete steps, usually at specific times. This distinguishes phase shift keying from phase modulation, where the amount of phase shift can be any value and not at specific times. Another way of summarizing the difference is that PSK is digital and phase modulation is analog. Analog signals, such as voice, can be first digitized and transmitted by PSK. This is the technique for voice in the new digital airborne communications.

The entire carrier cycle is divided into eight possible phases. This results in phase angles of 0, $\pi/4$, $\pi/2$, $3\pi/4$, π, $5\pi/4$, $3\pi/2$, and $7\pi/4$. When data are transmitted, assigned time slots are marked with a synchronizing word. Each time slot transmits a phase angle equal to one possible phase angle. Since there are eight possibilities, three binary bits may represent the phase angle. The three binary bits transmitted in a time slot is called a symbol. The symbol does not have to represent a character such as a letter or number. We could consider an octal digit, 0 through 7, as a symbol for this example, but the actual data transmitted is not octal; it represents various types including graphics and special characters. This is different from the secondary radar transponder, where entered data is four digits of octal.

Phase modulation requires a reference against which a phase angle measurement is made for demodulation. In many systems, a phase reference is transmitted and the receiver compares the reference to a local oscillator and records the phase difference. This is used as a phase reference to demodulate the entire data word. It is important that the local phase reference frequency be stable so the two carriers remain in phase coherence. The local oscillator must remain phase coherent to within a fraction of the minimum phase shift for the duration of a data transmission. This requires significant frequency stability. To understand how stable the transmitted signal and local phase reference must be, consider an example:

A digital transmitter sends messages 1 ms long. There are 4 levels of phase shift and the carrier frequency is 125 MHz. Each phase shift minimum is $\pi/2$ and, if the phase of the transmission drifts more than $\pi/4$, the decoder cannot determine the state of the transmitted bit because it is midway between states. Long before the phase error reaches $\pi/4$, noise begins to increase the received errors.

At the beginning of the transmission the phase reference is sent. If transmitter and local oscillator drift apart by $\pi/4$, the decoder cannot accurately decode. A phase shift of $\pi/4$ in 1 millisecond represents a frequency difference of 125 Hz. This error relative to a 125 MHz carrier is one part per million, PPM, frequency accuracy, representing the difference between two units. Therefore, each transceiver can add no more than one half of the one PPM.

Transmitter carrier frequency accuracy of 0.5 PPM is possible but expensive. Further, even if accuracy is 0.5 PPM, the Doppler shift caused by moving aircraft causes significant error.

Differential phase shift keying uses the phase of the previous symbol as a reference for the current symbol. Assume symbols are transmitted that are zeros and ones. This is transmission of simple binary data, a bit at a time. Only two phase angles are required and the obvious choices are 0 and π.

When a data bit is received, its phase is compared to the previous bit and, if phases are the same, the decoder outputs a logic zero. When the phase is different by π, the decoder outputs a logic one. Phase comparison is made by delaying the received signal by exactly one bit time and comparing the delayed phase of the received signal with the delayed signal, as shown in Fig. 6.12. It is important that a time delay does not introduce a phase delay. To insure this, the time delay of the delay line can be an integer number of cycles of the carrier frequency. These problems were discussed in a previous section on the mode S transponder.

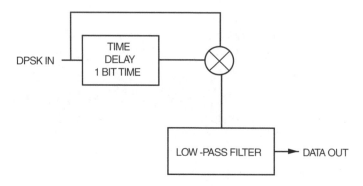

Figure 6.12 Decoder for binary DPSK

The significant advantage of differential phase shift keying is the reference has only been delayed one time slot, not the time of the entire message. If the message were, say, 32 bits long, there would be a 32-fold improvement in decoding accuracy using DPSK.

Differential phase shift keying implies that the difference in phase between the current and previous bit is the transmitted data. Let us explore an example. If the phase difference between the current and last bit is π radians, the symbol is 100, as shown in Table 6.1

There are eight possible phase differences, therefore, eight different symbols that may be transmitted during each bit time slot.

Phase Difference	Symbol
0	000
$\pi/4$	001
$\pi/2$	010
$3\pi/4$	011
π	100
$5\pi/4$	101
$3\pi/2$	110
$7\pi/8$	111

Table 6.1 Differential Phase Shift Keying (DPSK)

Generating phase shift for transmission can be done in a number of ways. The first operation is calculating the difference by subtracting the value of the current symbol, that is, the symbol to be transmitted during this time slot with the last symbol. This is done with a three bit subtractor. The difference is fed to an eight bit digital phase shifter. Another possibility is the difference can be transformed to an analog signal which drives an analog phase shifter.

Phase shifters tend to be for one frequency. The phase shifts are generated with Rs, Ls and Cs and are valid for only one frequency. There is an alternate method of producing phase shift that is not dependent on frequency, using orthogonal signals.

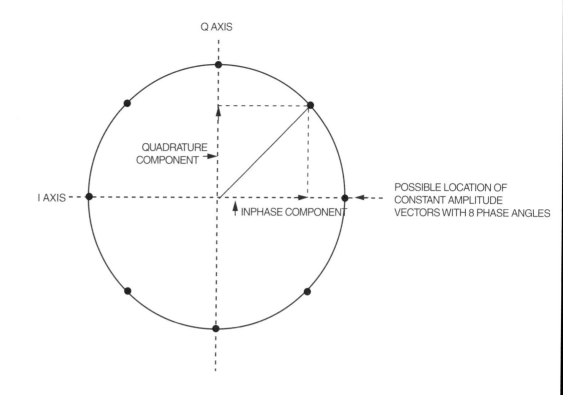

QUADRATURE COMPONENT

INPHASE COMPONENT

Q AXIS

I AXIS

POSSIBLE LOCATION OF
CONSTANT AMPLITUDE
VECTORS WITH 8 PHASE ANGLES

Fig. 6.13   Generating D8PSK with in phase and quadrature signals

Imagine a signal as a rotating vector (a valid view of any signal) constructed from two components. As for any vector, the two components are orthogonal and, for a rotating vector, the two components must rotate. Fig. 6.13 shows this concept. Two vectors make up the resultant vector. In the figure, they are shown on the X and Y axis, which implies that the entire coordinate system is rotating. We define a vector that lies on the X axis pointing in the direction of positive values as having a phase angle of zero. This is the "in phase" or I axis. A vector that points straight up or in the direction of increasing values is the "quadrature" or Q axis. The term "quad" is due to a vector being one quarter of a rotation around the axis.

Any vector can be created in this rotating coordinate system by vector summing two components. How this is done electrically is shown in Fig. 6.14. Two multiplying digital-to-analog converters, DACs, set the amplitude of the two components. One DAC has an input which is in phase with the carrier or I input, while the other DAC has the same carrier frequency, except shifted 90 degrees, which is the Q input. The DACs multiply the sinusoid I and Q inputs with a signed digital number. The term "signed" implies that component vectors can be both positive and negative.

271

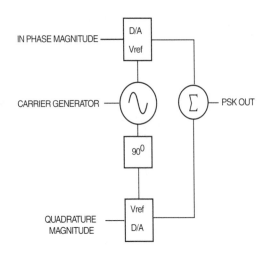

IN PHASE MAGNITUDE — D/A Vref

CARRIER GENERATOR — (∿)

90⁰

QUADRATURE MAGNITUDE — Vref D/A

(Σ) — PSK OUT

Fig. 6.14 D/A converters to generate 8DPSK

To see how phase shift keying operates, consider Table 6.2, based on an eight bit DAC.

Phase Angle	I component Analog Digital		Q component Analog Digital	
0	+1.000	+1111 1111	+0.000	+0000 0000
π/4	+0.707	+1011 0100	+0.707	+1011 0100
π/2	+0.000	+0000 0000	+1.000	+1111 1111
3π/4	-0.707	-1011 0100	+0.707	+1011 0100
π	-1.000	-1111 1111	+0.000	+0000 0000
5π/4	-0.707	-1011 0100	-0.707	-1011 0100
3π/2	-0.000	-0000 0000	-1.000	-1111 1111
7π/4	+0.707	+1011 0000	-0.707	-1011 0100

Table 6.2 Phase Shift Keying

There are only three numbers in the table; 0.000, 0.707 and 1.000. There are both positive and negative of 1.000 and 0.707. We don't need a DAC to produce 1.000 or 0.000, which can be done with an electronic switch. The DAC is needed only to provide 0.707, positive or negative.

It seems a waste of a DAC. This would be true if the only numbers generated were those shown in the table. To understand how the DAC is used to its fullest, however, consider the 8DPSK constellation. A constellation represents the location of points of arrows on vectors generated in the modulation. In the case at hand, there are eight points because there are eight levels of phase shift keying. They are on a circle with its center at the origin because only the phase is modulated, not the amplitude. For this discussion, it is not important where the points are in the constellation, but how to go from one to another. The obvious path is a straight line. Assume for a moment that we want to transition from one point to another on the opposite side of the circle. This results in a path through zero and a 180 degree phase shift. If this were done in a short time it would significantly change the waveform and use excessive spectrum.

Recall that the purpose of PSK in the first place is to minimize radio spectrum and increase the number of bits transmitted per Hz of bandwidth. With this in mind, let us make the transition in more time. Remember, the entire coordinate system is rotating. Increasing the time to make a transition would result in a more circular path, as shown in Fig. 6.15. There is now less change in more time, which results in narrower bandwidth.

272

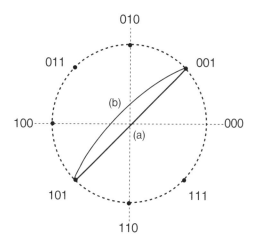

Fig. 6.15. Traces (a) and (b) show two possible paths between states 001 and 101. Notice that the most direct path causes carrier amplitude to go to zero

There is a limit to how much time may be taken to transition from one state to another. If there is too much time, the decoder has less time to determine the phase angle and decode the symbol.

If the required transition is not between opposite sides of the constellation but between adjacent points, the transition could still be a straight line, but there is little change. What it comes down to is minimizing the amount of generated spectrum. We could tailor the transitions based on the path between the initial and final points in the constellation. These transitions are made by several steps between the present and next state. This would require several states of the DAC in the modulator to minimize the spectrum.

6.10 Data Link Mode S

The mode S transponder was discussed in the previous chapter only as a secondary radar tool and as a part of ADS-B. In addition to its surveillance duties the mode-S transponder is capable of transmitting data. Of course, altitude and identity data are transmitted from the mode-S transponder when interrogated by a ground based radar. Other data is available upon interrogation. The mode-S transponder also has the ability to transmit spontaneously. This transmission is called a "squitter," which occurs about every second and was discussed in chapter 5. The data rate is 4 Mb/s for the down link, which means the mode-S data word is relatively long even for the short bursts of a squitter pulse. Most importantly, the mode S address is the standard ICAO 24 bit address used for the ATN. The significant disadvantage of the mode-S data link is the possibility of contention on the RF channel, particularly in areas of high traffic. The mode-S data link is a "transmit when ready" type and the only protection against conflicts is a repeat of the transmission. The mode-S transponder includes a very effective error detection algorithm which would satisfy the need for error-free transmission of data.

Chapter 6 Review Questions

6.1   What is the bandwidth of the current communications channel? What was the bandwidth of a communications channel when the VHF communications band was first used?

6.2   What is the air to ground radio range for a VHF communications transceiver at 37,000 feet?

6.3   Draw a block diagram of a VHF communications transceiver.

6.4   How much power is represented by a signal with a level of –100 dBm?

6.5   A signal of 20 watts is attenuated by 13 dB. What is the resulting power level in dBm? In watts?

6.6   What does a squelch circuit do?

6.7   If a receiver is to operate with an input of –97 dBm, what is the equivalent input in hard microvolts?

6.8   If a receiver is to operate with an input of –107 dBm, what is the equivalent signal in easy microvolts?

6.9   What is the significant disadvantage of a series modulator?

6.10   How does the synthesizer used for a transceiver differ from one used for a receiver?

6.11   When is the high frequency part of the spectrum used for communications?

6.12   What type of modulation is used for HF communications? Is this different from VHF communications? Why?

6.13   What type of demodulation is used for SSB?

6.14   Why is an antenna tuner used for an HF transceiver and not for a VHF transceiver?

6.15   What is a "clarifier" control and its purpose?

6.16   What are the categories of emergency locator transmitters?

6.17   How many different phase angles are used for data transmission in D8PSK?

6.18   How many symbols are in the symbol set for D8PSK?

6.19   What is a "constellation" relative to digital transmission?

References

Haykin, Simon, Communications Systems, 4th Ed., New York, John Wiley and Sons, 2000

Jain, Bijendra, Agrawala, Ashok, Open Systems Interconnection, its architecture and protocols, New York, McGraw-Hill, 1993

Chapter 7

Onboard Communications

7.0 Introduction

An important onboard system for voice communications and idents is the audio panel and interphone. A well-equipped business jet typically has two comm transceivers, two navigation receivers, an ADF, DME and marker beacon receiver. All six have audio outputs which must be monitored during flight. We would not like to hear all six in the ears during the entire flight, but need to identify a navigation aid or monitor a specific source for short periods.

Also required are voice communications between the flight crew and crew and passengers. Headphones block external noise and permit the flight crew to select audio sources independently. The flight crew also has microphones for communications radios and intercommunications with other crew members.

The requirements paint a clear picture for an audio panel which contains switching for audio sources and an interphone for communicating among users. It is common, particularly for small aircraft, to include the marker beacon receiver in the audio control panel. This is reasonable because the marker requires an audio connection. The usual arrangement is a bank of switches that add an audio source to a desired output. Outputs are usually headphones and cabin speaker. In some cases, there is a second headphone output; one for the pilot, a second for the copilot. The ideal arrangement, employed in larger aircraft, are three audio panels; one for cabin speaker, a second for the pilot and the third for the copilot. These panels are arranged so the speaker panel is in the center of the aircraft, while the two other panels are convenient to pilot and copilot.

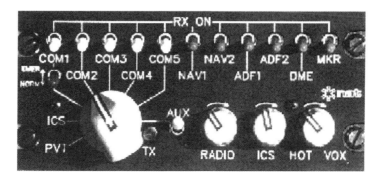

Audio Panel (Northern Airborne Technology)

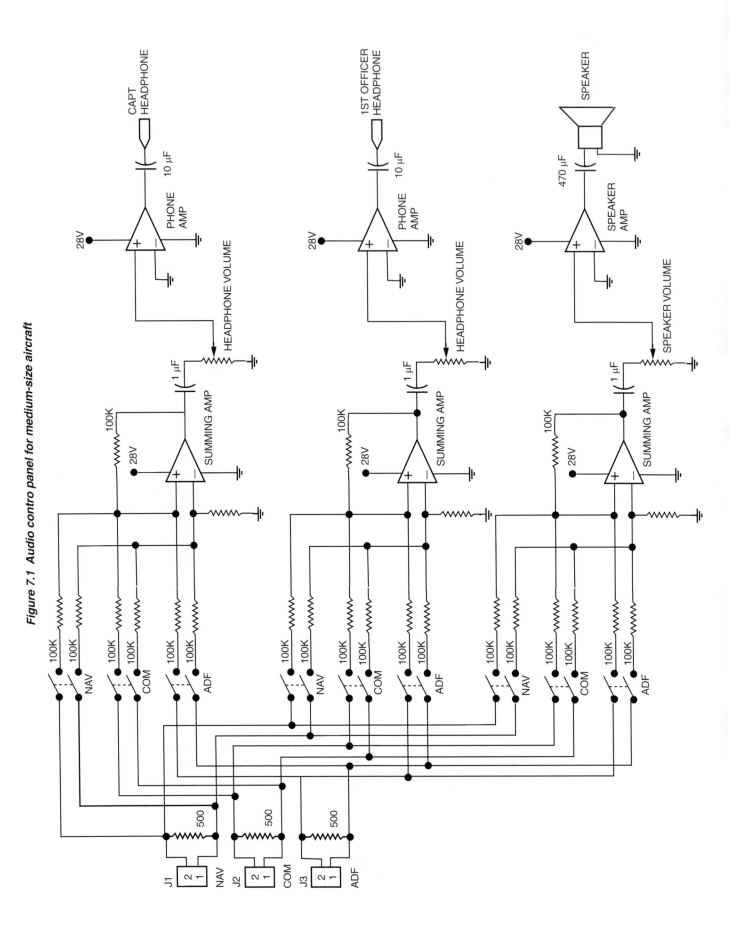

Figure 7.1 Audio contro panel for medium-size aircraft

276

The first rule is that all audio sources have the same output impedance. For aircraft, audio outputs that feed the audio panel are 500 ohms. (This is in contrast to the telephone industry, which uses 600 ohms for signal sources.) Every output is terminated with 500 ohms at all times. This is important. If the impedance seen by an audio output is allowed to change, it affects the level on the line. Users would perceive a change in audio volume. Changes in level to one pilot when the other pilot switches another audio source are to be avoided.

A technique in telephone systems is balanced audio transmission. This uses two outputs, where one voltage is opposite in polarity from the other. This is also called differential transmission and will be discussed later for data transmission in aircraft.

The advantage of balanced audio is that it rejects noise induced by electric and magnetic fields. Another technique for reducing noise is to use high signal levels, where the interfering signal is significantly lower than the desired signal. Balanced transmission is also used when a signal must travel a long distance through a noisy environment.

Figure 7.1 shows a simplified schematic of an audio panel for aircraft, from two-place to business jets. It provides two headphone outputs for pilot and copilot. A third channel is for a cabin speaker. This audio panel includes three rows of push switches, one row each for Captain, First Officer and cabin speaker, with one switch in each row for each audio source.

The audio panel also has two microphone inputs for the aircraft's two communications transceivers. Not only is microphone audio switched but the push to talk switch mounted on the yoke is switched as well. Only one transmitter may operate at one time. Both pilot and copilot must use the same communications radio.

The audio panel provides a constant impedance load on all audio sources supplied to the panel. The switching is done at a high impedance within the audio panel so there is no interplay of audio levels between pilot and copilot. The audio panel also contains a cabin speaker amplifier. The amplifier provides about 10 to 15 watts of audio power. The noise level in many aircraft is so high that cabin speakers must be robust and fed with considerable power. This is one reason headphones are recommended in aircraft, but for those who prefer the speaker, an audio amplifier is provided.

7.1 Microphones, Speakers and Headphones

Common microphones in aircraft are the hand and boom type. Attached to a pair of headphones, the boom mike allows hands-free communications. The push to talk switch is on the yoke; the hand microphone has it on the case. There are other types, such as a mask microphone for an oxygen mask and a throat microphone, which can be used with or without an oxygen mask.

The first type for aircraft was the carbon granule microphone, the same as in early telephone handsets. It is extremely rugged and a well-known technology. The carbon microphone was used in the first airborne radio and is still in operation to this day. If it is so good, why was it replaced? It is rugged, reliable and inexpensive—but it sounded terrible. Even though the carbon microphone is nearly gone, some of its requirements are still with us.

Let's examine the carbon microphone to see how its legacy lives on. The microphone has a container of carbon granules connected to a diaphragm, as shown in Fig, 7.2. Electrical resistance is reduced by squeezing the granules in the container. On the other hand, spread out the carbon granules and resistance increases.

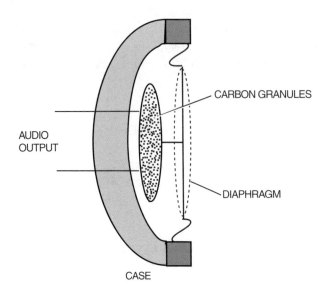

Figure 7.2 Carbon microphone

By connecting a diaphragm to the container, the variable pressure of sound waves compress and expand the carbon granules for a variation in resistance that *follows* the sound pressure. The phrase "proportional to the sound pressure" is used with great caution because this is the major problem with the carbon microphone; distortion. If resistance were truly proportional to sound pressure, we would still be using carbon microphones.

To use the variable resistance as a signal source, resistance is converted to a variable voltage. This is done by passing a constant, or nearly constant, current, through the micro-phone with a series resistor, as shown in Fig.7.3.

CARBON MICROPHONE

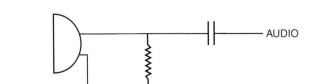

Figure 7.3 Carbon microphone circuit

Historically, aircraft transmitters provided the voltage source and resistance to operate a carbon microphone. There are other types, such as the crystal or ceramic microphone made with piezoelectric material, and magnetic microphones such as the so-called "dynamic" micro-phone. The crystal microphone is fragile and the ceramic microphone only slightly better. The dynamic microphone is rugged but does not provide a high level of audio voltage. Most impor-tant, once the series resistor is installed for the carbon microphone, no other microphone can be connected to that transmitter without chance damage. That is, except for amplified microphones.

278

As a replacement for the carbon microphone, manufacturers made several equivalents. The replacement behaved like a carbon microphone except it was a high quality dynamic or ceramic microphone.

Standard microphone technology today is the electret, a specialized ceramic with an extremely high dielectric constant. It can be made as a capacitor, where capacitance is a function of sound pressure applied to the capacitor. The electret is inexpensive, rugged and has superb frequency response and low distortion.

The electret microphone requires a source of voltage or current. The element operates into a high impedance, which makes it susceptible to electric fields. To avoid noise pickup, a preamplifier connects directly to the electret element. Connections between the electret material and amplifier are kept very short and signal level raised to a higher level. The electret microphone is no more susceptible to external fields than any other type. A source of current is needed to operate the amplifier and bias the electret material, achieved through a series resistor. Thus, the newest microphone technology uses the series resistor left over from the oldest technology, the carbon microphone.

The typical communications microphone allows sound waves to enter from the front. The operator holds the microphone to his mouth and talks directly into it. This appears to make sense, except that the large amount of background noise in the aircraft also enters the microphone. To reduce noise, a new microphone was designed with two sound entrance ports, one in the front and a second in back. The idea is that noise enters equally from front and back, causing equal pressure on the diaphragm. This helps cancel ambient noise. If the operator holds the microphone close to the mouth, sound pressure from the front is significantly greater than at the rear, so there is no cancellation of the voice. This is called noise cancelling and, throughout its development, the shape and location of sound entry holes have been optimized. This is the main type of microphone for aircraft.

Cockpit speakers are usually the common paper cone type used in most applications. No special speaker cabinets are used, which often causes problems in audio systems. High fidelity audio is not required since all sounds will be in the voice frequency range from 300 Hz to 3000 Hz, so aircraft manufacturers seldom provide any significant speaker enclosure volume. This results in bad fidelity and general inefficiency. Because the background audio level in many aircraft, particularly small aircraft where the engine is near the flight deck, is, in a word, loud. This results in the requirement of high power for audio amplifiers in audio panels. Unfortunately, many speakers cannot handle the power and distort, adding to the problem.

Headphones are preferred over speakers for cockpits with high ambient noise levels. Snug fitting headphones provide some ambient noise reduction, as well as provide audio from the audio panel. Recently, noise-canceling headphones have become available that use techniques similar to noise-canceling microphones. The noise-canceling headphone provides a microphone on the outside of the headphone which samples the ambient noise. Another microphone on the inside of the headphone samples sound on the inside of the headphone. Some audio energy from the outside of the headphone is fed to the earphone "out of phase" so that it adds with a negative sign and reduces the ambient noise inside the head set. Because background noise is a broad range of frequencies it is important that every frequency component of the background noise be fed back exactly out of phase. The microphone sensing the ambient noise should be as close to the headphone as possible so there is little phase shift between the sound outside of the headphone and inside.

The trick in making this technique work is to feed back just enough signal to reduce the ambient noise to zero. The amount of fed back signal depends on the attenuation provided by the basic headphone, which can change depending on how well the earphone is seated on the head. The most successful noise-canceling systems use adaptive gain adjusting circuits.

The final requirement is that noise-canceling circuits do not cancel the desired audio from the navigation or communications equipment. This is done by adding the desired signals with the correct phase relationships as to not cause cancellation. These same techniques are used in the so-called active noise cancellation systems which are capable of reducing the noise in an entire cabin by using strategically-placed microphones and large loudspeakers in the cabin. Because of the phase shifts involved within the cabin, which are much more involved than in the headphone, the cabin systems are only partially effective. The headphone systems are much more successful.

7.2 Digital Communication

One of the first requirements for onboard communications was to connect control heads with equipment in the avionics bay. The technique was to run as many wires as needed to control the remote units. If a switch had 6 wires, six wires were run. If an audio gain control on the instrument panel had three wires, the wires ran from receiver to instrument panel. If wires picked up noise, they had to be shielded. The problem with this philosophy is that the aircraft becomes heavy with wires and connectors.

The first technique to reduce wires was to multiplex switches. Take a transceiver that is remotely mounted with a control head in the cockpit. Frequency setting involves tens of MHz, MHz, 100s kHz and 25 kHz. The tens of MHz has only three positions, 1, 2 and 3. The MHz and 100's kHz switch has a possible ten positions each, and the 25 kHz switch has only 4 positions. To connect this switch using a normal single pole switch for each decade requires three wires for the tens of MHz, 10 each for the MHz and 100s kHz and four for the 25 kHz for a total of 27 wires. We assume that the common for the switch is ground, which is already required for other functions.

What if we encode the switches in binary coded decimal? Now the 10s MHz switch requires 2 wires, the MHz and 100s kHz, 4 each, and the 25 kHz switch two, for a total of 12, a reduction of more than one half the wires. We could reduce the number more by combining tens of MHz and MHz into one switch and 100s kHz and 25 kHz into another, which is done on many radios. The tens and MHz combined switch spans from 18 to 36 for a total of 19 positions. This is encoded using 5 binary bits. In the case of the combined 100 kHz and 25 kHz switch, there is a total of 40 different switch positions which can also be encoded using 6 binary bits. A total of 11 wires can communicate the frequency on the control head to the remote unit, but there is little improvement over the last example.

How far can we go with this technique? Let's go to the extreme and assume only one switch to select one of 760 channels. The 760 different states are encoded using 10 binary bits, which is a reduction of another two bits. The technique of encoding switch positions using binary codes is an example of parallel multiplexing. The number of wires is reduced by encoding information and communicating it to the remote unit, where it is decoded. Encoding can be mechanically generated by special switches, which was done in early avionics systems. Decoding is usually accomplished by electronic means.

Going back to the example of frequency programming for a communications transceiver, the wires can be reduced to the remote transceiver to *one* . This is accomplished by serial, rather than parallel, multiplexing. In serial multiplexing, the state of each switch is transmitted a bit at a time. In the example of two switches and 12 wires, the state of the twelve wires can be transmitted one at a time. If it is known which wire is sent first, in what order and how long between states, the 12 states can be decoded. A simple method of serially communicating switch positions of a frequency selector is shown in Fig. 7.4. The binary encoded state is loaded into a shift register and the contents transmitted a bit at a time.

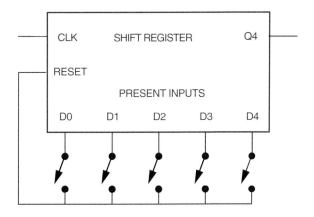

**Figure 7.4 Serially encoding switch positions
for communicating on a transmission line**

An early example of a standard for parallel onboard communications for navigation and communications frequencies is the "slip code". The name refers to characteristics of the code. If it is aligned against itself, then "slipped" one position, the code would not align in a unique way. This was implemented to suit motor driven switches. Another code for mechanical tuning is the 2 of 5 . Two of five parallel wires connect to ground at any one time. The codes were standardized by ARINC, as are the latest onboard communications techniques. This standardization enables the control head of one manufacturer to program another manufacturer's transmitter or receiver.

The first application of a standard ARINC communications code allowed a control head to interface with a COMM transceiver, NAV receiver, DME, etc. Encoding saves wires and ensures compatibility of systems of different manufacture.

As avionics became more complex, the need grew for serial communications. Installing more equipment on the flight deck and in the avionics bay led to the realization that any type of parallel communications would prove inadequate. A serial communications system, ARINC 429, was developed to meet this need and is widely installed in such aircraft as the Boeing 757 and 767, and in business aircraft. To use serial communications links, each unit must be ARINC 429 compatible.

7.3 Transmission lines

Consider, first, the transmission medium through which signals will pass on an onboard communications system which is a part of the physical layer. To send a signal from one point to another a simple wire would do. The fuselage of the aircraft could serve as a return path for current. This is how data were transmitted in the parallel communications just discussed. Why not do the same for serial data?

To a certain extent it's possible, but the earliest attempt at communicating via telegraph exposed the difficulties. If data is slow and the distance short, a single wire with a common return path may be used. Slow data in an aircraft are such tasks as turning on a warning lamp or pulling a flag in a VOR indicator. These signals are "discretes" in aircraft terminology. Most other signals require transmission lines to reliably connect one location with another.

What makes a transmission line different from a single wire and the aircraft for a return path? There are characteristics of a transmission line that distinguish it:

1. A perfect transmission line transmits signals of any rate or frequency without loss. This is the definition of a perfect transmission line. A practical transmission line has losses in the resistance of conductors, heating in the dielectric between conductors and radiation. Reducing resistance losses is achieved by high conductance material such as copper, silver or gold. Silver and gold sound prohibitively expensive, but high frequency signals travel on the surface of conductors and, therefore, the conductors only need to be gold or silver *plated*. The bulk of the conductor is common copper.

Reducing losses from heating is done with low loss dielectric material. There are reasonably priced materials such as Teflon, polyethylene and air. The mention of air as a dielectric may raise some eyebrows. To use air, a material is required to support conductors of the transmission line. Using air as a dielectric is done with small amounts of other material such as polyethylene in a few places to support the conductors, while the majority of the transmission line is air.

In some transmission lines thin disks of plastic support conductors, while the space between disks is air. Another method is plastic foam. The foam fills the space between conductors but foam is mostly air. When foams are part of transmission lines, only closed cell types are used. If cells are open, they eventually become contaminated by water or other substances.

2. Transmission lines provide immunity from signal egress and ingress. Creating a transmission line that has no signal egress implies that the line has no ingress. A transmission line with signal egress/ingress means the line acts as an antenna. Antennas can always transmit and receive. A transmission line with low radiation is necessary for low loss. If energy is radiated, it is lost from the signal in the line.

Signal egress and ingress are separated from other losses to understand what causes egress and ingress. Dielectric heating and resistive losses are due to the material of the transmission line, while egress and ingress are due to geometry.

There are two types of transmission lines, coaxial and parallel. Coaxial is more familiar and used for data transmission and RF signal distribution. Parallel conductor transmission line, often called twisted pair, is common but not always thought of as a transmission line. Twisted pair is used in telephone wiring. The length of telephone pairs probably exceeds all other transmission line applications added together.

The twisted pair is used in aircraft onboard communications. Short-range, wired communications use a mix of twisted pair and coaxial cables, with a movement to fiber optics, which has all the characteristics of a transmission line, as described later. Construction of a parallel conductor transmission line or twisted pair is shown in Fig. 7.5. The figure shows two parallel wires, although the line has been referred to as "twisted". The section of the line shown in Fig 7.5 is a very short section, so the twist is not evident.

Consider, first, how the parallel conductor transmission line prevents signal egress, that is, signal escaping the line. Assume the transmission line is driven with a signal and terminated with a load. Other than the load, there are no paths to ground or to other circuits. Drive current goes to the load and nowhere else. In this case, current in each wire of the transmission line is the same.

A magnetic field is generated around every current, in a wire or otherwise. The magnetic field lines are concentric circles with current at the center. The lines are orthogonal (right angle) to the current and thus the magnetic field must be circular with current at the center. In the case of parallel wire transmission line, there are two currents with the same magnitude but of opposite sign. If the two wires are close, each generates a circular magnetic field with very nearly the same center, same magnitude but of opposite direction; the fields cancel. This shows how signal egress is eliminated. If egress is eliminated is signal ingress (energy picked up from outside the line) also eliminated? Theoretically it can, but look at it from a magnetic field approach.

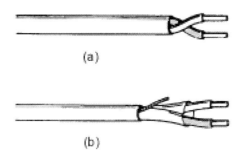

Figure 7.5 Twisted pair transmission line: (a) unshielded; (b) shielded

If a wire is in a *changing* magnetic field, current is induced in the wire. In the transmission line there are two close wires so it can be assumed they are subject to the same magnetic field. Thus the same current is induced in each wire. The load is connected across the two wires of the transmission line. To generate a voltage in the load, current moves into one end of the load and out the other end. An induced current, however, is either into or out of *both* ends and generates no voltage. Thus there is no signal ingress. This analysis relates to a changing magnetic field. The same results are obtained for a changing electric field.

The desirable characteristics of the parallel conductor transmission line depend on two conductors remaining relatively close throughout the length. If the wires separate, magnetic fields no longer cancel and there is a point of signal egress or ingress. To insure that the two wires remain close, a common practice is twisting them together. The wires could be physically attached to each other, which would insure that they did not separate.

A twisted pair transmission line rejects all signal egress and ingress in a perfect system. It was assumed that the load had no path to ground. Although transmission line drivers and receivers are very good, none is perfect. For added protection, some transmission lines are enclosed in a shield for additional protection against external electromagnetic fields. This is called a shielded twisted pair, or STP. Both shielded and unshielded twisted pair, UTP, are commonly used in airborne and ground installations.

One important attribute of a transmission line is characteristic impedance. Imagine a short pulse applied to the transmission line. The width is sufficiently short so all energy is within the transmission line. Assume a 10 ns pulse applied to a 10-meter transmission line. Pulses as narrow as 10 ns are readily generated with a pulse generator. When voltage of the pulse is applied to the transmission line, energy is transferred to the transmission line. Remember, one purpose of a transmission line is to transmit energy from one location to another and we assume that energy is transferred from the pulse generator to the transmission line during the pulse. The voltage applied to the transmission line must produce a current, for without current there could be no energy transfer. The ratio of voltage to current is called the characteristic impedance of the transmission line.

Energy coupled to the transmission line propagates to the far end. How is energy stored when contained in the line? It is in the electric and magnetic fields in the transmission line and propagates from the source to the load.

The next characteristic is the velocity at which energy propagates within the transmission line. Since energy is transferred through an electromagnetic field, maximum velocity is $c = 3E8$ m/s which is the speed of electromagnetic radiation in a vacuum.

Return to the example of a 10 ns pulse and 10 meter transmission line. Since maximum velocity of the pulse is 3E8 m/s, the 10 ns pulse travels less than 3.3 meters in the transmission line. Energy of the entire pulse is contained in the 10 m transmission line.

Energy is propagating in the dielectric material and velocity of propagation of electromagnetic energy in a dielectric is $c/(e_r)^{1/2}$, where e_r is the relative dielectric constant of the material.

Example: What is the velocity of propagation in a polyethylene coaxial cable? The dielectric constant in polyethylene is 2.45.

Solution: Substituting 2.45 for e_r we obtain $c/(e_r)^{1/2} = 3E8/(2.45)^{1/2} = 1.92E8$ m/s.

Example: How much transmission line does the 10 ns pulse occupy in the previous example?

Solution: The length is found by multiplying time duration of the pulse by velocity of propagation, which is $10E-9s \times 1.92E8$ m/s = 1.92 meters. The energy of a 10 ns pulse occupies less than 20 percent of the 10 meter cable.

The concept of a plug of energy traveling through a transmission line helps understand other characteristics. As energy travels, current remains a constant. This is true of voltage as well. Together this implies that impedance within the transmission line is a constant. What would happen if, suddenly, the characteristic impedance changed? This could happen if a section of transmission line is spliced with a different characteristic impedance. But how could current in a wire suddenly change? What happens is that some current and, consequently, some energy reflects back to the source.

Consider the ultimate change of impedance; an open or short circuit. All energy is reflected back to the source. For maximum transfer, a transmission line must drive a load equal to the characteristic impedance of the transmission line. The phenomenon of reflection, as we will see, is a troubleshooting tool to find faults in a cable.

To prevent reflections, transmission lines must terminate with a resistance equal to the characteristic impedance of the transmission line. When transmission lines are tapped, which means the application of a receiver or transmitter, the tap should not alter the impedance by much. This means that when a tap is placed in parallel with the transmission line, the impedance should be high. When the tap is placed in series with the transmission line the impedance should be low.

A tap of any sort causes a reflection. For short distances and low data rates in many aircraft systems, mild reflections cause no difficulty. When rates and distances increase, reflections can be catastrophic.

7.3.1 Line Codes

The earliest "code" for wire transmission was on-off keying or OOK. This was used for normal telegraphy and soon showed weaknesses. We must be careful to distinguish a line code from encoding. As an example, on-off keying transmits dots and dashes of the Morse code and is in the physical layer, layer 1.

There are a number of line codes in use in local area networks. For the most part, digital communications systems are divided into time slots during which a bit is transmitted. This discussion is relative to binary transmission where the physical layer transmits only one of two logic states in the designated time slot. What takes place in that time slot designates the line code. As an example, Fig. 7.6(a) shows a non return to zero, NRZ, data bit. This means that the line current or voltage goes to some value to transmit a logic one or zero and does not return to zero. In a unipolar system a logic zero is indicated by no current in the time slot. In this case the line current or voltage cannot return to zero as it is already at zero.

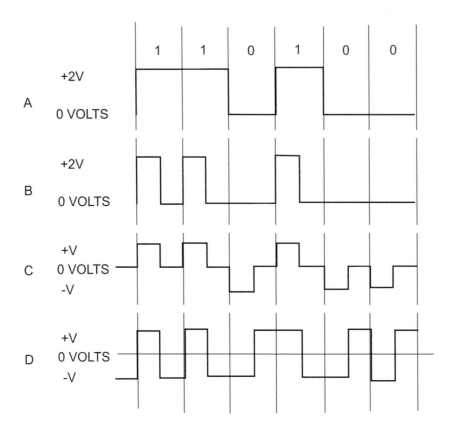

Figure 7.6 Example of line codes: (A) Non-Return to Zero, NRZ;
(B) Unipolar Return to Zero; (C) Bi-polar Return to Zero; (D) Bipolar Manchester

A bipolar line code uses both positive and negative polarities for data transmission. In this case a logic one is transmitted by a positive voltage on the transmission line while a logic zero is a negative voltage on the transmission line. For an NRZ code, the voltage or current on the transmission line is never zero. This is advantageous in that if a transmission line is open or shorted the situation is immediately recognized even though no data is being transmitted.

Some communications systems have a third state called "idle". This occurs when no data is to be transmitted and an idle state is entered. In many systems this is no voltage or current on the line. Not all data transmission systems have a zero voltage idle. Some transmit steady state logic zero or logic one. The significant advantage of a zero voltage or current idle state is a reduction of power dissipation when no data is being transmitted.

The unipolar line code has the advantage that a negative power supply is not required. This is an important advantage for small aircraft where the primary power is 28 volts DC. The bipolar line code has the advantage that when the number of ones and zeros are the same the average voltage on the line is zero.

Example: Assume a NRZ data communications system provides plus and minus 5 volts across a 130 ohm twisted pair transmission line. When not transmitting data the system provides a steady logic zero. How much power is dissipated in the terminating resistor?

The terminating resistor has 5 volts across it at all times. The power dissipation is
$P = V^2 / R = 25 / 130 = 192 \ mW.$

Power dissipation for terminating resistors may not sound like a difficult problem but when a unit must communicate on several busses the fractions of a watt begin to add up.

The next example of Fig. 7.6(b) is a unipolar return to zero code. There is little difference between the unipolar RZ and NRZ except that strings of ones have a transition between the bits, which can aid in timing and clock recovery. Fig. 7.6 (c) shows a bipolar RZ code. This code has taken on important characteristics. First, there are three levels on the line, a plus state, a minus state and a zero state. During periods of no data transition there will be zero volts across the line and thus no power dissipation in the terminating resistor. Secondly, there is a transition to zero for every bit transmitted. This will aid in timing and clock recovery.

Another important characteristic of the bipolar RZ code is there is no DC or average value when the number of ones and zeros are equal. Some data communications systems "scramble" the data to insure the number of ones and zeros are equal. When there is no DC value the data can be capacitively and transformer coupled, which offers some advantages.

The final line code shown in Fig. 7.6(d) is the bipolar Manchester. This method of coding was discussed relative to mode-S transponder replies. Since pulse amplitude modulation cannot have two polarities, the mode-S version of Manchester is similar to unipolar in a wired system.

To recall, Manchester encoding places a pulse in the early half of the time slot to transmit a logic one and, in the late half, to transmit a logic zero. Manchester encoding has the most advantages of all the line codes discussed. There is a transition from plus to minus or minus to plus in the middle of each time slot which is very important for timing. Secondly, the average value of the Manchester encoding is zero, regardless of the number of ones or zeros.

7.3.2 Transmission Line Drivers and Receivers

A line driver is the interface between the logic level signals of a digital subsystem to the line codes outlined in the previous section. A line driver usually does not contain any timing or buffering and receives logic level inputs and provides the two or three levels required to generate the line code.

The line driver must provide a source with an internal resistance equal to the characteristic impedance of the transmission line. For a twisted pair this is between 100 and 150 ohms. In addition, the line driver should be able to withstand several common faults without damage. One fault is shorting one of the two sides of a transmission line to ground. Another is shorting of one side or both sides to the 28 volt power supply. In some cases, the line driver must withstand a short to 115V 400 Hz, AC.

Line drivers, being connected to the "outside world," need to withstand various abuses other than shorts. One is induced voltages and currents from other wiring and electrostatic discharge.

Line drivers are often equipped with the ability to adjust the rise and fall times of the waveform. Very fast rise and fall times, that is, faster than needed, only cause problems with the system. First, fast rise and fall times cause a broad spectrum which can radiate and cause interference to on-board radio receivers. Also, fast rise and fall times produce reflections from poorly terminated transmission lines. Some on-board digital communications systems are designed to operate with improperly terminated lines and fast transitions will cause serious interference from poor terminations.

Line receivers convert line voltages to logic ones and zeros. In a system that has three states; plus, minus and zero, two logic outputs are required. A line receiver for a bipolar line code can actually have four states; a valid plus, a valid minus, a valid zero and an invalid state which is somewhere between valid states.

For simple two level line receivers, simple hysteresis is often used reduce the effects of noise and pulse distortion. Ringing on a pulse occurs on the leading and falling edge. Minimizing ringing is one of the reasons that rise and fall times are controlled. The use of hysteresis reduces the effects of ringing by not allowing a change of state.

Line receivers should offer rejection to common mode voltages. Common mode means situations where a voltage is induced on both lines of the transmission line. For a differential system these voltages should not affect the received signal. The ability to ignore common mode induced voltages is called the common mode rejection ratio and is given as a decibel figure. As an example, if a line receiver had a 60 dB common mode rejection ratio, a system that can operate with a 5 millivolt minimum signal should be able to reject a 5 volt common mode signal.

Just as a line driver can be programmed to limit the rise and fall time of the output voltage, a line receiver can be programmed to have a finite frequency response. A line receiver that has, say, a 1 MHz bandwidth is only inviting noise problems when used with a 10 kb/s data rate. It is also common to provide passive filters ahead of the line receiver to limit the frequency response of the data receiver.

7.4 ARINC 429

The characteristic ARINC 429 covers hardware and protocol for communicating on the ARINC 429 bus. In local area network, LAN, terms, ARINC 429 describes the physical layer and data link layer of the ARINC 429 LAN. When ARINC 429 was conceived in the mid 1970s, there were few LANs and these terms were not known.

ARINC 429 is installed in many Boeing 7X7 series of aircraft. The B-777 moved on to the later, more effective, ARINC 629 data bus. The Airbus A3X0 series of aircraft through the A340, helicopters and many business jets and general aviation aircraft also use ARINC 429. All 700 series ARINC-defined avionics are programmed with ARINC 429.

What's expected of a wired communications system for aircraft? The first requirement is transmitting the required amount of data per unit of time. Data rates for most aircraft are not unusually high. Digital communication for civil aircraft does not need to be more than a few megabits per second, Mb/s. In military aircraft, where electronic warfare, EW, is on board, a few Mb/s is not sufficient. Data generated by EW systems is tremendous. Modern civil aircraft with electronic displays and fly by wire are beginning to demand more data capability but at the time of this writing it is only a small fraction of that required by military aircraft.

Long wiring runs are not a high priority for an onboard communications system. The longest run in a large aircraft will usually be not be more than a 100 meters. Many wired digital communications systems are capable of tens of thousands of meters without exotic hardware.

Immunity from signal egress and ingress is important for airborne wired communications systems. Signal egress implies radiation from the system. This is dangerous on aircraft because so many radio-based systems could be affected.

Signal ingress is also important because of aircraft radio transmitters. Although many of these signals are not strong, there is a possibility of signal enhancement due to resonance within the airframe and high electric field intensities. One of the biggest field intensities that could be encountered in a civilian aircraft is a lightning strike.

Lightning strikes rarely cause aircraft accidents, but onboard communications systems should be not be allowed to fail, even temporarily. As an aircraft becomes more controlled by electronics, the more critical signals become. Two modern aviation systems whose criticality is especially significant are "fly by wire" and FADEC (full authority digital engine control). Fly by wire is a system where signals from the flight deck normally transmitted to control surfaces by mechanical means become electronic. The controlling element of the aircraft is not a massive yoke moved by the pilot, but can be a small "side stick" that requires one hand and little force. Electrical signals from the side stick are transmitted to a computer, which determines what signals should be sent to motors controlling ailerons, elevator and rudder. FADEC systems also communicate with sensors and controls throughout the aircraft and adjusts engine parameters.

A modern aircraft is a vast system where many elements must communicate and perform their functions reliably. Robust communications links are an absolute necessity for the success of this level of complexity. The thought of having to "reboot" every system in an aircraft while airborne is frightening.

The ARINC 429 digital interface is a one-way system, where a bus is driven by a single transmitter. The bus can have up to 20 receivers. ARINC 429 can be bidirectional by adding additional busses but each additional bus is one way. The basic hardware is a differential balanced digital communications system. The wire that connects the transmitter to the receivers is either a UTP (unshielded twisted pair) or STP (shielded twisted pair).

A differential system is where information is transmitted on two wires and one is the inverse of the other. For ARINC 429, if voltage measured to ground in one wire goes from zero to + 5 volts, the other wire goes from zero to –5 volts. The wire voltage is measured from wire to ground. If we measure across the two wires the voltage is seen to go from 0 to 10 volts. Whether it is plus or minus depends on which wire is the reference. The signal is received by connecting a receiver across the transmission line.

The advantage of the differential system is rejection of common mode voltage. Assume the two wires pass through a high electric field. We did not choose an electric field to show the transmission line characteristics of a twisted pair. This discussion is, essentially, that analysis. Conductors in an electric field have induced voltage, depending on how the conductors are arranged in the field. In the case of a UTP, since two wires are close together, whatever the field is, the two conductors are immersed the same way. Voltage introduced on one conductor is precisely the same as voltage induced on the other.

The signal is transmitted from wire to wire, or differentially. The signal is received by taking the voltage *across* the two wires. Since interfering voltage induced in both lines is the same, when measuring across the line there is no voltage due to an external field.

In the examples current in the transmission line went only to the load, there were no other current paths. If this is the case, the transmission line is said to be floating. This means voltage from transmission line to ground could become quite high and, if a charge accumulates on the line, voltage could become significant. Problems were discussed of the entire aircraft becoming charged to a high voltage and discharging to the atmosphere, and problems with the ADF. The transmission line is not hanging out in the airstream where it accumulates thousands of volts. Transmission line drivers and receivers operate from a power supply of 15 to 25 volts. If the transmission line becomes significantly higher than the power supply, circuits connected to the line could break down. This does not suggest the breakdown is a catastrophic failure, but the likelihood of breakdown causing loss of data is high. It is not desirable to allow the line to float but relate to a reference which is usually ground. This reference voltage is called the common mode voltage

In ARINC 429, when one line increases to +5 volts the other is exactly the same voltage but opposite in polarity. Relative to ground, the ARINC 429 common mode voltage is zero. The equivalent circuit is shown in Fig.7.7. If this system is balanced, the magnitude of the voltage sources of the driver, and the source impedance are exactly the same.

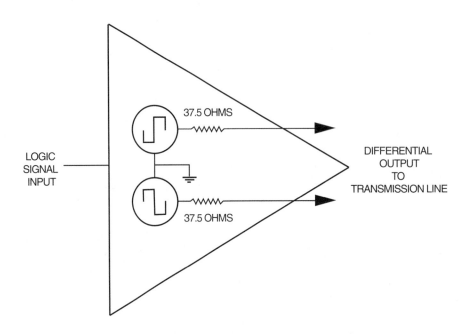

Figure 7.7   ARINC 429 transmission line driver and receivers

ARINC 429 has a high and low speed variant. The low speed operates at a nominal 13 kb/s and the high speed at 100 kb/s.

The ARINC 429 line driver, like most line drivers, has limited rise and fall times. The rise and fall time for the low speed variant is 10m +/- 5ms, while high speed rise time and fall time is 1.5m +/- 0.5ms.

ARINC 429 is balanced and differential. Voltage pulses are 20 volts, measured differentially, and the line code is a bipolar RZ as shown in Fig. 7.6(c) One significant advantage of an RZ code is it is "self clocking". Every data pulse has a rising and falling edge. The self clocking feature of the RZ code was an important feature when the ARINC 429 code was developed. Modern digital systems are blessed with microprocessors operating with crystal controlled clocks that can be used for controlling serial communications. Many early digital communications systems generated and decoded line codes using monostable multivibrators with RC time constants. Drift of the time constants was not uncommon and ARINC 429 line code, therefore, was made to be very tolerant of timing errors. The 100 kb/s high speed ARINC 429 was conceived at a later date when most digital communications were controlled by microprocessors and high speed 429 only permits timing errors of plus or minus 2.5%. Slow speed ARINC 429 permits variations in bit times from a minimum of 70 ms to 83 ms.

ARINC 429 is asynchronous. This implies that messages can begin at any time. When there are no messages the transmission line is the null state and there is no voltage on the transmission line, which is a power saving advantage. A message can start any time by simply sending the first bit. The receiver recognizes it and begins the receiving process. The data transmission is a timed communication where data bits occupy a time slot. To insure that the first bit is not confused with data bits, a minimum of 4 time slots of no data, i.e. idle, are required between data words. The four time slots of idle represent the minimum. If data is required, say, every second, it can be sent every second, which would keep the transmission line idle most of the time. Each ARINC 429 data bus is driven from one transmitter; the bus driver supplies up to 20 receivers. An identifier describes the data word. The transmitter can supply more than one data word, for example; a DME could provide distance and ground speed data words.

Receivers use only data words of interest to them. As an example, a transponder is connected to an air data computer in some aircraft. The air data computer provides parameters relative to the atmosphere; air temperature, MSL altitude, pressure altitude and others. The transponder uses pressure altitude and ignores other data words on the bus. If an outside air temperature indicator is connected to the bus, it ignores data words except for outside air temperature. ARINC 429 transmitter and receiver parameters are shown in Fig. 7.7. A certain amount of tolerance is permitted in the amplitudes of transmitted and received pulses. It is not possible or desirable to require transmitter pulses to be extremely precise because there are tolerances in components for the driver, and the bus can be lightly or heavily loaded.

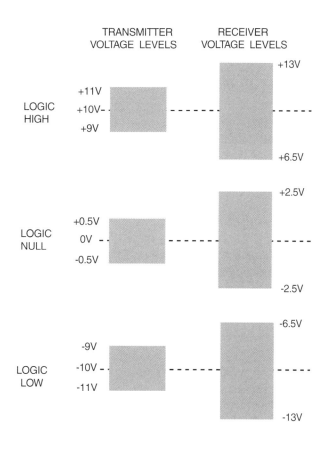

Figure 7.8 Transmitter and receiver parameters for ARINC 429

For the receiver, the voltages are configured so some signal loss in the bus, due more to loading rather than loss in the transmission line, can be accepted. As mentioned, there are three states in the ARINC 429 system; logic 0, logic 1 and null. At the transmitter, the line voltage representing a logic 1 is 10 volts plus or minus 1 volt. The null state is 0 volts plus or minus 0.5 volts. A logic zero is minus 10 volts plus or minus 1 volt. There are three ranges of voltages the receiver will accept. Notice there is a range of voltage the receiver will not accept for any of the three states. The null state at the receiver is plus and minus 2.5 volts.

Logic 1 state is between plus 6.5 and 13.0 volts, while the logic zero state is the same except for negative voltage.

What happens if voltage falls outside those ranges? In this instance, the receiver does not accept the voltage as valid. Let's see how this can increase reliability. When no data are transmitted, the bus is in the null state. Assume there are no pulses on the line but differential voltage is 3.0. This is recognized by the receiver and an alarm condition generated; the bus is flagged as faulty.

Another fault is detected by strict voltage ranges acceptable to the receiver. If one of the two lines of the twisted pair shorts to ground, transmitter voltage is cut in half; between 4.5 and 5.5 volts, which is in the unacceptable range of the receiver. Notice that half of the range of permitted transmitter voltage falls in the unacceptable region, which implies the system will cease operating. Whether the system detects the ground fault or ceases to operate is not important. What is significant is that the system will not operate with a serious flaw. The same holds true for shorting one of the transmission line wires to the 28 volt power source, rather than ground. The resulting voltage falls outside of the acceptable range for an ARINC 429 receiver.

It is important that the system not be damaged by connections to the 28 volt supply or to ground. While wires rarely short to ground or to the 28 volt supply, the system protects other receivers connected to the bus against damage during such failure.

The time slot for one bit depends on the speed of the ARINC 429 system. There are two rates: a high-speed variant, with a 10 ms time slot, and low speed, with a time between 69 ms and 83.3 ms. Data pulses have a duration of half the time slot and transition from null state to positive or negative 10 volts, depending on the data bit sent. The pulse returns to the idle state halfway through the data time slot. Each data bit has two transitions in each time slot. There is a transition at the beginning and midpoint of each time slot. This permits transition for generating strobe pulses for receiving data.

The ARINC 429 data word, consisting of 32 bits total, has several formats. One of the first applications was connecting control heads to navigation and communications equipment. Important words were for frequency programming, often in binary coded decimal, BCD. To handle this information a number of data words are BCD oriented. Some data words and discrete data are binary, as well There are alphanumeric oriented data words based on the ISO alphabet character set number 5.

The first 8 bits are a word identifier called the label. Most words, such as distance, frequency, bearing, heading, etc. , use an 8 bit identifier. Octal digits of 355 for the first 8 bits represent an acknowledgment word. Octal 356 or 357 indicate the word is a numerical or alphabetical character. What the character represents was indicated in a previous data word.

ARINC 429 has a standard set of data words, but they can expand as needed. An example is when GPS was installed in aircraft. GPS words were added to the standard list. All

ARINC 429 words also contain a parity bit for error detection. There is a set of file data transfer words for transmitting large amounts of data.

Bits 9 and 10 are the source/destination identifier or SDI. These two bits are used when more than one receiver is on the line that could use the data. In systems where there multiple sources of the same data, such as redundant systems, the SDI indicates the source of data. Multiple sources of data do not imply multiple transmitters on one data bus. When the SDI is not used, bits 9 and 10 are set to zero.

Bits 11 through 29 are the data bits. The format of the data depends on the data word being transmitted. They are defined in ARINC-429, which is updated when necessary. Some manufacturers have defined non-standard data words to suit specific systems.

Bits 30 and 31 is the sign/status matrix. This data set includes the status of hardware, the sign of the data and data validity.

Bit number 32 is the parity bit based on odd parity.

ARINC 429 hardware is shown in Fig. 7.9. The transmission line is driven by a line driver, usually from one end, rather than in the middle. The end of the transmission line may or may not terminate in the characteristic impedance of the line. For a short line and the slow ARINC 429 bus, the lack of termination will not cause significant difficulty. For a long line and high speed data, a termination is suggested.

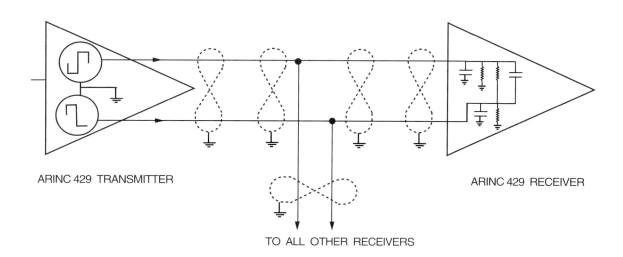

ARINC 429 TRANSMITTER

TO ALL OTHER RECEIVERS

ARINC 429 RECEIVER

Figure 7.9 ARINC 429 hardware

Receivers, as many as 20, are placed on the line with a minimum of 12K resistance. There are ARINC 429 interface chips that provide line drivers, receivers and logic translation from three-level signals to logic zeros and ones. More sophisticated chips include registers and interface circuits for direct application to a microprocessor bus.

7.5 MIL STD 1553

Designed for the military, MIL STD 1553 is used in limited cases for civilian aircraft. MIL STD 1553 defines layer 1, physical layer, electrical signals on the transmission line and layer 2, protocols for interfacing with the transmission line. For civilian aircraft, an SAE specification, AS-15531, is virtually the same as MIL STD 1553. There are a number of foreign equivalents and a NATO specification that is, essentially, MIL STD 1553. Only the newest aircraft use serial data transmission extensively. The F-16 was the first aircraft to use MIL STD 1553 shortly after 1553's introduction in 1973.

ARINC 629 is similar to MIL STD 1553 and superior to ARINC 429. It is expected that ARINC 629 will become more prevalent in new aircraft than ARINC 429. MIL STD 1553 is also used in aircraft ground test equipment and simulation.

MIL STD 1553 is a higher speed, more versatile data communications system than ARINC 429. One of the first differences is the speed of MIL STD 1553, which is 1Mb/s. There is only one speed as there are no variants of the system.

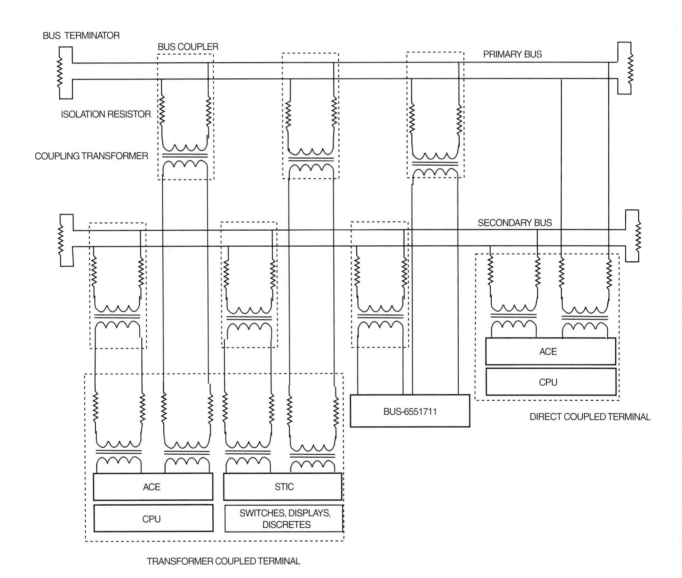

Figure 7.10 MIL STD 1553 communications system

The system operates with a shielded twisted pair using balanced differential signalling. This is common in advanced wired communications because, other than coaxial cable, anything less does not work. Data is transmitted in asynchronous packets of 20 bits each. Unlike ARINC 429, however, a bus can have more than one transmitter. This difference significantly affects the topology of the communications system and provides for high reliability.

Fig. 7.10 shows a MIL STD 1553 system. Subscribers to the bus are called remote terminals, or RTs. Like any terminal, RTs can receive and transmit. A bus controller reduces the number of collisions and other bus contentions. MIL STD 1553 permits redundant busses, a very important characteristic in a military system, which needs to function in spite of battle damage. In critical civilian applications, such as fly by wire, a similar advantage is obtained from redundancy.

A bus monitor is an RT that only listens to the activity on the bus. The monitor is primarily for the purpose of test and evaluation. It can be used to supply data to a back up controller in failure situations.

A bidirectional bus using RTs rather than a dedicated driver and only receivers significantly affects the way data are handled. First, in the single driver per bus, after data is transmitted, there is no acknowledgment of a successful receipt. The ability to perform two-way handshaking is an important part of a high reliability communications system.

In addition to improving data integrity, the bi-directional bus permits considerable flexibility and reduces the amount of twisted pair. A number of RTs with data to send and receive are present on the same bus. In the case of ARINC 429, each provider of data requires a bus for the provider and each recipient of data has a receiver on the bus. The only limitation on the number of data providers on a MIL STD 1553 bus is speed. For slow speed data, a large number of data sources can reside on the bus, as the 1 Mb/s data rate results in short data words and reduces the likelihood of collisions.

7.5.1 Bus Controller

One of the down sides to a bus using RTs is the greater possibility for collisions, since more than one device attached to the bus can transmit. A bus controller is used to control the traffic on the bus. The controller issues commands on the bus which insures that only one device transmits on the bus. Generally, the bus controller is not a stand-alone device but contained within a computer. Examples of a bus controller would be a mission computer or a fire control computer. In a civilian application the flight management system or air data computer would contain the bus controller.

Most bus controllers are message or frame controllers which allow one message at a time. The frame controller is capable of handling entire frames, which increases the speed of the bus and reduces some of the load on the host computer.

Data bits are applied to the bus using bipolar Manchester encoding. We met Manchester in our discussion of the mode S transponder reply. Recall that each data bit has a time slot and if the transmitted pulse is in the early part, the bit is a logic one. If the transmitted pulse is in the late part of the time slot, the transmitted bit is a logic zero. In the case of MIL STD 1553, the transmission is not of an RF carrier but voltage across a transmission line. For a logic one, a positive pulse followed by a negative pulse is placed on the line in the time slot. For a logic zero, a negative voltage is applied in the early part of the time slot followed by a positive voltage.

One advantage of Manchester coding for the mode S transponder is output power from the transponder is constant regardless of the number of zeros or ones in the message. In the case of MIL STD 1553 transmission, a positive pulse is followed by a negative pulse or vice versa. This means that regardless of message content, the average voltage on the line is zero. This is important because a signal with zero average voltage can be coupled through a transformer, which is used in attaching the RTs to the data bus.

One characteristic of Manchester is helpful in receiving data. In the center of the time slot is a transition from positive or negative voltage. Another way of stating this; received voltage passes through zero in the center of each time slot. This can synchronize reception of data.

Physical Layer Characteristics

(Signals are measured differentially, line to line)

Output	Transformer Coupled	Direct Coupled
Bit Rate	1 mb/s	1 mb/s
Output Level, (volts)	18.0 min, 27.0 max	6.0 min, 9.0 max
Rise time, fall time	100 ns, min, 300 ns, max	100 ns, min, 300 ns, max
Distortion	900 mv, peak	300 mv, peak
DC offset	250 mv, max	90 mv, max

Input		
Input Level, (volts)	0.86 min, 14.0 max	1.2 min, 20 max
Noise Immunity	0.2 volts	0.28 volts
Com. Mode Rejection	10 volts peak	10 volts peak
Input Impedance	1000 ohms	2000 ohms

7.5.2 Synchronization

Since the system is asynchronous, there must be a method of identifying the beginning of a transmission. Recall in ARINC 429 there were at least four bit times of no activity on the bus, or idle time. This represents four or more wasted bit times. The designator for the beginning of a word in MIL STD 1553 is a pulse that violates Manchester encoding. A normal data bit is one polarity for one half the bit time and the opposite for the other half. The state of the data transmitted doesn't matter; there is always a change of state in the center of the time slot. In addition, the voltage is never positive or negative for more than the time of one bit.

Synchronizing is a Manchester pulse three times the data bit. No positive or negative pulse has a width of 1.5 bit time and the wide Manchester pulse is recognized as the synchronizing pulse. The pulse has an average voltage of 0, as do all other Manchester pulses and does not affect the zero average voltage.

The first data of a message is a command word transmitted by the bus controller. The remote terminal, RT, address immediately follows the synchronizing bit. Next is the T/R bit, which is set to a logic one if the RT is to transmit, and logic zero if it is to receive.

The RT address is a 5 bit binary number. Of the possible 32 states of a 5 bit number, only 31 addresses are used. The number, 11111, is reserved for a broadcast mode. All RTs must receive messages destined for their own address and the broadcast address.

The 5 bits following the R/T bit are for a mode control indicator or subaddress for the RT. Of the possible 32 combinations of the subaddress field, two, 00000, 11111 are used for indicators that mode codes follow, leaving only 30 possible subaddresses. If the subaddress field does not contain a mode code indicator, the 5 bits following are a data word count. If the mode code is indicated, the 5 bits represent a mode. The final bit of the command word is a parity bit.

Following the command word are data words, in accordance with the data word count. The format for a data word is shown in Fig 7.11. The data word contains a start bit, 16 data bits and a parity bit.

MIL-STD-1553 WORD FORMATS

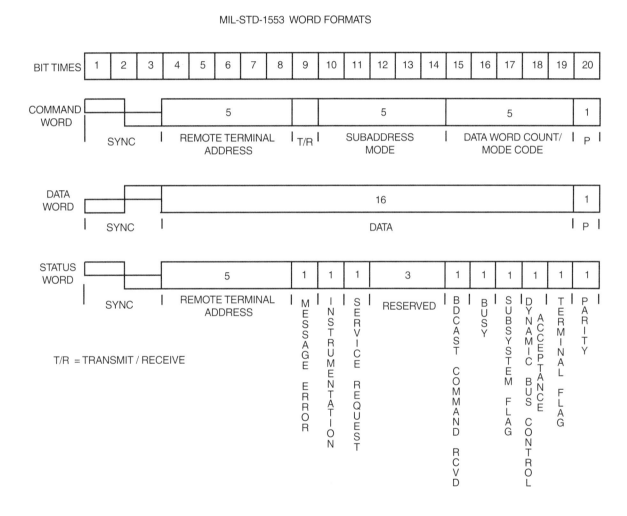

Figure 7.11   MIL STD 1553 data word format

Fig. 7.11 shows the connection of an RT to the 1553 bus with isolation resistors of $0.75Z_0$ each. This impedance, along with impedance reflected by the transformer, totals about $2.5\ Z_0$.

297

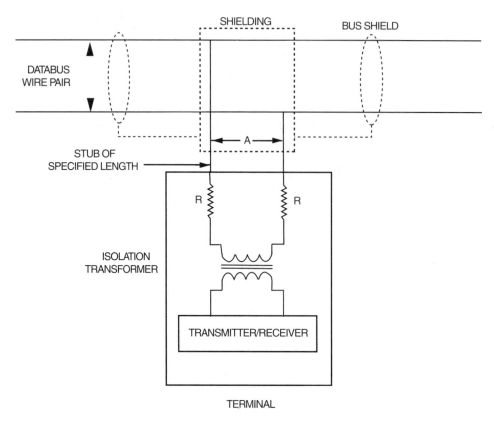

Figure 7.12   MIL STD 1553 RT tap

A transformer helps preserve the balance of the bus. As discussed, the ability of a balanced transmission line to reject noise from electromagnetic fields is a function of system balance. The transformer connects directly to the bus through a stub. Even with the transformer, isolation resistors and stubs aid in isolating user equipment from the bus. Length of the stub is kept as short as practical, typically less than 5 meters.

7.6 ARINC 629

A system similar to MIL STD 1553 but with significant improvements is ARINC 629. It operates at 2 Mb/s, twice the data rate of 1553. One attractive feature of ARINC 629 is that it will be defined for a fiber optic interface. ARINC 429 and MIL STD 1553 could be converted to light pulses in some fashion for fiber, but "some fashion" must be defined by an accepted specification.

The final significant difference between ARINC 629 and MIL STD 1553 is that ARINC 629 is defined for both voltage and current modes of operation. The systems discussed thus far use voltage coupling; receivers are high impedance and respond to voltage across the line. During a transmission, a voltage is placed on the bus. To prevent the bus from being loaded by RTs or receivers in the case of ARINC 429, there are series resistors between the terminal and bus for isolation. This is a problem because significant signal is lost in the resistors. An alternate to the voltage mode is the current mode.

An example of current mode is shown in Fig. 7.13. In this technique, the bus passes through the primary of a transformer. The impedance of the transformer is very low so there is no signal loss. In voltage mode transformer coupling, the transformer has a very high impedance so as not load down the bus. Because the transformer is in series with the bus in the current mode, a low impedance is desired.

ARINC 629 DATABUS

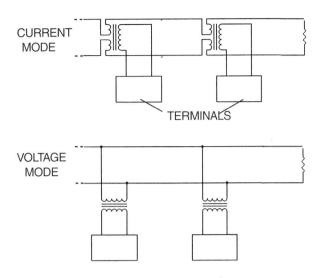

Figure 7.13 Current and voltage coupling modes for ARINC 629

What advantage is there to the current mode? The bus wire does not have to be broken to insert the RT and, if a unit is removed, the bus does not have to be reconnected. Fig. 7.14 shows an ARINC 629 coupler. The bus passes through the transformer and becomes its primary.

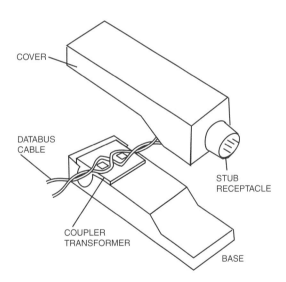

Figure 7.14 ARINC 629 bus coupler

Only one half turn is applied to the primary, which implies very low impedance, exactly what is desired. To keep loss low, impedance in series with the bus should also be low.

In addition to the convenience of adding and removing RTs without breaking the bus, the transformer coupler has the advantage of placing driver electronics in the coupling unit. This assures there is no stub, as found in ARINC 429 and MIL STD 1553 systems. Even though stubs in these systems are short, they are sources of signal egress and ingress. If eliminated, performance of the system is enhanced.

299

Another coupler type provides convenience for LRUs (line replaceable units). In this system, shown in Fig. 7.15, the primary of the transformer is located in the LRU mount and the secondary is in the LRU itself. Laminations of the coupler are separated so one half the transformer is located in the LRU with the second half in the mount. This couples the LRU to the bus magnetically without disturbing the bus. A unit on the bus can be removed and reinserted while the bus is operating. Because the system continues to function, it's called a "hot swap". This technique would never occur during normal flight even in a military operation, but while troubleshooting on the ground.

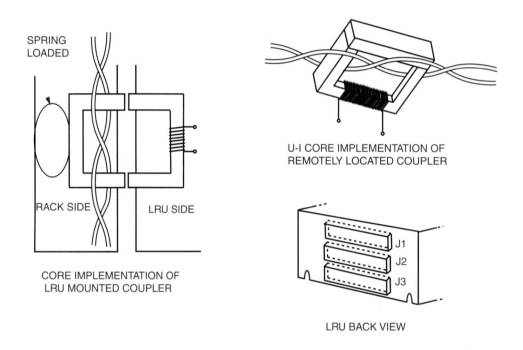

Figure 7.15 Split transformer ARINC 629 coupler

7.7 The Commercial Standard Digital Bus

The Commercial Standard Digital Bus, once known as the Collins Standard Digital Bus, is widely used in civil aircraft. The CSDB is a unidirectional asynchronous bus, two characteristics it shares with ARINC 429. Also similar to 429, two speeds are available; a low speed with a data rate of 12.5 kb/s and a high speed variant at 50 kb/s. The network topology is a linear network, meaning the transmission line is tapped as necessary without branches as in a tree network, or stubs as in a spine network. The transmission line does not return on itself as in a ring network. The transmission medium is a shielded twisted pair operating in an unterminated mode for distances of about 30 meters max.

Each data word, or byte, consists of a start bit, 8 data bits, a stop bit and a parity bit. The data are sent least significant bit first. Data are organized into frames, where the first data block is a synchronizing block. Several message blocks follow, separated by idle periods for the purpose of separating the message blocks. A message block consists of an address byte followed by several data bytes. The synchronizing block is the equivalent of sending the data word 1010 0101 a number of times with the normal start, stop and parity. Following a synchronizing block data blocks are transmitted. Data blocks can be various lengths, consisting of bytes. Simple parity is used with checksums for error detection. To insure that data can never appear as synchronizing the sequence, 1010 0101 cannot appear as an address or repeatedly in the data. A frame is a synchronizing block followed by message blocks separated by idle periods.

The CSDB is a character-oriented protocol where only one transmitter is connected to the bus, similar to ARINC 429. The physical layer is the EIA standard RS-422-A. This is a balanced differential system for which a large selection of drivers and receivers are available. There is a companion RS-423 which is an unbalanced system. It uses a non-return-to-zero format. Protection includes shorts to ground, connections to 28 volts, DC and 115 volts AC.

There is no maximum cable length specified in RS-422 but guidelines are provided as a suggestion for design. Lengths exceeding 1000 meters for data rates up to 100 kb/s are shown on many data sheets. However, much of this has to do with the noise and RF environment and in an aircraft it is not recommended that lengths even one tenth of this be used.

The EIA specification completely defines the electrical characteristics of the physical layer including the connectors and pin connection. This is similar to other EIA specifications that allow "mix and match" of components of different manufacturers for personal computers.

At the time of this writing, CSDB is used on regional jets and smaller commuter aircraft. Some older air transports have been retrofitted with the CSDB but usually in a situation where the aircraft had no multiplexing before the retrofit.

7.8 ARINC 573, 615, 708 and Other Data Bus Protocols

ARINC 573 is a data bus for flight data recorders. The data are streamed in 12 bit words and includes data from on board avionics systems. ARINC 717 will replace ARINC 573 and features several data rates and frame sizes. In addition ARINC 717 provides for a second redundant data stream.

ARINC 615 is a high speed data transfer protocol which uses ARINC 429 for the physical layer. There are two variants of ARINC 615, a portable data loader, or PDL, for the flight line and a version installed in the instrument panel. ARINC 615 is defined for data transfer from 3.5 inch floppy disks.

ARINC 708 is a high speed data bus for transferring data from a weather radar receiver/transmitter unit, RTU, to the display. The system is derived from MIL STD 1553 but is a simplex, one way, data transmission. Data words are 1600 bits long and consists of one 64 bit status word and 512 three bit data words. The data rate is 1 Mb/s.

With the tremendous increase of inflight entertainment systems, IFE, and retrofit to older aircraft, there is a need for a data bus. Not all of the "entertainment" system is actually entertainment. Included are functions in the cabin service system, or CSS. This includes such items as fasten seat belt sign, attendant call button and other functions.

There is a tremendous range of required data transmission in the modern aircraft, from simple discrete commands, such as the reading lamp or attendant call button, to high speed data such as video. The ARINC 628 IFE Interface defines a number of physical layer protocols to meet the diverse demands for the IFE. Those protocols include EIA 485, ARINC 429 and analog. It is expected that ARINC 628 will receive many changes and additions as IFE becomes more mature.

7.9 Fiber Optic Data Communications

The advantages of light energy along a glass fiber for onboard communications are great. Freedom from signal egress and ingress is beyond that of the most sophisticated wired system. Electromagnetic fields at frequencies below that of light will not interact with glass. As long as the fiber is shielded from light, easily accomplished even for intense light, the fiber is isolated from external radiated energy.

Wide bandwidth is another important characteristic of fiber optics. Bandwidths of gigabits per second; 1E9 bits per second are possible. It may appear this is more bandwidth than could ever be used in an aircraft, but EW (electronic warfare) equipment for the military has large requirements. Civil aircraft with graphics displays can also use gigabit per second rates. For most applications, 1E9 bits per second is more than enough.

Fiber optic systems have low losses. This is not critical for aircraft because distances between terminals are short. Losses are extremely important for telecommunications where losses translate to additional repeaters and high cost.

Fiber optics are lighter in weight than wired systems. Weight per unit length of fiber is less than the equivalent length of a twisted pair. It would seem that a small strand of glass is significantly lighter. However, when the fiber is encased in protective and strength members, the weight advantage is reduced.

Consider that fiber carries ten times the data of twisted pair, and compare weight per unit length to ten twisted pairs, the weight advantage of fiber becomes significant. To compare fiber to wired communications, therefore, the comparison should be kg per meter per bit per second, using the proper SI units.

The most important advantage of fiber for aircraft is immunity to high intensity radiated fields or HIRF (often from high power transmitters on the ground). This is particularly true for critical applications such as fly by wire, optics, or "fly by light".

Fiber optics are not without disadvantages. First, it is difficult to work with. If a copper wire breaks, it is repaired with a crimp connector or soldering. As long as wires touch, and electrical connection is made. It's not that simple with fiber optics.

Connectors are also a problem. A connector for copper wires is simply two conducting pieces that provide physical contact and a circuit. Connecting two fibers requires microscopic fibers to be perfectly aligned and joined so light energy couples from one fiber to the other.

The fiber is fragile. It can be protected by encasing it in a protective housing but the fiber can still be fractured. A common fiber damage is related to bending. If the fiber is bent in a tight radius, losses increase and there is risk of fracture. Mishandling causes fractures by pulling the fiber tightly over a sharp corner or stepping on it. This is dangerous and should be avoided for either technology. For wire, sharp bends do not usually cause immediate failure and, if the wire is straightened before installation is complete, no permanent damage may result. These problems are solved by training and procedures required of any new technology.

Fiber optics are the perfect solution to a communications system that needs immunity to HIRF. In spite of the disadvantages, more fiber will be applied in aircraft.

Let's investigate fiber and the physical phenomenon that transmits electromagnetic energy with little loss. Fiber optics operate on the principle of total internal reflection. If a light wave encounters a boundary between different indices of refraction, the light wave is both reflected and refracted. When a light wave passes from a higher to lower index of refraction, as shown in Fig. 7.16, the refracted wave deflects away from the normal, which is a line perpendicular to the surface where the two indices meet. If the light wave is at a shallow angle, that is, between the surface and light wave, refraction from the normal could cause light energy to travel along the border between the two materials. This means that light energy never enters the material with the lower index of refraction. All energy, therefore, is reflected and remains in the material with the higher index of refraction. The angle at which this takes place is the critical angle:

$$\theta_C = \arcsin(N_1/N_2) \qquad (7.1)$$

where θ_C is the critical angle, N_1 is the lesser of the two indices of refraction and N_2 is the greater of the two.

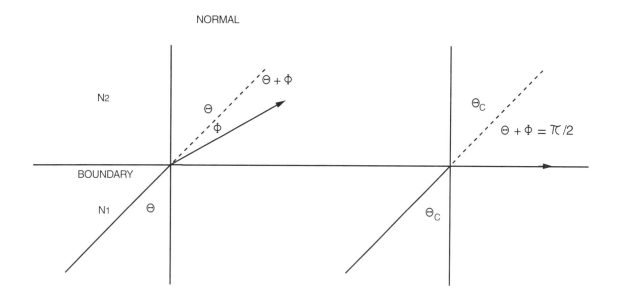

Figure 7.16   Light refraction

Imagine the two materials are glass and the shape is a cylinder, as shown in Fig. 7.17. The center of the cylinder, called the core, is the higher index of refraction and the outer part, called the cladding, has a lower index of refraction. Assume the diameter of the cylinders is small, on the order of 100 mm for the core and 200 mm for the cladding. This small dimension should be of no concern because the wavelength of light is on the order of 1000 nm or 1 mm. There is room for 10 waves of light in this fiber.

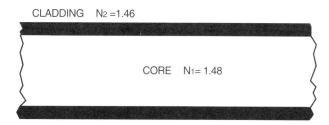

Figure 7.17 Basic construction of glass optic fiber

Example: What is the critical angle for a fiber constructed of glass with an index of refraction of 1.48 for the core and 1.46 for the cladding?

Solution: The angle is calculated by substituting in the above equation:

$$\theta_C = \arccos(N_2/N_1) = \arcsin(1.46/1.48) = 80.56 \text{ degrees}$$

Couple light energy into the fiber from a point source. Light travels in every direction from the point source and enters only where it intercepts the fiber. Only waves that travel at an angle less than the critical angle remain in the fiber. Waves greater than the critical angle enter the cladding and are eventually lost from the fiber. It can be seen from the figure that little energy from the point source remains in the fiber. Only waves within a cone, called the cone of acceptance, enter the fiber and remain there.

A point source is not ideal for coupling energy to a fiber. The ideal source emits light in a narrow cone so all light waves are at less than the critical angle. This causes all energy from the source to enter and remain in the fiber. The most effective emitter would be 100% efficient in coupling energy to a fiber, but the critical angle is different for various fibers; 100% efficiency is only an ideal. Coupling efficiency, however, can be quite high and a parameter to calculate efficiency is needed. The parameter, called numerical aperture, NA, is defined as:

$$NA = (N_1^2 - N_2^2)^{1/2}$$
$$\phi = \arcsin (NA)$$
(7.2)

Example: What is the acceptance angle for the fiber described in the previous example?

Solution: First the NA is calculated:

$$NA = (N_1^2 - N_2^2)^{1/2} = (1.48^2 - 1.46^2)^{1/2} = 0.2425$$
$$\phi = \arcsin (NA) = 14.0 \ degrees$$

The angle, ϕ, is often referred to as the half angle so the acceptance angle is 28 degrees.

Our example of a point source is the worst type for coupling light to a fiber. What is desired is a source with a relatively narrow beam width. It is also advantageous for the wavelength to be monochromatic, with a source capable of turning on and off quickly. The first light emitters that come to mind are LEDs and laser diodes. Most LEDs have a broad beam so they are visible from a wide angle. An indicator lamp with a narrow beam is not desirable. In fact, most LEDs used as indicators have integral lenses to increase the viewing angle. The beam angle of an LED depends on construction of the LED. An indicator LED uses a construction called a surface emitting diode. The light emanates from a large (for semiconductors) surface with a broad beam. A special diode made for coupling to fiber is the edge emitting diode.

The edge emitting diode has a higher power density and larger emitting area and is much smaller than the surface emitting diode. For maximum coupled energy, most LEDs for driving fiber optics have the fiber permanently attached to the diode. When the diode is purchased there is a short length of fiber called a "pig tail" that is spliced into the fiber optic system. Attaching the fiber to the diode is done with precision equipment at the factory for maximum energy transfer. The diode is then spliced to the fiber in the system.

An LED is a forward biased diode that emits light developed by high current density in the forward biased junction. LEDs are common in indicator lamps or as a part of a display to produce visible light. LEDs are monochromatic, producing light of one color. The wavelengths for fiber optic systems are longer than the visible spectrum because there is significantly less loss in glass at longer wavelengths. Wavelengths of 900 nm and 1350 nm are common in fiber optic systems.

A laser diode can drive a fiber optic line. Laser diodes come in different varieties but all are edge emitting devices. Light energy from the laser, by definition, is coherent (one frequency) and well collimated (emitted in parallel lines); it should be possible to couple the majority of light energy to the fiber from the laser diode. The laser diode is similar to the LED except the diode must operate above a current threshold to generate laser action. A laser requires the energy level of semiconductor atoms to be raised to a "metastable" state. This is somewhat stable in that the atom remains in this elevated energy state for some time before it returns to a ground energy state and emits a photon.

Atoms in the elevated metastable energy state can be stimulated to drop down to ground, or other energy states by a photon. To have laser action it is necessary to elevate a significant number of atoms to the metastable state, a condition called population inversion. This is the difficult part of making a laser diode, requiring high current density and the right semiconductor material. The energy level is raised by passing a relatively high current through a forward biased junction. If the current is not sufficiently high, an inadequate number of atoms will be in the metastable state and laser action will not take place. The laser diode then acts only as an LED; an expensive LED!

Once the majority of atoms in the diode junction are in the elevated metastable state, assume that an atom spontaneously emits a photon. The photon travels along the junction and stimulates other atoms to return to the ground energy state and emit a photon. More photons become available to stimulate atoms that are raised to the metastable state—to emit more photons. It is easy to see how a lot of light would be emitted by such a device, which is a characteristic of lasers; an intense source of light energy.

As photons propagate along the junction and stimulate other photons, the phase of stimulated photons is the same as for propagating photons. Light has a dual nature, being a particle as well as having characteristics of waves. Photons are phase coherent and, consequently, are exactly the same wavelength. Thus, the laser is very monochromatic (i.e., produces light of one color).

Finally, the laser diode has feedback. The simplest type, not used much any more but serves well for an explanation, is to provide reflective surfaces at both ends of the junction. Photons travel back and forth in the junction and only photons parallel to the reflecting surfaces remain within the junction. With a partial mirror on one end, some light passes out of the diode. The emerging light, therefore, is well collimated.

To summarize, light from the laser diode is intense, monochromatic and well collimated; the main characteristics of a laser.

The laser diode, LED, as well as any other device that couples to a fiber, including other fibers and connectors, have a numerical aperture which defines a cone of acceptance if it accepts energy or the cone of emission if it is an emitter. When the cone of acceptance of the receiver is greater than the source, nearly all energy is coupled to the fiber. If the cone of acceptance of the receiving device is smaller than the source some energy is lost. The numerical aperture can calculate maximum coupling efficiency for two fiber optic components:

$$\eta = (NA_2 / NA_1)^2 \qquad\qquad (7.3)$$

where η is the efficiency, NA_1 is the NA of the source and NA_2 is the NA of the receiving element; where $NA_2 < NA_1$.

Example: What is the cone of acceptance, cone of emission and coupling efficiency for an LED with a NA of 0.25 coupled to a fiber with a NA of 0.22?

Solution: The cone of emission of the LED is:

$$\phi = arcsin\ (NA) = arsin\ (0.25) = 14.5\ degrees$$

The cone of acceptance for the fiber is:

$$\phi = arcsin\ (NA) = arsin\ (0.22) = 12.7\ degrees$$

The angle of the cone is twice the values calculated or 29 degrees and 25.4 degrees. It can be seen that the LED has a broader emission than the fiber can accept and some energy will be lost.

The coupling efficiency is:

$$\eta = (\ NA_2\ /\ NA_1\ )^2 = (\ 0.22\ /\ 0.25\ )^2 = 0.774$$

It can be seen that 23% of the energy is lost coupling the LED to the fiber, where the NAs are very close, assuming there are no other loss mechanisms due to poor alignment, contamination, etc. This is shows why it is important to match NAs as closely as possible for an efficient system.

Glass fiber can transmit a broad range of light wavelengths. The glass is no different than glass in a common window and it is well-known that light of all colors passes through window glass. It is less known that ultraviolet does not pass well through window glass (which is good because ultraviolet energy fades colors on fabrics).

Glass transmits some wavelengths better than others. When choosing a wavelength for fiber optic data transmission, a wavelength is selected for low loss. Also needed is a wavelength that lends itself to construction of LEDs or laser diodes. Several wavelengths are suitable; one is around 900 nm, another at 1330 nm. Consider, next, the modulation to apply, and the sensor.

There are limitations in light sources and other components for light transmission when considering modulation applied to the LED or laser. First, LEDs and lasers produce photons of specific wavelength, which is set by energy levels in the emitting diodes. There is no way the frequency or phase of light emitted by laser or LED can be modulated. Secondly, the emission is not coherent. The laser comes closest to being coherent, but coherency of the diode laser doesn't begin to approach the coherency of a simple LC oscillator. We cannot think in terms of frequency modulation, superheterodyne receivers or other techniques to transmit and receive using radio waves; light waves from diode sources are different.

It is even difficult to control the amplitude of light from a laser diode or LED. Modulation, therefore, is on-off keying. A receiver, therefore, is nothing more than an energy detector. This leaves two basic detector types; the photo diode and photo transistor. A photo transistor is similar to the photo diode except the photo transistor has the advantage of added current gain. The photo transistor, however, is a slow device. Such a detector would prevent taking advantage of the fiber optic system.

The photo diode produces considerably less current but this is compensated for by an amplifier. To reduce noise pickup, diode and amplifier are mounted in a common package with short leads.

The weak signal performance of a communications system is a function of receiver noise level more than any other parameter. This refers to all communications systems, not just fiber optics. Weak signal performance is not a serious problem because the distance within an aircraft is short. It is important, however, that a fiber optic receiver be well shielded from electromagnetic fields.

Different coding techniques are applied to on-off keying, but a popular choice is Manchester. The Manchester coding of MIL STD 1553 is not the same because positive and negative voltage is involved. This is an important characteristic of 1553 encoding because it results in a zero DC component. If we offset 1553 Manchester coding so that instead of having an amplitude of +V and –V the voltage is 0 and +2V, we have the equivalent of on off keying, which could be converted to light pulses and placed on a fiber. Although MIL STD 1553 could be readily adapted to fiber optic, there is no specification for such an implementation.

A difficult problem with fiber optic transmission are the taps. A receiver in ARINC 429 requires a physical connection to the bus and a high impedance receiver so the bus is not loaded down. A similar technique is in the voltage mode of MIL STD 1553. ARINC 629 is easy to tap because the transmission line does not have to be physically disconnected. Tapping the fiber optic line requires special fiber couplers. Some taps intercept energy propagating in only one direction, which can be an advantage for some applications but a significant disadvantage for bidirectional communications. Nevertheless, suitable taps for fiber optics with newer designs are constantly introduced.

One method is to receive the fiber optic signal, tap off what is needed and regenerate the signal. This is undesirable because each repeater represents a point of failure. At the time of this writing, the most common application of fiber optics is fly by light, usually where data generated in the cockpit is transmitted to flight control systems. This system has few, if any, taps, and is often not bidirectional. The fiber's robustness in the presence of HIRF is the important characteristic.

The fiber that has been discussed here is multimode. Energy passing through the fiber as a ray of light reflects from the boundary between different glasses of different index of refraction. There are infinite paths light can take through the fiber. A path is called a mode.

Consider the path length. The shortest path is straight down the middle of the fiber. The longest path is at the greatest angle between the axis of the core and light ray. This produces most internal reflections and the longest path. Light moving through the longest path takes more time to traverse a length of fiber than light that takes the shortest path. If a pulse of light is fed to a fiber, and modulation is pulses of light, the energy is coupled to the fiber as a sharp rectangular pulse. When the energy exits at the other end of the fiber, the pulse is no longer sharp and rectangular. Some energy took longer to traverse the fiber. The pulse becomes distorted with longer rise and fall times. It would look more like a gaussian than a rectangular pulse and appear as if it had been through a low pass filter. This phenomenon is called modal dispersion because different modes disperse energy in the fiber.

The longer the fiber, that is physical length, the greater the difference in the longest and shortest propagation time. Longer fiber produces a distorted pulse with slower rise and fall times, as if it had passed through a low pass filter with a lower cut off frequency. Multimode fiber, therefore, causes distortions that are problematic for high speed data and long lengths.

One solution to modal dispersion is the graded index fiber. A type known as the step index fiber has a sharp boundary between the two glasses and is a viable method of constructing multimode fiber. An improved fiber has an index of refraction that is highest in the center and reduces as it reaches the outer periphery. The same refraction that causes light to be internally reflected still takes place, but instead of an abrupt boundary there is a gradual boundary.

Recall that electromagnetic energy has a velocity in material s equal to c/N where c is the velocity of electromagnetic energy in vacuum and N is the index of refraction in the material. The higher the index of refraction the slower the energy propagates. In the graded index fiber, the highest index of refraction is in the center and thus the slowest waves are in the center. But it is also the shortest distance. If the index of refraction is adjusted so light takes the same time to traverse the center of the fiber, as it did making a large number of reflections, the amount of spreading of pulses is reduced. The index of refraction is adjusted to provide a significant reduction of pulse spreading in the graded index fiber.

The ultimate reduction of modal dispersion is to lower the number of modes to one. The diameter of multimode fiber we have been discussing is on the order of 125 μm. A common wavelength for fiber optic systems is 900 nm, which implies that the diameter is 139 wavelengths. What would happen if the diameter of the core is reduced to 10 μm? This is only 11 wavelengths, and the fiber could not support a large number of modes. In fact, the number of modes supported by such a narrow fiber is one.

Why not make all fibers with a narrow core and eliminate problems of modal dispersion? The smaller core is not without problems. First, 10 mm is *very* small. Coupling emitters and detectors is difficult. Splicing broken fibers and making connectors are difficult, too. As a result, improved methods have been developed to use narrow core fiber.

A laser diode is necessary for a single mode fiber system. The laser's well-collimated beam is relatively easy to couple into the narrow fiber.

There is one more distortion in glass fiber called material dispersion. The index of refraction of glass is a function of wavelength. This is a well-known mechanism behind the prism's ability to break white light into constituent colors. In a glass fiber, this variation in index of refraction changes transit time for different wavelengths. Problems of material dispersion occur at high data rates or long fibers. Generally, in aircraft, length is quite short by telecommunications standards. Very high data rates may be required, though, and material dispersion could be a problem. Even single mode fiber, which solved the modal dispersion problem, is susceptible to material dispersion.

A glass suitable for fiber has zero material dispersion at 1300 nm which, conveniently, is a wavelength within the capability of LEDs and lasers. However, 1300 nm does not have low loss in glass fibers. The low loss window is about 1550 nm. Special fibers called "dispersion shifted" change the point of zero material dispersion to the same as the wavelength of the lowest loss, but they are made for long distance telecommunications. In aircraft, most fiber is multi mode, with some single mode. Emitters are mostly LEDs with some lasers.

A fiber for future aircraft is plastic, now commonly found in toys and decorations. The problem is tremendous loss, although distance is not a problem in aircraft. Recall that the major reason for fiber optics in aircraft is protection from HIRF interference. Cheap plastic fiber can offer as much protection from HIRF as the most expensive, fragile, dispersion shifted single mode fiber. Manufacturers are developing inexpensive plastic fiber components for short distance applications.

7.10 Glass Fiber as a Transmission Line

Does glass fiber meet the definition of a transmission line? It does, perfectly. Consider the characteristic impedance; is there an attribute of a glass fiber that is similar to characteristic impedance? To couple maximum energy into a wire transmission line the generator must have same impedance as the characteristic impedance of the transmission line. To couple maximum energy out of a transmission line, the load must have a value equal to the characteristic imped-ance of the line. To couple maximum energy into and out of glass fiber requires the source or load to have the same numerical aperture, NA. Therefore, NA is analogous to characteristic impedance.

What would happen if a load is applied to a transmission line that did not match the characteristic impedance of the line? The same would happen if the fiber terminates in a load with a different NA; energy reflects back to the source. The velocity of propagation of a glass fiber is equal to c/N, where N is the index of refraction of the glass and c is the velocity of light in a vacuum. The velocity of propagation in a transmission line is $1/(e_r)^{1/2}$. In both cases energy propagates via electromagnetic fields through a dielectric. It is also true that in a dielectric the index of refraction, N, is equal to $(e_r)^{1/2}$ and the equation for the velocity of propagation in a fiber is the same as for a transmission line.

This similarity of a glass fiber and transmission line allows transmission line measure-ment and terminology to be used. One example is the measurement of power in a fiber ex-pressed in dBm. The total power delivered from a fiber is expressed in decibel form referenced to 1 mw.

Example: How much power is delivered to a photodiode from a fiber optic system that has an emitter of +2 dBm, and a NA of 0.24, a multi mode fiber with an NA of 0.22 and a loss of 12 dB per km, and two connectors of 0.8 dB loss each. The NA of the receiver diode is 0.20? The total length of fiber between the emitter and receiver is 37 m.

Solution: The loss of the cable is 12 dB(37E-3 km) = 0.44 dB. The loss of the two connectors is 1.6 dB. The loss of the mismatch of the coupling between the emitter and the fiber, in dB is

$$\eta = 10 \log (NA_2 / NA_1)^2 = 10 \log (0.22 / 0.24)^2 = - 0.76 \, dB$$

The loss of the receiver diode is calculated in a similar fashion.

$$\eta = 10 \log (NA_2 / NA_1)^2 = 10 \log(0.20 / 0.22)^2 = - 0.083 \, dB$$

The total loss is: 0.44 + 1.6 + 0.76 + 0.083 = 2.9 dB
The power at the detector diode is – 0.9 dBm.

7.11 Time Domain Reflectometry

A troubleshooting technique for transmission lines, time domain reflectometry , can apply to wired and fiber optic systems . The tool senses reflections in a transmission line to find faults. A reflection occurs whenever there is an impedance mismatch. Time domain reflec-tometry is abbreviated TDR for wired systems and called, appropriately, optical time domain reflectometry, or OTDR, for fiber optics.

The TDR injects narrow pulses of energy and looks for reflections from the transmis-sion line. When there is a mismatch, a reflected pulse of the same polarity results when the fault has a lower impedance than the characteristic impedance; the opposite polarity reflects back when the fault has a higher impedance.

The most common fault is an open or shorted cable, which causes a complete reflection of energy. More than determining a fault on the line is the ability to precisely locate it. The TDR measures the time from transmission of the incident pulse and receipt of the reflected pulse. If the velocity factor of the transmission line is entered into the test set, the TDR calcu-lates distance from the TDR to the fault.

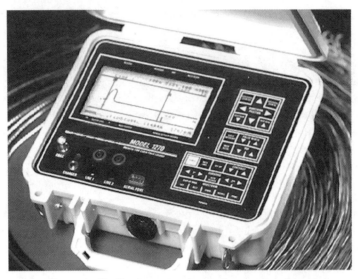

Time Domain Reflectometer launches pulse through connector or cable under test. Pulse is reflected back from a fault (an open or short circuit). Location of fault is indicated as a "bump" on the display. (RLW)

Chapter 7 Review Questions

7.1	What are problems with the carbon microphone?
7.2	What is a noise-cancelling microphone?
7.3	What are characteristics of a transmission line?
7.4	What is a twisted pair transmission line?
7.5	A transmission line has a velocity of 0.66c. The transmission line has a fault, which reflects energy. What is the elapsed time from the signal being injected into the line and receipt of the fault if the fault is 15 meters from the line end?
7.6	What is the characteristic impedance of a transmission line?
7.7	What is the pulse applied to an ARINC 429 transmission line for a logic one? What is the pulse for a logic zero?
7.8	What prevents an ARINC 429 system from continued operation with a short or an open circuit?
7.9	How many line drivers may be applied to an ARINC 429 bus?
7.10	How many line receivers may be applied to an ARINC 429 bus?
7.11	What is an asynchronous digital communications system?
7.12	What is the purpose of a label in an ARINC 429 system?
7.13	What is the data rate in a MIL STD 1553 bus?
7.14	What type of encoding is used for data applied to a MIL STD 1553 system?
7.15	Which types of coupling may be used in the ARINC 629 bus system?
7.16	Which data bus permits transmission of data by fiber optics?
7.17	What is multimode fiber? How does it differ from single mode fiber?
7.18	What are the advantages of single mode fiber?
7.19	What semiconductor devices can drive a fiber optic fiber?
7.20	What semiconductor devices can be used for receivers in single mode fiber?
7.21	What advantages do fiber optics offer over wired systems in aircraft?
7.22	What is the numerical aperture of a fiber that has a core index of 1.51 and a cladding index of 1.50?

7.23   What is graded index fiber and why is it used?

7.24   What is the maximum coupling efficiency of an LED with a numerical aperture of 0.31 and a fiber with a numerical aperture of 0.33?

7.25   What types of modulation are used for light in an optical fiber?

7.26   What is an OTDR?

References

Hebrawi, Baha, Open Systems Interconnection; upper layer standards and practices, New York, McGraw-Hill, 1993

Hecht, Jeff, Understanding Fiber Optics, 4th Ed., Upper Saddle River, N.J., Prentice-Hall, 2002

ILC Data Device Corporation, MIL STD-1553 Designer's Guide, 4th Ed., Bohemia N.Y., ILC Data Device Corp. 1993

RTCA, Design Guidelines and Recommended Standards to Support Open Systems Interconnection for Aeronautical Mobile Digital Communications, Washington D.C., RTCA, DO-205, 1990

Sloane, John P. ed., Handbook of Local Area Networks, Boca Raton Fl., Auerbach 2000

Walrand, Jean, Varaiya, P. P., High Performance Communications Networks, San Francisco, Morgan Kaufman, 2000

Chapter 8

Indicators

8.0 Introduction

Indicators on aircraft are often simple dials or gauges to display engine performance, communications and other information. Navigation instruments, on the other hand, are more complex because position is defined in three dimensions; latitude, longitude and altitude. Navigation involves not only the present, but the future. Engine pressure, for example, is reported as present pressure, there is no indication of what it should be in an hour. Beside showing present position, navigation may have to indicate where the aircraft will be. Heading, track and ground speed could calculate whether the aircraft will follow the course, but these data are not candidates for simple dials. What is needed is a three dimensional picture of where the aircraft is, the destination, the course and other references such as navigation aids and fixes.

Early developers realized that a pictorial presentation of navigation was the most desired. Technology that produced such displays for aircraft was 60 years in the future when the first instruments were invented. The best picture presented to the pilot depended mostly on mechanical technologies.

The first navigation instrument, the magnetic compass, was not truly pictorial, but a simple dial gauge. The artificial horizon, another early instrument is, in fact, a pictorial display. The indicator has a background of blue and brown, or blue and black. Blue is the sky and dark brown or black, the earth. Where colors merged, a straight line border represents the horizon. A silhouette of an aircraft, as viewed from behind, gave a simple picture of the aircraft relative to the horizon.

The first experimental electronic navigation system had an indicator which displayed angular deviation from a desired course. It was a vibrating reed indicator, which moved left and right from a center position to show deviation from course. The direction finding receiver had a manually rotated antenna which pointed to the NDB. It may not appear that such pointing gives the pilot a picture of his navigation situation. If one were in a strange town and asked where to find the post office and a local resident pointed in a direction and said, "it's over there", you would have some idea of the location.

VOR was invented to provide navigation information relative to a selected course. The indicator shows the amount of *angular* deviation and whether the aircraft is travelling to or from the station. The VOR indicator provides reliable information when the heading of the aircraft is approximately equal to the selected VOR course. If the CDI (course deviation indicator) points left, flying left corrects the deviation only if the aircraft heading is approximately equal to the omnibearing. The CDI indicates absolute deviation from the selected course regardless of direction.

If we supplement the CDI with a VOR indicator that points, in a similar fashion as the ADF indicator, we have the "it's over there" picture that an ADF provides. This device is the "radio magnetic indicator", or RMI. If angular deviation and location of the VOR relative to the airplane heading are known, we have a picture of position relative to the desired course. If a DME is used with a VOR the "it's over there" picture would be "it's over there, so many miles," which is an improvement.

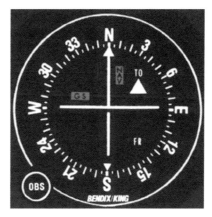

VOR/Localizer/Glideslope indicator

To point to a VOR, we need to know the VOR radial and heading. Normally, a VOR radial is not measured, but a course selected and deviation from the course is measured. Finding the VOR radial is a matter of measuring a phase angle, which is a simple task using integrated circuits. However, the RMI was implemented using vacuum tube technology and a bit of mechanics. Mechanical instruments are still used in great numbers in aircraft and electronic displays will eventually replace them. It will be a while before aircraft are all electronic and we need to understand how mechanical instruments function.

How can a pilot know which radial he is receiving? It would be a "TO" radial if he wants to point *to* the VOR, as he would an NDB. All that needs to be done is turn the OBS until the indicator shows a centered CDI and a "TO" indication. By using a motor to turn the OBS and electronic circuits to read the TO/FROM flag and the CDI to drive the motor, the OBS could be made to show the VOR radial the airplane is on.

To make the arrow point to the VOR, the heading of the aircraft is used. If heading is exactly the same as the VOR radial, the pointer should be straight ahead; the airplane is heading to the VOR. If the aircraft turns to the left, the pointer should turn to the right by the same angle as the aircraft were turned to the left. In other words, the RMI pointer depends on the *difference* angle between heading and VOR radial.

8.1 Gyroscope

To create any pictorial indication, the aircraft magnetic heading is required. The source is the aircraft's compass. It is the ultimate source of heading but the compass has annoying problems that are eliminated by a gyroscopic heading indicator for short term heading information. The magnetic compass periodically corrects the gyro.

The compass is a magnet in a low friction mounting. It aligns itself with the earth's magnetic field and indicates magnetic north. A low friction mounting is required because torque from the weak earth magnetic field cannot overcome high frictional forces.

The lightweight compass tends to oscillate because low torque allows little damping. There are error sources, such as magnetic fields within the aircraft. These fields can appear and disappear, such as the magnetic field generated by a landing gear, flap motor or other device that consumes heavy current. The currents through interconnecting wires emit magnetic fields that can temporarily affect a compass.

Another important error is due to turning. When the aircraft turns, the wings bank around the roll axis. Aircraft and compass are no longer horizontal relative to the surface of the earth and its magnetic field lines. If the aircraft is heads exactly north or south, there are no errors due to banking. If the aircraft heads in other directions, there is a worse error than when the aircraft heads east or west. These turning errors continue as long as the aircraft is in the turn and banked.

A turn results in an aircraft taking up a new heading. During a turn, an indication of heading is important, but during this time the magnetic compass is least accurate. What is needed is a reliable indicator of heading not affected by these errors.

A spinning wheel has "rigidity in space," which means it is difficult to displace the wheel from its position. The more massive the wheel and the greater its angular velocity, the more it resists displacement. The is the basis of the gyroscope or "gyro". In an aircraft, the spinning wheel is aligned with the magnetic compass when the magnetic compass is most accurate; during straight and level flight and on the ground. The gyro can be used as a heading indicator in lieu of the compass, but it has bad habits, too. The first is drift.

If a gyro wheel were perfect, once set in a direction it would remain in that position forever. The wheel, however, has friction, which causes it to wander. Friction is made as small as possible and a massive gyro wheel spins at 20,000 RPM or more to insure as much rigidity as possible to overcome friction . In spite of all this care, the gyro drifts a few degrees per hour. It does a splendid job of providing heading when the compass is the most affected, and drift is overcome with a manual correction to the gyro every 15 minutes or so.

There is another good reason to adjust the gyro periodically. First, the gyro is rigid in space, which means relative to the universe. Magnetic north is located on a sphere, our planet, and we are not flying a straight line relative to space; we are flying over the surface of the sphere. The magnetic compass is pulled toward the magnetic north pole by magnetic force. The gyro remains absolutely rigid in space and does not always point to magnetic north.

Another reason for adjusting a gyro is precession. If an aircraft is on the ground, even though the airspeed indicator says zero, the aircraft is moving at up to 464 meters per second. The motion is the rotation of the earth, and this accelerated motion causes the gyro to precess, or wobble, in its axis. The earth rotates once every 24 hours and precession is small, but large enough to be noticed in time.

The gyro is our source of heading information. When it is only a simple heading indicator, a compass card is mechanically connected, which is called a directional gyro or DG. In an RMI we take the difference between the VOR radial and heading to produce the pointer indication. The difference can be taken with a gear assembly connected to the gyro wheel. The RMI and heading indicator usually share the same indicator. Inexpensive instruments have the

DG mounted in the instrument with a mechanical connection to the heading card.

Mounting the DG in the instrument is cost-saving, but undesirable. First, the size of the gyro wheel is severely restricted due to the size of the indicator. The larger the wheel, the better the gyro performs. Secondly, the gyro performs best when mounted near the center of gravity of the aircraft. Seldom is an instrument panel near that location. Finally, vibration in an instrument panel can be high. Although there is no guarantee that vibration near the center of gravity is any better, the gyro can be mounted on vibration isolators. There is usually no room in an instrument housing for vibration isolation.

The remotely mounted gyro is the choice for large aircraft. It uses a generous vibration-isolated gyro wheel in a sealed container.

The gyro wheel must remain rigid in space while the aircraft rotates around it. In the case of the directional gyro, where the axis of rotation is horizontal, the aircraft must be capable of changing pitch angle without forcing the gyro from its vertical position. The aircraft must also roll without disturbing the gyro. To achieve this, the gyro wheel is mounted in a frame called a gimbal, as shown in Fig. 8.1.

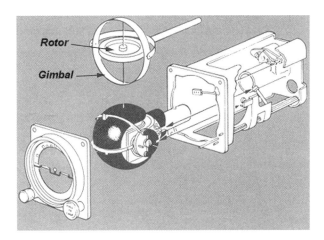

Fig. 8.1 Artificial horizon. Rotor and gimbal are removed and shown simplified

When mounted in the gimbal, the gyro wheel remains oriented in its original position, relative to the earth, while the aircraft can rotate around the gyro in all three axes. In the case of the directional gyro, the angle between the current aircraft's position and the initial angle of the gyro wheel is the desired information, the heading of the aircraft. The part of the gimbal assembly that permits rotation around the yaw axis is connected to a heading indicator.

When the axis of the gyro is vertical, the gimbal assembly allows the gyro to remain vertical while the aircraft can rotate on all three axes. In this case, the indicator is an artificial horizon, shown in Fig. 8.1.

Gyros can be electrically or air driven. Both techniques have advantages and disadvantages and one type does not excel over the other. Any aircraft can have both types as a matter of redundancy. If the electrical system fails, air driven gyros continue to function.

8.2 Synchros

When a gyro does not directly control its indicator, because it is not in the same case, it connects to a synchro transmitter. A synchro is a specialized motor for servo systems. We met a similar device, the resolver, in the OBS of a VOR receiver. Synchro and resolver are similar except the synchro has three stator windings with 120 degrees of separation , while the resolver has two stators with 90 degrees separation. The synchro is not a motor in the normal sense of turning something, but is a position sensor. In the group called "servo motors" there are normal power-producing motors.

One important characteristic of servo motors, particularly for position sensing , is very low friction. Gyro performance is degraded by friction, so a minimum amount may be applied. Otherwise, there is an increase in gyro drift. The rotor is driven by 400 Hz AC and output from the synchro is the three stators.

The frequency of 400 Hz is not only for instruments, but a major power source in larger aircraft. With the universal use of 50 and 60 Hz throughout the world, why was 400 Hz selected for aircraft? The major reason is that higher supply frequency permits smaller magnetic components such as servo motors and power transformers. In large air transports many items are powered from AC sources. This is a holdover from vacuum tube days where high voltage was required. An AC power source permits a transformer to generate various high voltages for vacuum tubes. Large aircraft have both AC and DC supplies. DC powered items are usually required before engines are started and for emergency equipment. DC is obtained from storage batteries which are recharged by generators driven by aircraft engines.

In small aircraft, only DC is employed because of the high cost of the AC generator with its constant speed drive. This requires a method of generating high voltage without a transformer or creating AC from DC. Some inefficient methods were used to generate high voltage, including the popular motor-generator combination called a dynamotor.

When transistors were introduced to avionics, the need for most high voltage was eliminated. High voltage, if required, could use a transistor to chop the DC supply into AC. One application of AC aboard an aircraft today is for servo motors. To satisfy this need, most aircraft have a "static inverter," a solid-state system which generates a small amount of 400 Hz AC for instruments.

To understand the synchro, assume the rotor, called the transmitter synchro, is supplied with AC which produces a magnetic field vector within the synchro (Fig. 8.3). Applied to the transmitter rotor is the excitation voltage. The three stator coils have current induced within them as a function of the angle between stator and rotor coil.

316

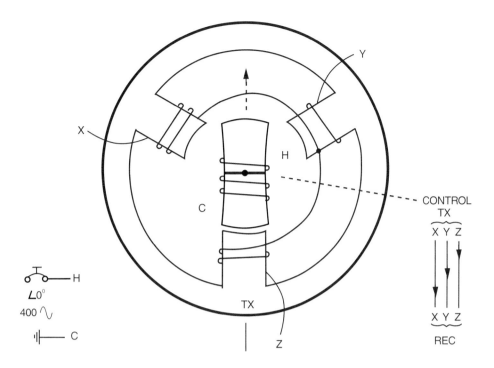

Fig. 8.3 Operation of synchro motor

If stators of the transmitter synchro are connected to stators of the receiver synchro, a magnetic field is generated in the receiver synchro, as shown in Fig. 8.4. Does this sound like the description of the goniometer used with a direction finder in chapter 2? The goniometer is nothing more than an RF servo motor.

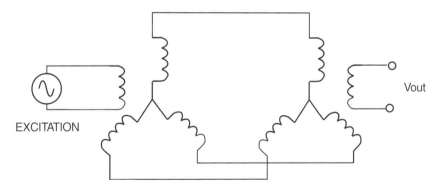

Figure 8.4. Transmitter synchro connected to receiver synchro

In the receiver synchro, the rotor produces an output voltage, Vout, that is a function of rotor angle. The magnetic field produced in the receiver synchro has the same orientation as the rotor in the transmitter synchro. If the rotor in the receiver synchro is set to the same angle as the transmitter rotor, output voltage is maximum. If the receiver rotor is turned until it is orthogonal to the magnetic field in the receiver synchro, the voltage induced is zero. This represents a shaft angle 90 degrees away from the transmitter.

Take the output voltage from the synchro receiver's rotor and use a synchronous rectifier to change AC to DC, amplify the DC and drive a DC motor with the amplified output, as shown in Fig. 8.5. If there is any voltage at the receiver's rotor, called the error voltage, the motor turns in the direction of the null. A massive object with friction, therefore, can be positioned at exactly the same shaft position as the transmitter synchro. The mechanical input has little inertia and friction and will not cause excessive drift in the gyro. The motor can turn a large assembly. What about the 90 degree difference between transmitter and receiver synchros? This is taken care of by offsetting the transmitter shaft by 90 degrees.

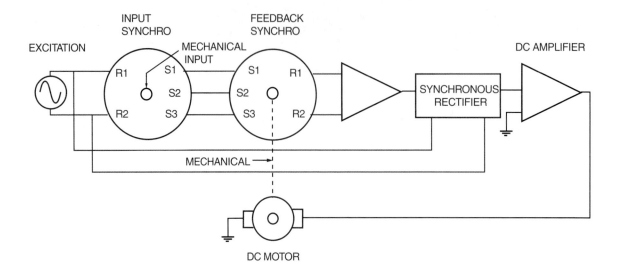

Figure 8.5   Servo system using a synchro

Return now to the synchronous rectifier mentioned above. If AC from the receiver's synchro is rectified, it has the same polarity each side of the null. Also, there are two nulls. This is the same problem with ADF. It was solved by using the electric field, which served as a reference unaffected by position of the loop. The same is done by using excitation voltage as a reference.

A synchronous rectifier is shown in Fig. 8.6. Output of the receiver rotor has only two phase angles, zero and 180 degrees, while amplitude of the output can vary. This can also be thought of as having only one phase angle, zero, but the amplitude includes the sign.

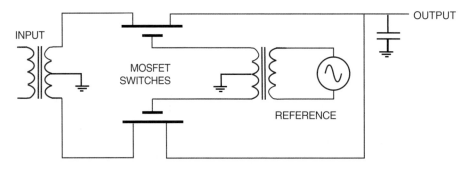

Figure 8.6 Synchronous rectifier

By providing an amplifier and multiple outputs, several indicators can display DG information. Any number of indicators can be driven from the same gyro with no danger of overload and excessive drift.

8.3 Flux Gate Compass

What would be convenient and less of a workload on the pilot is an automatic method of keeping the gyro adjusted. An electronic magnetic compass is the ideal candidate. This requires sensing a magnetic field, but the difficulty is that field intensity is low. This implies

318

that the amplitude of signals from the sensor is low and must be protected from interference aboard a typical aircraft. These assumptions are correct and signals must be handled carefully when sensing the earth's magnetic field.

A widely used sensor of the earth's magnetic field is the flux gate. It has an iron alloy, ferromagnetic material in the shape of a wheel, as shown in Fig. 8.7. This is placed in the earth's magnetic field, usually at a wing tip to prevent interference from motors and other devices in the fuselage. The wheel has a center post wound with wire so it can be magnetized.

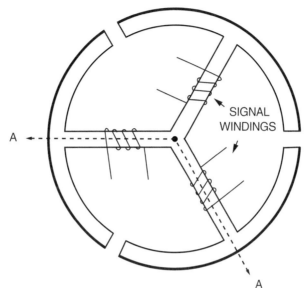

Figure 8.7 Flux gate compass.

Ferromagnetic properties of the wheel are important in the operation of the flux gate. Shown in Fig. 8.8 is the flux density of ferromagnetic material as a function of magnetizing force. When a coil of wire is wound on ferromagnetic material, the magnetizing force is proportional to current in the coil and the number of turns. Flux density as a function of current has the shape in Fig 8.8.

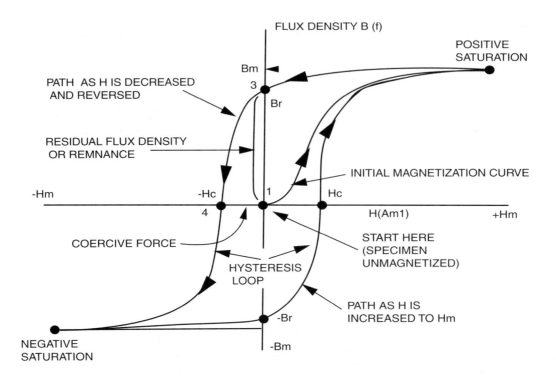

**Figure 8.8 Relationship between magnetizing force
and flux density in ferromagnetic material**

A property of any material is permeability, usually designated by the Greek letter m. This is the ratio of flux density to the magnetizing field or m = B/H, where B is the flux density in Tesla and H is the magnetizing field in amperes per meter. Permeability is the ability of a substance to concentrate magnetic field lines. Materials that are non-magnetic, such as wood, have a permeability of zero. This implies that wood has no effect on magnetic field lines. Place a compass inside a wooden box and it works normally.

If a material has high permeability, such as iron, it distorts the magnetic field lines. For example, a compass in a steel-frame building could have serious errors. This is also why magnetic north has significant deviation in areas of large iron ore deposits.

The permeability of material is the slope of flux density as a function of magnetizing force. Examine the plot of B as a function of H in Fig. 8.8, and the slope is not constant; the material is non-linear. This is an important characteristic. Ferromagnetic materials have a steep slope for small magnetizing forces and suddenly saturate where the slope is zero. Assume the flux gate "wheel" is immersed in the weak magnetic field of the earth; because the material is ferromagnetic and earth's field is weak, the value of m is very high and the wheel concentrates the flux as shown in Fig 8.9(a). Apply a magnetizing force so the wheel is magnetized to saturation, and permeability is decreased to zero. The wheel would have as much effect on magnetic field lines as the piece of wood in the example. This means magnetic flux passes through the flux gate wheel as if it were not there.

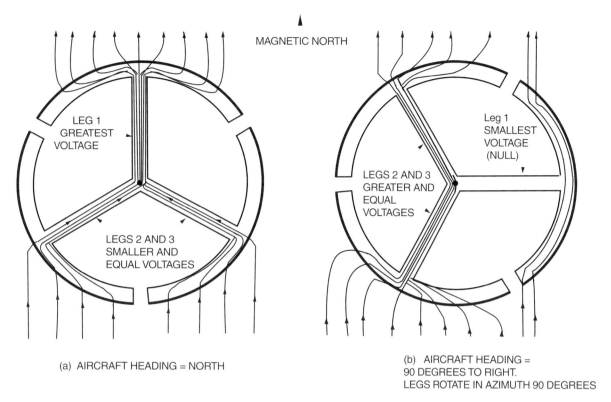

MAGNETIC NORTH

LEG 1
GREATEST
VOLTAGE

LEGS 2 AND 3
SMALLER AND
EQUAL VOLTAGES

Leg 1
SMALLEST
VOLTAGE
(NULL)

LEGS 2 AND 3
GREATER AND
EQUAL
VOLTAGES

(a) AIRCRAFT HEADING = NORTH

(b) AIRCRAFT HEADING =
90 DEGREES TO RIGHT.
LEGS ROTATE IN AZIMUTH 90 DEGREES

Figure 8.9 Magnetic characteristics of flux gate

The center post of the flux gate is driven from a 400 Hz source, with a resulting magnetic field that drives the wheel into saturation. There is nothing special about 400 Hz except it is the common frequency of AC in aircraft. Since there is saturation in two polarities, positive and negative, each cycle of 400 Hz "excitation" (the same term to describe synchro rotor voltage) in the flux gate wheel is in saturation 800 times a second. Since excitation changes permeability from a high value to zero 800 times a second, it is as if a gate opens and closes to the flux due to the earth's magnetic field. When the gate opens flux passes through the arms of the wheel; when the gate closes, flux passes through, shutting out the flux.

Consider a wire winding, called a pick-up coil, around spokes of the flux gate wheel. Because excitation drives the flux gate into saturation, the flux in the spokes turns on and off. Whenever a coil of wire surrounds a changing magnetic flux, current is induced in the wire. This is the basic physics of a transformer. The flux due to the earth's magnetic field is responsible for flux in the spokes. Wouldn't the flux due to the excitation cause a huge signal in the pick-up coils? Wouldn't this flux overwhelm the smaller flux of the earth's magnetic field? Take a careful look at the flux gate from a side view, as shown in Fig 8.10. Notice that flux due to excitation passes in both directions through the pick up coil. The net flux due to excitation is zero. This is not the case with flux from the earth's magnetic field. This flux passes in only one direction.

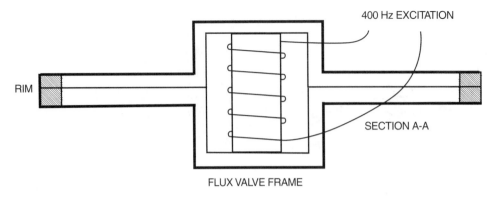

400 Hz EXCITATION

RIM

SECTION A-A

FLUX VALVE FRAME

Figure 8.10 Side view of flux gate

The amount of flux gated on and off through the spokes is a function of   flux gate orientation in the earth's magnetic field. As an example, if one spoke is parallel to the magnetic field lines, that spoke has maximum flux. If one spoke is perpendicular to the field lines, it has zero flux, as shown in Fig. 8.9(b).

Voltage induced in windings around spokes of the flux gate wheel have a frequency of 800 Hz. This is because the flux gate is driven into saturation at twice the excitation frequency. The amplitude of the induced voltage is a function of the angle between the flux gate and magnetic lines or magnetic north. Since the angle between spokes of the wheel is the same as a synchro, the induced voltage has the same relationship to magnetic north as the relationship between the stator windings and shaft position in a synchro.

This relationship is important; the flux gate can be treated as if it were a synchro. If the three pick-up windings are connected to stators of a synchro and the rotor synchronously demodulated, an error voltage is obtained. The voltage is proportional to the difference in shaft position of the synchro and orientation of magnetic north. Remember that the frequency of the flux gate is twice the 400 Hz excitation frequency. When the output of the synchro is demodu-lated, the second harmonic of the 400 Hz excitation voltage is used. This uses full wave rectification on both halves of the 400 Hz supply.

The orientation of the spokes is not important. The pick up coils are connected to the stator windings of a synchro which, in this case, is a control transformer, and nothing more than a specialized synchro. The shaft of the control transformer is connected to the gyro. The control transformer is adjusted so that when the gyro indicates the same heading as the magnetic head-ing, output of the control transformer is zero.

When the magnetic heading of the aircraft and gyro differ, the rectified output of the control transformer, which is a DC voltage, is proportional to the error. The error voltage is amplified and pulls the gyro into the correct position.

This "pulling" of the gyro wheel should be done with a small amount of torque. As-sume a large torque so the torque motor can easily move the gyro. This loses the advantages of the gyro. The purpose of   the gyro is to take advantage of its rigidity in space. In spite of vibration and other disturbances, the gyro provides a steady indication of heading. Signals from the flux gate are likely to be noisy and, if   the flux gate makes significant changes in the gyro through a motor with large torque, the gyro would become erratic. Correcting gyro drift and changes in direction of magnetic north are both slow phenomenon. To insure the gyro is cor-rected for slow errors without overwhelming the desirable characteristics of the gyro, a motor with a small amount of torque, called a gyro torquer,   gently pulls the gyro into a position that points to magnetic north.

322

A gyro with this error-correcting system is called a slaved gyro. When a synchro drives indicators, which usually results in the gyro wheel mounted near the center of gravity of the aircraft, the assembly is called a "remote slaved gyro".

8.4 RMI: Radio Magnetic Indicator

Consider, next, a more pictorial indicator for the VOR so it points to the station as an ADF indicator points to the NDB. For this to happen, the aircraft's heading is required. The bearing from the aircraft to the VOR is the difference between the heading of the aircraft and the VOR radial. A motor can drive the OBS resolver to the TO radial, and the remote gyro, a motor-driven synchro which follows orientation of the DG.

To create an instrument that has a compass card slaved to the DG, the compass card is connected to one input of a differential gear set, which subtracts one shaft position from another. The other input of the differential gear set connects to the motor-driven OBS resolver. The output is the difference between aircraft heading and VOR radial, which points to the VOR. An example of this instrument, the radio magnetic indicator, RMI, is shown in Fig. 8.11

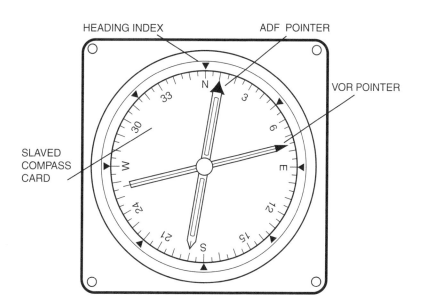

Figure 8.11   Basic construction of RMI (Radio Magnetic Indicator)

The figure shows two pointers, one for VOR and a second for ADF. The ADF pointer is simple to implement because it points to the NDB. The second pointer could also be used for a second VOR and , in some cases, the second pointer is switched from a second VOR to the ADF.

How does this two-pointer plus compass card instrument form a navigational situation for the flight crew? First, examine the information this instrument provides. Heading is provided by the compass card. Secondly, two navigation sources are displayed simultaneously in the same format.

The instrument improves several flight maneuvers. Assume an aircraft is flying to a VOR. If there is any crosswind, the station will not lie directly ahead of the aircraft. The offset of the VOR and the heading, or crab angle, is the difference between the VOR pointer and top of the instrument. It is a simple matter to subtract the OBS setting from the heading to obtain crab angle, but the RMI provides a visual indication without computation.

*RMI (Radio Magnetic Indicator) combines
compass and radio bearing information
for better view of navigational situation.
Pointer at top left is ADF indicator.
Pointer at top right is VOR indicator.*

The RMI is useful when approaching for landing, altering course, or changing navigation, for example; from VOR to NDB. As an example, assume a non-precision approach to an airport which only has an NDB. The procedure calls for flying a VOR radial until the airport is abeam, or off to the side, of the aircraft. Assume we are flying TO the VOR and the airport is to the left of the aircraft. As we fly to the station, the indicator points to the VOR and is different from the heading of the aircraft by the crab angle. The ADF pointer starts by pointing to the left but to the front of the aircraft. Near the airport the ADF pointer moves towards the left of the aircraft. Just before the pointer is exactly to the left, a turn brings the ADF pointer to the top of the RMI indicator, which indicates homing to the NDB. At this time an estimate is made of the wind. If there is a cross wind from the left it will now be a headwind , and so on. Once the NDB is reached, we take up a heading equal to the runway while watching the compass card on the RMI and make the final approach.

8.5 HSI: Horizontal Situation Indicator

Much en route flying involves airways, where a specific VOR radial is flown. What if an OBS and CDI are added to the RMI? This would provide all the information needed; selected course, heading, and a pictorial display which points to the VOR. Called the horizontal situation indicator, or HSI, it is the ultimate in mechanical pictorial displays. The HSI is shown in Fig. 8.12. Like the RMI, the instrument has a compass card, with heading shown under the pointer at the top of the display. The line that points to the heading is the "lubber" line. The compass card is positioned by the DG, which uses a synchro-based servo system in the same fashion as employed in the RMI.

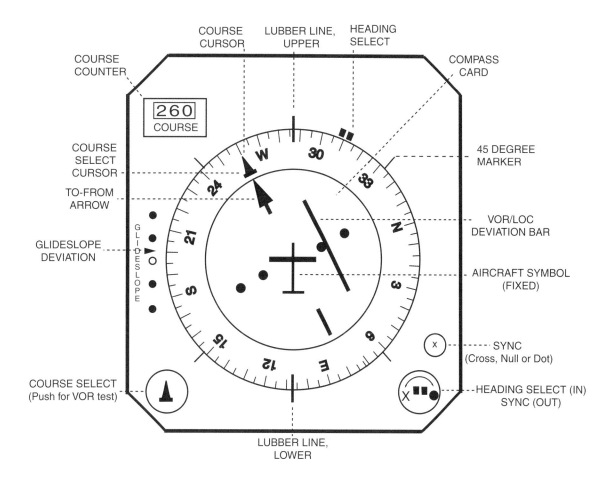

Figure 8.12   Horizontal Situation Indicator (HSI)

Attached to the compass card is an OBS and CDI, meaning the entire assembly, OBS and CDI rotates with the compass card. Consider what happens when the OBS and CDI rotate with the DG.

Horizontal Situation Indicator, HSI. (S-Tec)

One problem of VOR is the receiver has no knowledge of the aircraft heading. This was apparent in our discussion of VOR; the CDI points in the proper direction only if the aircraft heading is roughly in agreement with the OBS setting. As an example, fly a 180 degree FROM radial but head to the VOR on 0 degrees, and the CDI points in the wrong direction. Flying "into the pointer" takes us further off course. But note what would happen if the entire CDI and OBS rotate with the DG. First consider a situation where the OBS is set to 0 degrees and heading is about 0 degrees. The OBS/CDI indicator in the HSI would be in its normal upright position and the CDI would point correctly.

Next, turn the aircraft 180 degrees so it is heading in the opposite direction and the CDI points in the wrong direction. But would the CDI point in the wrong direction? No! The entire OBS/CDI has turned upside-down because it is attached to the compass card, which rotated 180 degrees when the aircraft turned.

What would happen if we turn the aircraft only 90 degrees? Now, the CDI is horizontal. If there is a small outline of an aircraft on the glass face of the indicator, it shows the aircraft flying perpendicular to the CDI. If the CDI is the course, it shows us flying perpendicular to the course. Since the CDI deflects as the airplane deviates from the course, flying perpendicular will, eventually, put us to one side of the course. As we move off course, the CDI moves and puts the small aircraft to one side or the other of the course. This is what is happening. As the airplane flies perpendicular to the course, that course is ahead or behind it.

If the course is intercepted, the HSI shows the intercept angle and distance to the selected course. The VOR CDI is a function of angle. The HSI requires the CDI to be proportional to the *distance* from the aircraft to the selected course.

The HSI is also superior for flying a localizer. On an approach, the OBS knob is set to the runway heading. There is no "omnibearing" associated with a localizer, and new nomenclature is required for the control that changes the angle of the CDI in the HSI. The knob is "course," usually abbreviated CRS.

As with the RMI, runway and aircraft heading are slightly different if there is a crosswind. This is clearly visible on the HSI. The same instrument shows course deviation and, if a second pointer is employed, glide slope deviation; all the information for an ILS approach is on one instrument. The glide slope is not part of the "horizontal situation" since it is vertical guidance, but its inclusion is valuable for ILS approaches.

The HSI also provides a solution to the back course approach (non-precision approaches may be made to the backside of a localizer). The problem is, the CDI deflects in the opposite direction. One solution is to reverse connections to the CDI with a switch, but the switch must be carefully annunciated so the reversed sense of the CDI is not used for the normal front course approach.

When runway heading is set into the HSI, it is the front course. This may be confusing so consider an example. Assume an airport has an ILS on runway 9, with a heading of 90 degrees. The other end of the runway is 27, which implies that when landing from the east runway heading is 270 degrees. More often than not, only one of two possible runway headings is equipped with ILS. For our example, assume that runway 27 has an ILS. ILS equipment provides a front and back course, but the ILS runway is 27. Even though an aircraft can approach runway 9 on a back course, the back course is to ILS equipment on runway 27. Therefore, the approach is a back course to runway 27. One way to remember it is: a "backwards" approach to runway 27.

When making a back course approach, the runway heading is 180 degrees different from the actual heading of the aircraft. The HSI turns the CDI upside down and the deflection of the CDI is correct without reversing wires.

Another setting on most HSI's is the heading "bug," usually marked HDG. It moves a pointer around the periphery of the compass card. The main purpose of the heading bug is to control an autopilot, which is on a heading hold mode. When an autopilot is not controlling the aircraft, the heading bug often reminds the pilot of the desired course.

As mentioned previously, the CDI is a part of an HSI and should represent distance rather than angle. In a VOR receiver, the CDI provides an indication proportional to angular deviation, not distance. Unless distance to the VOR is known, the VOR signal does not provide sufficient information to determine distance from the desired course. This distance is called the cross track error, or XTE, and was discussed in the sections for GPS and long range navigation.

By using DME distance, XTE is:

$$XTE = D \sin \theta \qquad (8.1)$$

Where D is the DME distance and θ is the angular course deviation.

Since DME is required to generate the HSI CDI deflection, it is a valuable addition to the HSI display of DME distance.

The HSI was originally designed to be used with VOR and DME but may operate with other navigation systems. When based on GPS or LORAN-C, for example, a waypoint is selected, usually by latitude and longitude or a fix which is stored in a database. CDI and distance indications are now relative to the waypoint.

8.6 ADI: Attitude Director (Direction) Indicator

The artificial horizon indicates the aircraft's orientation relative to the horizon. The instrument is based on a gyro with a vertical axis. This provides a reference to the vertical and a measurement for two aircraft attitudes; pitch and roll.

A basic artificial horizon contains the gyro inside of the panel instrument. The gyro is mechanically connected to the brown disk (earth) and a blue disk (sky) representing the horizon. Held in a gimbal, the gyro remains vertical for both yaw (nose left-right) and pitch (nose up-down) axes. The vertical gyro, as in any gyro, drifts but is not slaved to any other source. Only if an aircraft never flew straight and level would drift be a problem. The vertical gyro is designed with a tendency to align with gravity, which torques it (to borrow a term from the slaved DG) and corrects drift.

An improvement over the artificial horizon is the Attitude Director Indicator, or ADI (Fig. 8.13). It is also known as an Attitude *Direction* Indicator. Primarily an artificial horizon, the ADI is the obvious place to put glide slope and localizer pointers. The ADI also contains the indicator for the radar altimeter and DME distance. A specialized version of the ADI, when combined with an HSI, is called a flight director and contains other indicators.

Figure 8.13 Attitude Director Indicator

8.7 Electronic Displays

The first instruments for aircraft borrowed technology from ships, railroad locomotives and automobiles---transportation of the period. For simple parameters, dials and gauges were adequate. Even the first radio navigation instruments used simple pointer indicators for the ADF and CDI. When pictorial displays were invented, they contained special meter movements, rotating compass cards and a host of mechanical contrivances. In spite of the complexity, many aircraft are still full of mechanical displays.

The ultimate navigation instrument, however, would be a map with the familiar "You are here" arrow. On the display is your flight plan, destination, location of bad weather, obstructions and collision hazards. This display depends on the ability to pictorially present information. Other data can be displayed with numbers and letters, or alphanumerics. Examples are engine parameters, radio frequencies, airports, outside air temperature, airspeed and so on. Any parameter that is scalar can be shown with an alphanumeric display, while data that are vectors, such as courses, tracks, and headings, are best indicated with a graphic display.

A *reflective* display (like a painted number) requires ambient light to be visible; it does not generate light. All mechanical pointer displays are reflective. For alphanumerics, numbers are painted on rotating drums mounted behind a window on a panel. The drum rotates and displays characters similar to the way a mechanical odometer operates in an automobile. The first DMEs were made this way; with distance displayed on rotating drums.

An early *emissive* display was the warning lamp An example is a gear up - gear down light and a marker beacon indicator. One requirement of a warning light is high brightness; it must be seen in sunlight, which can be very bright in a cockpit. There are no trees or clouds to shade the sun from an aircraft at high altitude. To reduce direct sunlight, a glare shield creates a "roof" at the top of the instrument panel. Even with this shield, emissive displays must be very bright.

At the other end of the emissive brightness scale is the dark of night, where displays are reduced in intensity. There could also be a single warning light with so much illumination that night vision of the crew would be affected. (This is more critical in military flying than in the civil world.) The required range of light intensity is large and some display types cannot provide it.

8.8 Display Technologies

8.8.1 Incandescent

One of the first technologies in aircraft was the incandescent lamp, leading to the first alphanumeric electronic displays. The incandescent was probably the first application of the segmented numeric display, where digits are formed by seven segments. Illumination comes from filaments stretched between posts as shown in Fig 8.14. The display provides 10 decimal digits.

Light emitted by the display is close to white. When intensity is reduced, the color shifts to longer wavelengths and appears more orange. This was not a bad characteristic because redder light does not affect night vision as much as shorter wavelengths. Filters over a display can generate colors other than white. This is a problem, however, when the display is reduced in intensity and shifts toward red. Displays filtered for shorter wavelengths such as blue, are more reduced in intensity than longer wavelengths. It causes an imbalance between colors.

Although the incandescent is still found in many aircraft, there are limitations. First, it is not suitable for alphanumeric displays. There are alphanumeric displays with 16 segments and numerals are acceptable. Letters of the alphabet, however, are difficult to read. Another problem is efficiency. At daytime brightness, the display becomes hot, limiting its life to approximately 5000 hours at moderate brightness. However, when the display operates at sunlight-readable intensities, life is reduced considerably. The final problem is cost. When incandescent displays became available, the high cost was acceptable since they were the only choice. Later technologies are much less costly.

8.8.2 Light Emitting Diodes

The next display technology was the light emitting diode, or LED. It has intriguing characteristics. First, it is much less expensive. It is a tiny semiconductor chip which can form a seven-segment arrangement or, in more complex arrays such as 5X7, generate acceptable-looking alphabetical characters. Compared to incandescent, LED is more efficient. Also, when reduced in intensity or dimmed, color does not shift. The color of the LED was its biggest problem; early LEDs were only red. This color is reserved for danger warnings, and would be lost in a sea of other red indicators in the cockpit. In spite of this there is some application of red LEDs in aircraft.

It wasn't long after the first red LEDs that other colors became available. First was amber, then yellow, green and, finally, blue. Early amber and yellow LEDs were bright and sunlight readable, opening the way toward more application in instrument panels.

Large arrays of LEDs are used for graphics display but not in significant numbers. One problem is energy efficiency. The LED is moderately efficient but when thousands form an array, heat buildup is significant. Also, a blue LED was not available until recently to provide full color. Another difficulty is yield. During manufacture, when thousands of LEDs are attached to a substrate, there is a possibility of one failure. LED arrays are mainly used in small arrays such as 5X7 for alphanumeric characters, where they have proved successful.

8.8.3 Plasma

A display technology used in significant numbers before LEDs is plasma. It is based on orange light emitted from ionized neon gas. An example is shown in Fig. 8.15. Neon gas is contained between two flat glass plates. The rear glass is coated with a conductive material, usually a metal. Deposited on the inside of the front glass are metal segments. These can be a seven segment configuration or a customized pattern. The metal segments are very thin and transparent to light. If a sufficiently high electric potential is applied between the rear conductive coating and a metal segment, the neon gas ionizes. Orange light is emitted when neon atoms return to their zero energy state. By selectively energizing segments, numeric digits are generated.

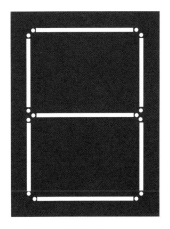

Figure 8.14 Seven segment incandescant display

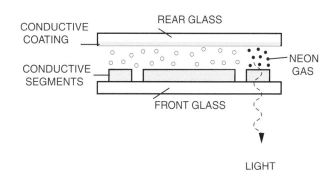

Figure 8.15   Plasma display

The color of ionized neon gas includes several spectral lines but appears to the eye as orange. A filter can extract other colors, but the intensity is less. A plasma display can be sunlight readable and dimmed for night time use. Energy efficiency is reasonable but specialized drivers and high voltage are used for these displays. When energy consumption is considered, efficiency is no better than the LED.

Plasma displays have been used in avionics, especially before LEDs became available in bright yellow and orange. One difficulty with plasma displays is they are usually custom assemblies. LEDs are purchased as standard parts and arranged as needed for the design. There are standard plasma displays but they tend to be larger and not suited for miniature avionics displays.

Another disadvantage is that plasma requires high voltage. About 90 volts are required to start ionization and about 60 volts to sustain the display. High voltage comes from an additional power supply and high voltage drivers. Since plasma displays are no longer common in new designs, the lack of high voltage drivers precludes their use in new designs.

8.8.4 Liquid Crystal: LCD

A premier technology for avionics is the liquid crystal display. LCD is unique in that it can be reflective, emissive or both. The basic function is that of a light valve. The LCD turns ambient light on and off or it can be supplied with a light source. Thus, it is reflective or emissive. Fig 8.16 shows the basic construction; the heart of the LCD is a fluid, the liquid crystal, between two clear glass plates. The rear glass is coated with a thin, transparent metallic film. The front plate is coated in specific areas with metallic material. LCD construction to this point is similar to the plasma display described.

LCD display for engine torque (BFG)

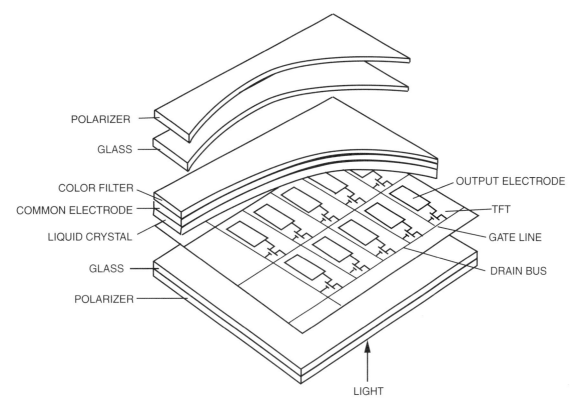

POLARIZER
GLASS
COLOR FILTER
COMMON ELECTRODE
LIQUID CRYSTAL
GLASS
POLARIZER

OUTPUT ELECTRODE
TFT
GATE LINE
DRAIN BUS

LIGHT

Figure 8.16   Construction of LCD display

Outside of the front and rear glass plates is a polarizing film. This creates plane polarized light out of randomly polarized light. Polarization occurs when the electric field of the light is parallel to a plane. A polarizing film is like a microscopic window blind. When light strikes the polarizing film where the electric field can pass through the blind, light passes. Light of other polarization is blocked.

If two polarizing films are aligned so polarization is the same, we see through the two films. On the other hand, aligning the films so polarization is different blocks the light; the result is darkness.

Crystals, liquid or solid, have a unique characteristic of being able to rotate the polarization of light. Crystals have an ordered array of molecules which can have characteristics similar to the window blind example above. Another important characteristic is that the crystalline structure reacts to electric fields. In a liquid crystal, the ability to rotate the polarization of light is a function of the applied electric field.

Assume the polarizing films are arranged so polarization is the same front and back. Pass light through the films and there would be little attenuation. By applying an electric field across the liquid crystal material in the space between films, polarity of the light is rotated.. If that rotation is 90 degrees the area where the electric field is applied becomes dark. Polarized light was rotated 90 degrees so it cannot pass through the rear polarizing film.

Selective application of an electric field, therefore, causes areas to become opaque. A light source behind the rear polarizing film generates characters such as 7-segment digits and alphanumerics.

If the polarizing filters are oriented 90 degrees to each other, the display appears dark unless there is rotation in the space between front and back polarizers. In this case, the electric field causes a bright area, as the additional 90 degree rotation allows light to pass through the LCD. By orientation of front and back polarizing films, the LCD can be configured as a white on black display or black on white.

A static electric field produces the desired results but continuous application of an electric field can cause unwanted chemical reaction in the liquid crystal material. To prevent this, the applied field alternates, with no DC component.

The LCD is a shutter, allowing light to pass or be blocked. If a light source is placed at the rear it emits light and becomes an emissive display. If the glass panel is replaced with a mirrored surface, ambient light is reflected from the rear glass plate and no illumination is required. Here, the display is a reflective type. If the mirror is partially transparent, the light can be reflected or transmitted. This is called transflective.

A major advantage of LCD is low power. Only an electric field is required to pass or shut off light. Virtually zero energy achieves this change of state. When an LCD is in the reflective mode, a low power display provides sunlight readable results with nearly zero power. With back lighting, energy is required. For a sunlight readable emissive display, the light energy is significant and only highly efficient back lighting may be used, such as fluorescent. Incandescent lighting may be used for nighttime viewing. A common arrangement is a transflective display with incandescent lighting for night, reflective mode for sunlight and emissive mode for night viewing.

Because power to the liquid crystal is very small, a large number of segments may be used. As pointed out for the LED, a large array has problems with the amount of energy in a small area. A bright LED consumes 10 to 20 mw and, for a large matrix such as 1024 elements, all segments on can dissipate 20 watts. Clearly, 20 watts cannot be highly concentrated in the front panel of an avionics display. On the other hand, 1024 LCD segments may occupy a small area with no danger because power is extremely low. What does become a problem, however, is how to connect 1024 segments to the driving electronics.

Graphics displays produce pictures with a large number of emitters or light shutters. As an example, a reasonable picture can be made with a matrix of 256 by 256 picture elements, or pixels. This represents 65,536 pixels. The word "reasonable" is used in this example; a picture of 256 by 256 pixels is not television quality, which is approximately 500 by 750 pixels. A good quality computer monitor is 1024 by 1024 or more than a million pixels. It is not possible to have a million-pin connector to connect the LCD to one million drivers on a printed circuit board. Before generating LCD graphics, connections need to be reduced to individual pixels.

The technique is to place the driving electronics on the glass with the segments. Very small thin film transistors, TFT, are deposited on the glass and connected to the segments. Each pixel is addressed sequentially. For a large LCD with a 1024 by 1024 matrix, each pixel is addressed by horizontal and vertical lines where the lines intersect. When segments are addressed, a transistor acts as a storage element to keep the segment activated until addressing returns to that pixel. With X-Y multiplexing, the number of lines addressed is now 2048, still a large number. A 2048 pin connector is impractical and further reduction of interconnects is required. By mounting integrated circuits directly to the glass and using electronic multiplexing, the number of interconnects is reduced to a handful. This display is called the active matrix liquid crystal display, or AMLCD.

The shape of a pixel is considered to be square. If a display has an aspect ratio of 4 to 3, meaning width is 4/3 that of height, pixels are arranged as a matrix of 4N columns by 3N rows. If a display has a resolution of 1024 pixels along the horizontal, it requires 4N columns to be 1024 or N equals 256. The number of rows is 768. The total pixels is 1024 X 768 or 786,432 pixels. Another way of describing this display is to specify a resolution of 1024 X 768, which may be recognized by as a computer monitor specification.

LCDs generate color graphics by providing three light shutters, one for each additive primary color at each pixel. Every shutter also has a microscopic filter; red, green or blue. This implies that if there are 1 million pixels in a 1024 by 1024 display, there are 3 million LCD light shutters. (That fact does make one shudder!) A major problem with AMLCD displays at the time of this writing is cost, which is driven by manufacturing yield. If we start the manufacture an AMLCD with a piece of glass and perform all steps, a finished product results only if every step is a success. If just one pixel doesn't work it is not a viable product.

What is the probability of getting 3 million pixels to work? It is small, and there is a lot of scrap in the AMLCD industry. The product, therefore, is expensive. This is changing as manufacturing techniques grow more refined

LCD displays have limitations. Most early problems have been solved but one remains; temperature range. An LCD can be destroyed by excessively high or low temperature. Low temperature freezes the LCD material and causes possible permanent damage. Response time also slows. For an instrument display, where there is no high-speed motion, slowness can be tolerated. At a low temperature that renders an LCD television worthless, the LCD display is satisfactory for an indicator. Noticeable slowing occurs at temperatures below about 10 degrees C and freezing occurs below –20 degrees C. Permanent damage results below about –40 degrees C. With the possible exception of bush planes in Alaska, aircraft are not usually flown with a cockpit temperature below –20 degrees C. And aircraft are rarely stored below –40 degrees C.

Backlighting LCD displays is an art. To be sunlight readable requires significant intensity. Any backlight must be reasonably efficient if the display is not to get overly warm. For color LCDs, the backlight should have a white color that does not shift with dimming, as would an incandescent. Of all the potential lamp technologies, fluorescent tubes emerged as the choice of illumination. Specialized fluorescent tubes with steady illumination are mounted behind the LCD.

Fluorescent tubes require high voltage and a "kick" to start an internal arc. The lamps are a constant current device so they need current limiting. A power supply is usually included as a part of the lamp assembly. In spite of the fact that fluorescent tubes are more efficient than other lamp technologies, they dissipate energy. The power supply also needs to dissipate heat so backlight assemblies often have heat sinks.

8.8.5 Cathode Ray Tube: CRT

Although AMLCD displays dominate the cockpits of new aircraft, the CRT has long been one of the most popular technologies . It has been manufactured for more than 75 years and installed in aircraft since World War II. The first application as an airborne display was military radar screens. In the mid fifties, it was applied to weather radar for airliners. When color was added, different hues, rather than a gray scale, could designate the intensity of rain.

Weather radar screens were also enhanced with overlays and manufacturers started to use the CRT as a multifunction display, where check lists and other items are displayed. The weather radar was the first true electronic flight instrument system.

Construction of the CRT is shown in Fig 8.17. It is a vacuum tube with components enclosed in an evacuated glass bottle. At the end away from the screen, in the neck, is a heated cathode to provide a source of electrons. The electrons accelerate toward the screen with increasingly higher positive voltages. Electrodes near the cathode focus the beam into a narrow spot on the screen. The final accelerating electrode has a very high potential, typically from 10 to 25 kV, depending on CRT size.

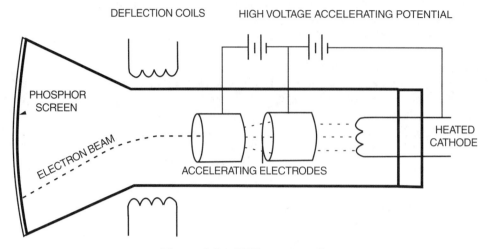

DEFLECTION COILS   HIGH VOLTAGE ACCELERATING POTENTIAL

PHOSPHOR
SCREEN

ELECTRON BEAM

ACCELERATING ELECTRODES

HEATED
CATHODE

Figure 8.17 CRT construction

The electron beam is deflected by a magnetic field. An electric field could be used, but a magnetic field deflects the beam through a greater angle. This permits the design of shorter tubes, but even these tubes often have a length that is objectionable for aircraft. A magnetic field is generated with a ferrite yoke that fits around the neck of the CRT.

The screen is coated with a phosphor material. Single color (monochromatic) tubes have one phosphor deposited on the front glass. A thin coating of aluminum is evaporated onto the glass to provide a return path for current of the electron beam. When an electron strikes phosphor atoms they emit light photons. Green is a common color for CRTs in oscilloscopes and computer screens and is still used in aircraft instruments.

CRT phosphors become sunlight readable by increasing beam current and forcing more photons from the phosphor. The disadvantage is a reduction in tube life. A CRT for a television receiver in the home, where ambient light is low, can last tens of thousands of hours. A CRT in an aircraft will last thousands of hours.

A reduction of beam current decreases CRT brightness without a color shift and is an effective method of dimming the display.

There are two basic methods of creating an image on a CRT. The first is raster scan, the same as in television and computer screens. The second is stroke writing, which generates a display as you might draw with a pencil. To understand their advantages and disadvantages consider how the two different, yet common, displays are generated.

The idea of an electronic display is to show any parameter by simply selecting it As an example, to fly an ADF approach, an ADF indicator is selected and displayed . Fly a VOR approach and we select an HSI on the same CRT. But if the aircraft has electronic flight instruments (EFIS) , one CRT can show either indicator, or even both simultaneously. If the indicator is an RMI, a compass card is displayed on the perimeter of the display with two pointers.

A CRT beam is not only deflected anywhere on the screen but turned on and off. This is equivalent to moving a pencil across a paper and pressing it down make marks. Assume the image will be an artificial horizon. This display does not have fine detail such as numbers and "tic marks" of a compass rose but areas of solid color. The artificial horizon has a section representing blue sky and another representing the brown earth. There are a few tic marks and the outline of an aircraft but it is mostly large areas of color. Returning to the pencil and paper idea; large color areas are done by tracing a line back and forth until the area is filled.

We could pass the pencil over the whole sheet of paper to create any image, including large areas and fine marks. This is also done with a CRT by scanning the whole screen and turning the beam on and off for each symbol or letter. The benefit is that the beam deflection is the same for any display; the beam is deflected left to right, top to bottom. This is called raster scan and simplifies the scanning electronics. It illuminates large areas such as an artificial horizon. Raster scanning, which is also used for television broadcast images, can picture almost anything.

A raster-scanned image consists of raster lines which can be considered lines of pixels. The resolution of raster scanning is equal to the number of lines. The lines are usually horizontal, as for television and computer screens, but this is not always the case with aircraft instruments. The selection of horizontal scanning lines for television and computer screens is because they are wider than they are high. Some aircraft displays, however, are taller than they are wide and use vertical scanning lines.

For conventional horizontal scanning, resolution in the vertical direction can be no better than the number of scanning lines. Anything that falls between scanning lines cannot be resolved. Resolution along the scanning line depends on the frequency of turning the electron beam on and off, which is called the video response. A pixel is usually square in a raster display, and resolution in the horizontal direction should produce a square pixel. The ratio of width to height of a scanned display is called aspect ratio or A. If there are N horizontal scan lines, there are NA square pixels in one scanning line, which is also resolution in the horizontal direction.

Example: A television display has 525 scanning lines and aspect ratio is 4:3. What is the equivalent resolution of the display in lines?

Solution: The equivalent lines is M = 525 (4/3) = 700 lines.

Example: How many pixels in a television picture?

Solution: The total number of pixels is the horizontal resolution in lines multiplied by vertical resolution in lines or 525 X 700 = 367,500. This may sound high but television is not considered a "high resolution" display. Digital television with "high definition" has much higher resolution.

The color CRT was developed in the early 1950s for television. The most common type is the shadow mask tube. There are other designs but only the shadow mask and certain refinements of the design survive. One is the Trinitron, a trade name of the developer, Sony Corporation.

The concept behind the shadow mask CRT is a metal plate with microscopic holes located just behind the phosphor screen, as shown in Fig. 8.18. The screen consists of phosphor dots rather than a continuous coating, as in a monochrome tube. There are three dots for each pixel, each emitting a different primary color; red, blue and green. Three electron beams are aimed so each strikes only phosphor dots of one color. In other words, one beam strikes only red dots, another beam hits green and the third strikes blue.

One panel of an EFIS (Electronic Flight Instrument System). This 8 x 8-in. panel is the pilot's primary flight display, which replaces the earlier artificial horizon or attitude director indicator, ADI. (Honeywell)

335

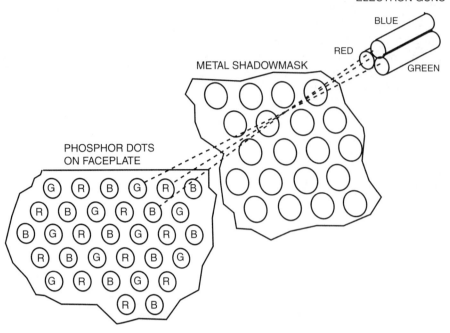

ELECTRON GUNS

BLUE

RED

GREEN

METAL SHADOWMASK

PHOSPHOR DOTS
ON FACEPLATE

Figure 8.18 Shadow mask color CRT

Red, green and blue are additive primaries which mix in various ratios to produce any color.

The holes in the shadow mask are small and any misalignment relative to the phosphor dots causes errors in color. Mechanical misalignment of the electron beams can also cause false colors. Many improvements have been made, however, in the 50 years the color CRT has been in production.

If the beam is incorrectly deflected it shifts colors. Deviations can be caused by strong magnetic fields near the CRT so the tube may be protected by metal shield. If color is not uniform over the screen, the raster is adjusted during the scan.

The Trinitron uses color stripes rather than dots, so the shadow mask has slots rather than holes. The dot-type color tube requires three electron beams arranged in a triangle. The Trinitron places three electron beams in a line. Because of the color stripes, alignment of the electron beam is in the horizontal direction. With the Trinitron it is easier to preserve color purity. Since the color phosphor is a stripe there is no wasted space between dots on the CRT face. More phosphor is also available to produce light and the tube is somewhat brighter than the dot matrix CRT.

Most CRT technology was developed for television receivers. For the first EFIS (electronic flight instrument system), smaller CRTs of high brightness were developed . The tubes have deflection yokes, where color purity adjustments are made at the factory and bonded in place. With the growing popularity of EFIS displays, newer CRT displays are as large as a small television receiver.

To review the positive features of the CRT:
1. Full color
2. Graphics display
3. Good resolution
4. Sunlight readable
5. Dimmable
6. Reasonably power efficient

7. Relatively inexpensive
8. Wide temperature range
9. Proven technology
10. Life span as good as most technologies

On the negative side, the CRT :
1. Requires several power supply voltages
2. Requires very high voltage
3. Generates magnetic fields which can radiate
4. Is constructed with a fragile glass envelope
5. Is heavier than other display technologies
6. Requires *significant* depth behind the front panel

Item 5, on weight, includes magnetic deflection components and transformers for generating high voltage. Item 6 on panel depth is the most significant CRT problem. Depth represents wasted volume. Space behind the instrument panel is always tight in an aircraft and small assemblies are highly desirable.

Most EFIS displays in aircraft at the time of this writing are CRT-based. The flat panel AMLCD, however, is replacing the tubes in many existing and new-design aircraft.

8.8.6 Field Emission Displays

A promising technology is the field emission display, or FED. It is almost a flat CRT. In the FED there are three electron emission centers per pixel. Each center is a sharp pointed electrode or emission cone charged by a voltage. The sharp shape concentrates a high electric field at the tip of the cone. This is the same phenomenon that causes lightning rods to attract lightning . With the high electric field, electrons eject from the metallic cone and travel in the direction of the electric field. The phosphor is very close to the emission cone so electrons strike it, then return through a conductive coating below the phosphor.

Except for arrays of cones for emitting electrons, the FED contains dots of phosphors, one for each primary color and a plate similar to a shadow mask. The difference is that the FED is a flat display. Since the FED is, essentially, a flat CRT, it should have all the advantages of a CRT without the disadvantages. This is, in fact, the case and most, but not all, disadvantages are reduced. The technology is still expensive and has not yet matured.

The emission cones are addressed with a logic element and high voltage driver. Since the cones are behind the display, it is not necessary to deposit transparent transistors on the front glass, as done with the AMLCD. Although the need for several supply voltages is removed, there is still a high voltage requirement, but nowhere as near as high as that required for a CRT. The field emission display, however, eliminates CRT problems of radiating magnetic fields, substantial weight and considerable depth behind the panel.

8.8.7 Colors and Gray Scale

A television receiver and computer display provide primary colors in any ratio for nearly an infinite number of colors. Assume the intensity of three primary colors (red, blue and green) is digitized with three bits or eight levels of color. The total color combinations is 512. This is calculated by realizing that three groups of three binary bits is the same as 9 bits, which has 512 different states. One state is 000 or no emission of light, which is black. Some argue that black is not a color and we will not take up that argument here. There is, however, a need for black and it is included as a color.

In aircraft there isn't a requirement for large number of colors in the "palette". Color distinguishes magnitude changes rather than a wide range of parameters. Humans cannot easily discern differences among a large number of different colors.

The simplest and, in many displays, effective color palette is created by turning primary colors on or off with no gray scale. With just one primary color at a time there is red, green or blue. All three together produce white. Red and green create yellow; red and blue, cyan; and blue and green equal magenta. No colors, that is, no light emission, produces black. This is a palette of 8 colors, the total number of anything defined by three binary, on or off, bits. This eight-color palette has been used for many years in weather radar, including the most recent turbulence radar.

8.9 Display Systems

The concept of an electronic display system is the flexibility of providing any indicator at any location. An HSI, for example, may be displayed directly in front of the captain while the first officer checks the weather radar. Later in the flight, the first officer makes the approach to land and requires an HSI and ADI. The first officer selects the instruments needed, while the captain retains the same instruments or selects a different display. This versatility provides a high level of convenience, reduces pilot workload and unclutters the instrument panel.

A block diagram of EFIS (electronic flight instrument system) is shown in Fig 8.19. The size is noted by "tubes" (the CRTs). A typical arrangement is a "four tube" system, with two tubes for the captain and two for the first officer.

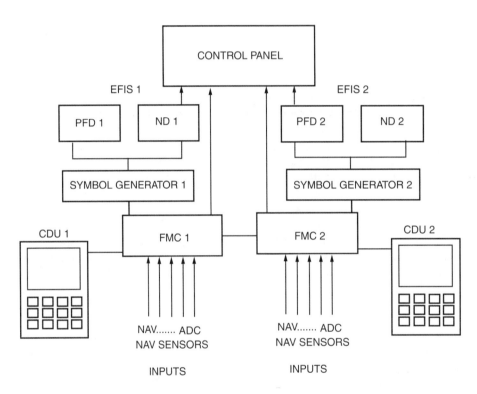

PFD = Primary Flight Display   **ND = Navigation Display**
FMC = Flight Management Computer   **CDU = Control and Display Unit**

Figure 8.19   EFIS (Electronic Flight Instrument System)

A three-tube system usually has two tubes for the captain and one for the first officer. This might be found in a business jet, air taxi or commuter aircraft. Four tubes can be implemented several ways. A common arrangement is two each for the captain and first officer. Another is two for the captain, one for the first officer and one for a center console display of engine parameters and other data. The center screen is often called an MFD, or multifunction display.

EFIS installations also have five and six panels, for a flight deck with virtually no mechanical instruments. This is often call an "all glass cockpit". The typical arrangement of a six tube cockpit has two displays each for captain and first officer. There is one tube in the center for engine instruments and one multifunction tube on the center console for flight plans, waypoints, radio frequencies, etc.

Referring to the block diagram of a typical EFIS, each tube contains the CRT, its power supply , and deflection circuits. In an aircraft, circuit sharing reduces cost and weight. In the case of displays, each has its own power supply and deflection circuits. Theoretically, one power supply could drive all tubes as well as deflection circuits. The practical reason for independent supplies is that voltages for a CRT span from hundreds up to as much as 30,000 volts. The cost and size of a connector to distribute 30 kV to displays is prohibitive, not to mention fire and health hazards. Deflection circuits can have voltages of several hundred but problems arise because of fast rise time of the waveforms. This enhances the likelihood of radiation and interference to other avionics systems.

Circuit sharing can be done, however, and a major example is the symbol generator. This subsystem generates displays from standard libraries. Many displays originate from common elements; for example, alpha and numeric characters. Text for flight plans and radio frequencies are standard characters, which appear in other displays. For example, the compass rose of an HSI or RMI has numbers representing magnetic bearings.

Graphics displays also have standard shapes. An HSI has a compass rose, a lubber line, a heading bug, course arrow and CDI. These items are always present and have the same shape. The basic elements are rotated and the CDI deflected from the central position. To generate an HSI, the image of a compass rose is stored in a read-only memory, ROM, and rotated to the correct position. Rotation is done by the symbol generator which reassigns the location of pixels in the compass rose image, depending on data from the directional gyro, or DG. The math is simple trigonometry.

The course arrow is also stored in ROM and retrieved for the compass rose. This image is rotated according to the setting of the OBS. The CDI section of the course arrow is a straight line and generated with a mathematical equation. The CDI is rotated and deflected from the central position. Both operations involve simple mathematics and input from the OBS, VOR receiver and DME for course deviation. The CDI is added to the compass rose and course arrow.

The lubber line is always in the same location and has the same appearance. It is read from ROM and added to the display. Many HSIs have other stationary items read from ROM, along with the lubber line. The heading bug is another rotating item. The input for the heading bug is from the autopilot.

Compare the EFIS display with a broadcast television picture. The TV image is updated 30 times each second (actually half the picture 60 times each second). Relatively fast motion can be displayed; a baseball player swinging a bat or race cars travelling down the backstretch at nearly 200 miles per hour. Navigation displays for aircraft have far slower motion, allowing update rates down to twice per second.

A display on a CRT must be rescanned about 30 to 50 times per second; any slower and the pilot sees flicker. This is particularly true if there is low frequency vibration in the aircraft.

There are two methods of scanning a CRT display. The first is from top to bottom a line at a time. An alternate method scans every other line, say the odd-numbered ones, and returns the beam to the top to scan even-numbered lines. Used in broadcast TV, it's called interlace scanning and reduces the flicker effect in the eye.

Although scanning may occur up to 60 times per second, the display does not change at that rate. Once the display is created, say twice every second, the same image is displayed 30 times before the image can change. Images are constructed, then stored in a fast RAM or a shift register, and recirculated 30 times or so, and rewritten. Construction of the image is slow; for each display it occurs every 500 ms or so.

Example: Calculate how much memory is required to store an image, which contains green, red and white elements. The image is displayed as a one to one aspect ratio with a raster scan of 512 lines.
Solution: With a one to one aspect ratio there are 512 X 512 = 262,144 pixels. Four colors, green, red, black and white can be stored with 2 bits. Therefore, the total is 524 288 bits. Since memories are usually

organized in groups of 8 bits, a 65,536 byte, (8 bits), memory will suffice. This is commonly referred to as a "65 K memory" which is not very large.

8.10 Instrument Placement

What is the most effective location for these displays? The FAA recognized that key instruments should be placed in specific positions so there is no confusion over where to find them. Every person who has rented an automobile knows that it takes a while to become familiar with the controls in an unfamiliar vehicle. Imagine if brake and accelerator pedals were placed where it suited the manufacturer.

Standardizing controls for a complex machine has been a problem for hundreds of years. One of the first efforts was more than 400 years ago when pipe organ builders realized that an organist could not readily play an unfamiliar instrument. The organ guilds drew up plans outlining where keyboards and pedals were located, the names and locations of stops, and even the size and arrangement of keys. Modern standard pitch and temperament grew out of the pipe organ trade and was championed by history's most famous organist, Johann Sebastian Bach.

The FAA plan addresses the most basic instruments; attitude indicator, altimeter, airspeed indicator and heading indicator. It applies to aircraft, from the simplest single-engine GA to the most sophisticated air transport jet. If a pilot looks at a specific location to determine heading, the information will be there. The indicator could be a simple self-contained gyro or state-of-the-art graphic display.

Figure 8.20 shows the location of what is called the "basic six". This is an instrument panel found on small aircraft. At the top center is the artificial horizon, which is the indicator associated with the vertical gyro. Below is the DG, the other gyro instrument on small aircraft. At top left is the airspeed indicator, with the vertical speed indicator, VSI, in the upper right. The lower left is the altimeter and lower right the turn and bank instrument, which is the rate gyro instrument on small aircraft.

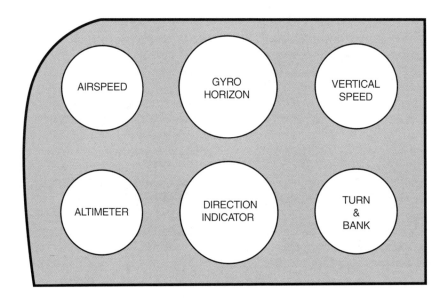

Fig. 8.20   Basic six instrument layout

Let us see what happens for more sophisticated instruments. Shown in Fig. 8.21 are instruments in what's called the basic "T" arrangement. At the top center is the attitude director indicator, or ADI. When an ADI is available , a turn and bank instrument is not needed.

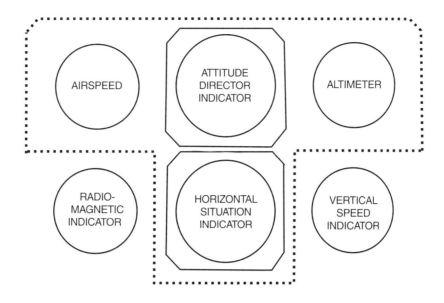

Fig. 8.21 "T" configuration of flight instruments

Below the ADI is the HSI which, in addition to other information, is the main indicator of heading. The VSI is in the lower right and altimeter at the upper left.

A radio navigation instrument such as an OBS/CDI or ADF or, most likely an RMI, is located in the lower left of the T configuration.

In an EFIS system any instrument can be placed anywhere. However, the basic T convention is followed. In the EADI (electronic attitude director indicator), it is common to include with the attitude indicator, airspeed, altitude, vertical speed and heading. This compact grouping is convenient for navigating and particularly for instrument approaches. Even when the EADI includes this additional information, it follows the basic T configuration. Airspeed is to the left of the attitude indicator, altitude and vertical speed to the right and heading below the attitude indicator.

8.11 Head Up Display

To fly in very low visibility, the head up display is widely used in military aircraft and, increasingly, in civil aircraft , It projects images on a transparent screen in front of the pilot. The concept can be understood by the analogy of an automobile windshield. The windshield provides a view outside for driving, but also visible are reflections on the windshield from inside (usually objects near the top of the dashboard). Since this is undesirable in automobiles, windshields are positioned for minimal reflection. What if we mount the speedometer on the top of the panel so its reflection is intentionally visible to the driver? . This would allow the driver to keep his eyes on the road, and see the speedometer at the same time.

This is a good beginning toward a safer display of the speedometer, but there is a problem. The reflection of the speedometer is a meter or so away, while objects of interest outside the automobile are at several hundred meters. When the driver reads the speedometer image, his eye focuses at about a meter, but needs to refocus on infinity for objects beyond the windshield.. This calls for a method of making the speedometer appear at infinity so the eye sees both instruments and the outside world simultaneously. He would not have to refocus his eyes

It is also important for the image reflected from the windshield not to block the outside view. This means the image must have thin lines and translucent areas. The system, known as HUD, or head up display, is highly successful in aircraft and also adapted for automobiles.

In aircraft , the image is not projected on the windshield because windshields may curve and have embedded heaters. The windshield, too, is not a good quality optical component. Therefore, a transparent projection screen is lowered between the pilot and windscreen.

Images are projected from a CRT or LCD light shutter with back lighting. A lens system focuses the image on infinity. The projector is below the screen and pointed up, or located behind the pilot and projected over the head. The major application of the head up display in civilian aircraft is for approach and landing. Military aircraft also use HUD for fire control.

The end of every instrument landing is most often a visual touchdown. This is not true for CAT IIIC approaches but these are not yet operational. The most important goal on approach is to keep the aircraft on the glide path, then visually acquire the runway. During a typical airline approach in low visibility, one pilot flies "head down", looking at the instruments, while the other looks through the windscreen for the runway environment. When the head up pilot announces "runway in sight," the head down pilot looks up. His eyes now shift from the ADI display to the windshield. This means the flying pilot must quickly refocus from the instrument panel to the outside, and from near to far vision. The task becomes even more difficult if the airplane re-enters low-lying cloud which is often hidden at night. Now the flying pilot must look back and forth several times in the critical seconds before touchdown. The head up display, however, provides a simultaneous view of instruments and the outside world without the pilot changing head position or eye focus.

Chapter 8 Review Questions

8.1   What characteristics make the gyroscope valuable in navigation?
8.2   What phenomena causes a gyro to drift?
8.3   What is a synchro? How does it differ from a resolver?
8.4   How does the output from a flux gate compass compare to a synchro?
8.5   If a flux gate is excited from a 400 Hz source, what is the frequency of the output?
8.6   How does ferromagnetic material play a role in the flux gate?
8.7   What information is available from an RMI?
8.8   What information is available from an HSI?
8.9   How does the HSI provide a picture of the horizontal situation?
8.10   The left/right deviation of the CDI shows the correct deviation only if the heading of the aircraft is close to the selected omnibearing. How does the HSI solve this ambiguity problem?
8.11   What is cross track error?
8.12   What information is shown on the ADI?
8.13   What type of data appears on incandescent displays?
8.14   What problems were associated with early LEDs as airborne indicators?
8.15   What types of displays are best suited for sunlight readability?
8.16   What is an emissive display?
8.17   What is a reflective display?
8.18   What is a transflective display? Which display technology can be transflective?
8.19   What is an AMLCD type of display?
8.20   If a display has 1024 pixel resolution in the horizontal direction and aspect ratio is 4:3, what is the total number of pixels?
8.21   What are advantages of the CRT for a graphics display?
8.22   What are disadvantages of the CRT for airborne displays?
8.23   What do the field emission display and CRT have in common?
8.24   What is a symbol generator?

Chapter 9

Air Data Computers

9.0 All About Air

In one of his comedy routines Bill Cosby was describing his sister. She was a philosophy major and went about asking intellectual questions such as "Why is there air?" Cosby was incredulous. It was obvious to Cosby, an athlete, that air was for blowing up footballs and basketballs. Aviators have an answer in the style of Cosby; "Air is for holding up airplanes". Our question here is not why is there air, because we agree it's to hold up aircraft. We want to ask *what* is air?

A gaseous mixture, air is 80 percent nitrogen and 19 percent oxygen. There are other gasses, notably carbon dioxide at 1.5 percent and small amounts of argon and other inert gasses. Water vapor is also in the air but considered negligible.

Air in the atmosphere, in addition to holding up airplanes, makes weather, delivers water to the soil, protects life from harmful radiation of the sun, holds in heat and delivers life-supporting oxygen. Since air is the medium of aviation travel, the parameters of air masses are carefully measured.

The atmosphere extends from the surface of the earth to about 105,000 feet. It is divided into three regions: troposphere, from the surface to 36,089 feet; stratosphere, from the troposphere to 65,617 feet; and chemosphere, from the stratosphere to 105,000. What's above 105,000 feet and higher? That's space travel.

Altitudes for the boundaries between regions of the atmosphere seem odd. Does something unusual take place at *exactly* 36,089 feet? Not at all; 36,089 feet is 11,000 meters. The altitude 65,617 feet is 20,000 meters. But 105,000 feet is an exact multiple of 1000 feet and not a multiple of 1000 meters. These boundaries are an example of how units can be mixed in aviation.

Units of Measurement. Earlier, we discussed non-standard units in aviation such as nautical miles. During World War II it was recognized that for aviation to succeed there must be worldwide practices and procedures. The United States and England were prominent in the aircraft industry, but were at war with other countries that did not participate in standardization. It was no surprise that ICAO adopted English as the standard language and English units of measurement.

Although non-English speakers may not agree, in the more than 50 years since English was declared the language of aviation, it has served well. The same cannot be said of English units of measurement. Even the English abandoned the system.

One standard of measurement in use over most of the world, with notable exceptions such as the U.S., is the so-called "metric" or International Standard, SI, units. SI units are used in equations and scientific calculations. Generally, converting English units used in aviation to SI is not difficult. There are 3.28 feet in one meter and to convert altitude in feet to meters divide by 3.28. One nautical mile is exactly 1852 meters and a knot is one nautical mile per hour. Thus, nautical miles and knots are "quasi" metric.

For temperature, it is often in Celsius, but there is some use of Fahrenheit. The SI standard unit of temperature is the Kelvin, which is Celsius plus 273.

The fun begins when we consider pressure. Atmospheric pressure is used to set aneroid altimeters with the so-called "baro set". This is usually obtained from the ground via a communications link such as voice radio. Pressure is force per unit area or Newtons per square meter, N/m^2 in SI units. A common unit for atmospheric pressure is "inches of mercury"! It is the height of a column of mercury supported by atmospheric pressure.

The pressure of the atmosphere varies with weather, but average pressure, also called standard pressure, is 29.92 inches of mercury. If this is converted to SI units the result is $101,325\ N/m^2$. One Newton per square meter is also a Pascal in the SI system of units. Standard atmospheric pressure is 101.3 kilo Pascals or 101.3 kPa. A large number would be difficult to transmit via voice radio and a more convenient unit was desired. A unit called a "bar," from "barometric," was defined so that $100,000\ N/m^2$ is one bar. This results in atmospheric pressure at sea level of about 1 bar. Standard sea level pressure is 1.013 bars. Using a decimal point in voice communications is also difficult. What is desired is a whole number with sufficient significant figures to be useful. With millibars, one thousandth of a bar, the result would be atmospheric pressures in whole numbers and four significant figures. Therefore, standard atmospheric pressure at sea level is 1013 millibars.

9.1 Atmospheric Temperature

Dividing the atmosphere into three regions is based on characteristics of each region. The lowest, or troposphere, has a linear relationship between temperature and altitude. Temperature decreases linearly until the altitude which marks the beginning of the stratosphere.

The stratosphere has a nearly constant temperature of 217K or –56C. In the chemosphere, temperature rises with increasing altitude.

Since temperature rises linearly with altitude in the troposphere, we can write a simple equation:

$$T = T_0 - LH \qquad\qquad (9.1)$$

where T is temperature, T_0 is zero altitude temperature, L is lapse rate and H is altitude. This equation can be used for any units as long as constant L matches the units. L is 6.5E-3 K/m. Since the change of temperature in Kelvin is exactly the same as in Celsius, this lapse rate will serve calculations in Kelvin or Celsius. The lapse rate is changed to be used with Fahrenheit temperature.

Example: What is the temperature at an altitude of 25,000 feet when the temperature at sea level is 15 C?

Solution: There is a lapse rate per meter which converts to "per foot" by substituting the equivalent of feet for one meter; thus, the lapse rate, L is:

L = 6.5E-3 K/m = 6.5E-3 K/3.28 ft = 1.98E-3 K/ft

The temperature at 25,000 feet is:

$$T = T_0 - LH = 15 - 1.98E\text{-}3 \; X \; 25E3 = -34.5C$$

Example: What is the temperature at 10,000 meters when temperature at zero altitude is 85 F?

Solution: In this case, altitude is in meters and temperature is in Fahrenheit. We change the lapse rate by substituting for degrees K, nine fifths, 9/5, degrees F:

$$L = 6.5E\text{-}3 \; K/m = (9/5)6.5E\text{-}3 \; F/m = 11.7E\text{-}3 \; F/m$$

The temperature is:

$$T = T_0 - LH = 85 - 11.7E\text{-}3 \; X \; 10,000 = -32 \; F$$

We are not concerned with temperature or other characteristic of the chemosphere because no civil aircraft, and few military aircraft operate in this region.

9.2 Atmospheric Pressure

The atmosphere is held to the earth's surface by gravity. Air is a compressible fluid and its pressure depends on how much air is above the point where pressure is measured. Called static pressure, static implies the measurement is made from a stationary platform. Motion through a fluid causes pressure to vary.

If a fluid is contained in a vessel, pressure anywhere in the vessel depends on the weight of the fluid above the measurement point. If the fluid is incompressible and the vessel not so high that acceleration due to gravity can be considered a constant, pressure is a linear relationship. This is the case for pressure under the sea. In the case of the atmosphere, there are two considerations for calculating pressure. First, air is compressible, and height of the atmosphere is such that gravity cannot be considered a constant. The equation for pressure, in millibars, as a function of altitude in the troposphere is:

$$P_S = 1013(\; 1 - 2.256E\text{-}5 \; H_p)^{5.256} \qquad (9.2)$$

where P_S is the pressure in mb and H_p is the pressure altitude in meters.

To review; pressure altitude is the altitude, MSL, that an altimeter reads if set to the standard sea level atmospheric pressure of 1013 mb. Using pressure altitude in this equation eliminates the effect of ambient atmospheric pressure. Pressure altitude is also used for altitude during high level flight. Rather than state altitude in feet, pressure altitude uses the term "flight level". Flight level is pressure altitude in feet divided by 100. For example, 27,000 feet, pressure altitude, is flight level 270 or FL270. Flight levels are generally not used below 18,000 feet.

In the stratosphere, pressure in millibars, as a function of altitude is:

$$P_S = 226.2 \; \exp(-1.577E\text{-}4(H_p - 11,000))$$

For the troposphere, the relationship between pressure and altitude is the altitude raised to a power. For the stratosphere, pressure is an exponential function of altitude. The 226.3 is the pressure at 11,000 meters, where the troposphere ends and the stratosphere begins, a boundary called the tropopause.

These equations are tested by inserting pressure altitude for the tropopause, 11,000 m and verifying that both arrive at the same pressure. For the troposphere, pressure at 11,000 m is:

$$P_S = 1013(1 - 2.256E\text{-}5\ H_p)^{5.256} = 1013(1 - 2.256E\text{-}5 \times 1.1\ E4)^{5.256} = 226.2$$

This result is exactly that calculated by the equation for pressure as a function of pressure altitude for the stratosphere; the exponent in that equation is zero.

Example: What is the pressure at 10,000 feet pressure altitude?

Solution: The first step is to convert 10,000 feet to meters. (The equations require SI units but the examples use feet because it is the internationally accepted unit of altitude.) The altitude is in the troposphere, so we use the equation for that region.

$$10,000\, ft = 1013(1 - 2.256E\text{-}5 \times 10,000/3.28)^{5.256} = 696.5\ mb$$

9.3 Air Speed

As the name suggests, airspeed is the velocity of the aircraft through the air. If air is moving relative to the ground, speed is the vector sum of aircraft velocity in the air and the vector velocity of the air relative to the ground. In aviation groundspeed is always given in knots as are subsonic airspeeds. Some antique aircraft have airspeed indicators calibrated in miles (statute) per hour, MPH.

There is a definite airspeed known as the sound barrier. Anyone familiar with the story of Chuck Yaeger, first man to break the sound barrier on October 14th 1947, knows that aircraft must be designed and flown for this type of flight. There were incidents of fighter pilots in early aircraft who unwittingly broke the sound barrier during steep dives. Fortunately, they were flying strong aircraft and narrowly escaped the hazards of in-flight breakup.

Jet airplanes are widely flown for their ability to cruise near the speed of sound. And a fast aircraft is worth the investment to many owners. It is desirable to fly as close to the sound barrier as possible, but never exceed it. Why not place a big red line on the airspeed indicator at the speed of sound with a "never exceed" warning? This idea has a major problem; the speed of sound is not constant but a function of temperature.

The speed of sound is given by:

$$V_S = 20\ (T)^{1/2} \tag{9.3}$$

where V_S is the speed of sound in m/s and T is the temperature in K.

Example: What is the speed of sound in the stratosphere?

Solution: The temperature of the stratosphere is –57C or 216 K. Therefore:

$$V_S = 20\ (T)^{1/2} = V_S = 20\ (216)^{1/2} = 294\ m/s$$

A measure of airspeed in high-performance aircraft is called mach number, an airspeed relative to the local speed of sound. The word "local" indicates the location of the aircraft while flying, not on the ground or under laboratory conditions. Because the speed of sound is a function of temperature, the value may be different at other locations. Mach number, M is:

$$M = V_T/V_S \qquad (9.4)$$

where V_T is the true airspeed which is derived from the indicated airspeed and correction factors.

Example: An aircraft is flying at an assigned altitude of 15,000 feet MSL. The temperature at sea level is 24C and the true airspeed is 525 knots. What mach number is this aircraft flying?

Solution: The first chore is to convert all of the non SI units to the correct SI.

525 knots = 270 m/s
15,000 feet = 4573 m
24C = 297K

The next item to handle is to find the temperature at the altitude in order to find the speed of sound.

$$T = T_0 - LH = 297 - 6.5E\text{-}3 \; X \; 4573 = 267 \; K$$

Knowing temperature, calculate the speed of sound

$$V_S = 20 \, (T)^{1/2} = 20 \, (267)^{1/2} = 327 \; m/s$$

Finally, calculate mach number

$$M = V_T/V_S = 270 \, / \, 327 = 0.83 \; mach$$

Next, consider airspeed. If an open end of a pipe is placed in the air stream, the motion of the aircraft forces air molecules into it. This will increase air pressure in the pipe above normal atmospheric pressure. Placing the open end of a pipe on the side of the fuselage would have the air stream passing across the opening and not increase ambient pressure. Air that does not increase pressure due to moving air is called static pressure. Pressure due to air forced down the open end of the tube due to aircraft movement is called total pressure. The difference of them is used to calculate airspeed.

The ratio of total pressure, P_T and static pressure, P_S is

$$P_T/P_S = (\, 1 + 0.2 \; M^2 \,)^{3.5} \qquad (9.5)$$

9.4 Temperature

If the bulb of a thermometer is pushed through a hole in the fuselage it would read air temperature outside the aircraft. When the aircraft is moving, temperature tends to rise due to the kinetic energy of air molecules striking the probe. Temperature rise at high velocities, that is above mach 1, due to air friction can be significant. It is the temperature rise of air that causes meteors to burn up in the atmosphere and the reason ceramic tiles are attached to the bottom of the Space Shuttle. The temperature read by the thermometer in the air stream is called "total outside air temperature," or TOAT. If the thermometer bulb is shielded from the air stream, the temperature would not include effects of the kinetic energy of air molecules and would read the "outside air temperature," or OAT.

Temperature measurement is important for warnings of ice. The amount of moisture is also a factor. When water evaporates, there is a reduction in temperature and possibility of icing when air temperature drops near 0 C. The TOAT (total outside air temperature) probe registers the effects of evaporating water and is a more accurate factor in airframe or propellor icing.

9.5 Sensors

Early aircraft had altitude, temperature and air speed indicators as dedicated mechanical instruments. If there was a pilot and copilot, each had an airspeed indicator and altimeter but the systems were totally redundant. This was a safety enhancement but involved twice the equipment and the annoying situation of two indicators showing different values.

For later aircraft, airspeed, temperature, altitude and mach are required for several systems. We noted the need, for example, of pressure altitude for the radar transponder, and "real" altitude for the altimeter, which includes the baro set. For high altitude flight, pressure altitude is also used. In high velocity flight, mach number becomes the reference. When a fast aircraft slows for approach and landing, the crew reverts to conventional airspeed. Large, modern aircraft use an air data computer (ADC) that converts pressure and temperature to electrical signals. The processed signals are sent to indicators, typically electronic, and to the automatic flight control system.

The ADC takes signals from different points around the aircraft, processes them and distributes data to indicators and other systems. This places the ADC central to sensors and indicators, giving rise to the "central ADC", or CADC.

ADC has been around for a long time and older models include many mechanical parts. Their computers calculated air parameters using mechanical devices. The modern ADC converts pressure and temperature to electrical signals and calculates them electronically.

The relationship between a desired air data parameter and the input is not a simple one. Mechanical instruments display air data with levers, cams and non-linear springs. The non-linear spring is where the stiffness of the spring is adjusted by advancing set screws to create a piece-wise linear approximation to a complex function. These instruments had to be hand calibrated with complex test equipment and highly skilled technicians. The result was a heavy, fragile and expensive instrument. Now, sensors can digitize the output and compute a parameter with high accuracy, reliability and low cost.

Once air data is calculated, the information is communicated to onboard systems such as the transponder, TCAS and autopilot. An EFIS system can display all parameters such as mach, true airspeed, pressure altitude, etc. The major sensor for ADC is pressure, both static and pitot. This is the basis for altitude, airspeed, mach, rate of climb and others. Temperature is the other parameter. Between the two, all necessary data can be calculated.

Virtually every pressure sensor involves partially evacuated container walls that deform from differential pressure between outside and inside. The most common shape of this container is a cylinder, where the flat ends deform. Often, one end is stiff while the other end operates as a diaphragm. The key to using this evacuated chamber is to sense the amount of deformation of the diaphragm.

Expansion is one method of measuring deformation and this was done on old mechanical instruments. For this to succeed, the diaphragm must be capable of considerable motion. In old mechanical altimeters the partially evacuated chamber allowed both ends to deform and had corrugated diaphragms for both. The capsule had to expand as much as practical because the altimeter turns the indicator ten times for a 0 to 10,000 feet change in altitude.

As crude as it sounds, the mechanical altimeter was one of the first digital air data sensors. An encoding disk attached to the altimeter provides a digital output for the transponder. Called the Gilham, or gray, code, it is positioned before the baro set so digitized altitude is pressure altitude. Generally, pressure altitude in the gray code was used only for the transponder. However, enterprising engineers developed a simple device called an "altitude alerter," which is a simple device to warn

348

the crew when an aircraft reaches a preset altitude or strays from a desired altitude. For example, if an aircraft is to climb to a predetermined altitude, the altitude alerter is set to the assigned altitude; when it ascends, say, within 200 feet of that altitude, an alert sounds. This is one example of air data used for a number of systems.

There should not be much expansion of the pressure capsule in an altimeter to avoid non-linearity and fatigue. In an electronic sensor it is not necessary to turn an indicator pointer and a large deformation is not required. Therefore, it is necessary to sense a small deflection.

There are several methods for detecting small mechanical deflections. Two diaphragms can form plates of a capacitor, as shown in Fig. 9.1. The capacitor is measured or inserted in a resonant circuit which controls the frequency of an oscillator. For this method to be effective, the change in capacitance should be a significant part of the total capacitance. This requires that spacing between capacitor plates be as close as practical. If the plates touch, the use of diaphragms as a pressure sensor is lost. What is the highest pressure the altimeter will see? This would occur at the lowest place on earth with the highest meteorological pressure. A safe number is –3000 feet pressure altitude. To understand the importance of close spacing in capacitor plates, let us work two exercises.

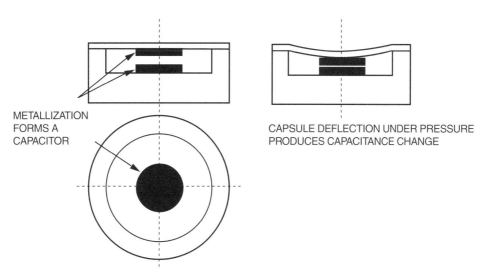

Figure 9.1   Capacitive pressure sensor

Exercise: How much will the capacitance change of a pressure transducer if, at –3000 feet pressure altitude, the separation of the plates is 0.5 mm and total deflection from –3000 feet to 50,000 feet is 1 mm?

Solution: The capacitance of parallel plates is inversely proportional to the distance separating them. Thus capacitance varies as the ratio of maximum separation to minimum separation or:

$$\Delta C = X_{max} / X_{min} = 1.5 / 0.5 = 3$$

Exercise: How much will the capacitance change of a pressure transducer if at –3000 feet pressure altitude the separation of the capacitor plates is 5 mm and the total deflection from –3000 feet to 50,000 feet is 1 mm?

Solution: $\Delta C = X_{max} / X_{min} = 6 / 5 = 1.2$

As we can see, the change of capacitance is much greater when separation is reduced. It would appear that closest separation is best for a capacitive pressure sensor. However, as with many physical devices, with the good comes the bad. If we permit separation to become microscopic to achieve maximum capacitance change, there is also greatest sensitivity to temperature variations. Whatever the material, it expands and contracts with temperature. If we know the temperature and expansion and contraction as a function of temperature, corrections can made in the ADC. But if expansion causes the capacitor plates to touch, the sensor fails. Consequently, there is a compromise between minimum separation and material with a low coefficient of thermal expansion. A major problem with this sensor is that diaphragms are sensitive to vibration---they become microphones! A recurring problem in electronics, it's called "microphonics".

Besides low thermal expansion, it is important that the pressure sensor not leak air; the material should be hermetic. Most metals and glass meet the leakage criteria and the challenges are the seals where pieces of the capsule connect and wires enter . Fortunately, hermetically-sealed packaging has been a requirement for electronic equipment for many years and the technology is highly advanced. .

There are two methods of converting capacitance to an electrical signal in the ADC. The first is to use the capacitor in an oscillator. This is effective because counting frequency is a simple operation and done with great accuracy. The oscillator, however, must be stable so frequency change of is a function of capacitance, not temperature instability in other oscillator circuits. To gain an appreciation of the problem, assume the sensor in the previous example as the sole capacitor in the oscillator.

Exercise: How much would the frequency of an oscillator change if a pressure sensor with a separation at –3000 feet of 0.5 mm and a separation of 1.5 mm at 30,000? The capacitance of the pressure sensor is the sole resonating capacitor for the tuned circuit.

Solution: The capacitance ratio of the sensor is 3:1. The frequency of the oscillator, when the sensor is the sole capacitor, is inversely proportional to the square root of the capacitance. Thus, the oscillator frequency would vary by $(3)^{1/2} = 1.732$.

Accuracy of an altimeter should be better than 50 feet. For an altimeter that covers –3000 to 50,000 feet, 50 feet is one part in little more than a thousand. Designing an oscillator with a stability of less than one part in a thousand is reasonably easy. Designing a frequency measuring system that can resolve one part in a thousand is also not difficult.

One advantage of an oscillator with the capacitive transducer is that microphonics cause the frequency of the oscillator to increase *and* decrease. Average frequency, however, is not seriously affected. The relationship between oscillator frequency and pressure is not linear so linearizing is applied.

Another method of measuring the small mechanical deflection of the diaphragm is the strain gauge. One technique attaches four strain gauges, as shown in Fig. 9.2. When the diaphragm deforms with pressure, it stretches toward the center. This causes strain along any radius from the center of the diaphragm to the edge.

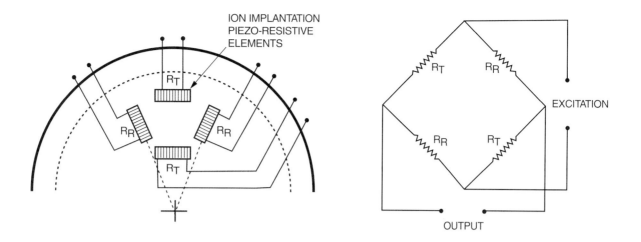

Figure 9.2 Strain gauge pressure transducer

Strain gauges on radius increase resistance when the diaphragm is subject to higher pressure, while strain gauges perpendicular to the radius decrease in resistance. To measure pressure, the strain gauges are connected in a Wheatstone bridge and error voltage measured. Again, the relationship between error voltage and pressure is not linear and linearization is performed. The bridge is excited from a DC source so its output can be low-pass filtered to eliminate microphonics.

Another required sensor is for temperature. There are three basic devices; resistive, semiconductor and thermocouple. The thermocouple is reliable and accurate over a broad range of temperature, but it does not have the sensitivity of other sensors. Output voltage is low, in the millivolt region. The major advantage is high temperature capability, especially for measuring exhaust gas temperature. The thermocouple is not used for air data application.

The semiconductor sensor measures voltage across a semiconductor junction, which is forward biased with constant current. A major drawback is operation at very low temperature. The semiconductor junction itself provides an output to determine temperature, while other electronics provide the constant current source and can amplify junction voltage.

The final sensor is the resistive thermal device, or RTD, often called a thermistor. This is a resistor that changes resistance with temperature. The common method of reading the resistance is to apply a constant current and measure the resulting voltage. The RTD operates over the full range of temperatures required. Unlike the thermocouple, output voltages can be high, on the order of a few volts, which helps prevent noise problems.

9.6 Pitot and Static Systems

A tube in the air stream measures the speed of the aircraft through the air. Called a pitot tube, the sensor is shown in Fig. 9.4. Care is taken to avoid mounting the tube in turbulent air from the airframe which would cause errors in total air pressure. A typical location is on the leading edge of a wing, away from the fuselage and propeller wash. In large multiengine aircraft it is most often mounted on the side of the fuselage, several feet back from the nose.

We can't simply stick a tube in the air stream without encountering problems. One is water; it shouldn't enter the pressure sensors and cause damage. Water can also block the tube and cause serious pressure errors. Unfortunately, the atmosphere is full of water, not only as vapor, but liquid and solid in the form of rain, snow and hail. A drain is provided for water to escape the pitot tube. This hole is considerably smaller than the diameter of the pitot tube so it will not cause errors in pressure measurements.

Another problem is ice. Because the pitot tube is in the air stream, temperature does not need to be below freezing to form ice; evaporating water lowers the temperature further. The solution is to heat the tube. Heated air, however, may introduce an error because pressure of a gas is a function of temperature. It is important to heat the tube only where icing is most likely. In light aircraft, the pilot is instructed to turn on the pitot heat whenever the aircraft enters visible moisture, such as a cloud, and outside air temperature is near freezing. Airliners, however, often have their pitot heaters on continuously, even when on the ground, because icing and loss of air data can cause an accident soon after takeoff. The ADC in large aircraft compensates for errors due to heating in the probe.

Static pressure is sensed with a port, a hole usually in the side of the fuselage. Like the pitot tube, the static port requires a drain hole for purging water and a heater to prevent freezing. One arrangement is a common static and pitot port on a single probe. Static holes are provided on the side of the pitot probe. A common drain and heater may be used.

Even after every precaution, the pitot system can get plugged up. It is commonly caused by bugs. The pitot tube should be covered after flight so insects do not take up residence, but airplanes also collide with them in the air, as well as with birds. A plugged-up pitot tube is not rare. Most aircraft except small GA airplanes have dual systems, which include ports, piping and sensors.

9.7 Angle of Attack Indicator

The angle between the vector indicating motion of the aircraft through the air and the chord of the wing is angle of attack. The wing chord is a line drawn through the vertex of the trailing edge to the center of the leading edge. When an aircraft flies straight and level, the angle of attack is a small positive angle of a few degrees. When climbing, angle of attack increases. When an aircraft descends at low air speed, angle of attack increases. These assumptions may not hold for high performance aircraft such as military fighters. Because of other considerations, such as engine power, some can fly straight up on takeoff; so the normal concept of angle of attack does not apply.

Fig. 9.3 Angle of attack sensors are usually mounted on the side of the fuselage. Three models are shown. (Gull)

Not all aircraft display angle of attack but it plays a role in aircraft performance. The ability of a wing to produce lift is a function of angle of attack. When it increases sufficiently, the airplane ceases to fly and begins to fall. The warning for this dangerous maneuver is generated by the angle of attack indicator.

Other information from angle of attack assures accuracy of the pitot system. Maximum pressure is developed when the pitot probe is parallel to the motion of the aircraft through the air. When angle of attack increases or decreases, pitot pressure decreases, which reduces the airspeed indication. Knowing angle of attack, the air data computer provides corrections for pitot pressure

The angle of attack sensor is a vane, much like a weather vane for wind direction, as shown in Fig. 9.3. It is mounted so the vane rotates around a horizontal axis. It aligns with the relative wind, in this case, relative to the chord line of the wing. The shaft angle is transmitted to the ADC by a synchro, the classic method. It also may be done with a shaft encoder that digitizes the angle and transmits it through a data bus to a computer. Like the pitot tube, the angle of attack sensor is heated to prevent ice build up

9.8 Air Data Computer System

We have described sensors for measuring pressure, temperature and angle of attack. They derive quantities for direct display or other calculations. Shown in Fig. 9.4 are inputs and where they are used.

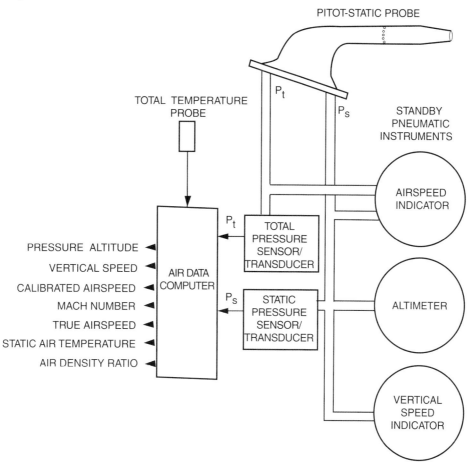

Fig 9.4 Air Data Computer (ADC) system

When an aircraft has an electronic ADC, sensors provide inputs for calculating parameters. The ADC generates outputs which drive indicators that may appear much like old mechanical types. To the flight crew there is no difference in appearance in the instrument that provides a parameter directly, or one that is driven from the ADC. What is different, and not immediately evident, is that the computer-generated instrument is more accurate and stable. When an aircraft has EFIS (electronic flight instrument system), the ADC is the sole source of air data for the display. Air data is also supplied to engine controllers. To obtain maximum power and efficiency from a turbine engine atmospheric pressure, airspeed and temperature are important. FADEC (full authority digital engine control) relies heavily on air data.

Air data ramp tester. Technicians connect pitot and static lines to aircraft to simulate airspeed and altitude. This verifies accuracy of instruments aboard aircraft. (Kollsman)

Shown below are inputs, calculations and systems, which receive data for an ADC. The first section shows calculations for a simple indicator. The second section shows data provided other systems that use data for additional calculations and control.

Sensor	Used to Calculate	With	Displayed As	On
Static Pressure	Altitude	Baro Set	Altitude, MSL	Altimeter
Static Pressure	Pressure Altitude	Nothing	Altitude	Altimeter
Static Pressure	Flight Level	Nothing	Flight Level	Altimeter
Static Pressure	Vertical Speed	Nothing	Vertical Speed	Vert. Speed Indicator
Total Pressure	True Air Speed	Static Pressure	Air Speed	Air Speed Indicator
		Angle of attack		
Total Pressure	Mach	OAT	Mach	Mach Meter
		Angle of attack		
Total OAT	OAT	True Airspeed	OAT	OAT Indicator
Angle of Attack	Angle of Attack	Nothing	Stall warning	Stall warning horn

Calculated Parameter	Used with
Pressure Altitude	Transponder, TCAS, Altimeter, Altitude Alerter, Auto Pilot, FADEC
Altitude	Altimeter, Autopilot, FADEC
True Airspeed	Airspeed Indicator, Autopilot, FADEC
Mach	Mach Meter, Auto Pilot, FADEC
Vertical Speed	Vertical Speed Indicator, Instantaneous Vertical Speed Indicator, TCAS, Autopilot, FADEC

Old ADCs have mechanical components, mostly the sensors. As an example, the altimeter pressure capsule is contained in the air data computer. This is undesirable because the ADC has hose and pipe connections. These pressure inputs are open to the outside world, which introduces one of the greatest enemies of aircraft, water. Any static system with piping more than a few centimeters long has drains to release water that could contaminate the system. If the ADC had no pipes, the problem would be eliminated and the unit can have quick-disconnect fittings for replacement. Data to and from the ADC is better handled through such databuses as ARINC 429 or 629

Chapter 9 Review Questions

9.1   If the temperature at sea level is 10C what is the temperature at 10,000 feet?

9.2   What are the three divisions of the atmosphere?

9.3   What characteristics do the three divisions of the atmosphere exhibit?

9.4   What is pressure altitude?

9.5   If sea level barometric pressure is 1000 mb what is absolute pressure at 8000 feet?

9.6   What is the speed of sound at 0C?

9.7   If an aircraft is flying at 230 kts true airspeed, and temperature of the air is 15C, what is aircraft speed in mach number?

9.8   What is the difference between total outside air temperature, TOAT, and outside air temperature, OAT?

9.9   What techniques are used to measure pressure?

9.10   What technique is used to measure airspeed?

9.11   What is a static system?

9.12   Why must a pitot tube be heated?

9.13   What is angle of attack?

9.14   What devices measure air temperature?

Chapter 10

Flight Control Systems

10.0 Introduction

One enhancement of avionics is to reduce tedium in the cockpit. Long hours of flying, staying on course and maintaining altitude are fatiguing to the crew. Near the end of a long flight the crew may not have a high level of situational awareness, just when it's needed most. Because automatic flight control has long been valued for air safety, it is installed on most aircraft engaged in long range flight. Small GA aircraft often have autopilots to reduce the workload in single-pilot flight. In commercial operations that allow a crew of one, an autopilot is often required, especially for instrument flight rules (IFR).

These systems, developed for ships before being applied in aircraft, were called "autopilots" and the name survives today. As they became more sophisticated than simple steering, they acquired such names as AFCS, for automatic flight control system, or simply FCS for flight control system.

In addition to easing crew workload, the FCS increases accuracy of flight because it can control an aircraft with greater precision than a human operator. In fact, some CAT III landings must be performed with an FCS because there is not yet adequate guidance on the instrument panel for touchdown and roll out. (There are exceptions to the FCS rule for CAT III (a) landings using a head up display, HUD.)

Autopilots are categorized by the number of axes they control. The simplest is one-axis which controls roll (through the ailerons). This simple FCS in light aircraft is often called a "wing leveler" because it relieves the pilot during long legs. Many wing levelers can also hold a compass heading and track a radio course.

The next level is two-axis FCS, which controls the roll and yaw (rudder) axes. This can not only keep wings level but control the direction of flight. This type of FCS can become sophisticated particularly in the ability to be coupled to navigation equipment. This type of FCS can be found on small aircraft up to relatively large business aircraft including jets.

The next level is three axes. This system keeps wings level, holds a course and maintains an altitude or rate of climb or descent. Climbing and descending usually involve pitch changes to move the nose up or down, as controlled by the elevator. In simple systems, pitch mainly serves to hold steady altitude. It should be noted that raising the nose will not sustain an airplane in a climb unless there is sufficient engine power. However, for minor adjustments needed for altitude hold, pitch alone is adequate. When a flight control system combines roll and pitch, it's called a "two-axis" autopilot. The third autopilot axis is yaw, referring to nose left/nose right, as controlled by the rudder.

There is some confusion in classifying autopilots in light aircraft. Many pilots say "3-axis autopilot" to mean roll, heading and altitude. Roll and heading are both functions of the roll axis. Roll can turn an aircraft to a heading by coupling compass information from another source. Note that in most light aircraft autopilot systems, rudder is not used in turning. Because the turns are gentle, roll alone is sufficient for the maneuver.

A higher level of flight control involves all three axes and adds engine power. The added control is called "autothrottle". Generally, only air transport aircraft enhance their flight control with autothrottle.

The most advanced control system is autoland. It includes all three axes, throttle control, the ability to flare, straighten the nose (decrab) and transition for roll out. Typical aircraft with autoland are widebody airliners.

10.1 Control Systems

The FCS requires inputs, a method of control and feedback to compare the present situation to the inputs. Assume an aircraft is to follow a VOR radial. The input is clear; the omnibearing selector, or OBS. By rolling and yawing the aircraft it will turn and fly to the desired radial. Motors attached to control surfaces respond to the flight control system and turn the aircraft. Finally, the airplane's situation needs to be compared with the desired result. In this case, how far off the airplane is from the selected radial needs to be known.. The course deviation indicator, CDI, provides this information.

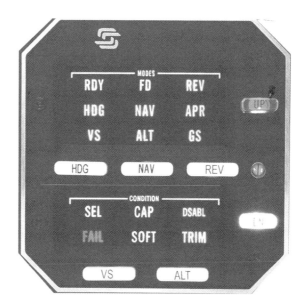

Autopilot Controller (S-Tec)

Consider, first, the simple wing leveler. To keep the wings of a small aircraft level, a reference is required, such as looking out at the horizon and rotating the yoke or pushing the stick left and right. Looking at the horizon is fine in good weather but an electrical signal is needed by the FCS for roll angle. The artificial horizon is controlled by a vertical gyro which can supply the reference signal. To operate the ailerons, an electric motor connects to the aileron control cable. The FCS is shown in Fig. 10.1.

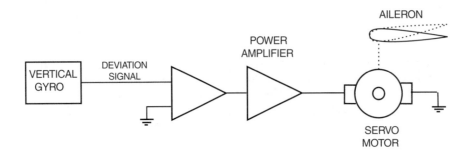

Fig 10.1 Single axis flight control system

How much power is required from the motor? The error signal is amplified so the motor strongly pushes the aircraft back to wings level after a gust. The restoring maneuver could cause the aircraft to overshoot the vertical and lean to the other side, whereupon the process is repeated. As in the example of intercepting the VOR radial, the back and forth action causes instability. The answer could be a smaller motor or less gain to reduce the powerful restoring action. This is a step in the right direction.

Consider what could happen with a smaller motor. If a gust lifts one wing, the motor cannot push the yoke to the other side and cause oscillations. In fact, if the motor is too small, it may not counteract the gust and the aircraft does not return to level flight. It is possible the aircraft will fly, leaning to one side or another. The control system is said to have a steady state error when there is no return to the vertical.

What if a powerful motor is used and limited in its ability to make the rapid motion that causes oscillations, but not restrict the motor from correcting steady state error? If the motor did not have the torque to overcome the restoring forces, it could not fully correct the aircraft. There will be a steady state error, even without a gust.

What is needed is a motor sufficiently powerful to overcome the restoring forces of the wind, and a bit more to counteract wind gusts. This can be done by limiting the rate at which the motor can turn, so overshoot is reduced. The inertia of the aircraft and natural restoring forces counteract the tendency of the aircraft to maneuver rapidly and overshoot.

The mention of restoring forces infers that an aircraft returns to stable flight. Most aircraft have inherent stability; if flown with hands or feet off the yoke or rudder pedals, the aircraft tries to fly straight and level. The FCS, therefore, would not have to provide significant effort. This is generally the case and a stable aircraft needs only small nudging to fly straight and level.

Some aircraft are designed to be unstable. Air transport aircraft fly straight and level most of the time and maneuvers are usually shallow turns, climbs and descents. A military fighter, on the other hand, survives on maneuverability. A fighter is designed to have a propensity to turn if prodded to do so. Rather than return to straight and level, the fighter will rise, descend and turn at the slightest provocation. The difficulty is that an unstable airplane may be virtually impossible for a human to fly. An FCS is required at times to control an aircraft of such high maneuverability and instability.

In a stable aircraft, most FCS systems are used only when the aircraft is flown by the autopilot. In helicopters, which are unstable and difficult to hand-fly while looking only at instruments, there are "stability augmentation systems" (SAS). It a flight control system which allows the pilot to fly manually but prevents him from getting into dangerous attitudes.

Returning to the basic flight control, a filter is placed between the error voltage and motor amplifier. Filter parameters are adjusted so the dynamics of the aircraft and FCS create a stable system. This filter must match the aircraft on which the FCS is installed.

10.2 Servo Motors

The units that control ailerons, horizontal stabilizer and rudder are called servo motors. They are a class of devices that include synchros and resolvers. Servos for the FCS have important characteristics; they will not jam or cause other parts to become entangled in the motor. If an FCS fails, the aircraft returns to manual control. In light aircraft, control surfaces are directly connected via mechanical devices such as cables and push-pull tubes to the yoke. Servo motors are connected to the control system by clutches so when the FCS is engaged, servo motors pull or push tubes or cables controlling the aircraft. If the clutch fails to disconnect, the pilot can still overcome the drag of the motors connected to the controls. It is also important that cables to servo motors do not slip off pulleys and become entangled in the motor. The drag of pulleys when the FCS is disconnected must not cause excessive drag on control cables.

In many large aircraft, control surfaces are moved with motors. A pilot does not have the strength to move control surfaces in some aircraft and, like power steering in an automobile, the controls are "servo assisted".

In the most advanced aircraft, where control surfaces are manipulated by a simple wrist action controller called a side stick, surfaces are moved only by servo, with no mechanical connection to the controller. This is "fly by wire," where signals from the side stick are transmitted to a computer which adjusts the control surfaces. In the largest aircraft with conventional servo-assist controls, the system is, essentially, fly by wire. The difference between fly by wire and servo assist is that fly by wire uses digital data and control surface positions are determined by a computer. Conventional servo assist typically uses analog signals and does not involve a computer. Servo assist, even in the largest aircraft, is a simple feedback control system. The important point in servo-assisted control systems is that there are motors already in place. When an aircraft is to be controlled by an FCS, new motors do not need to be installed; they are already there for the servo assist system. All that needs to be done is drive the servo assist motors from the FCS, rather than from the yoke or side stick controller.

10.3 Flight Control System Modes

The FCS can perform several modes beside intercepting a VOR radial or leveling wings. The most fundamental is heading hold mode; whatever the heading of the aircraft when the FCS is engaged, the aircraft will hold it. The only input is the DG (directional gyro), but a means of remembering what the DG was when the FCS is engaged is required. In this age of digital electronics, "remembering" a parameter is trivial. However, even though the digital FCS is increasing in aircraft, most FCSs flying are analog.

The input from the DG to the FCS is a synchro, as shown in Fig. 10.2. The FCS takes this input and "servos" another synchro to follow the DG. This is what is done in the remote DG, HSI and RMI. The difference is that when the FCS is engaged, the motor that turns the servoed synchro is disabled so the synchro can no longer turn. The position of the synchro is exactly the position of the DG when the FCS was engaged. Also, error voltage from the synchro, used to turn the servo motor that kept the synchro aligned to the DG, is now the error voltage for the FCS.

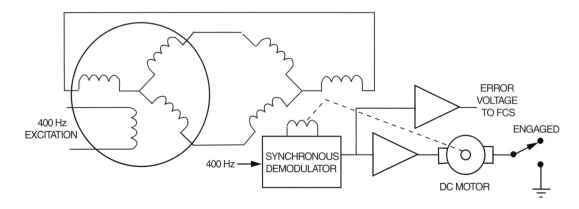

Fig 10.2   Input circuit to Flight Control System (FCS) from Directional Gyro (DG)

To summarize, when the FCS is disengaged, a servo motor causes the heading synchro in the FCS to track the DG. When the FCS is engaged, it turns the aircraft to keep the DG at the same heading as the heading synchro in the FCS computer, which is stopped at the heading just before the FCS was engaged.

Another mode of operation is altitude hold. This operates in similar fashion except the last altitude is held when the FCS is engaged. Altitude is usually in digital form because it's required for the transponder. This is pressure altitude, which has no effect on the altitude hold mode of the FCS; altitude is held regardless of its form in the aircraft. The altitude hold mode controls the pitch axis of the aircraft.

Another example of a hold mode is mach hold. This requires data from the mach meter, which is available from the air data computer. To control the mach number of an aircraft, the throttles also have to be controlled.

Deviation from the last heading in the heading hold mode is available from the turn knob on the FCS control panel. This control causes a constant rate of turn as set by the knob. The feedback for controlling a constant rate turn is from the rate gyro or by differentiating the DG. A similar knob is used on the pitch axis, which is the climb and descend knob.

10.4 FCS Control Panel

An example of an FCS control panel is shown in Fig. 10.3. The panel is often referred to as the mode selector. An important function is engaging the FCS. Most aircraft have disengage switches on the captain's and first officer's yoke. Usually, the engage switch is magnetically held. When the switch is pushed to engage the FCS, if all systems are in a valid state, an electromagnet holds the switch in the engaged position.

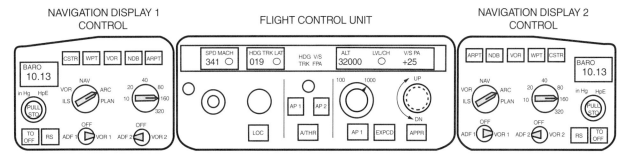

Figure 10.3. Flight Control System (FCS) panel

There are situations when the FCS refuses to engage, where the switch returns to the disengaged position. There are reasons that do not represent a failure. One is if the FCS is in the radio navigation mode and the VOR signal is too weak to remove the NAV flag. It can happen for any navigation signal, such the localizer, glide slope or GPS.

If the FCS is disconnected, the holding magnets are de-energized and FCS switches go to the down position, usually with a resounding "thud" that can be seen and heard. The FCS also causes an audible alarm to alert the crew that the aircraft is no longer on automatic control.

In addition to the engage switch, the control panel contains the selector for choosing such modes as heading hold, altitude hold, VOR, GPS, ILS or mach hold. Many modes can operate at the same time. As an example, heading hold, altitude hold and mach hold can be activated together. This is because heading hold involves the yaw axis of the FCS while altitude hold mode involves the pitch axis. Also, altitude hold can be used with the VOR mode. Using the VOR mode is also referred to as "coupling" the FCS to the VOR.

10.5 Aircraft Dynamics

There are a number of forces operating on an aircraft and as many resisting forces. Lift is provided by the wing and overcomes gravity. Drag is a byproduct of lift and is overcome by thrust of the power plant. A wing produces lift by causing a differential in air pressure between its top and bottom surface. The angle of attack is between the relative wind and a straight line drawn from the center of the leading edge and the center of the trailing edge.

Increasing angle of attack increases lift and drag to a point. There is an angle at which lift drops off quickly and drag increases rapidly. At this angle an aircraft stalls and begins to fall.

An aircraft has six degrees of freedom. This refers to the basic three dimensions of space and three to describe rotation around the same three dimensions. Translation in three axes is the ability to go up and down, left and right and forward or back. Rotation around the vertical axis, the "up/down" part of translation is called yaw. Rotation around the "left/right" axis is called pitch and rotation around the "forward/back" axis is roll.

When an aircraft flies straight and level, the sum of the moments about a point is equal to zero. The point around which moments are summed can be located anywhere; it serves only as a reference. Two points that play an important role in the summation of moments are the center of gravity and center of lift.

The center of gravity is found by suspending the aircraft at a point that would cause perfect balance. Lack of rotation about the point of support implies that the sum of the moments around the point from each part of the aircraft is zero, which is the definition of center of gravity.

Another point is the center of lift. The definition is similar to the center of gravity except all moments due to lift of the wing and any other surface is zero. The tail provides lift, which can be negative, that is, pushing the tail down rather than up. The value of center of lift and center of gravity is seen by considering how lift and gravity are applied, as shown in Fig 10.4.

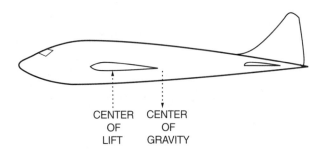

CENTER CENTER
OF OF
LIFT GRAVITY

Fig 10.4 Center of lift and center of gravity

For the aircraft to remain aloft, lift must equal weight. If the center of gravity is ahead of the center of lift, the upward lift, along with downward force pitches the nose downward. This is overcome by a downward force on the elevator of the aircraft. The downward force works against lift of the wing but is much smaller.

If the center of lift is behind the center of gravity, the aircraft tends to pitch downward and a negative force is required from the elevator. Both center of gravity and center of lift can vary due to passengers, fuel and cargo. The center of lift is a function of the angle of attack, airspeed and position of wing flaps.

To account for changes in the location of centers of lift and gravity and the amount of lift provided by the wing, lift provided by the elevator is adjustable. This is the purpose of the elevator in causing pitching action. The elevator, part of the horizontal stabilizer, is connected to the yoke to provide pitch control.

In operation, the neutral position of the elevator is adjusted so the aircraft flies level. The position can also be adjusted for a specific rate of climb or descent. What happens if an aircraft adjusted for straight and level is buffeted by a gust? If the aircraft is stable, after the gust passes, the forces restore straight and level flight. Let's investigate lift to understand how the aircraft can be designed for stability.

The first item is lift generated by a wing. It results from compression of air passing under the surface of the wing and an expansion of air passing above it. The shape of the wing provides a longer path over the top than the bottom. This implies the same amount of air passes over the top of the wing as below it, which causes the same air mass to be spread out over a longer path and results in lower air pressure.

The centerline of the wing is tilted up at a small angle relative to the motion of the wing through the air mass as shown in Fig. 10.5. The collision of air against of the bottom surface of the wing generates a force with an upward component. This adds to lift. If the angle between the wing centerline (chord) and relative wind, called angle of attack, is increased, lift increases. This is because of a greater upward force due to the collision of air. Further increasing angle of attack increases lift until the flow over the top of the wing pulls away. Once lower pressure air pulls away from the top surface of the wing, it is replaced with air at atmospheric pressure, which significantly and suddenly reduces lift. This is the stall condition and the wing no longer produces lift to support the aircraft. A typical lift versus angle of attack plot is shown in Fig. 10.6.

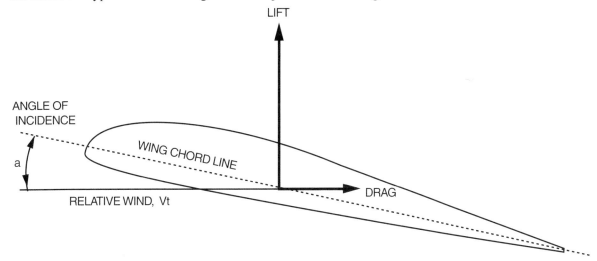

Figure 10.5 Cross section of an aircraft wing

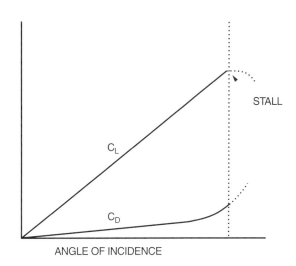

Figure 10.6 Lift of wing as a function of angle of attack

Assume an aircraft that has a center of lift behind the center of gravity. This causes pitching down if it weren't for the elevator. In this case there is downward force on the elevator to counteract the tendency to pitch down. The horizontal stabilizer is a wing and the amount of lift is a function of the angle of attack.

Next, consider a gust that pitches the aircraft up. This increases the angle of attack of the horizontal stabilizer, which increases drag and lift. The increase causes a counterclockwise rotation of the aircraft and tendency to restore straight and level flight.

Consider a gust pitching the aircraft down. In this case, the angle of attack of the elevator decreases, reducing lift and rotating the aircraft clockwise. This tends to restore straight and level flight. If the aircraft is trimmed for a rate of climb or descent, after displacement by a gust the aircraft returns to the trimmed rate of climb or descent.

Now, for the case of lift ahead of the center of gravity. When the aircraft pitches from a gust, increased angle of attack increases lift of the wing. This added lift, however, causes the aircraft to pitch up more. This continues until the wing stalls. When a gust causes a down pitch, the lift of the wing decreases and adds to the down pitching motion. This arrangement of center of lift ahead of center of gravity causes instability. When loading an aircraft , it is extremely important not to move the center of gravity behind the center of lift; the pilot might run out of control and be unable to recover.

In an unstable aircraft a gust causes an immediate and severe up or down pitch. If the pilot reacts quickly, the pitch might be overcome with flight controls. But it could be virtually impossible to fly an unstable aircraft because the slightest provocation may cause it to pitch violently. There is also the probability the aircraft may pitch into a deep dive or stall before the pilot can regain control.

The same discussion applies to roll and yaw. Actions affecting stability are complex, particularly for roll and yaw stability. In the discussion of pitch stability, not considered were the contributions of lift and drag from fuselage, engine nacelles, thrust , altitude, airspeed and temperature. To make the situation more difficult, some of these relationships are not linear.

There are times when a high degree of stability is not desirable. This is true for an aerobatic aircraft or military fighter. Stability is the tendency of an aircraft to return to its trimmed position. A stable aircraft resists being diverted from a trimmed flight path.

Even a stable aircraft can have instability, but not the type that causes stalling and other violent results. Consider what happens when the pitch of an aircraft changes. If yoke or sidestick moves, the pitch change is not immediate because of the moment of inertia of the aircraft. Response time is faster for less stable aircraft and slower for stable aircraft. Fig. 10.7 shows the position of the yoke or controller and the resulting pitch of the aircraft.

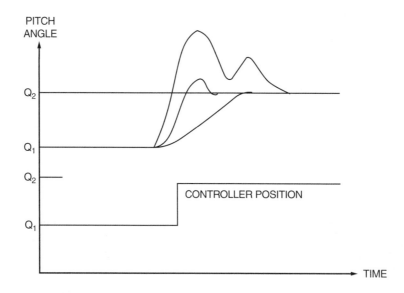

Fig. 10.7 Aircraft response to pitch changes from yoke or sidestick controller

Notice that pitch lags behind controller position, caused by inertia of the aircraft. There is also a small overshoot when the aircraft reaches the desired pitch angle. This is common in any mechanical system with forces and inertia. The overshoot includes an oscillation, which typically has two components; one short-lived, the second, a lower frequency, longer lasting oscillation.

10.6 Yaw Damper

In a well-designed aircraft, oscillations are not severe . Some oscillations, particularly around pitch and yaw axes, exist continuously in trimmed flight. There are no significant oscillations around the roll axis; they have a period of one to ten seconds or so. The amplitude of oscillations is no more than a few degrees and is more annoying than dangerous. When an FCS navigates on a radio signal or heading hold, it can counteract oscillations. A mode of operation, called yaw damper, counteracts oscillations during all phases of flight including times when the aircraft is flown by hand. The yaw damper can also remove adverse yaw encountered during turns (the tendency of the nose to move opposite from the direction of the turn). The yaw damper is engaged, but the aircraft is still controlled by hand.

The yaw damper is different from other FCS modes in that it does not have full authority. This means that the amount of control is limited. Not much movement of the control surfaces is required to damp out yaw and pitch oscillations. If the FCS fails, the amount of movement is limited and the pilot can easily overcome the failure.

This concept of full authority was mentioned in the discussion of robust data communications. The "full authority digital engine controller," or FADEC, was described as a critical system. There are also limited authority engine controllers. A common and useful controller is the automatic synchronizer for multiengine aircraft. It adjusts the throttles to match the RPM of the engines. After engines are manually matched, the automatic synchronizer keeps them perfectly synchronized. Should the synchronizer fail, the amount of throttle variation causes no hazard of excessive or inadequate power. In the case of FADEC, engine power is set throughout the full range.

Depending on the whether the FCS is a two or three axis system, the yaw damper works on just the yaw axis or on both yaw and pitch. Since the yaw damper does not hold a course, input can be the rate of turn gyro. Theoretically, the heading gyro can control the yaw damper by removing the DC component and using only AC. The implementation is more than capacitor coupling the gyro output; it's done with a component called the "wash out" filter. It "washes out" the DC and prevents new oscillation.

The yaw damper is an example of auto stabilization. In a stable light aircraft, auto stabilization only on the yaw axis provides reasonable results. In large aircraft, particularly military aircraft, at least two and often all three axis are required for complete stabilization. Pitch and yaw auto stabilization are often employed, and pitch-roll auto stabilization included in many high-performance aircraft.

The most important characteristic of auto stabilization is to damp out oscillation and not create new ones. To understand stability and performance of a control system we model the aircraft and diagram it in flight. The model must include not only moments due to aircraft inertia and reaction to the air mass, but flexure of the fuselage. Flexure is important because auto stabilization can cause detrimental effects. Auto stabilization might respond to the resonant frequency of fuselage flexure and set up oscillation. Fuselage flexure does not play a significant role in aircraft stabilization and the control loop should have no gain at the resonant frequency of the fuselage. This is accomplished with notch filters in the control loop to reduce gain at the resonant frequency. The oscillations will not be sustained.

10.7 Fly By Wire

A servo assist system is required in large aircraft to help move control surfaces because the forces are more than a pilot can handle. In medium size aircraft, the servo assist is a mechanical link to the control surfaces and servo motors for positioning control surfaces. Motion of control surfaces can be felt in the control yoke in the same manner the driver of an automobile with power steering feels the road. For large aircraft, a mechanical connection to the control surfaces is difficult to construct. The yoke is connected to an electrical transducer which signals a computer to calculate position of the yoke and desired positions of the control surfaces. Digital signals transmitted to control surface actuators set the required positions. This is a basic fly by wire system. This system differs from the servo-assisted system in a number of ways. First, there is a computer between input from the yoke to control surfaces. Secondly, the input is electrical; there is no mechanical connection to the control surfaces. This is evident in the diagram of the fly by wire system in Fig. 10.8.

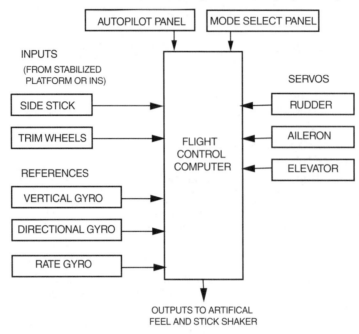

Fig. 10.8 Fly by wire system

The strictly electrical input permits a small controlling element. Historically, large aircraft had large controls. This was necessary because those aircraft had non-assisted controls and those with servo-assist could be flown if the servo system failed. An electrical transducer can be made quite small and the need for a large control is not necessary. A small side-mounted controller with two degrees of freedom has been developed for aircraft control. It would appear that pilots, used to the conventional large control, would find the small side stick strange and difficult to use. Pilots who have used the sidestick controller have found the device easy to get used to.

A disadvantage of an input device that has no mechanical connections to the control surfaces is lack of "feel" to the pilot. If a mechanical control surface encounters turbulence, it is felt in the control yoke. To provide these missing forces, the side stick controller produces an artificial feel. The resisting forces on the side stick give the feeling of a mechanical connection to the control surfaces.

The artificial feel system can also implement a stick shaker. The device is not unique to fly by wire. In fact, the stick shaker is not a part of an avionics system except fly by wire. It alerts the pilot to a potential disaster such as a stall. Before the stall develops, the aircraft yoke shakes in the pilot's hand. In an aircraft with mechanical controls, it's done by energizing a motor with an eccentric mass. Attached to the yoke shaft, the eccentric mass shakes the yoke violently enough to be felt in turbulence.

10.8 Inertial Navigation

The navigation techniques discussed thus far, other than the historic use of light beacons and so-called dead reckoning, which used charts and visual landmarks, involved radio signals. Early systems used earth-based radio transmissions, while later systems employ space-based signals. Radio navigation reached high levels of sophistication, such as the extreme precision and global coverage of GPS. ILS and VOR/DME are tailored to aviation users and provide reliable navigation with relatively simple equipment. En route airways and approach procedures are constructed around these legacy radio navigation systems.

As good as they are, there are disadvantages to radio navigation. First, all radio-based systems are vulnerable to interference, unintentional or deliberate. Military users expect deliberate jamming and design alternate systems for when signals are compromised. GPS, being a military system, has a certain level of immunity to deliberate interference but is not totally immune. Not all interference is from man-made sources; many are caused by nature.

Sources of interference are varied. There are natural causes, such as noise from lightning strikes. There are unusual propagation paths such as ducting and sporadic E skip which can cause interference from co-channel transmitters that would normally be out of range. As discussed previously, VHF and shorter wavelength signals were used for radio navigation to minimize the vagaries of longer wavelength propagation, but there are isolated cases of long distance VHF propagation. Some sources of interference are from onboard equipment or multipath signals. Interference can originate in the aircraft itself. Avionics equipment is tested for generating interfering signals but there are other equipment that has not been tested, such as portable electronic devices carried aboard by passengers.

Another disadvantage of radio-based navigation is the time delay to respond to track changes. Most radio navigation systems are for long distance en route navigation and thus longer response times are acceptable. An exception is the ILS, but even in that case, the system is built around a gentle 3-degree glide path angle. ILS works fine for most fixed wing aircraft but forces helicopters to fly a long, protracted approach.

With the exception of ADF, radio navigation systems have no information relative to the heading of the aircraft and cannot anticipate maneuvers.

There are instruments aboard an aircraft for navigation but more in an ancillary way, including artificial horizon, gyrocompass, barometric altimeter and vertical speed indicator. These instruments respond very quickly to changes in aircraft flight path. As an example, the gyrocompass keeps an aircraft on a specific course while a VOR insures long term adherence to the course.

These instruments do not depend on signals in space but gather information mechanically from motion of the aircraft and, therefore, are immune to interference or variations in radio signal propagation.

The gyro that controls the artificial horizon gives roll and pitch guidance. The directional gyro provides a North and East heading reference. If acceleration is sensed in the vertical, east and north directions, these accelerations can be mathematically integrated over the time variable and the result is velocity, as a function of time.

Performing a second integration over time of the three components of velocity results in the three components of position of the aircraft as a function of time.

The input to the determination of position is acceleration, which requires two integrations. If velocity is available, the number of integrations is reduced from two to one. This double integration introduces problems, which will be discussed later. However, there is no purely mechanical method for an airborne system to determine velocity.

Acceleration, on the other hand, can be sensed. One simple form of accelerometer uses a mass attached to a spring. Because displacement of a spring is directly proportional to the force applied to the spring and the force needed to accelerate a mass is proportional to the acceleration, a spring/mass device can sense acceleration.

If three mutually-orthogonal accelerometers are provided, aligned to north, east and vertical, each accelerometer provides the component of the aircraft's acceleration in each of those three axes. The acceleration as an electrical signal is integrated in either an analog integrator or converted to a digital value and integrated with a digital routine to provide velocity, and integrated a second time to provide position.

When each integration process is performed, it is necessary to know the initial conditions. The integration of acceleration to obtain velocity requires, as an initial condition, the velocity of the aircraft at the beginning of the integration process. Likewise, the second integration from velocity to position requires the initial position of the aircraft. In a navigation system, integration is continuous and it can be assumed when the system is energized the aircraft is on the ground and stationary. This gives an initial velocity of zero and the initial position is that of the aircraft at system turn on. Aboard an aircraft carrier, or for an INS used in airborne missiles, the initial conditions are obtained from the host vehicle.

Integrating acceleration to calculate velocity and integrating again to obtain position is applying Newton's laws of motion, which only work in an inertial frame of reference. Therefore, the technique is called an inertial navigation system or INS.

Relative to an aircraft there are three accepted axes; roll, pitch and yaw. Roll is the axis along the fore/aft line. Pitch is around a line laterally through the wing at approximately the center of lift, and yaw is around the up/down line and orthogonal to the roll and pitch axis. If linear accelerations are measured along these axes it produces components of the acceleration vector as aligned to the aircraft. The angles, roll, pitch and yaw, also called the Euler angles, are the three axes of a Cartesian co-ordinate system called the body co-ordinate system. Unlike vehicles that are constrained to the surface of the earth or oceans, aircraft are free to assume any roll, pitch or yaw angle, and accelerate in any direction in three-dimensional space. Furthermore, the aircraft can move along all three axes, i.e. it can go left or right and up or down. Therefore, it is said that aircraft have 6 degrees of freedom.

Gyros sense angular motion, three of the six degrees of freedom. Angular acceleration of an aircraft is recorded by gyros immediately, which is an important reason to use a directional gyro rather than a magnetic compass; the gyro is "rock steady" and provides excellent feedback for heading control. This implies the INS, because it relies on mechanical inputs, would have an immediate response to aircraft position changes and provide 3D navigation. Over the short term, INS is an excellent performer but as time passes, errors begin to grow because of the integrations. If an accelerometer has an error; after integration the velocity error will continue to grow and velocity gets progressively less accurate. In the INS, velocity is integrated continuously to determine the aircraft's position. Thus, velocity, with its increasing error, will now be integrated to produce an error in the aircraft's position that grows even faster than the velocity error.

In the short term, the INS provides accurate position and velocity, while in the long term, it has increasing errors. Radio-based systems, in particular GPS, do not suffer from this problem. They are the opposite; in the short term they are slow to respond but in the long term have no degradation of accuracy.

An inertial navigation system needs to be corrected periodically for these accumulating errors. The obvious method is to use information from a radio-based system to correct the INS. This method exploits the virtues of radio-based and inertial navigation systems and will be discussed later.

10.8.1 Frames of Reference

Acceleration is a vector and, as any vector, can be described by components in a three dimensional co-ordinate system. Integrating the acceleration vector twice, the resulting position vector is in the same coordinate system as acceleration. A vector in three dimensional space may be described by three orthogonal components relative to the coordinate system. For navigation, the most convenient coordinate system is latitude, longitude and altitude relative to mean sea level, MSL.

Latitude, longitude and MSL would certainly be sufficient to navigate anywhere on earth. However, a problem is immediately evident. Lines of latitude and longitude are not straight but are circles. Lines of longitude are circles of constant radius, which are equal to the radius of the earth. Lines of latitude have a radius which is variable and equal to the radius of the earth at zero latitude, the equator, and reduce to zero radius at the poles. Even more distressing is the radius of the earth is not a constant because of its oblateness. Even the "constant" radius of lines of longitude are not quite constant. The problems associated with an oblate earth were discussed relative to GPS orbits.

10.8.1.1 Locally-Level Frame of Reference

For the desired frame of reference for navigation, altitude is measured along the local up/down or vertical line. The second axis is parallel to lines of longitude or north/south since all lines of longitude pass through the poles, and the third axis is parallel to lines of latitude or east/west. If accelerometers are aligned along those axes and integrated twice while accounting for the initial conditions, latitude, longitude and altitude are calculated directly. This was alluded to earlier in this section by the suggestion that acceleration be measured along the axis of the artificial horizon gyro and directional gyro.

A Cartesian coordinate system is suggested by the lines of latitude and longitude and up as described, which is fine for plane geometry but the geometry at hand is actually spherical. For small areas of the earth's surface, differences are slight but eventually the geometry must be corrected to account for the spherical earth.

Assume for a moment our interest is in a small portion of the earth's surface, such that the surface of the earth can be considered to be a plane. Align the frame of reference so the Z axis is vertical. This is easy to do if there is no motion of the aircraft by simply aligning the Z axis to the pull of gravity. If the Y axis is aligned to true north, the coordinate system is aligned to latitude, longitude and altitude. This is also called the locally-level coordinate system.

Consider some characteristics of this coordinate system. The need to determine up and down was discussed earlier as one of the first requirements for instrument flight. The device providing this information to the flight crew was the artificial horizon based on a gyroscope. Knowing up from down is not a problem to a pilot when visibility is good and the pilot can see the horizon. Even when visibility is bad, humans can tell up from down until the aircraft experiences accelerated motion. Acceleration vectors from aircraft motion add to the gravity vector and the pilot cannot distinguish the gravity vector from the acceleration of the aircraft and no longer knows up from down. The gyro has a characteristic of "rigidity in space" which can be aligned to the local vertical and maintains its alignment during accelerated motion.

However, an aircraft at rest, stationary on the ground is, in fact, experiencing accelerated motion as the earth rotates on its axis. This has very little affect on the artificial horizon because the gravity vector and acceleration vector due to rotation of the earth around its axis are, essentially, in the same direction. But it is intended to integrate the acceleration vector in the vertical direction to obtain vertical speed and a second integration to determine altitude. As discussed, small errors of acceleration grow to large errors when integrated twice. Accelerometers cannot distinguish force due to gravity and acceleration due to rotation of the earth or acceleration of the aircraft. Acceleration as sensed by the accelerometer in the vertical direction has three components; gravity, centripetal acceleration due to rotation of the earth and acceleration of the aircraft in the vertical direction. Of these three terms, only the acceleration due to motion of the aircraft should be integrated. The other terms need to be subtracted from the acceleration sensed in the vertical direction.

The definition of the constant, $g = 9.8$ m/s^2, or gravity used in so many familiar physics equations, is acceleration due to the mass of the earth having an effect on a mass on the surface of the earth and is nearly constant but changes due to the oblateness of the earth. The constant, g, is a function of latitude and has its minimum value at the poles and maximum at the equator. The actual effect of oblateness does not fit a simple formula and involves empirically-derived parameters discussed in the section on GPS.

Centripetal acceleration is also a function of latitude. The magnitude of the centripetal acceleration decreases as latitude increases either north or south. This is because the radius of the circular path of motion decreases; becoming zero at the poles. This radius decreases as the cosine of the latitude. The direction of the centripetal force vector goes from the local vertical at the equator and moves towards the horizontal as the latitude is increased. Therefore, the magnitude of the centripetal force and the component of the centripetal force in the vertical direction are proportional to the cosine of the latitude and the magnitude of the centripetal force in the local vertical is proportional to the cosine of the latitude squared.

The constant, g, takes into account the effects of centripetal force due to the rotation of the earth about its axis. The simple physics equation that calculates weight from mass, $W = mg$ where W is the weight and m is the mass, the g is the "local" gravity.

Latitude is the angle that would exist between the equatorial plane of the earth and a line drawn from the center of the earth to the point of interest on the earth's surface. This is called the geocentric latitude.

If a surveyor's plumb bob were dropped at the point of interest, the angle subtended by that vector and the equatorial plane is the geodetic latitude.

If the plumb bob were only affected by gravity, it would be aligned towards the center of the earth. Because of the additional centripetal acceleration, the alignment of the plumb bob is slightly different from a line drawn to the center of the earth. Because surveyors use plumb bobs to align surveying instruments, maps and navigation charts are based on geodetic latitude. Although the difference is usually quite small, precision navigation requires that the distinction be made.

Exercise

Calculate the mean gravity vector and centripetal acceleration.

The nominal radius of the earth is 6378 km.

The acceleration at a distance, R, from the center of mass of the earth, which is very close to the geometrical center would be;

$$G = gM/R^2,$$

where G is the acceleration due to gravity at a point on the earth's surface, M is the mass of the earth, R is the distance between the surface of the earth at the point of interest, and g is Newton's gravitational constant.

The term gM is used in the discussion of GPS orbits and the value is 398601 km³/sec². The km units are quite handy for satellite orbits but g in terms of m/sec² would be more appropriate and, therefore, gM is redefined as:

$$gM = 3.98601E14 m^3/sec^2$$

Thus:

$$G = (3.98601E14 m^3/sec^2)/(6.378E6m)^2 = 9.798 \ m/s^2$$

Example:

Calculate the centripetal acceleration at the surface of the earth at the equator.

Again, from the discussion of GPS orbits, the earth rotates at a rate of 145.8E-6 radians/sec.

The centripetal acceleration is

$$a = R\omega^2$$

where R is the mean radius of the earth and ω is the angular rotation rate of the earth. (The radius of the earth at the equator is greater than the mean. For this example, the effect of using the mean rather than the actual radius is small and ignored.)

Therefore,

$$a = 6.378E6 X (145.8E-6)^2 = 0.136E-6 \ m/s^2$$

An observer standing at the pole would not perceive a significant difference in the acceleration experienced at the equator, but the centripetal acceleration's effect on calculations required for inertial navigation is significant.

Example:

Assume that the effect of centripetal acceleration is ignored. How much error would be created for an aircraft not in motion by the centripetal acceleration after an hour? Use the worst case for an aircraft at the equator.

Since the centripetal acceleration is 0.136E-6 m/s² and is a constant, simply multiplying by 3600 seconds, one hour, the error is,

878.6m

An error of this magnitude of altitude is completely unacceptable, therefore, the effects of centripetal acceleration must be corrected for.

Navigation is relative to the surface of the earth. The motion of the earth through the celestial sphere needs to be considered. Certainly, the earth travels around the sun in 365.25 days but navigation is relative to the center of the earth. A coordinate system that is "earth centered" or where the origin of the coordinate system is the center of the earth will provide the desired navigation guidance. A locally vertical coordinate system is an earth centered system as it was aligned it to the lines of latitude and longitude. At this time, the subtle distinction of the center of mass of the earth relative to the geometrical center as the difference will be ignored, as it is quite small.

The locally level coordinate system is also called "earth fixed" as it is tied to lines of latitude and longitude and rotates with the earth around its axis.

Exercise:

How much does the attraction due to gravity change from sea level to an altitude of 33,000 feet?

Since gravity is inversely proportional to distance squared the change in gravity is proportional to the square of the ratio of 6378km/6378km + h, where h is the altitude or about 10 km in this example.

Therefore,

$$[6378/(6378 + 10)]^2 = 0.997$$

The difference is only 0.3% but this error is a constant. To determine the vertical acceleration due to motion of the aircraft, the gravity component, which is usually much smaller than the aircraft acceleration, must be corrected for altitude.

Because of the number of error terms in determining altitude and the criticality of altitude, barometric altitude is often used as an aid to calculating altitude in an inertial navigation system.

The "ultimate" in frames of reference is the "inertial" frame of reference, where all of Newton's laws hold. This is a frame that experiences no acceleration and is tied to the universe. This implies that the inertial frame does not rotate with the earth about its axis or orbit the sun. It is fixed relative to the celestial bodies. Only in this frame of reference would there be no errors but such a frame of reference is only useful for space travel.

10.9 The Stabilized Platform

The locally-level frame of reference is of interest in inertial navigation in that the vertical is always the true up and down reference. If a physical "platform" were provided so that accelerometers may be attached to the locally-level platform, the Z-axis accelerometer would provide the Z component of acceleration to be processed. If the platform was also oriented towards true north the accelerometer oriented towards north would provide the north component of acceleration, while the third accelerometer can be oriented towards the east.

It was shown how gyros can create an artificial horizon, which provides an indication of vertical guidance, while the gyrocompass provides aircraft orientation to true north.

In its simplest form, the artificial horizon and directional gyro simply added indicators to free gyros and were used as instruments. In larger systems, indicators were "slaved" to gyros in more convenient locations. This involved resolver outputs from a gyro and a control system to mimic the position of the gyros which were connected to an indicator located in the instrument panel.

Consider a platform connected to a set of gimbals such that the platform could be aligned and kept in one position even though the aircraft can rotate around the pitch, yaw and roll axis. This means if the platform was aligned relative to north and to the vertical, it would remain that way regardless of aircraft attitude or heading. If gyros are used to stabilize this platform, rather large gyros would be required if the platform were directly connected to the gyro. A very similar technique to slave remotely mounted gyros is used to keep the platform aligned. Rate gyros are mounted to the platform, usually one per axis. A rate gyro is one where the output signal is proportional to the rate of rotation around an axis. Once the platform is aligned, it is desired to have no further rotation and thus the rate gyro outputs should be zero at all times. This is insured by amplifying the rate gyro output and using the amplified signal to drive torque motors that apply an opposing torque to counteract the rotation. This is called the stabilized platform and has been employed for inertial navigation systems, INS, for a number of years.

The difficulty of such a system is that the platform should remain oriented relative to the local vertical regardless of aircraft motion. For an air transport aircraft, where maneuvers are mild and relatively slow, the stabilization of the platform is an easy task. However, for high performance aircraft, where maneuvers can be rapid and through a large range of roll and pitch angles, keeping the platform stabilized becomes difficult. The gyros do not have to go through a large range of angles assuming the torque motors provided the correct amount of restoring torque. However, if torque from the motors cannot keep up with rotation of the aircraft, the platform takes on large error angles. If the platform cannot be maintained locally level, it is said to have "tumbled" and the INS ceases to function until the platform is restored and initial conditions are established.

In the discussion of the stabilized platform, it was suggested that if the platform were initially aligned to the vertical, rate gyros would sense any deviation from that initial alignment. One might be tempted to assume the platform would remain vertical.

With the exception of the poles, there is a constant rotation of the local vertical due to the rotation of the earth around its axis and the motion of the earth orbiting around the sun of 15 degrees an hour. Recall from the discussion of GPS orbits that the earth rotates about its axis in slightly less than 24 hours, solar time, but the combination of the earth's rotation around its axis and the orbit around the sun is exactly one revolution per solar day or 15 degrees per hour. If the platform only sensed the rate gyro around the north axis it would rotate one complete revolution every day. In order to keep the platform vertical it is necessary to introduce a precise 15 degree per hour rotation.

Thus, a stationary, stabilized platform must rotate about 15 degrees an hour in inertial space to remain locally level for an aircraft that is not moving. When an aircraft is in flight, the amount of rotation is variable, depending on the direction and speed of the flight. An output bias from the X and Y accelerometers must be provided to cause a rotation of 15 degrees per hour to keep the platform locally level.

A stabilized platform is always perfectly level and aligned towards true north and can be used to drive the artificial horizon and direction indicator. The gimbals of the platform are fitted with either resolvers, synchros, or digital shaft encoders and provides attitude and heading information for indicators or navigation computers.

Although three gimbals are all that is theoretically required to keep a platform locally level, the use of four is common to prevent gimbal lock.

The accelerometers on the stabilized platform can be perfectly aligned to the X, Y and Z axis and, theoretically, be integrated once to determine the X and Y component of velocity, and the vertical speed. If the platform is locally vertical there is no gravity component in the X and Y direction. Only the Z axis has the gravity component and needs to be subtracted from the sensed acceleration. A second integration provides the X and Y components of the aircraft position. It is important to remember that what is desired is the position of the aircraft along the surface of the earth, or a case of spherical geometry. With the locally-level stabilized platform, the X and Y axes are always parallel to the surface of the earth and, therefore, the acceleration and velocity and position obtained from the acceleration are along the surface of the earth.

The stabilized platform is aligned to an earth-centered, earth-fixed, ECEF coordinate system. The ECEF coordinate system that is important is the latitude, longitude and sea level altitude system used for navigation.

10.9.1 Orientation of the Stabilized Platform

A north pointing platform has a serious problem when at the poles. An aircraft flying, say, to the north pole, on a line of longitude must rotate 180 degrees at the pole. Unless very large torque motors are used, the platform will not be able to rotate rapidly at the pole crossing and the system will develop errors that are unrecoverable.

One method is to permit the platform to be oriented in a direction that is not north pointing. When an aircraft is directly over the pole, the INS cannot provide an azimuth indication but the non-north pointing platform does not need to rotate and does not suffer an unrecoverable error. For a short time the INS cannot provide an accurate heading indication but fully recovers. Systems that use a non north-pointing platform are called free-azimuth platforms. The convenience of having accelerometer outputs that are perfectly aligned with east and north are lost but modern computers can perform the necessary transformations.

10.9.2 Problems Associated with a Stabilized Platform

It would appear that the stabilized platform would be the obvious method of maintaining alignment of the accelerometers. For this reason, early INS used the north pointing stabilized platform. Early INS relied on analog circuits and the complexity of a non north-pointing platform was not easily handled by the circuits of that era. Although the north-pointing platform is seldom found in newer designs, the stabilized platform continues to be used.

The platform approach does have problems and is not perfect. First, the accuracy of a platform-type INS is strongly dependent on the accuracy of maintaining orientation of the locally level platform. Since gyros are the sensors used to achieve platform stability, gyro errors affect the accuracy of the platform. Three gyros are involved in stabilizing a platform and all three add to system error. Three accelerometers are involved and since the acceleration is integrated twice, accelerometer errors are very important.

Another potential problem with a stabilized platform is the ability to follow aircraft maneuvers. Keeping a platform from tumbling in high performance aircraft is a difficult design requirement.

Another disadvantage of the stabilized platform is that the rate of roll, pitch and yaw, the body rates, are not directly available. Rate gyros are used for the platform but are mounted on the platform to provide feedback signals for stabilizing the platform and since those gyros do not rotate they do not provide a rotation rate. The body rates are used to drive flight instruments such as the turn and bank indicator, attitude direction indicator, and directional gyro.

Other disadvantages of the stabilized platform are the need for gimbals, and slip rings to provide input and output signals for the platform. Three rate gyros are required to sense platform motion and three torque motors to keep the platform rigid in space. The good news about gyros is they are used as a part of a feedback loop. This means that if the feedback loop is working properly, the actual rotation of the gyros is virtually zero and thus dynamic range of the gyro is small.

10.9.3 Strapdown

Instead of providing a stabilized platform, accelerometers and gyros can be mounted rigidly relative to the aircraft, or "strapped down". This implies that the sensing elements, gyros and accelerometers, are aligned to the "body" frame of reference; the aircraft itself. There are a number of advantages to the strapdown system; no gimbals, no platform to tumble, no torque motors and no problems at the poles. Also, body rate signals are directly available for use but this is more of a tradeoff as the body angular rate signals have been traded for the convenience of accelerometer signals directly aligned with north, east and vertical. The added complexity is that the body frame of reference is not as convenient for processing. Before the advent of capable microprocessors this would be a serious disadvantage.

In the strapdown scheme, the gyros, being rigidly attached to the airframe, experience the entire dynamic range of the aircraft. This implies a full 360 degrees of rotation for the yaw axis for all aircraft and somewhat less for the roll and pitch for non-military aircraft. Many military aircraft can be expected to perform maneuvers with angles exceeding 360 degrees in all axes at rather significant rates. For air transport aircraft, the total dynamic range can be considerably less. In a strapdown system, the performance of gyros and accelerometers will have a great effect on overall performance of the system.

Modern gyros such as the ring laser gyro (RLG), fiber optic gyro (FOG) and electrostatic gyro have provided the necessary performance to permit precision navigation from the strapdown INS. The older mechanical spinning gyro is virtually worthless for strapdown INS.

The advantage of the north pointing stabilized platform is the three axes are the exact axes required for navigation east, north and vertical. For the free azimuth platform, the platform remains locally vertical and the frame of reference conversion is only in two dimensions. In the case of strapdown INS, the body frame of reference can experience rapid and large changes in all three dimensions from the locally vertical north-reference frame. The conversion between reference frames requires significant calculations.

In order to discuss conversion from one reference frame to another, the three frames that are involved with inertial navigation must be understood:

Inertial Frame, Earth Centered; The X and Y axes are in the equatorial plane while the Z axis is along the axis of the earth. Although designated an inertial frame it is not exactly that for two reasons. First, it is earth centered, meaning that it moves about the universe with the earth in its orbit around the sun. Secondly, the earth's axis "wobbles" around over a period of many years and the Z axis of this frame wobbles. Both of these departures from a true inertial frame of reference are slow processes and do not affect the implementation of inertial navigation.

Earth Centered Earth Fixed; this is the same as the earth centered frame except the X and Y axes rotate with the earth. When the Z axis is locally-vertical the reference frame is the earth-centered, earth-fixed, locally-level frame.

Body Frame; the X axis is parallel to the aircraft's roll axis, the Y is parallel to the aircraft's pitch axis and the Z is parallel to the yaw axis. This is not an inertial frame of reference due the motion of the aircraft in the inertial frame.

Since the accelerometers are fixed in the body frame of reference, and the goal is to provide position information in the ECEF, vertically-level frame, it is clear that the many of the calculations required of a strapdown INS will involve converting from one frame of reference to another. The strapdown system still relies on continuous integration from the accelerometers but those integrations need to be translated to another frame of reference.

When a vector in a frame of reference is viewed from another frame of reference, determining the coordinates in the new frame of reference is called a vector transformation.

A vector can be described by its components, which for a Cartesian coordinate system are the X, Y and Z components. To transform a vector from one coordinate system to another it is necessary to convert the components of the original vector to the components of the new vector in the new coordinate system.

The original and new coordinate systems can be related by rotation and translation. When comparing the stabilized platform coordinate system to a strapdown coordinate system imagine either system located at the same place in an aircraft. The stabilized platform maintains the platform locally level and oriented in the same direction but it is physically attached to the aircraft. In the case of the body coordinate system it, too, is physically connected to the aircraft. Therefore, the origin of either of the two, the stabilized platform or the body coordinate system is the same. Therefore, the difference in the two coordinate systems is strictly rotation not translation.

In the case of a strapdown inertial navigation system, the origin of the body system relative to the locally-level system is only rotation.

When a transformation is made from one coordinate system to another where the origins are coincident, each component of the transformed vector is a sum, which consists of each component of the original vector multiplied by a conversion factor.

To understand the mechanics of vector transformation the concept of direction cosine will be explained.

A direction cosine defines the relationship of a vector to a coordinate system. In a simple 2D coordinate system a vector has two direction cosines one is the cosine of the angle between the vector and the X axis and the other is the cosine of the angle between the vector and the Y axis.

As an example, assume a vector, P has an angle θ between the X axis, the reference from measuring angles and an angle $(90 - \theta)$. Therefore the X component of the vector is

$|P| \cos(\theta)$

and the X component is

$|P| \cos(90-\theta) = |P| \sin(\theta)$.

When a vector is transformed from one coordinate system to another where the origins are coincident, each component of the vector in the new coordinate system is the component of the vector in the original coordinate system multiplied by a constant.

For the case of three dimensions, assume that a vector, P, has the components of Px, Py and Pz for the X, Y and Z components, respectively. Transforming this vector to another coordinate system where only rotation is involved the components of the transformed vector are,

$P'x = K_{11}Px + K_{12}Py + K_{13}Pz$
$P'y = K_{21}Px + K_{22}Py + K_{23}Pz$
$P'z = K_{31}Px + K_{32}Py + K_{33}Pz$

where P'x, P'y, and P'z are the X, Y and Z components of the vector P in the transformed coordinate system and Kmn are the conversion factors.

Arranging the equations above in a matrix form results in;

$$\begin{vmatrix} P'x \\ P'y \\ P'z \end{vmatrix} = \begin{vmatrix} k_{11} & k_{12} & k_{13} \\ k_{21} & k_{22} & k_{23} \\ k_{31} & k_{32} & k_{33} \end{vmatrix} X \begin{vmatrix} Px \\ Py \\ Pz \end{vmatrix}$$

This can be written as a simple vector equation;

$P' = \mathbf{k} \; X \; \mathbf{P}$

where P' is the vector notation for the transformed vector of P, and k is the transformation matrix.

The strapdown INS computer calculates the **k** transformation matrix from the body angles and accelerations.

10.9.4 Initializing the Gimballed Platform

All inertial navigation systems must be initialized due to the very nature of INS. Because the acceleration vector is integrated to obtain velocity and then a second time for position, two constants of integration are required, the initial velocity and the initial position. If an INS is powered up when an aircraft is stationary the initial velocity is zero. This would appear to be obvious but there are some considerations. First, for aircraft aboard an aircraft carrier or for missiles launched from aircraft using INS, zero velocity may not be the case. In most cases where inertial navigation systems are initialized from a moving vehicle the needed initial values are obtained from the host vessel. For aircraft carriers the SINS or ship's inertial navigation system is used and is transmitted to the aircraft via a wired or wireless connection.

The position of the INS is also required at turn on. It is often safe to assume the aircraft is located where it was when the INS system was last shut down but there are many instances where this position if far from correct. Clearly, the situation mentioned in the previous paragraph for aircraft aboard an aircraft carrier. It would not be uncommon for an aircraft to be moved after the INS was shut down. An aircraft could be tugged to a maintenance hangar after being shut down at a terminal gate, which could be several nautical miles after shutdown at a large airport.

Present position can be entered manually but this is problematic as the precise latitude and longitude is not always known and manual entries are subject to error. In the current technology, most aircraft have an on board GPS system and the latitude and longitude from the GPS can be used to initialize the INS. As will be discussed, the GPS will play an important role in correcting for INS drift.

There are several orientations that a gimbaled platform must initialize. The vertical axis is reasonably obvious and the orientation of that axis can be determined simply by the use of a gravity sensor. This sensor would align the platform to "plumb bob gravity" which, as previously discussed, is the geodetic latitude. This is a good choice because it is the basis for charts and maps. A simple gravity sensor, such as a pendulum, is very effective assuming the aircraft is stationary. However, if an aircraft is moving, the motions associated with taxiing, for example, will decrease the accuracy of the vertical initialization. Filtering can be employed and most aircraft spend a few minutes before taxiing to "warm up" all the aircraft systems, so there is a reasonable period of time when the aircraft is not in motion. If the initialization routine can be completed quickly, the platform can be initialized before taxiing.

An alternate method of setting the gimbaled platform to the local vertical is to null out the outputs of the X and Y accelerometers. If both X and Y accelerometers are perpendicular to the local vertical, their outputs will be zero, which means the platform is horizontal. Since the outputs of the X and Y accelerometers are near zero, the effects of noise must be minimized, for an accurate initialization. Noise can be reduced by filtering, but this implies that the process will be slow. The advantage of using the X and Y accelerometers is that the offsets, both electrical and mechanical, of these accelerometers are eliminated. That the actual platform is not absolutely horizontal does not matter; as long as the X and Y accelerometers "thinks it is" by providing zero output for an aircraft that is not experiencing acceleration other than gravity.

To speed up the initialization process, coarse and fine adjustments are made; the coarse adjustment is made using the gravity sensor and the fine adjustment is made using the output of the X and Y accelerometers.

For stationary aircraft, determining the horizontal is relatively easy. When a platform is aligned properly, the vertical accelerometer will produce its maximum output while the two horizontal accelerometers produce their minimum output. Because of the motion relative to inertial space due to the earth's rotation, and depending on the azimuth of the platform, there will be some acceleration from the two horizontal accelerometers. If the azimuth is adjusted so that the accelerometers are exactly north and east, the east accelerometer will produce a zero output.

When the platform is perfectly aligned and assuming the aircraft is not in motion, the vertical accelerometer produces an output approximately equal to the local g, the east accelerometer produces an output equal to zero and the north accelerometer produces an output equal to the north component of the earth rate acceleration.

One of the problems associated with initializing is the need to accomplish the task before the aircraft begins movement. Even while taxiing, aircraft remain relatively horizontal but are subject to wind buffeting and bouncing over uneven pavement making initializing the horizontal axis difficult. Filtering can be used but this makes the initialization slower. In the case of azimuth initialization the heading of the aircraft will not change the direction of the earth rotation but the motion makes the initialization more difficult. Therefore, many initialization mechanisms perform a coarse but rapid initialization followed by a fine adjustment. Using the magnetic heading of an aircraft would permit the rapid alignment of the azimuth to within a few degrees.

10.10 Improving the Long Term Accuracy of an Inertial Navigation System

Because of the accumulative effects of errors in the INS, most modern systems combine it with navigation solutions from other systems. The most suited system is GPS. The GPS navigation solution is most precise in latitude and longitude and least accurate in altitude. A GPS/INS navigation solution using a Kalman filter would provide short term and long term navigation accuracy. Use of barometric altitude along with radar altimeter altitude with a ground MSL data base, again with Kalman filtering would provide a respectable altitude component of the navigation solution.

GPS data can also enhance INS initialization.

10.11 Accelerometers

Based on the deflection of a mass, accelerometers are restrained by some type of force. The restoring force can be a magnetic field, electric field, piezoelectric force or mechanical source. Many structures have been designed to accurately measure acceleration. Two parameters key to successful accelerometers are accurate scale factor and low offset. The problem of offsets has been addressed, and it is an important characteristic.

A simple pendulum accelerometer serves as an example. As shown in Fig. 10.9 a pendulum has a leaf spring with a mass at the end. A wire coil attaches to the end of the pendulum. A first thought after describing a mass at the end of a leaf spring is that deflection from the neutral, unaccelerated position is measured to indicate acceleration. This could, in fact, be done but it has problems. First, using a spring to measure force suffers from non linearity. There are other problems of temperature and vibration.

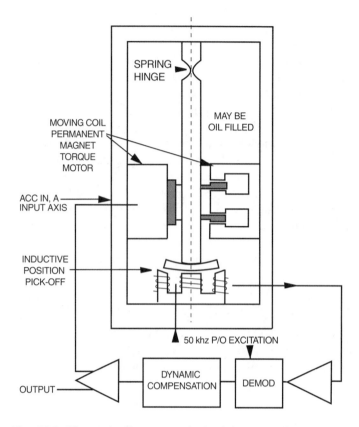

Fig. 10.9 Magnetically restored pendulum accelerometer

To make the accelerometer independent of spring characteristics, the pendulum is restored to the undeflected position by a magnetic field. The mass of the pendulum is in a constant permanent magnet field. Current may pass through a wire coil around the pendulum, producing a field that interacts with the static magnetic field and generates a force between the pendulum and static magnetic field.

The force of acceleration is counterbalanced by the magnetic fields. A current passed through the coil counteracts the force due to acceleration, such that the pendulum is restored to its undeflected position. The current is directly proportional to acceleration. Because the magnetic field restores the mass, there is no contribution of force from the spring, thus the spring constant and non linearities are not involved.

To provide the right amount of restoring force a method of detecting deflection is required. There are several methods, including capacitive pick ups, inductive pick ups and optical. The latter is one of the more effective methods. A small slit is etched into the pendulum and a light source provided. If the pendulum deflects in one direction, more light falls on one of two photo diodes or photo transistors. When the pendulum deflects in the opposite direction, more light falls on the other detector. When the pendulum is not deflected, equal light falls on both photo detectors. A differential amplifier provides bipolar current to the pendulum coil, which forces the pendulum to the neutral position.

10.12 Lightwave Gyros

Our discussion of stabilized platforms for accelerometers mentioned that the gyroscope is a key component of the platform. The conventional gyro wheel, however, is not the most effective item to carry aboard an aircraft. The wheel is massive---and the more massive, the more effective.

The wheel spins at a high rate and develops considerable mechanical energy. Bearings are critical, causing friction and drift. The gyro must also survive the temperature, altitude, shock and vibration of an aircraft. It is often mounted in a heated and cooled location, shock-isolated and sealed from dust and contamination. In spite of the problems, gyros have operated successfully from the earliest days of flying because of excellent mechanical construction. This also makes them very expensive to buy and maintain.

As for most mechanical devices, engineers strive for an electronic replacement. Two alternatives can eliminate the spinning wheel; the ring laser gyro, RLG, and fiber optic gyro, FOG. Although the name survives, neither device is a true "gyro" because they do not exhibit rigidity in space. They are, instead, angular rate sensors.

The FOG and RLG are found only in strapdown inertial systems but, theoretically, could be mounted in a stabilized platform. To recall, the strapdown system measures roll, pitch and yaw and corrects the outputs from linear accelerometers mounted along those axes. The output of an angular accelerometer is integrated to calculate angle, which is the angular counterpart to integrating linear accelerometers to determine distance.

10.12.1 Ring Laser Gyro

The RLG operates on the principle of the interferometer. A helium-neon gas laser is a major component, as shown in Fig. 10.10. The laser generates coherent light in the area of the gas. Light energy propagates in two directions; away from the laser section of the gyro and combines at the opposite apex.

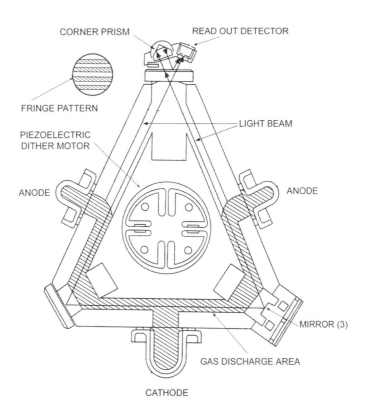

Fig. 10.10 Ring Laser Gyro

When two coherent light sources are phase locked they combine because of phase coherency. The light energy adds constructively or destructively. Because the light has a finite radius, interference "fringes," alternating light and dark rings form where light beams combine. This is due to the slight difference in path length for the light beam. Located at the apex where the beams combine is a photo detector which produces an electrical signal proportional to the intensity of light.

If the RLG rotates about its axis, motion of the light path is in the same direction of the light propagation on one side of the RLG, and against the direction of motion on the other side. In the short time it takes light to travel from source to detector the RLG rotates. The optical path in one direction, therefore, is shorter than the other direction, thus causing a frequency shift.

This is called the Sagnac Effect and is an outgrowth of the special theory of relativity. It is similar, but not equal to, the Doppler effect. The frequency shift causes the interference fringes to move because of a "beat frequency," which is the difference between the frequencies of the two light beams. The difference is directly proportional to the rate of rotation. Another way of stating this is, the number of fringes passed is directly proportional the angle of variation. The RLG determines angle by counting output pulses from the photo detector that senses the interference fringes. The counter must be bidirectional so that it counts up for rotation in one direction and down for the other.

The Sagnac effect is due to the time difference between the time of the clockwise and counterclockwise path, given by;

$$\Delta T = (4 A \omega)/c^2 \tag{10.4}$$

where ΔT is the time difference, A is the area enclosed by the optical path, and ω is the angular rotation rate of the gyro. This relationship is from the general theory of relativity and is stated here and not derived. From this relationship, equate an apparent change in the optical path length, ΔL,

$$\Delta L = c \, \Delta T = (4A/c) \, \omega \tag{10.5}$$

The change in optical frequency relative to nominal frequency is proportional to the change in optical length relative to the total length, L, or,

$$(\Delta L/L) = (\Delta f/f) \tag{10.6}$$

Solving for Δf we obtain:

$$\Delta f = (4Af/cL) \, \omega \ = (4A/\lambda L) \, \omega \tag{10.7}$$

where λ is the wavelength of the light. Angular rotation is not a constant, but a function of time and thus we rewrite the equations as:

$$\Delta f (t) = (4A/\lambda L) \, \omega (t) \tag{10.8}$$

The RLG operates by counting fringes from the photodetector. This is the same as integrating frequency and we integrate both sides of the above equation

$$\int_{t-t_0}^{t} \Delta f (t)dt = (4A / \lambda L) \int_{t-t_0}^{t} \omega(t)dt \tag{10.9}$$

If fringes are counted, the output of the RLG is directly proportional to the angle through which the RLG has rotated.

Example: If an RLG has a total optical length of 30 cm, an enclosed area of 0.022 m² and uses an He-Ne laser with a prominent wavelength of 633 nm, how much angular displacement will cause the counting of one fringe. This will represent the resolution of the gyro.

Solution: In this problem it does not matter that elapsed time, τ_0, is, the integral of $\omega(\tau)\,d\tau$ over that period of time is the angle represented by one fringe, which is to say the left side of the equation above is equal to 1. Therefore, the minimum detectable angle, which we shall call ζ is:

$$\zeta = \lambda L / 4A = (633E\text{-}9 \times 0.03)/(4 \times 0.022) = 215.8E\text{-}9 \ rads$$

$$= 12.36E\text{-}6 \ degrees = 1.113E\text{-}3 \ minutes \ of \ arc = 0.0445 \ seconds \ of \ arc$$

Counting interference fringes is not the same as counting frequency. The fringes have positive and negative values and the counter must count up and down. The photodetector is constructed with several photodiodes so the direction of the fringes may be determined. The direction of fringe movement determines the sign of the frequency counter.

The key to a drift-free RLG is to make the assembly from temperature-stable material, usually glass. Any expansion causes the fringes to drift. Another phenomenon of the RLG is the opposite of drift; it's "lock in". For small angular rotation, the difference frequency is also small. This is a phenomenon common to high Q oscillators. Some energy from one beam becomes back scattered into the laser portion of the RLG. Because of gyro rotation, the two frequencies are different. The frequency of a high Q oscillator can be "pulled" from the nominal frequency by small external signals very close to the natural frequency of the oscillator. It takes little energy from an external signal to cause pulling. Backscattered energy which is shifted in frequency slightly, therefore, can shift the oscillator to the backscattered signal. This implies that the frequency difference goes to zero. This phenomenon only occurs at low angular velocities, but is equivalent of an offset.

To prevent this, the RLG is "wiggled" around its axis so there is never very low angular velocity. This is called "dithering". The secret to dithering is; the amount of rotation is small, but the average of dithering is zero. Let us say the dither (created by a motor) causes the RLG to oscillate plus and minus 1 degree in sinusoid fashion. Dithering causes an instantaneous error of as much as 1 degree, but an average of zero. Counting the fringes is the digital equivalent of integrating and integrators are low pass filters. If the dither frequency is sufficiently high, its effects are removed by integration.

10.12.2 Fiber Optic Gyro

In the fiber optic gyro, FOG, shown in Fig. 10.11, light from a laser diode is injected into both ends of a fiber. One beam travels in a clockwise direction, the other in a counterclockwise direction. The term "light" is used here but a more practical wavelength is 1330 nm. It has very low loss in glass fiber because it falls into a low loss "window". The fiber is single mode because path length is very important and each mode of a multimode fiber represents a different path length. The fiber is constructed as described in the section on fiber optic communication. Since the fiber is located within the gyro housing, however, there is no protective covering or need for splices and connectors.

Considerable fiber is used, as much as 1000m, so low loss is important. After traversing the fiber, the two beams combine in a detector. Since the beams traverse exactly the same path, they should emerge in phase and add constructively.

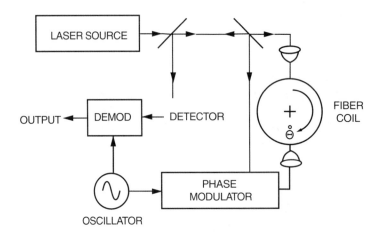

Fig. 10.11   Fiber optic gyro

Due to the Sagnac effect, rotating the fiber optic coil results in a time delay, as previously calculated for the RLG or,

$$\Delta T = (4\,A\,\omega\,)/c^2 \qquad\qquad (10.10)$$

The area, A, in the equation represents the area enclosed by the fiber. In the FOG, the fiber is wound on a cylinder with a number of turns, N. Therefore, each turn encloses the area, A. Thus, the total area enclosed is $N\,(\pi r^2)$, where r is the radius of the cylinder.

The length of the fiber, L, is

$$L = 2\,N\,\pi\,r$$

Solving for ΔT, we obtain,

$$\Delta T = (4\,N\,(\pi r^2)\,\omega\,)/c^2 = (\,2\,L\,r\,/c^2\,)\,\omega$$

The phase shift due to the Sagnac effect is

$$\Delta \Phi = (\,2\,\pi\,c\,/\lambda\,)\,\Delta T = (\,4\,\pi\,L\,r\,/\lambda\,c\,)\,\omega$$

Example: Calculate the Sagnac phase shift for a rotation rate of 1 degree per second for a FOG with 1000 meters of fiber wound on a 7.5 cm diameter cylinder. The fiber is driven with a 1330 nm laser diode.

Solution: If we leave ω in degrees per second, we will calculate the phase shift in degrees. Thus,

$$\Delta \Phi = (\,4\,\pi\,L\,r\,/\lambda\,c\,)\,\omega = (\,4\,\pi\,X\,1E3\,X\,3.75E\text{-}2\,/\,1330E\text{-}9\,X\,3E8\,) = 1.18\ degrees$$

The gyro should be capable of measuring angular rates as low as 1 second of arc per second (of time). The phase shift for the FOG in the previous example is 0.33E-3 degrees.

A photodiode measures the intensity of the combined beams from clockwise and counterclockwise paths. The intensity is:

$$I(\Delta\Phi) = 1 + \cos(\Delta\Phi) \tag{10.11}$$

Output of the photodiode is measured to determine Φ which leads to several difficult problems. The accuracy of Φ depends on accurately measuring light intensity. There are many variables in measuring with the photo diode. These include gain of the photodiode, loss in the fiber, light output of the laser diode, offsets in the photo diode and amplifiers.

A technique to solve problems of measuring very small phase angles is to phase-modulate one of the two fiber paths. Rather than a constant phase difference there is a variable phase angle. The modulation is typically sinusoid but other waveshapes can be used, so long as the waveform is symmetric about zero.

As shown in Fig. 10.10, the nominal phase shift is 0 for no rotation of the gyro. Phase modulation varies the phase shift above and below the nominal phase shift by the same amount, due to the symmetric modulation. If there is a phase shift, the waveform becomes asymmetrical. The asymmetry is detected by a synchronous detector; the result represents phase shift and, thus, the rotation rate.

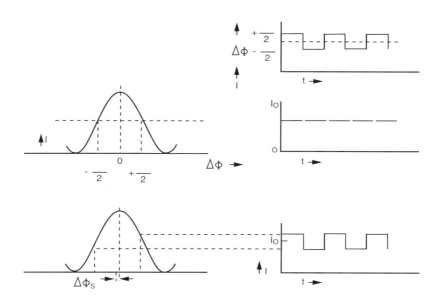

Fig. 10.12 Output of photodetector measuring phase angle between clockwise and counterclockwise paths in the fiber optic gyro (FOG)

There is even greater improvement by placing the output of the photodetector in a feedback loop. The output is amplified and used to drive a phase shifter in the opposite path of the modulation phase shifter, as shown in Fig. 10.13. In this feedback loop, accuracy is dependent mostly on the phase shifter. Like any feedback system, a multitude of non-linearities and gain variations due to temperature and other sources are removed from the equation.

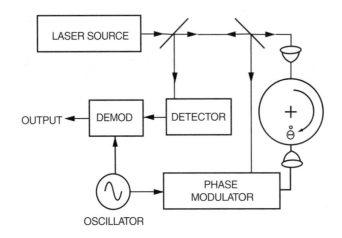

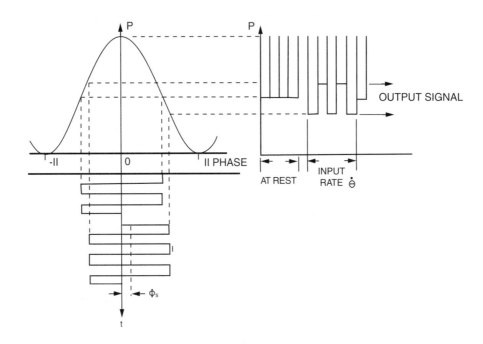

Fig. 10.13 Phase shifter in feedback loop for Fiber Optic Gyro

The inherent phase shift, θ, of light energy travelling through the length of fiber, F, with an index of refraction, n, is:

$$\theta = (2 \pi f L) / (c/n) = \theta = (2 n \pi f L) / c \qquad (10.12)$$

Take the derivative of both sides of this equation to obtain:

$$\delta\theta = ((2 n \pi L) / c) \delta f \qquad (10.13)$$

Recalling the Sagnac phase shift:

$$\Delta\Phi = (4 \pi L r / \lambda c) \omega \qquad (10.14)$$

The closed loop FOG inserts a phase shift such that phase shift due to the Sagnac shift is exactly equal to the path phase shift, plus or minus 2Nπ:

$$\Delta\theta = \Delta F \qquad (10.15)$$

$$((2\,n\,\pi\ L\,)/c\,)\Delta f = (\,4\,\pi\,L\,r/\lambda\,c\,)\,\omega \qquad (10.16)$$

$$\Delta f = (\,2\,r\,\omega\,)/n\,\lambda \qquad (10.17)$$

Example: What is the output frequency of a FOG with a rotation rate of 1 degree per second? The laser diode provides a 1330 nm wavelength for 1000 meters of single mode fiber on a 150 mm diameter cylinder in the gyro. The index of refraction of the core of the fiber is 1.48.

Solution: The equation for Δf provides an answer in Hz for a ω in radians per second. Therefore, the 1 degree per second is converted to radians per second, which is:

$$\omega = 1/360 = 17.45E\text{-}3\ rad/s$$

$$\Delta f = (\,2\,r\,\omega\,)/n\,\lambda = 2\ X\ 0.075\ X\ 17.45E\text{-}3\ /\ 1.48\ X\ 1330E\text{-}9 = 1330\ Hz$$

Next, calculate how much rotation of the FOG produces one cycle of output frequency. In one second there is movement of one degree or 3600 seconds of arc, producing 1330 cycles. One cycle is equal to 2.7 seconds of arc. The factor:

$$2\,r/n\,\lambda \quad is\ called\ the\ gyro\ calibration\ factor.$$

Example: What is the gyro calibration factor for the previous example?
Solution: Inserting the given values:

$$2\,r/n\,\lambda = 2\ X\ 0.075\ /\ 1.48\ X\ 1330E\text{-}9 = 76.2E3\ Hz\ /\ rad\ /\ sec$$

The technology of FOG uses digitally generated phase modulation for making phase angle measurements, and to digitally control the phase shift of the closed loop system. When an aircraft turns, the external phase shift cannot provide infinite phase angle and has to be reset every time phase angle progresses 2π. The phase shift is set back to zero and the number of times the phase shifter resets is counted. With microprocessor control and self-calibration, the FOG is one of the most promising gyros available.

Chapter 10 Review Questions
10.1   What is a servo motor?
10.2   What types of modes can a flight control system operate?
10.3   What controls are found on an autopilot control panel?
10.4   What characterizes a stable aircraft?
10.5   In what circumstances would an aircraft be deliberately designed to be unstable?
10.6   What purpose does a yaw damper serve?
10.7   What is FADEC?
10.8   What is "fly by wire".
10.9   What is artificial feel?
10.10   What does a stick shaker do?
10.11   In an RLG what is proportional to the frequency of the output from the device?
10.12   What is "strapdown" INS.
10.13   Why is single mode fiber used in a FOG?
10.14   Why is 1330 nm a common wavelength for the FOG?
10.15   What type of laser is used in the RLG?

Chapter 11

Complete Avionics System

11.0 Introduction

We have discussed avionics sensors, communications (on board and air to ground), computers and indicators. The final step is integrating these elements into an airborne system. Ground stations as well as space segments are an important part of CNS (communications, navigation, surveillance) systems and, when studying airborne avionics, be aware that success is dependent on ground and space portions. Next, consider the physical environment; ambient temperature, pressure and humidity, as well as electric and magnetic fields, static and dynamic, and the power supply

11.1 Power Sources

Power for avionics systems includes DC and 400 Hz AC. In large aircraft, both sources are available; AC for the majority of avionics, DC for items that must operate during an emergency. DC voltage in large and, more recently, light aircraft, is 28 volts from batteries, which are charged while the aircraft operates. DC is used for critical equipment to provide energy from batteries if mechanically-driven generators fail. Battery power starts aircraft engines and rotating machinery. Electrical energy comes from engine-driven generators or an auxiliary power unit (APU).

11.2 Batteries

Aircraft have used batteries in a variety of ways since the earliest aircraft. Simple aircraft that had no avionics, no running lights or cockpit illumination and relied on hand "propping" to start the engine, could be designed with no electrical energy storage. Later aircraft had at least one storage battery and a generator with a voltage regulator to provide primary power. These electrical systems were identical to that used on automobiles. For turbine-powered aircraft the battery is a crucial part of starting, not only the main engines but auxiliary power units, as well. Starting and recharging from turbines placed severe requirements on batteries.

The major applications of a battery in an aircraft are starting an engine and generating electricity using a mechanically-driven generator. The need to use a battery for starting is obvious but the battery is also required in producing electrical power due to the nature of the engine-driven generator. Because the generator, or alternator, does not turn at a constant speed and the output of an alternator, after rectification, is a pulsating voltage, the storage battery is used as a smoothing device.

In modern aircraft, batteries are not only for supplying primary power but keeping data alive in memories and operating emergency equipment.

The term "battery" has been misused to the point where it has become acceptable. A battery is two or more cells. A flashlight might have two cells which, taken together, is a battery. For understanding battery behavior it is necessary to distinguish between a battery and a cell. Also, there are two types of cells, primary and secondary. Primary cells cannot be recharged. Once cell chemistry is depleted, the cell must be discarded. A secondary cell can be recharged through reversing the chemical action by applying a charging current so the cell can, again, supply energy. An example of a primary cell is the common alkaline cell, while the lead acid automobile storage battery is a secondary battery.

In its simplest form, a cell is constructed of two electrodes and an electrolyte. Often, the electrodes are called "plates" because, in many cells, electrodes are in the shape of rectangular plates of metal. The energy is stored in chemical reactions involving all elements of the cell. The electrolyte in most batteries is a strong chemical capable of causing corrosion and other undesired chemical reactions should it leak from the cell. The chemical reaction in the cell also creates gasses, which can be explosive or toxic. The electrodes are just as dangerous. Many batteries contain such toxic metals in their electrodes as lead and cadmium.

11.2.1 Characteristics of Cells

A number of characteristics describe electrical energy in storage cells. The first is energy capacity; the amount of energy a battery can provide between full charge and full discharge.

Another characteristic is cell voltage. This is a highly variable parameter, being a function of state of charge, temperature, rate of discharge and age of the cell.

Each cell has an equivalent resistance, which limits the maximum current obtainable under charge and discharge. Certain cells produce very low internal resistances and these technologies are for applications that require short bursts of high current, such as engine starting.

Like cell voltage, internal resistance is a function of state of charge, temperature and age of the cell. Even the energy capacity of a cell or battery is not a constant. Understanding that cell or battery characteristics is like shooting a moving target, it can be appreciated how difficult it is to safely and efficiently charge and discharge batteries.

For the simplest application, starting engines and generating power, using inexpensive and forgiving technologies, such as lead acid, the techniques often used are simply, "abuse the battery and replace it often".

Lead acid batteries for both automobiles and aircraft are very robust. They have a lot of space below the plates to collect debris generated from the abuse of extremely heavy starting currents. Older-design lead acid batteries had removable caps so electrolyte that was vaporized due to abuse could be replaced. They are made to handle overcharging and withstand the high temperatures of an engine compartment. Lead acid batteries are relatively inexpensive and replaced often.

Cells are of two types; vented and sealed. The chemical reactions of charging and discharging produce various gasses, depending on cell type. To prevent unsafe pressure within the cell, vents are provided. In the vented cell, a low pressure vent permits almost all of the generated gas to escape to the environment. When pressure lowers, the vent seals again. In the sealed cell, a vent is supplied but this is a safety measure. The vent is set to a high, abnormal pressure and opens to prevent an explosion, and may not reseal. Gas generated in the sealed cell recombines to prevent continued build up of pressure. A cell that vents is losing electrolyte; therefore, vented cells that are charged repeatedly to the point of venting must have the electrolyte periodically replenished .

Another characteristic of cells is the disposition of the electrolyte. In the typical automotive battery the electrolyte, which is dilute sulphuric acid, is a liquid which covers the plates. If the battery is turned upside down, the electrolyte would pour out. In an aircraft this could be a problem. This type is called the "flooded" cell and is found in some aircraft applications. The cell is sealed against electrolyte leakage but still permits gas venting. Flooded cells are seldom used in modern aircraft.

An alternative to the flooded cell is to constrain the electrolyte in either a sponge-like material or gelled form. The gelled electrolyte cell finds uses where a sealed, non-leaking cell is desired. The major problem with gelled electrolyte is that charging current must be limited because the cell is easily damaged if overcharged. This is because gelled electrolyte can pull away from the plates as gas forms when overcharging. This leaves a void and reduces capacity of the battery.

The alternative for the gelled type of lead acid battery is the "starved electrolyte" cell. The electrolyte is absorbed in a boron silicate glass mat at about 96% of saturation. This prevents the electrolyte from leaking but will not form voids if the cell is overcharged. These batteries are called absorbed glass mat or AGM batteries. Modern lead acid batteries for aircraft are the sealed AGM type.

Lead acid cell voltage is about 2.1 volts. The common automobile battery is called a "12 volt battery", and is made from six lead acid cells. However, actual cell voltage is 12.6 volts, assuming cell voltage is 2.1 volts.

In the typical aircraft DC power system using a lead acid battery, after the engine starts, the battery is under constant charge. The battery now has a terminal voltage higher than the nominal cell voltage due to the charging current. Typically, a lead acid storage battery has terminal voltage of 13.6 to 13.8 volts. This is the voltage that equipment powered from the charging battery will be operating at while the engine is running. In automotive terminology the 6 cell lead acid battery is referred to as a 12 volt battery, while in the aviation world, the 6 cell lead acid battery is called a 14 volt battery to reflect the real operating voltage.

Many older aircraft use a 14 volt system. But most modern aircraft have a 28 volt system using 12 cells if a lead acid battery is employed. This was done to reduce the size of the wiring, as each load would have half the current than it would draw if powered from a 14 volt system.

11.2.2 Defining Battery Capacity

Before looking at battery capacity, charged and discharged states must be defined. One of the easiest parameters to use is open circuit cell voltage. Cells have a reduction in cell voltage when the cell approaches the discharged state. Declaring a cell fully discharged when open circuit voltage reaches a certain value at a specified temperature is an acceptable criterion for the discharged state. More energy could be extracted from the cell but this could result in damage. This is particularly true for a battery with several cells in series. Many cell technologies do not have a significant change in voltage as the cell discharges. In many technologies there is little change in cell voltage between a safely-discharged and potentially-damaged cell.

A cell's one hour discharge rate, which means the current that would take the cell from full charge to the discharged state is called C. As an example, a 10 ampere-hour battery, or C = 10 amperes, can supply 10 amperes for an hour before cell voltage reaches the minimum value.

Interestingly, energy capacity is typically given in ampere hours, which is not energy. However, if the voltage at which current is delivered is known, the ampere hour capacity can be multiplied by cell voltage and ampere hour capacity becomes watt hour capacity, and that is energy. This would work well if cell voltage was a constant but, unfortunately, it is not.

11.2.3 Nickel Cadmium Cell

An alternative technology to lead acid is the nickel cadmium cell, sometimes called NiCad; an attempt at pronouncing the chemical symbols, NiCd.

The NiCad battery is used in many applications to take advantage of its more salient characteristics;

1. Long life

NiCad batteries are good for about 1000 charge-discharge cycles while maintaining near full capacity. Higher quality lead-acid batteries, particularly those with absorbed glass mat, AGM, electrolyte, come close to this number. However, the lead acid capacity tends to continually reduce during the lifetime of the battery.

2. High current output

NiCads are capable of very high currents, without damaging the cells. This characteristic is also a disadvantage; if there is a failure in equipment powered by NiCads, the results can be fire and explosion. It is important that NiCads be carefully protected from overloads.

3. Wide temperature operation

NiCads operate over a much wider range of temperatures than lead acid, being able to provide more than 60% of rated capacity at –30C. In addition, the equivalent series resistance of the cell does not deteriorate as much as other battery technologies and NiCads provide high currents at low temperatures. This makes NiCads attractive for turbine engine starting in cold climates.

4. Capable of being overcharged without damage

NiCads do not suffer damage for moderate overcharges, assuming the cell is not otherwise stressed, such as heat. This makes the battery technology attractive for trickle-charging applications, such as emergency lighting, including aircraft, power tools and other rechargeable applications.

5. Cell voltage remains constant during discharge

Cell voltage is not absolutely constant but more constant than most other battery types. A steady output voltage and low equivalent resistance to the end of charge makes the NiCad a star performer for battery operated tools.

6. Capable of fast charging

NiCads can be safely charged up to and beyond C. This means that a fully depleted NiCad can be recharged in less than an hour. The longest life of a NiCad is for cells charged more slowly, say, C/10. However, well-designed NiCads specifically made for rapid charge applications such as cordless power tools can provide 1000 charge/discharge cycles.

7. Good energy density

The energy capacity of a NiCad is on par with lead acid but not as good as some of the newer technologies. NiCads can usually supply more capacity at a discharge rate less than the one hour rate which permits NiCads, in some applications, to be superior to lead acid. However, NiCads are not suited for very long discharge times such as powering solid state memories for years. The NiCad's self-discharge rate from internal leakage currents is such that the battery would self-discharge before the year is up. Generally, secondary batteries are not used for long-term low current applications.

11.2.4 Methods of charging

Two basic methods of charging have been employed in past years; constant voltage and constant current. If constant current charges a NiCad without determining full charge state, the charging current must be less than the safe trickle charge current. This produces a slow but safe charge with a simple circuit.

When a battery used with an engine generator is the primary source of power for avionics and other equipment, the charging method is usually constant voltage. As discussed previously, the actual voltage avionics equipment receives is the charging voltage. Fig. 11.1 shows a simplified diagram of a power generation system using constant voltage. The output from the generator is regulated and that voltage applied to the storage battery. The charging current is a function of the state of charge, in that a depleted battery has reduced cell voltage and will then cause higher charging current. This produces the desirable effect; the more a battery is discharged the greater the charging current.

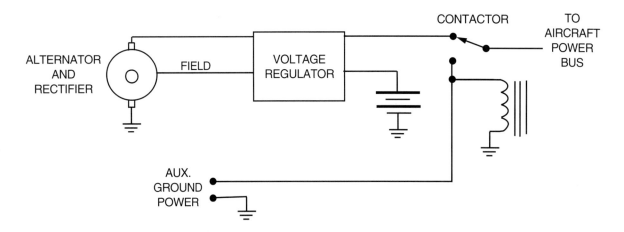

Fig. 11.1 Simplified aircraft battery charging system

For a fast charge, a constant voltage source with low series resistance produces a quick charge because charging current can be much greater than the trickle charge current. If the charge voltage is equal to the full charge cell voltage, charge current will automatically stop when full charge is reached. The problem with this method is that cell voltage is a function of temperature, age of the cell and other factors, and they must be taken into account when setting the charging voltage.

392

11.2.5 Determining Full Charge

Some positive characteristics of the NiCad battery make it difficult to determine when full charge is reached. As mentioned previously, the cell voltage of a fully charged NiCad cell is higher than a discharged cell. However, this must be corrected for a variety of factors. Actual cell voltage is difficult to use as an end-of-charge indicator but the rate of rise is easy to detect.

The temperature of a cell increases as full charge approaches. This is because more energy is being dissipated as heat, rather than transferred to the chemistry of the cell. This temperature rise affects full charge voltage but is also a good indicator of end of charge.

Also, the NiCad begins to outgas as it reaches full charge and the internal pressure of the cell rises. This is difficult to measure and is seldom used.

A good determination of full charge during the charging process can be obtained if cell voltage, charging current and cell temperature are analyzed to determine full charge condition. Circuits that analyze these parameters are usually called, "smart chargers".

11.2.6 Memory Effect

The NiCad battery is notorious for a phenomenon that many other battery technologies exhibit. If a NiCad battery is repeatedly charged, then only partially discharged before being recharged, the apparent capacity of the cells is reduced. This is called the "memory effect" as the battery seems to remember it was asked only to provide a small portion of its capacity, then adjusts so capacity reduces to that amount.

This effect can be "erased" by conditioning the battery. Essentially, to erase the memory effect, a battery is fully discharged and then recharged. This process is repeated and, with each charge/full discharge cycle, capacity of the battery will increase. Eventually, full capacity is restored.

Large NiCad batteries are removed from service and reconditioned in a shop environment. Small NiCads can be reconditioned automatically by a battery monitor circuit.

11.2.7 Nickel Metal Hydride

One problem with NiCad batteries is the extreme toxicity of cadmium. In the quest to find a replacement for cadmium, the nickel metal hydride, NiMH, cell was developed. Many characteristics of the NiCad cell are present in the NiMH cell, but there are advantages and disadvantages. Since the technology is new, many of the disadvantages may be reduced or eliminated by improved designs.

A main advantage of the NiMH cell is increased energy capacity for equivalent volume and weight, up to 50%. Also, high temperature capacity is somewhat greater.

On the other hand, the NiMH is inferior in cold temperature operation, particularly for charging. Also, the NiMH self discharge rate is somewhat greater than the NiCad but neither technology was intended to be a long-term storage device.

NiMH cell voltage, discharge profiles, cutoff voltages, the ability to provide very high discharge currents and charging processes are virtually the same as for the NiCad. In spite of the similarities there are small differences that dramatically affect battery performance. The voltage rise at end of charge is not as pronounced with NiMH and it is more temperature dependent than NiCads. On the other hand, the internal temperature rise rate is greater than NiCads and an accurate charge indicator should use a temperature sensor.

NiMH cells are less tolerant of overcharging. Trickle charging and long term charging rates of 0.03C to 0.05C should be used where C is the one hour rate.

The NiMH cell exhibits a memory effect similar to, but not as predominant as, NiCad and can be erased by conditioning.

11.2.8 Cell Reversal

Cell reversal is a danger in any series-connected battery. For battery applications requiring a voltage higher than the voltage of one cell, multiple cells are wired in series. Fig. 11.2 shows a battery consisting of three cells, where the equivalent circuit of a "real" cell is shown. The battery is discharging and providing energy to a load. Each cell shows an ideal voltage source and an internal resistance. The complete equivalent circuit of a battery cell would include a self-discharge current, a capacitance and a method of including the temperature dependence of the cell. These elements are not needed for this example. For Fig. 11.2 it is understood the cell voltage and internal resistance is a function of state of charge and temperature.

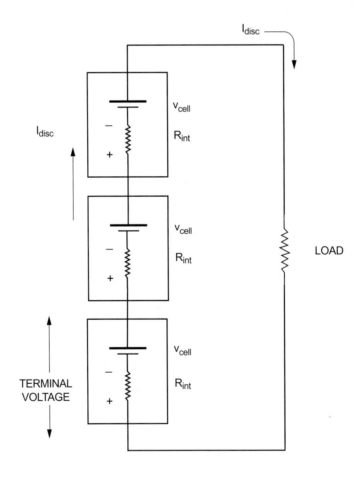

Fig. 11.2 Three-cell battery under discharge

As long as the terminal voltage of every cell is greater than zero, the life of the cell is not seriously jeopardized during discharge. The situation that would insure a positive cell terminal voltage is:

$$I_{disc}R_{int} < V_{cell} \qquad (11.1)$$

Where, I_{disc} is the discharge current, R_{int} is the internal resistance and V_{cell} is the cell voltage. The internal resistance and cell voltage are a function of the state of charge and temperature.

If the situation were modified to show a charging battery, it is impossible to reverse bias a cell and thus, cell reversal is only a problem during discharge.

Cell reversal usually affects only a single or small number of cells. Because of many factors, such as manufacturing tolerances, damage, temperature and state of charge, the internal resistance of cells could be quite different. This implies that one cell would enter cell reversal before others. When a battery consists of dissimilar cells, one cell will be much more prone to cell reversal than the remaining cells. Dissimilar in this context does not imply a battery was made with different capacity cells but that the cells have become different capacity because of wear and tear.

11.2.9 Thermal Runaway

Thermal runaway is a problem for the charging process. As shown in Fig. 11.3, a simple method for charging NiCad and other batteries is to provide a constant voltage source where there is a limiting resistance and the open circuit voltage of the charger is the actual end of charge voltage of the battery. This method of charge, although simple, provides a cessation of charge when the battery reaches full charge. Because differences in cell voltages between an incomplete charge and full charge is small in a NiCad battery, in order to generate significant charging currents, the charger's internal resistance needs to be small. The charging current is set by the sum of the internal battery resistance and charger resistance.

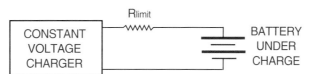

Fig. 11.3 Constant voltage charging

Because the full charge cell voltage is a function of temperature, the voltage in a constant voltage charger for NiCads should be a function of temperature. Because the difference between charger voltage and cell voltage is a function of so many variables, it is possible the charger voltage is higher than it should be.

Other factors come into play in this situation and that is the internal resistance of the NiCad cell. Internal resistance goes down with increasing temperature and capacity of the NiCad cell decreases with increasing temperature. These factors, coupled to the fact that overcharged cells increase in temperature, leads to a situation of thermal runaway. Decreasing internal resistance of the cells permits higher charging currents which only increase the internal temperature of the cell and current increases more. The reduced capacity implies that the battery is becoming increasingly overcharged. This leads to potential catastrophic battery failures. If a cell should short, this exacerbates the problem and serious consequences ensue.

The obvious solution to this problem is to not use constant voltage to charge NiCads. Many aircraft electrical systems charge their battery with constant voltage, which is not a serious problem with lead acid cells, as they do not exhibit thermal runaway.

To prevent thermal runaway in a constant voltage charging system is to reduce factors that cause the condition and implement preventative maintenance items. Some of the factors are:

A. Excessive engine cranking without cooling-off periods
B. Excessive charging voltage
C. Poor battery condition
D. Poor battery ventilation
E. Cells low on electrolyte
F. Cell imbalance

11.2.10 Battery Reconditioning

To prevent thermal runaway and other battery failures, batteries should be inspected and reconditioned on a regular schedule. This includes checking for imbalance between cells, "erasing" the memory effect, cleaning, checking leakage currents for individual cells and checking electrolyte levels. The battery box should be cleaned of any electrolyte and vents checked or replaced. Lead acid batteries are not usually reconditioned, as they are much less expensive than NiCads and are simply replaced.

Most aircraft NiCad batteries have replaceable cells so that imbalances can be repaired by replacing individual cells.

There are battery maintenance shops that provide these services using computer-operated equipment that insures safe and long battery life.

11.2.11 Primary Cells for Aircraft Use

There are applications for primary cells in aircraft. One universal application is emergency locator transmitters, ELTs. Another application is for real-time clocks for the time-keeping portion rather than the display. Another application is powering memories to hold data during power down periods.

There are long life batteries with a shelf life of 5 to 7 years. These include lithium manganese dioxide, $LiMnO_2$, lithium thionyl chloride, $LiSoCl_2$, and $LiSO_2$ lithium sulphur dioxide.

The $LiSO_2$ battery has outstanding characteristics, making it an excellent candidate for long shelf life applications. However, some years ago, $LiSO_2$ batteries got a bad reputation when some early models exploded, leaked and caught fire. This prompted the FAA to issue TSO C-97, which mandates testing of $LiSO_2$ cells for a variety of safety issues.

$LiSO_2$ cells are suited for applications that require short bursts of energy, such as the 406 MHz ELT. They are also suited for wide temperature applications from -40C to 70C. Shelf life is from 5 to 7 years. The battery has a constant output voltage until discharge.

Ultrasonic "pingers" which locate flight data recorders and cockpit voice recorders are typically powered by lithium batteries.

For the ELT, common alkaline technology is sufficient. Alkaline batteries are much less expensive but have to be replaced on a shorter schedule.

11.2.12 Battery Safety

Batteries are potentially dangerous devices, containing toxic and corrosive chemicals. When a battery is charged, it gives off gasses which may be flammable, toxic and corrosive. The battery can build up excessive pressure, or generate unsafe amounts of heat and catch fire. The battery can supply huge amounts of electrical energy, which can cause fires outside the battery. Although some battery technologies are safer than others in some regards, there is no safe battery. The FAA in FAR 23.1335 has addressed this fact.

The FAR states that safe battery temperature and pressure must be maintained under all possible charge and discharge conditions. The rule specifically mentions charging a completely discharged battery and the dangers of a fully charged battery with a short circuit.

The FAR recognizes that batteries will emit liquids and gasses but orders that these emissions not damage surrounding structures or equipment. Generally, this implies that batteries be enclosed in a sealed container with venting to the atmosphere for gasses.

NiCads are addressed by FAR 23.1335. The regulation requires that the charging system be designed to prevent overheating which would lead to thermal runaway. Also, an over temperature warning system must be provided which includes a means of disconnecting the battery from the charging source.

Small batteries have been a source of news, particularly in notebook computers. Potentially exploding and flammable batteries have precipitated massive recalls. It is true that batteries that are dropped can cause internal shorts and subsequent failures but this is rare, and once a battery has been properly installed in a well-designed holder, there are no incidents of exploding batteries.

New-design batteries with very high energy density are technologies that have the largest potential for catastrophic failures because high energy density does not allow for rapid heat removal. However, modern batteries are constructed with internal sensors and used with "smart chargers" which reduce the chances for catastrophic failures.

11.2.13 Quality of the Power Supply

In addition to variations in average DC voltage, the DC supply is contaminated with fast voltage variations due to changing loads. If a motor is turned on then removed from the DC supply, the sudden loss of load can sharply increase supply voltage. This transient is due to energy supplied from equipment on the power supply line back to the line in response to the sudden change in battery voltage. Transient voltage can be up, down or both, depending on the nature of the load change.

Transient voltages can be high and last for microseconds. Avionics must be tested to be sure they are not damaged by transients. The problem is that we cannot predict the nature of the transient. What is needed is a representative transient against which avionics are tested, with an estimate of the worst case. Passing the test should raise confidence for installed avionics.

Such a voltage transient is described in RTCA document DO 160E. It outlines the nature of the

DC power supply, as well as a large number of environmental conditions for avionics equipment. Levels of voltage transients and other parameters were determined by experience in a typical aircraft environment. To gain a feeling for the environment affecting avionics, it is enlightening to look at DO 160E.

Generating AC in an aircraft presents obstacles. Generators are typically powered from engines operating at varying shaft speeds. For generating DC, shaft speed determines output voltage. Rotating shaft generators are AC generators, with DC output obtained by mechanically or electronically changing AC to DC. The historical mechanical method is a commutator on a rotor, while the present method uses solid state rectifiers to change alternator AC to DC. The frequency of the AC output is not important. Voltage can be regulated by means other than affecting the alternator's shaft speed.

In the case of AC power, frequency may not be allowed to vary by a large amount. Transformers, power supplies and motors are designed for 400 Hz. A frequency variation of ten percent will cause no problems. But to any one who has inadvertently tried it, 400 Hz equipment does not operate safely at 60 Hz, a nearly seven to one ratio of power supply frequency. Since the frequency of an AC generator is directly proportional to angular shaft velocity, a seven to one change in frequency is equivalent to a seven to one change in shaft speed. Such variation is not unknown in a reciprocating or turbine engine.

An AC generator is coupled to the aircraft engine with a constant speed drive. The device is large, heavy, expensive and critical because it directly connects to the engine. There are alternatives. The first is a dedicated turbine with constant shaft velocity for generating electrical power. This is the auxiliary power unit or APU. Not only does it provide 400 Hz electrical power but DC power, hydraulic pressure and compressed air. Hydraulic pressure operates such items as exit stairs and cargo doors, while the compressed air starts turbine engines. In most aircraft, the APU is used only when the main engines are not operating. One advantage of power generated by main engines is that, in larger aircraft, there are at two to four engines. This provides important redundancy without installing multiple APUs.

In smaller aircraft, where only a small amount of 400 Hz power is required, a static inverter is the source. This device changes 28 or 14 volts DC to 400 Hz AC at constant voltage and frequency. The term static means that nothing rotates, in contrast to older DC to AC converters with moving parts. Early converters used DC motors operating at a constant speed that turned an AC generator to create 400 Hz AC. These devices are called "rotary converters". It is a toss-up on which is the ugliest; a constant speed drive or a rotary converter, but if 400 Hz AC is required, one of the two was often used. Modern switching power supplies now generate AC power with high purity, stability and efficiency. It is expected that future AC power, when needed, will be provided by a large static inverter.

11.3 Avionics Environment According to DO-160

The avionics environment is a function of so many variables it is not possible to set clear limits. Environment is a statistical playing field, with variations in temperature, pressure, humidity, power supply voltages, etc. Equipment may operate at elevated temperature and high power supply voltage---or at each extreme individually, but not together. If equipment is subject to high temperature and high supply voltage simultaneously it may fail. There is also time. Equipment at extremes of temperature and power supply for an extended time increase the chance of failure.

The most accurate test is to operate the equipment in its intended environment. Will all extremes occur together? Should equipment be subject to the highest power supply voltage, highest temperature and lowest atmospheric pressure simultaneously? For this example, it is unlikely that highest temperature and lowest atmospheric pressure would occur together. The lowest temperature usually occurs at the highest altitude or lowest pressure, not the highest temperature.

On the practical side, it is expensive and time consuming to test at all environmental extremes simultaneously. Some manufacturers test under simulated aircraft conditions such as a cold start, application of vibration, temperature increase, atmospheric pressure decrease and so on. This simulates an aircraft from a cold start, engines running, taking off and reaching cruise altitude. The tests are done in real time; if a test runs 100 hours, the simulation is of 100 hours' flying time. Since the mean time between failure, MTBF, is usually measured in thousands of hours, the tests take that time. The good news is they may be performed 24 hours a day, seven days a week with automatic test equipment. It still takes over 41 days to accumulate 1000 hours of test time.

Not all aircraft are started cold, then warmed up. An aircraft sitting on the ramp at a desert airport in summers starts hot, then cools at altitude. Simulated tests can follow any profile, but are still done in real time. One method of shortening environmental reliability tests is to conduct them under conditions beyond the real world. Accelerated life tests and reliability testing using overstresses are not uncommon in the industry.

RTCA document DO-160(E) outlines environmental conditions for all avionics unless otherwise specified. When a piece of equipment is tested for TSO (Technical Standard Order) compliance, operational characteristics are covered in the DO- document for that type of equipment , while the environment outlined in DO-160(E) is applied. The test limits in DO-160(E) represent the worst possible conditions. These limits are not considered overstresses and tests performed to these limits are not considered accelerated life tests. Tests performed to DO-160(E) are *minimum* performance compliance tests for the purpose of granting a TSO.

Before looking into DO160(E), it is helpful to see how location affects the environment. The least hostile location for avionics is in the passenger cabin. The area is heated or cooled and often pressurized. Passengers are isolated from the harshest environment of the aircraft.

The second location is in an unheated, unpressurized area. This is a common, often essential, site for avionics. Pressure can decrease to the aircraft's maximum altitude, which is more than 40,000 feet for jet transports. The temperature extreme is usually of low, rather than high, values. However, in an uncooled area or one without moving air, hot locations in summer can cause problems on or near the ground.

The worst location is near engines, an area not always possible to avoid. The full authority digital engine controller, FADEC, is an example of electronic components that must be near an engine. This is also a critical system where failures cannot be tolerated. The engine nacelle is not heated, cooled or pressurized, and it's close to powerful vibration. Depending on the location relative to the engine, high temperature is a significant problem.

RTCA DO-160(E) is summarized in the following section to show a range of environments by stating the easiest and most difficult conditions. In many cases there are many more than just two categories.

The examples here are tests where the greatest difference exists between classes of equipment. Not specified are complete test configurations; the numbers demonstrate the significant difference between avionics environments. The figures, however, are for the same test.

Temperature:
Least difficult; -15 - +55 degrees C
Most difficult; -55 - +70 degrees C

Pressure:
        Least difficult; 0 - 15,000 feet
        Most difficult; 0 - 70,000 feet

Temperature Variation:
        Least difficult; 2 degrees C per minute
        Most difficult; 10 degrees C per minute

Humidity: Least difficult; 95% relative humidity, 50 degrees C, 48 hours
        Most difficult; 95% relative humidity, 65 degrees C, 240 hours

Vibration: Least difficult: 0.5 G
        Most difficult: 40 G

Note: Vibration tests include a range of acceleration, displacement and frequencies. The numbers quoted here are highest and lowest accelerations in all tests. They illustrate how much the vibration environment varies with aircraft type. Helicopters have large displacement vibration at low frequencies, while turbine powered aircraft have higher frequency, lower displacement, but higher acceleration, vibration.

DC Power Supply, Operating
        Least difficult: 24.8V – 30.3V
        Most difficult; 22.0V – 29.5V

DC Power Supply, Emergency
        Least difficult; 20V
        Most difficult; 18V

DC Power Supply Surge Voltage
        Least difficult; 46.3V
        Most difficult; 80 V

Audio Frequency Audio Susceptibility
        Least difficult; 1.4V RMS up to 15 kHz
        Most difficult; 1.4V RMS, linearly decreasing with frequency from 15 kHz to 150 kHz

Induced Signal Susceptibility
        Least difficult; 360 volt/meter
        Most difficult; 1800 volt/meter

Radio Frequency Susceptibility
        Least difficult; 1 mV
        Most difficult; 5000 mV

Radiated Radio Frequency Energy
        Least difficult; 55 dB mv/m
        Most difficult; 35 dB mv/m

Lightning Induced Transient Susceptibility
        Least difficult; Test voltage = 50V. Test current = 100 amps.
        Most difficult; Test voltage = 1600V. Test current = 5000 amps.

11.4 HIRF

HIRF, high intensity radiated fields, is sometimes called high intensity RF. HIRF has been an environmental consideration in recent times. Many tests and requirements outlined in DO-160 have developed over much of the history of avionics. (Actually, DO-160 replaced an earlier document that was in existence since the 1950s.) The current document, DO-160(E), was approved in 2004. Certainly, temperature, pressure and power supply disturbances affect any technology including vacuum tubes in the 40 or so years before solid state devices found their way into aviation electronics.

Solid state devices brought great improvements; smaller, low power operation and seemingly unlimited life. The first devices could not operate at high frequencies but that quickly changed. Solid state devices could do anything a vacuum tube could, and more.

In spite of the benefits, there were significant deficiencies. Solid state devices are vulnerable to burnout from excessive voltage or current. If the devices are overheated they "run away" that is, become even hotter and self-destruct. Engineers were not accustomed to this fragility. Vacuum tubes operated at high voltage in the first place and additional high voltage from a power supply might cause arc-over but most tubes survived. As far as temperature, vacuum tubes operated at high temperatures, becoming so hot they glowed cherry red. Engineers needed to be aware of overstresses to solid state devices and provide protection from over voltage, over temperature and electrical transients.

Specifications and tests for high transient voltages for power sources and external electric fields were developed in RTCA documents to protect the new solid state equipment.

The appearance of computers in aircraft electronics brought forth additional concerns about electric field and power supply transients. The microprocessor had a nasty habit of becoming "glitched" and running amok. Although the microprocessor was an ideal candidate for aircraft control, the thought of it running wild while connected to control surfaces brought new concerns about high electric fields.

Electromagnetic field generators and wiring abound in an aircraft. Some of the more significant generators are the many radio transmitters carried aboard. Transmitting power ranges to 500 watts and higher. Carrier frequencies start at a few MHz for HF communications and progress to 10 GHz for weather radar. Fortunately, higher frequencies can be filtered from wires that enter an avionics unit because the carrier frequencies are much higher than a typical signal frequency.

One electromagnetic field too low in frequency to be filtered but very in high amplitude is a lightning strike. In a military aircraft, a large electric field similar to a lightning strike results from an atmospheric nuclear detonation. Another source of HIRF is the large number of high power FM broadcast stations emitting megawatts of power on frequencies close to the VHF communications and navigation bands.

An aircraft struck by lightning is not uncommon. Although flying on an aircraft that takes a direct hit is a memorable experience, aircraft are not often seriously damaged. What is dangerous, however, is when avionics are affected by high electric fields. Because of this, more recent versions of DO-160 include tests that simulate lightning effects.

11.5 EMC: Electromagnetic Compatibility

The environmental problems of avionics systems discussed thus far concern external disturbances. It is also important that equipment not interfere with other systems aboard the aircraft by generating electromagnetic fields or transient voltages on power sources. Electromagnetic compatibility, EMC, is to design equipment that neither generates, nor is susceptible to, interference.

It is not possible to design an electronic system more elaborate than a flashlight that does not generate electromagnetic fields. A certain amount of radiation emanates from everything. Similarly, it is not possible for electronic systems to withstand all electric fields, regardless of amplitude. The concept is to reduce radiated fields as much as possible and operate with a comfortable margin. Techniques include shortening leads, insuring lines with high frequency signals do not run parallel to those that exit the equipment and other techniques. Shielding encloses circuits with signals that are likely to radiate in a conductive container, such as high frequencies and high voltages.

Digital signals are notorious for causing interference. Voltages are significant, typically 5 volts peak to peak. Rise and fall times are short. Finally, the typical digital system synchronizes signals to a master clock, so harmonics are phase coherent. This means harmonic energy increases the field intensity. The good news is that supply voltages for logic circuits are decreasing. On the other hand, clock frequencies of digital devices are increasing.

11.6 LRU: Line Replaceable Units

To understand line replaceable units, consider the term "line". When an aircraft is in service it is said to be "on line". For civilian aircraft, to be on line, the aircraft is carrying passengers, cargo or both. The aircraft may have passengers on board at the time maintenance is performed. In the case of the military, on line means an aircraft is ready for immediate flight or is in service training for tactical missions.

In the civilian sector, when an aircraft is not carrying passengers, even for a short period such as the middle of the night, significant maintenance is performed and the aircraft is not considered on line. With this understanding, let's look at characteristics of equipment that can be replaced on line.

First, a line replaceable unit, LRU, must not require complex removal procedures. Typically, an avionics LRU is removed and a replacement installed with minimal or no tools. Also, an LRU depends on where it is located. An example is an antenna which can be removed from the outside of the aircraft and its cable withdrawn from the hole. The old antenna can be replaced by one person from the outside. Take the same antenna and mount it with nuts on the inside of the fuselage. Now, two persons are required; one to hold the nuts on the inside and a second to turn the screws on the outside. It is likely that interior parts of the aircraft must be removed, such as a section of floor, to gain access to the nuts. This antenna is no longer an LRU.

Secondly, an LRU must be replaced without extensive testing. Ideally, there should be no testing or adjusting. Some avionics need to be adjusted for other items in the aircraft. An example is an inexpensive ATCRBS transponder. When a transponder is installed, it is often necessary to adjust its frequency to compensate for the antenna on the aircraft. This calls for a test set and, for larger aircraft, two persons. Even though the procedure can be performed in less than an hour, this transponder pushes the limits of the LRU definition.

Third, an LRU must be rugged. There should be no delicate appendages to become damaged while transported to the line. Typically, an LRU has recessed connectors and rugged cases to avoid damage. An LRU is stored in a shop, tossed in the back of a pickup and driven over speed bumps to the aircraft. There's often an aircraft full of passengers that can't take off until the replacement black box is installed.

The most common LRUs are the so-called "black boxes" that can be removed by manually operated fasteners and pulled from the mounting tray. Usually, an operating check insures that the new LRU fixed the problem.

11.7 ARINC Type Equipment

If a light bulb needs replacing, one thinks nothing of installing a new one in place of the failed one. The reason is that old and new bulbs share common characteristics. Socket dimensions are the same, as are voltages. This concept is called "form, fit, and function". A major factor is that the standards don't describe what is *inside* the bulb---but only the external factors which assure interchangeability. There are, in fact, energy-saving lamps with a power supply which allows an energy-efficient fluorescent to directly replace an incandescent lamp. Light from the energy-saving lamp is whiter and it takes a second to strike an arc, but it screws into an incandescent fixture. This meets the criteria of "form, fit, and function".

There are several series for avionics form, fit, and function, which include the most common LRUs defined by AEEC, the Airlines Electronics Engineering Committee, a branch of ARINC. These black boxes, have the same physical dimensions and fit into the same mounting hardware. Pins on connectors are the same and compatible. Not only do the same signals appear on the same pins, levels are specified. The black box of any manufacturer can be installed with the assurance that size and connections are the same.

Some new LRUs consume less current than older versions. If a replacement LRU has lower power consumption, it will operate satisfactorily . A maximum current drain is specified so the circuit breaker for primary power handles the current for units of any manufacture.

Many ARINC-type LRUs have forced air cooling applied through the mounting shelf. ARINC boxes fit into mounting hardware that positions them over cooling holes. The amount of air is controlled by the size of the openings in the LRU. Small LRUs requiring less cool air reduce the flow with smaller holes.

The LRU is mounted in a slide-in tray with tie down fasteners. The fasteners are fitted with finger knobs that can be tightened without tools. Later mounts have torque limiting knobs. This prevents a technician from exerting excess force that could damage or overtighten the fastener. Performance of the unit is specified by ARINC so when an LRU is replaced with that of another manufacturer, operation will be the same.

An important point about ARINC avionics: It does not matter *how* specifications are met. One manufacturer may design only with silicon transistors, while another adopts integrated circuits. As long as the LRU functions the same way, fits into the same mounting and gives the same level of performance, there are no restrictions on how this is accomplished.

11.8 Fault Tolerance

It is unlikely that complex aircraft always have every component functioning. If an aircraft were grounded until every component was flawless, it would never take off! There is no doubt that virtually all aircraft are flying with something broken. A darkened reading light over a cabin seat may cause an unhappy passenger, but is no reason to cancel the flight . If the reading light is over the captain's seat, the situation changes. Some equipment is simply more important than others. Even an essential item such as a communications radio can be inoperative without compromising safety of flight. With three radios, for example, one faulty unit allows sufficient remaining communications. Many aircraft have only two communications radios.

Flying safely with known, malfunctioning equipment is called fault tolerance. The three communications radios are a simple example of the concept. One more radio than is normally found on aircraft provides more than minimal safety if one radio is out of service.

There is a limit on how much and what equipment, must operate. A minimum equipment list, MEL, describes what a specific aircraft absolutely requires to be functional before flight. The list includes obvious items such as engine instruments, lights and navigation equipment. It contains not-so-obvious items such as "fasten seat belt" lights, exit indicators, fire extinguishers and life rafts. The MEL may contain small, apparently insignificant, items that can ground an aircraft.

The concept of fault tolerance provides a backup or substitute when equipment fails. Let us look at this in a slightly different way. Many items of equipment aboard an aircraft contain a computer. Imagine a VOR receiver and DME operating together. Each has a computer. Let us say the DME's software is installed in the VOR computer and vice versa. Imagine that communications lines are added so the two units can exchange data. Now if the DME computer fails, the VOR computer processes DME data and the DME continues to operate. Both DME and VOR are now using the same computer and should it fail, both units become inoperative. The two units, however, may have to function only a few hours, until the defective DME is replaced. The flight crew, in fact, may never be aware that a computer failed!

This scenario raises interesting questions. First, if there is no indication of failure, the DME computer will not be fixed until the VOR computer fails---and both units cease functioning. Now the flight crew is painfully aware of the failure---and the advantages of fault tolerance are lost. In fact, it caused *two* units to fail. If the DME computer failure were not known to the pilots, but known to the maintenance crew, the DME computer will be fixed in due time and the advantages of fault tolerance preserved. There are maintenance panels or terminals where a fault can be annunciated outside the cockpit. The second question is, if one computer can do the job for DME and VOR , why not use one computer? This is a valid question and considered in a later section.

Fault tolerance has difficult problems to be addressed. First, it is necessary to determine that a system has failed. It may appear that the flight crew could easily spot a failure and press a "fault" switch. It is not always possible, however, to determine a failure. For the DME example, a failure can be the wrong distance. How would the flight crew know the displayed distance is wrong? If two DMEs are on board, one distance may be compared to the other, a technique pilots often use. But what would happen if two units disagreed? Which one is wrong?

One solution is to perform "test" calculations and compare results to the known answer. These tests may read data from a port, adding constants, inverting, and a variety of other manipulations, and outputting the answer to a port where a hardware comparator determines if the result is correct. If the computer makes errors, a hardware "watch dog" can shut it down. These "calculations" can be distributed within software so certain actions take place in proper order only when the program is running correctly.

The problem with this type of fault detection is the test must not interfere with normal operation of the computer. There should be no situation where a program running properly will not run the test, or vice versa. A second problem is the hardware comparator; its failure could cause a functioning computer to shut down.

Generally, any device, hardware or software that detects a fault, is itself a possible fault. The fault detector can overlook a fault or cause an unwarranted shut down. It is very important that any fault detection scheme be simple, so all failure modes are easily and accurately analyzed. Fault tolerance also requires a method of detecting the fault and a method of "patching around" it.

The "patch" in this context is not used to stop a leak. In a broadcast studio, audio signals in and out of various pieces of equipment are brought to a "patch panel". It has a large number of electrical jacks for inserting and removing cables. When no jacks are connected, the studio is operating in the normal mode. If the mode has to be changed, to use a microphone in another studio, for example, it's quickly connected by inserting a patch cord into the panel.

Now imagine that an amplifier fails. If the studio has a spare, it can be used in place of the failed unit by inserting two patch cords from the input of the failed amplifier to the substitute amplifier and from the output of the substitute amplifier to the failed amplifier. This is called "patching around" the failed amplifier.

Another concept is the nature of a failure. A failure is usually thought of as a circuit that ceases to operate because of a bad component. But this is only a part of the story. Software can also fail. When it is developed, software is exercised every possible way to determine what failures may occur. One that's readily detected is when a software routine does not produce the desired result. Software errors that are very difficult to locate produce errors for only a specific set of inputs. It is nearly impossible to test software for every sequence of inputs. There can be a sequence that causes failure only once in a very long time.

Detecting failure is a key item in fault tolerance. Besides a "watchdog," another method provides redundancy and compares results of redundant systems. Two systems performing the same function are required if a failure is detected because a good system must be patched in to replace the faulted system. If only two systems are available, the results of one system can be compared to the other. Should they disagree, however, there is no way of knowing which is functioning correctly. It is similar to a tie in voting; there is no winner. If three systems are used, there would be a winner. If two systems failed simultaneously, there would be no agreement, resulting in a three-way tie with no winner, but this highly improbable.

What if two systems fail simultaneously and agree, and a third system disagrees? This is particularly bad because the two failed units would appear to be good, while the remaining good unit would be faulty. This situation, as we will see, must be avoided.

To use a voting technique, three systems must be performing the same function. Systems that benefit most from fault tolerance are autopilots, navigation computers and other complex systems. Three identical systems will not accomplish the desired result. If a fault is due to hardware, it produces a false output which is detected. If the fault is a software bug, all three units exhibit the same behavior and the error goes undetected. If two of the three units share the software with the bug, the good unit appears to be faulted .

Assume each of the three units has different software. It is unlikely, in this case, that three disparate programs would produce the same error. The word disparate is key in this. The development of software involves tools to develop code and to convert it to machine language for the computer. Errors can be introduced at any step of software development. If an error is due to a compiler, and all three use the same compiler, simultaneous error can result. The microprocessor, itself, can make errors. There was a well-publicized case of a microprocessor that erred only in division. It was exceedingly small but if an algorithm requires considerable division, the error accumulates.

Finally, there are program errors. A programmer might have a favorite, but flawed, algorithm that is used frequently. Even if the flaw is slight, the algorithm might fail under certain conditions. The result is software with a potential failure mode.

Ideally, if three computer-based systems participate in a voting process, they should use different microprocessors, be programmed in different languages and not share any algorithms. This should extend to avoiding the same programmers developing any part of the computer algorithms.

11.9 Computer Architecture

Computers are everywhere aboard aircraft. The first airborne computer was the Norden bombsight during World War II. It took air speed, heading and ordinance information and accurately calculated the drop point. It vastly improved bombing accuracy. Computers of this sort also improved navigation by using much the same information, such as wind velocity and heading.

In spite of peacetime application of airborne computers, most were found in military applications. Electronic computers followed the war but airborne computers were mainly mechanical. The original bombsight was improved, but with later mechanical technology.

The vacuum tube was not suited for computers. Early machines were behemoths that spent a significant part of their life being repaired, primarily for failed vacuum tubes. There were attempts to install electronic computers in military aircraft using rugged subminiature vacuum tubes.

Airborne computers had to wait for the transistor. Semiconductors became available in the late 1950s and it did not take long before solid state digital computers appeared in aircraft. A decade after the
introduction of transistors, the integrated circuit became a reality. Progress was now on a high-speed roll. Advanced computers got aboard military and larger civil aircraft, but the trip was far from ended.

About a decade after integrated circuits appeared, a silicon chip that would change electronics forever was introduced. Called the microprocessor, it was a "computer on a chip"---well, most of the computer. It processed four bits at a time and was programmable. This means the same chip could solve navigation problems, fly the airplane or control the front panel of a communications radio. The only difference is the software.

The microprocessor is small, versatile, and uses minimal power, making it an excellent component for aircraft large and small. In the civil world, technology progressed from no computers on aircraft to one in almost every new system

As large numbers of computers were installed, questions of duplication were posed. If two communications transceivers each had a microprocessor, why couldn't one microprocessor service two transceivers? There is some validity in this question. One answer is reliability, due to the redundancy of two computers. On the other hand, some computers work together, such as a navigation receiver and DME. If each has a computer, they must communicate, as VOR and DME operate as a pair. If one computer fails, the VOR/DME *system* is down. Therefore, it takes only one of the two computers to bring the complete system down; there are more chances of a computer failing because there are twice as many than required. In this example, it is more reliable to provide one computer to handle both DME and VOR.

With multiple computers aboard aircraft, it was becoming evident that distributing computing power would affect cost, reliability and performance of an airborne electronics system. The layout of such a system is its computer architecture. There are three basic types: distributed, central, and federated. Let's look at their relative advantages and disadvantages.

11.9.1 Central Architecture

All, or nearly all, computing power takes place at one location when using central architecture. The first advantage is there is only one computer. One LRU is stocked and there one software package to be developed and updated. Software can be shared among all subsystems. Since there is only one computer, more expensive hardware and software can be justified because they are shared among subsystems. A high-speed computer results in faster throughput for some applications. Since the computer is shared, a high-speed processor is necessary.

The disadvantage; there is only one computer and should it fail, so does every system using it. Every effort must be taken to insure highest reliability in the central computer. It makes sense to locate it in the most benign environment. Since there is only one computer, the investment in a heated, cooled and pressurized location is not as great as if the entire avionics suite is in a benign location. This alone enhances reliability of the computer.

Other methods of increasing central computer reliability include redundancy. This would seem contrary to the concept of the central computer. The idea was to reduce the number of computers and redundancy increases the number to two, three or more. If we consider the arithmetic, it may not be that bad. Assume that the central computer is calculating for 10 subsystems. This means the computer has replaced ten smaller computers. If the central computer is made triply redundant with a voter, ten computers are replaced with three, plus a voter. This is still an advantage.

When computer redundancy is employed, is it applied to ancillary devices such as the cases and power supplies? When a single supply powers three redundant computers, the supply becomes the critical item. In fact, the design must be very careful not to permit one computer to fail in a way that brings down an otherwise good power supply, or cause the other two computers to glitch or cease operating. Using protective devices between power supply and computers can prevent this failure.

Could there be a failure of the case, connectors and other mechanical components? It would seem unlikely that a case could cause a computer failure . However, a case provides important functions, such as cooling. Some systems have internal fans while others obtain cooling from the mechanical mounting of the case. Fans can fail and air filters clog with dirt. Mounts become loose and lose external cooling air. Temperature sensors fail to turn on cooling fans.

To provide true redundancy requires two or more computers with their own cases, mounts and cooling systems. This further reduces the attractiveness of the central computer. However, if the central computer is calculating for ten subsystems that otherwise would require ten computers, the economics favor the central computer.

To have pure central architecture, all calculations and processing are done by the central computer. By this we mean everything. If a signal is analog, the analog to digital conversion is performed in the central computer. Thus, an analog signal is transmitted to the computer where it is converted. If the output is analog, it is converted in the computer and transmitted as an analog signal. This insures that sensors and actuators, virtually, have no electronics at the sensor. This is one concept of central computer architecture. The central computer, which represents all the electronics, is located in a well-protected location. Peripherals are often in hostile locations and benefit from having the least amount of electronics.

Another disadvantage of central architecture is evident from the above. Signals transmitted from sensors to the central computer could be vulnerable to noise pickup. This is particularly true of analog signals. The solution is to convert analog signals to digital and transmit data via a digital data link with error detection to insure highest data integrity. This is, in fact, a good solution, but is against the concept of the central computer.

11.9.2 Distributed Architecture

The opposite of central architecture is distributed architecture. Computation is done at the sensors and only results are transmitted to other systems. As an example, consider a VOR receiver. When microprocessors appeared in aircraft, they were for specific calculations. A processor was included in the DME which controlled the transmitter, timed receipt of the reply, calculated distance and ground speed. Processors were slow, performing DME functions at a significant percentage of their maximum capability. It was common for even a basic DME to use two processors, one for the transmitter/receiver for distance and ground speed, a second processor to control displays. A modern processor can control several DMEs, VOR receiver, glide slope and more. It is possible for one fast processor to control all standard avionics systems---- and this is the attraction of centralized architecture.

In central architecture, analog signals for course deviation and even the navigation composite signal are transmitted to the central computer to be converted to digital and processed further. The indicator, which contains a resolver, transmits resolver output signals to the central computer for conversion and calculation. Resolver signals are analog and can be low level.

In distributed architecture, resolver signals are converted to digital at the indicator and transmitted to the VOR receiver as digital signals. Error detection can added , as in the case of transmission via ARINC 429 or 629. The receiver calculates course deviation and transmits a digital data word to the indicator, which converts digital to analog to drive the meter. Other equipment requiring the OBS resolver setting and CDI, such as an autopilot or navigation computer, are provided the information via a digital data bus.

Because there is no central computer, systems of this sort require significant communications between subsystems. The advantage is that if the VOR subsystem in the example fails, only the VOR system is affected. Any other system receiving data from the VOR that fails will have to resort to another system for data. This means, as an example, the autopilot isn't able to couple to the failed VOR but could couple to other VOR receivers, or continue to operate in other modes.

To understand how distributed architecture uses electronics at the sensor and how central architecture reduces electronics at the sensor, consider a ram air sensor. The device uses a pressure transducer to measure airspeed. Temperature is introduced into the calculation of airspeed for accuracy. In distributed computer architecture, ram air pressure is measured and converted to digital at the sensor, as well as temperature. A microcomputer at the sensor makes corrections as required by temperature and transmits the data on a data bus such as ARINC 429 or ARINC 629 to systems that require the data. Receiving systems in this example are airspeed indicator and air data computer.

Central computer architecture requires wires from temperature and pressure sensors to the central computer, which performs the A/D conversion and corrects for temperature. Wires from sensors to the computer can be long, as the computer is located in an interior, benign location. Data produced by these calculations, on the other hand, do not have to be transmitted any significant distance since the central computer performs the calculations, including the air data computer. Thus, data is stored in memory and available for calculations that require it.

The ram air sensor is outside the fuselage in the aircraft slip stream, about as harsh as an environment can be. The electronics can mount just inside of the fuselage, which is a little better. On the positive side, a small computer is required for such simple conversions and calculation, so electronics are minimal.

Another advantage of distributed computing is shown by the ram air sensor. In many cases, correction of ram air pressure as a function of temperature varies from one sensor to another. There could be variations from one manufacturer to another, or even from one unit to another. For the example of the ram air sensor, a manufacturer can store calibration factors specific to the sensor in the ROM of the unit. When a sensor is replaced, new calibration factors are automatically implemented. In a central processor, it necessary to provide the central processor with new calibration factors.

Distributed architecture provides faster computation because computers typically calculate only a small number of parameters. The computers are not required, therefore, to share computation time with other systems and maximum efficiency results.

11.9.3 Federated Architecture

A compromise between central and distributed is federated architecture. Instead of one central computer, aircraft functions are partitioned into a small number of sub systems. A "small number" means more than one and significantly less than the number of computers in a distributed system. As an example, in a civil aircraft, there may be a computer for navigation, one for communications, another for flight management and a third for engine control. A federated system can still employ some distributed computing when it makes sense.

Ideally, partitioning major subsystems should be such that serious failure in one subsystem does not greatly affect another area. As an example, an engine control subsystem has little to do with communications. Thus, the entire communications subsystem could be down, leaving the aircraft with emergency communications, but engine controls are unaffected.

Other partitions are not as easily separated. Flight management, communications and navigation systems are closely interconnected. A failure in the flight management system requires frequencies and navigation data to be manually entered, but not cause these systems to fail.

In most federated architectures, partitions are such that only the most critical processors require redundancy. In the previous example of partitioning the engine control computer is a definite candidate for redundancy, while flight management, although convenient, is not as critical. Communications and navigation computers could also be provided without redundancy as long as there are emergency back up modes for basic navigation and communications.

The future of airborne computer architecture is tending toward the federated, primarily in the airlines. The most difficult facet of centralized computer architecture is insuring interface compatibility. On the military side, the avionics system is purchased from one vendor who dictates compatibility. In the case of airlines, the concept of ARINC interchangeability fosters multiple vendors and cost competition. Thus, individual vendors of avionics sensors desire to use their own processors and software. If another vendor's computer will perform calculations, the ability to tailor the computer to hardware is lost.

Vendors choose computers and software to suit transmitters, receivers and other hardware in their units. Tradeoffs can be made between computation and hardware. To successfully implement highly centralized computing, it is necessary to define a large number of signals, both analog and digital, to connect sensor to computer. If data from the sensor is calculated in the sensor and transmitted to the central computer, interfacing is simplified. An example is DME; data is distance and ground speed. A standard data bus supplies the central computer with these data words. If the DME has no computing power, the central computer would tell the DME when to transmit, receive the reply, make calculations to determine distance, etc. The transmitter must transmit at specific times and a number of valid pulse pairs are received after the interrogation. The data bus is tied up during the time after transmission of the interrogation because it is not known when replies will be received. None of the data exchanged between DME and the central computer has error detection or correction and noise will degrade the system. The computing power has been removed from the DME at the expense of a critical communications link.

Glossary

A

ABS	Absolute
AC	Advisory Circular
A/C	Aircraft
ACARS	Aircraft Communications And Reporting System
ACAS	Airborne Collision Avoidance System
ACC	Area Control Center
ACP	Audio Control Panel
ADC	Air Data Computer
ADF	Automatic Direction Finder
ADI	Attitude Director Indicator/Attitude Direction Indicator
ADIRS	Air Data Inertial Reference System
ADIRU	Air Data Inertial Reference Unit
ADLP	Aircraft Data Link Processor
ADM	Air Data Module
ADS-B	Automatic Dependent Surveillance - Broadcast
ADSEL	Address Selective
AEEC	Airlines Electronic Engineering Committee
AES	Aircraft Earth Station
AFC	Automatic Frequency Control
AFCAS	Automatic Flight Control Augmentation System
AFCS	Automatic Flight Control System
AFSK	Audio Frequency Shift Keying
AGC	Automatic Gain Control
AGL	Above Ground Level
AHC	Attitude Heading Computer
AHRC	Attitude Heading Reference Computer
AHRS	Attitude Heading Reference System
AIDS	Aircraft Integrated Data System
AIM	Aeronautical Information Manual
AIMS	Aircraft Information Management System
ALC	Automatic Level Control
AM	Amplitude Modulation
AMLCD	Active Matrix Liquid Crystal Display
AMSRS	Aeronautical Mobile Satellite Route Service
AMSS	Aeronautical Mobile Satellite Service
AOA	Angle of Attack
AOC	Aircraft Operational Control
AOG	Aircraft On Ground (aircraft grounded due to component failure)
APU	Auxiliary Power Unit
ARINC	Aeronautical Radio, Inc.
ARSR	Air Route Surveillance Radar
ARTCC	Air Route Traffic Control Center
ASDE	Airport Surface Detection Equipment
ASDL	Aeronautical Satellite Data Link
ASM	Airspace Management
ASRS	Aviation Safety reporting System
ASTA	Airport Surface Traffic Automation
ATA	Air Transport Association, Actual Time of Arrival
ATC	Air Traffic Control
ATCC	Air Traffic Control Center
ATCRBS	Air Traffic Control Radar Beacon System
ATCSS	Air Traffic Control Signaling System
ATE	Along Track Error; Automatic Test Equipment
ATIS	Automatic Terminal Information System
ATLAS	Abbreviated Test Language for Avionics Systems
ATM	Air Traffic Management
ATN	Aeronautical Telecommunications Network
AUX	Auxiliary

B

BCAS	Beacon Collision Avoidance System
B CRS	Back Course
BER	Bit Error Rate
BFO	Beat Frequency Oscillator
BITE	Built In Test Equipment
bps	Bits Per Second
Bps	Bytes Per Second
BPSK	Binary Phase Shift Keying

C

C/A	Coarse/Acquisition
CAS	Calibrated Air Speed
CAT I	Category One ILS
CAT II	Category Two ILS
CAT III	Category Three ILS
C band	4 to 8 GHz
CCIR	International Radio Consultative Committee
CCITT	International Telegraph and Telephone Consultative Committee
CDI	Course Deviation Indicator
CDMA	Code Division Multiple Access
CDTI	Cockpit Display of Traffic Information
CDU	Control Display Unit
CFIT	Controlled Flight Into Terrain
CLR	Clearance (antenna)
CMC	Central Maintenance Computer
CMN	Control Motion Noise
CMU	Communications Management Unit
CNS	Communications, Navigation, Surveillance
CODEC	Coder/Decoder
COM, COMM	Communications
COP	Cross Over Point
CPA	Closest Point of Approach
CRC	Cyclic Redundancy Check
CRS	Course
CRT	Cathode Ray Tube
CSB	Carrier and Side Bands (ILS ground station)
CTOL	Conventional Takeoff and landing
CVR	Cockpit Voice Recorder
CW	Continuous Wave

D

DABS	Discrete Address Beacon System
DADC	Digital Air Data Computer
DADS	Digital Aid Data System
dB	Decibels
dBm	Decibels above one milliwatt
DDM	Differential Depth of Modulation
DFDR	Digital Flight Data Recorder
DFDU	Digital Flight Data Unit
DG	Directional Gyro
DGNSS	Differential Global Navigation Satellite System
DGPS	Differential Global Positioning Position
DH	Decision Height
DITS	Digital Information Transfer System (ARINC 429)
DLV	Detected Log Video
DME	Distance Measuring Equipment
DMU	Data Management Unit
DoD	Department of Defense
DPSK	Differential Phase Shift Keying
DSB	Double Side Band
DSBSC	Double Side Band Suppressed Carrier
DSP	Digital Signal Processing
DTMF	Dual Tone Multiple Frequency
DVOR	Doppler VHF Omni Range

E

EADI	Electronic Attitude Director Indicator
EASA	European Aviation Safety Agency
ECEF	Earth Centered, Earth Fixed
EFD	Electronic Flight Display
EFIS	Electronic Flight Instrument System
EGNOS	European Geostationary Navigation Overlay System
EGPWS	Enhanced Ground Proximity Warning System
EHSI	Electronic Horizontal Situation Indicator
EICAS	Engine Indicator and Crew Alerting System
ELBA	Emergency Locator Beacon, Aircraft

ELM	Extended Length Message		IRU	Inertial Reference Unit
ELT	Emergency Locator Transmitter		ITU	International Telecommunication Union
EMI	Electromagnetic Interference		IVSI	Instantaneous Vertical Speed Indicator
EPIRB	Emergency Position Indicating Radio Beacon			
ERP	Effective Radiated Power		**J**	
ESD	Electrostatic Discharge		JAA	Joint Aviation Authority
ETOPS	Extended Twin Operations			

F

FAA	Federal Aviation Administration
FAC	Flight Augmentation Computer
FADEC	Full Authority Digital Engine Control
FAF	Final Approach Fix
FANS	Future Air Navigation System
FAR	Federal Aviation Regulation
FBL	Fly By Light
FBO	Fixed Base Operator
FBW	Fly By Wire
FCC	Federal Communications Commission
FD	Flight Director
FDDI	Fiber Distributed Data Interface
FDM	Frequency Division Multiplexing
FDR	Flight Data Recorder
FEC	Forward Error Correction
FM	Frequency Modulation
FMC	Flight Management Computer
FMS	Flight Management System
FOG	Fiber Optic Gyro
FRUIT	Friendly Replies Unsynchronized In Time
FTE	Flight Technical Error

G

GA	General Aviation
GDOP	Geometrical Dilution of Precision
GEO	Geostationary Earth Orbit
GES	Ground Earth Station
GIC	GNSS Integrity Channel
GICB	Ground Initiated Comm B
GLNS	GPS Landing and Navigation System
GLNU	GPS Landing and Navigation Unit
GLONASS	Global Orbiting Navigation Satellite System
GLS	GPS Landing System
GMT	Greenwich Mean Time
GNSS	Global Navigation Satellite System
GPIB	General Purpose Instrumentation Bus
GPS	Global Positioning System
GS	Glide Slope, Ground Speed

H

HDG	Heading
HDOP	Horizontal Dilution of Precision
HF	High Frequency, 3 – 30 MHz
HIRF	High Intensity Radiated Field, High Intensity RF
HOW	Hand Over Word
HPA	High Powered Amplifier
HSI	Horizontal Situation Indicator
HUD	Head Up Display

I

IAS	Indicated Air Speed
IATA	International Air Transport Association
ICAO	International Civil Aviation Organization
ID	Identify
IF	Intermediate Frequency
IFE	In Flight Entertainment
IFF	Identification Friend or Foe
IFR	Instrument Flight Rules
ILS	Instrument Landing System
IMA	Integrated Modular Avionics
IMC	Instrument Meteorological Conditions
INMARSAT	International Maritime Satellite Organization
INS	Inertial Navigation System
IRS	Inertial Reference System

L

L1	GPS frequency 1 (1575.42 MHz)
L2	GPS frequency 2 (1227.60 MHz)
LAAS	Local Area Augmentation System
LADGPS	Local Area Differential GPS
L Band	750 MHz to 1550 MHz, approx.
LCD	Liquid Crystal Display
LED	Light Emitting Diode
LF	Low Frequency, 30 kHz – 300 kHz
LMM	Locator, Middle Marker
LO	Local Oscillator
LOC	LOCalizer
LOM	Locator Outer Marker
LOP	Line Of Position
LORAN	LOng RAnge Navigation
LORAN-C	Improved version of LORAN
LOS	Line Of Sight
LRM	Line Replaceable Module
LRU	Line Replaceable Unit
LSB	Least Significant Bit, Lower Sideband

M

MAP	Missed Approach Point
MASPS	Minimum Aviation System Performance Standard
MB	Marker Beacon
MDA	Minimum Descent Altitude
MEL	Minimum Equipment List
MF	Medium Frequency, 300 kHz to 3 MHz
MFD	Multi Function Display
MKR	Marker (beacon)
MLS	Microwave Landing System
MM	Middle Marker
MMIC	Monolithic Microwave Integrated Circuit
MOCA	Minimum Obstacle Clearance Altitude
MODEM	MOdulator DEModulator
MOPR	Minimum Operational Performance Requirement
MOPS	Minimum Operational Performance Standard
MSB	Most Significant Bit
MSL	Mean Sea Level
MTBF	Mean Time Between Failure
MTBR	Mean Time Between Removal
MTBUR	Mean Time Between Unscheduled Removal
MTI	Moving Target Indicator
MTL	Minimum Trigger Level
MTTF	Mean Time To Failure
MTTR	Mean Time To Repair
MTTUR	Mean Time To Unscheduled Removal

N

NAS	National Airspace System
NAV	NAVigation
NAVCOM	NAVigation/COMmunication
NDB	Non Directional Beacon
NIST	National Institute of Standards and Technology
NRZ	Non Return to Zero code
NTSB	National Transportation Safety Board

O

OAT	Outside Air Temperature
OBS	Omni Bearing Selector
OM	Outer Marker
OOK	On-Off Keying
OSI	Open System Interface

P

P1	First pulse (DME, transponder)
P2	Second pulse (DME, transponder)

P3	Third pulse (transponder)
PAM	Pulse Amplitude Modulation
PAR	Precision Approach Radar
PCIP	Precipitation
PCM	Pulse Code Modulation
P-Code	Precision code
PDME	Precision DME
PDC	Pre Departure Clearance
PDOP	Position Dilution Of Precision
PDS	Primary Display System
PFD	Primary Flight Display
PN	Pseudo Noise
PPI	Plan Position Indicator
PPM	Parts Per Million
PPS	Precision Position Service
PRF	Pulse Repetition Frequency
PRN	Pseudo-Random Noise
PRX	Proximity

Q

QPSK	Quadrature Phase Shift Keying

R

RA	Resolution Advisory
RAD ALT	Radio Altimeter
RAI	Radio Altimeter Indicator
RAIM	Receiver Autonomous Integrity Monitoring
RCS	Radar Cross Section
RGB	Red Green Blue
RLG	Ring Laser Gyro
RMI	Radio Magnetic Indicator
RMP	Radio Management Panel
RMS	Root Mean Square
RNP	Required Navigation Performance
RT	Remote Terminal, Receiver Transmitter
RTCA	Formerly "Radio Technical Commission for Aeronautics," now "RTCA Inc."
RTU	Radio Tuning Unit
RVR	Runway Visual Range
RVSM	Reduced Vertical Separation Minimums
RZ	Return to Zero code

S

SA	Selective Availability
SAR	Search And Rescue
SARSAT	Search And Rescue SATellite
SARPS	Standards and Recommended Practices
SAS	Stability Augmentation System
SAT	Static Air Temperature, Satellite
SATCOM	Satellite Communications
SBO	Side Bands Only
SCAT-1	Special CATegory One
SELCAL	SELective CALling
SID	Standard Instrument Departure
SLM	Standard Length Message
SLS	Side Lobe Suppression
SNR	Signal to Noise Ratio
SPI	Special Pulse Identification
SPS	Standard Positioning Service
SSB	Single Side Band
STAR	Standard Terminal Arrival
STC	Sensitivity Time Control, Supplemental Type Certificate
STP	Shielded Twisted Pair, Standard Temperature and Pressure

T

TA	Traffic Advisory
TACAN	TACtical Air Navigation
TAS	True Airspeed
TAT	Total Air Temperature
TAWS	Terrain Awareness Warning System
TBO	Time Between Overhaul,

TC	Type Certificate
TCAS	Traffic Alert and Collision Avoidance System
TFM	Traffic Flow Management
TDM	Time Division Multiplexing
TDMA	Time Division Multiple Access
TDOP	Time Dilution of Precision
TKE	Track angle error
TOAT	Total Outside Air Temperature
TOW	Time Of Week
TRACON	Terminal Radar Control
TRK	Track
TSE	Total System Error
TSO	Technical Standard Order
TT	Total Temperature
TWDL	Two Way Data Link

U

UHF	Ultra High Frequencies, 300 MHz – 3000 MHz
ULB	Underwater Locator Beacon
USB	Upper Side Band
UTC	Universal Coordinated Time
UUT	Unit Under Test
UTP	Unshielded Twisted Pair

V

VASI	Visual Approach Slope Indicator
VCO	Voltage Controlled Oscillator
VDL	VHF Data Link
VFR	Visual Flight Rules
VHF	Very High Frequency, 30 MHz – 300 MHz
VMC	Visual Meteorological Conditions
VOR	VHF Omnidirectional Range
VORTAC	VOR and TACAN (co-located facilities)
VOX	Voice
VSI	Vertical Speed Indicator
VSWR	Voltage Standing Wave Ratio

W X Y Z

WAAS	Wide Area Augmentation System
WGS-84	World Geodetic Survey 1984
WOW	Weight On Wheels
WPT	Waypoint
WX	Weather
WXI	Weather Radar Indicator
WXR	Weather Radar
X Band	8 GHz – 12.5 GHz
X channel	DME X channel
XCVR	Transceiver
XMTR	Transmitter
XPDR	Transponder
XTE	Cross Track Error
Y Channel	DME Y channel
Y-Code	Encrypted GPS code
YSAS	Yaw Stability Augmentation System
YD	Yaw Damper
Z	GMT (Greenwich Mean Time)
ZULU	GMT

412

Appendix A

ARINC Documents

ARINC No.	Description	Abbrev.	Issued	429 ID
701-1	Flight Control Computer System	FCCS	4/83	001
702-6	Flight Management Computer System	FMCS	6/94	002
703-2	Thrust Control Computer System	TCCS	10/83	003
704-7	Inertial Reference System	IRS	3/99	004
705-5	Attitude Heading Reference System	AHRS	4/85	005
706-4	Subsonic Air Data System	ADS	1/88	006
707-6	Radio Altimeter	RALT	4/97	007
708-6	Airborne Weather Radar	WXR	11/91	008
709-8	Airborne Distance Measuring Equip.	DME	10/88	009
710-10	Mark 2 Airborne ILS Receiver	ILS	11/97	010
711-10	Mark 2 Airborne VOR Receiver	VOR	2/02	011
712-7	Airborne ADF System	ADF	7/92	012
714-6	Mark 2 Airborne SELCAL System	SELCAL	8/90	014
715-3	Airborne Passenger Address Amplifier	PA AMP	7/84	015
716-10	Airborne VHF Comm. Transceiver	VHF COM	1/98	016
717-10	Flight Data Acquisition and Rec. Sys.	DEFDARS	4/98	017
718-4	Mark 3 Air Traffic Control Transponder	ATCRBS/S	12/89	018
719-5	Airborne HF/SSB System	HF	7/84	019
723-3	Ground Proximity Warning System	GPWS	1/88	023
724-9	Aircraft Comm Addressing and Rpt. Sys	ACARS	9/98	024
725-2	Electronic Flight Instruments	EFI	11/84	025
726-1	Flight Warning Computer System	FWCS	9/81	026
727-1	Airborne Microwave Landing System	MLS	8/87	027
731-3	Electronic Chronometer		11/98	031
732-1	Airborne Passenger Audio Tape Rep.		3/96	032
735-2	Traffic Alert and Collision Avoidance	TCAS	3/93	033
737-1	On Board Weight and Balance System		4/88	037
738-3	Air Data and Inertial Reference System	ADIRS	7/01	038
739-1	Multi Purpose Control and Display Unit	MCDU	6/90	039

ARINC No.	Description	Abbrev.	Issued	429 ID
743	Global Positioning System Receiver	GPS	3/90	043
745-2	Automatic Dependent Surveillance	ADS	6/93	045
746-4	Cabin Communications System	CCS	4/96	046
747-2	Flight Data Recorder	FDR	1/99	047
750-3	VHF Data Radio	VDR	11/00	050
751	Gate-Aircraft Terminal Link	Gatelink	1/94	051
752-1	Terrestrial Flight Telephone System	TFTS	12/95	052
753-3	HF Data Link System		2/01	053
755-2	Multi-mode Receiver	MMR	1/01	055
756-2	GNSS Navigation and Landing Unit	GNLU	2/00	056
757-2	Cockpit Voice Recorder	CVR	12/00	057
758-1	Communications Management Unit	CMU	2/98	058
760-1	GNSS Navigation Unit	GNU	3/00	060
762-1	Terrain Awareness and Warning System	TAWS	9/00	062
none	Thrust Management Computer	TMC		02A
none	Digital Fuel Gauging System (A310)			02C
none	Propulsion Discrete Interface Unit			03A
none	Autopilot Buffer Unit			03B
none	Tire Pressure Monitoring Unit			03C
none	Vibration Monitor, (737, 757, 767)			03D
none	Center of Gravity Control Computer			03E
none	Full Authority EEC-B			03F
767	Enhanced Airborne Flight Recorder		11/06	
781-1	Mark 3 Aviation Satellite Communication System		11/06	
801	Fiber Optic Connector		1/06	
802	Fiber Optic Cable		2/05	
803	Fiber Optic System Design Guidelines		1/06	
817	Avionics Digital Video Bus, Low Data Rate		6/06	
818	Avionics Digital Video Bus, High Data Rate		12/06	

Appendix B

RTCA Documents

ICD   Interface Control Document
MASPS Minimum Aviation System Performance Standards
MIS   Minimum Interoperability Standards
MOPS Minimum Operational Performance Standards
MPS   Minimum Performance Standards

DO No.	Type	Title	Issued
294A	-----	Guidance on Allowing Transmitting Portable Electronic Devices	2006
293	**MOPS**	Nickel-Cadmium and Lead Acid Batteries	2004
292	----	Assessment of Radio Frequency Interference Relevant to the GNSS L5/E5A Frequency Band	2004
291	----	Interchange Standards for Terrain, Obstacle, and Aerodrome Mapping Data	2004
289	**MASPS**	Aircraft Surveillance Applications (ASA)	2003
286A	**MASPS**	Traffic Information Service – Broadcast (TIS-B)	2005
285	----	Next Generation Air/Ground Communications (NEXCOM) VDL Mode 3 Interoperability	2003
283A	**MOPS**	Required Navigation Performance for Area Navigation	2003
282A	**MOPS**	Universal Access Transceiver (UAT) Automatic Dependent Surveillance – Broadcast	2004
276A	----	User Requirements for Terrain and Obstacle Data	2005
275	**MOPS**	Integrated Night Vision Imaging System	2001
274	----	NEXCOM Principles of Operation	2001
271	**MOPS**	Aircraft VDL Mode-3 Transceiver	2001
270	**MASPS**	Aeronautical Mobile Satellite Service as Used in Data Links	2001
269	----	Concepts for Integrating Flight Ops. and ATM Using Data Link	2001
267	**MASPS**	Flight Information Service Broadcasts Using Data Link	2001
266		Govt. and Industry Guidelines for NAS Analysis and Redesign	2000
265	**MOPS**	Aeronautical Mobile HF Data Link, HFDL	2000
264	----	Guidelines for Approval of the Provision and use of Air Traffic Services Supported by Data Communications	2000
263	----	Application of Airborne Conflict Management	2000
262	**MOPS**	Avionics Supporting Next Generation Satellite Systems	2000
260	**MOPS**	1090 MHz Automatic Dependent Surveillance-Broadcast, ADSB	2000
261	----	NAVSTAR/GPS L5 Signal Specification	2000
259	----	Applications Descriptions of Cockpit Display of Traffic Information, CDTI	2000

DO No.	Type	Title	Issued
258	----	Interoperability Requirements for ATS Applications Using ARINC 622 Data Communications	2000
257	MOPS	Depiction of Navigation Information on Electronics Maps	2000
256	----	Minimum Human Factors Standards for Air Traffic Services Provided via Data Communications Utilizing the ATN	2000
255	----	Requirements Specification for Avionics Computer Resources	2000
254	----	Design Assurance Guidance for Airborne Electronic Hardware	2000
253A	MOPS	GPS Local Area Augmentation System Airborne Equipment	2001
252	MIS	Automated Meteorological Transmission, AUTOMET	2000
251	----	NAS Plan for Air Traffic Services Data Link	2000
250	----	Guiding Principles for Air Traffic Services Provided via Data Communications Utilizing the ATN	2000
249	----	Development and Implementation Planning Guide for ADS-B	1999
247	----	The Role of the Global Navigation Satellite Services in Supporting Airport Surface Operations	1999
246B	ICD	GNSS-Based Precision Approach, LAAS	2001
245	MASPS	Local Area Augmentation System , LAAS	1998
243	----	Guidelines for Initial Implementation of Cockpit Display of Traffic Information	1998
242	MASPS	Automatic Dependent Surveillance- Broadcast, ADSB	1998
240	MOPS	Aeronautical Telecommunications Network, ATN, Avionics	1997
239	MOPS	Traffic Information Service, TIS, Data Link Communications	1997
238	----	Human Engineering Guidance for Data Link Systems	1997
236A	MASPS	Required Navigation Performance, RNP, for Area Navigation	2000
235	----	Assessment of Radio Frequency Interference Relative to the GNSS	1997
233	----	Portable Electronic Devices Carried Aboard Aircraft	1996
232	----	Operations Concepts for Data Link Applications of Flight Information Services	
229C	MOPS	GPS Wide Area Augmentation System	2001
228	MOPS	Global Navigation Satellite Systems Airborne Antenna Equipment	1995
227	MOPS	Lithium Batteries	1995
224A	MASPS	Advanced VHF Digital Data Communications Including Compatibility with Digital Voice Techniques	2000
223	MOPS	Context Management Equipment	1994
220	MOPS	Airborne Weather Radar with Forward-Looking Windshear Detection Capability	1993
219	MOPS	ATC Two-Way Data Link Communications	1993
218B	MOPS	Mode S Data Link Processor	2001
217	MASPS	DGNSS Instrument Approach System, Special Category I, SCAT I	1993
216	----	Minimum General Specification for Ground-Based Electronic Equipment	1993
215A	----	Guidance on Aeronautical Mobile Satellite Service, AMSS	1995
214	MOPS	Aircraft Audio Systems and Equipment	1993
213	MOPS	Nose-Mounted Radomes	1993
212	MOPS	Airborne Automatic Dependent Surveillance Equipment, ADS	1992
210D	MOPS	Geosynchronous Orbit Aeronautical Mobile Satellite Services, AMSS	2000

416

DO No.	Type	Title	Issued
204	**MOPS**	406 MHz Emergency Locator Transmitters, ELT	1989
202	**MASPS**	Global Positioning System	1988
199	----	Potential Interference to Aircraft Electronic Equipment from Devices Carried Aboard	1988
197A	**MOPS**	Active Traffic Alert and Collision Avoidance System I, Active TCAS I	1994
196	**MOPS**	Airborne VOR Receiving Equipment	1986
195	**MOPS**	Airborne ILS Localizer Receiving Equipment	1986
194	**MOPS**	Airborne Area Navigation Equipment Using LORAN-C Inputs	1986
192	**MOPS**	Airborne ILS Glide Slope Receiving Equipment	1986
191	**MOPS**	Airborne Thunderstorm Detection Equipment	1986
189	**MOPS**	Airborne Distance Measuring Equipment, DME	1985
186A	**MOPS**	Airborne VHF Communications Equipment	1995
185A	**MOPS**	Traffic Alert and Collision Avoidance Equipment II, TCAS II	1997
184	----	Traffic Alert and Collision Avoidance Functional Guidelines	1983
183	**MOPS**	Emergency Locator Transmitters	1983
181C	**MOPS**	ATCRBS/mode S Transponder	2001
180A	**MOPS**	Airborne Area Navigation Using a Single Co-located VOR-DME Sensor Input	1990
179	**MOPS**	Automatic Direction Finding, ADF, Equipment	1982
178B	----	Software Considerations in Airborne Systems and Equipment Certification	1992
176	----	FM Broadcast Interference Related to Airborne ILS, VOR and VHF Communications	1981
175	**MOPS**	Ground-Based Automated Weather Observation Equipment	1981
167	----	Airborne Electronics and Electrical Equipment Reliability	1977
163	**MPS**	HF Radio Communications	1976
161A	**MPS**	Airborne Ground Proximity Warning Equipment	1976
160D	----	Environmental Conditions and Test Procedures for Airborne Equipment	1997
143	**MPS**	Airborne Radio Marker Receiving Equipment Operating on 75 MHz	1970
62	----	Calibration Procedures, Test Standard Omni Bearing Selectors and Omni Bearing Selector Test Sets	1954
56	----	VOR Test Signals	1954
52	----	Calibration Procedures for Signal Generators used in the Testing of VOR and ILS Receivers	1952

417

Appendix C

DME Channel - Frequency - Spacing Correlation

VORTAC Freq. MHz	AIRBORNE DME Freq. MHz	Spacing μsec	TACAN Freq. MHz	Spacing μsec	TACAN Channel	MLS Channel	GS Freq. MHz
108.00	1041	12	978	12	17X		
108.05	1041	36	1104	30	17Y		
108.10	1042	12	979	12	18X	500	334.70
108.15	1042	36	1105	30	18Y	542	344.55
108.20	1043	12	980	12	19X		
108.25	1043	36	1106	30	19Y		
108.30	1044	12	981	12	20X	502	334.10
108.35	1044	36	1107	30	20Y	546	333.95
108.40	1045	12	982	12	21X		
108.45	1045	36	1108	30	21Y		
108.50	1046	12	983	12	22X	504	329.90
108.55	1046	36	1109	30	22Y	550	329.75
108.60	1047	12	984	12	23X		
108.65	1047	36	1110	30	23Y		
108.70	1048	12	985	12	24X	506	330.50
108.75	1048	36	1111	30	24Y	554	330.35
108.80	1049	12	986	12	25X		
108.85	1049	36	1112	30	25Y		
108.90	1050	12	987	12	26X	508	329.30
108.95	1050	36	1113	30	26Y	558	329.15
109.00	1051	12	988	12	27X		
109.05	1051	36	1114	30	27Y		
109.10	1052	12	989	12	28X	510	331.40
109.15	1052	36	1115	30	28Y	562	331.25
109.20	1053	12	990	12	29X		
109.25	1053	36	1116	30	29Y		
109.30	1054	12	991	12	30X	512	332.00
109.35	1054	36	1117	30	30Y	566	331.85
109.40	1055	12	992	12	31X		
109.45	1055	36	1118	30	31Y		
109.50	1056	12	993	12	32X	514	332.60
109.55	1056	36	1119	30	32Y	570	332.45
109.60	1057	12	994	12	33X		
109.65	1057	36	1120	30	33Y		
109.70	1058	12	995	12	34X	516	333.20
109.75	1058	36	1121	30	34Y	574	333.05
109.80	1059	12	996	12	35X		
109.85	1059	36	1122	30	35Y		
109.90	1060	12	997	12	36X	518	337.80
109.95	1060	36	1123	30	36Y	578	333.65
110.00	1061	12	998	12	37X		
110.05	1061	36	1124	30	37Y		
110.10	1062	12	999	12	38X	520	334.40
110.15	1062	36	1125	30	38Y	582	334.25
110.20	1063	12	1000	12	39X		
110.25	1063	36	1126	30	39Y		
110.30	1064	12	1001	12	40X	522	335.00
110.35	1064	36	1127	30	40Y	586	334.85
110.40	1065	12	1002	12	41X		
110.45	1065	36	1128	30	41Y		

DME Channel - Frequency - Spacing Correlation

VORTAC Freq. MHz	AIRBORNE DME Freq. MHz	Spacing μsec	TACAN Freq. MHz	Spacing μsec	TACAN Channel	MLS Channel	GS Freq. MHz
110.50	1066	12	1003	12	42X	524	329.60
110.55	1066	36	1129	30	42Y	590	329.45
110.60	1067	12	1004	12	43X		
110.65	1067	36	1130	30	43Y		
110.70	1068	12	1005	12	44X	526	330.20
110.75	1068	36	1131	30	44Y	594	330.05
110.80	1069	12	1006	12	45X		
110.85	1069	36	1132	30	45Y		
110.90	1070	12	1007	12	46X	528	330.80
110.95	1070	36	1133	30	46Y	598	330.65
111.00	1071	12	1008	12	47X		
111.05	1071	36	1134	30	47Y		
111.10	1072	12	1009	12	48X	530	331.7
111.15	1072	36	1135	30	48Y	602	331.55
111.20	1073	12	1010	12	49X		
111.25	1073	36	1136	30	49Y		
111.30	1074	12	1011	12	50X	532	332.30
111.35	1074	36	1137	30	50Y	606	332.15
111.40	1075	12	1012	12	51X		
111.45	1075	36	1138	30	51Y		
111.50	1076	12	1013	12	52X	534	332.90
111.55	1076	36	1139	30	52Y	610	332.75
111.60	1077	12	1014	12	53X		
111.65	1077	36	1140	30	53Y		
111.70	1078	12	1015	12	54X	536	333.5
111.75	1078	36	1141	30	54Y	614	333.35
111.80	1079	12	1016	12	55X		
111.85	1079	36	1142	30	55Y		
111.90	1080	12	1017	12	56X	538	331.10
111.95	1080	36	1143	30	56Y	618	330.95
112.00	1081	12	1018	12	57X		
112.05	1081	36	1144	30	57Y		
112.10	1082	12	1019	12	58X		
112.15	1082	36	1145	30	58Y		
112.20	1083	12	1020	12	59X		
112.25	1083	36	1146	30	59Y		
112.30	1094	12	1157	12	70X		
112.35	1094	36	1031	30	70Y		
112.40	1095	12	1158	12	71X		
112.45	1095	36	1032	30	71Y		
112.50	1096	12	1159	12	72X		
112.55	1096	36	1033	30	72Y		
112.60	1097	12	1160	12	73X		
112.65	1097	36	1034	30	73Y		
112.70	1098	12	1161	12	74X		
112.75	1098	36	1035	30	74Y		
112.80	1099	12	1162	12	75X		
112.85	1099	36	1036	30	75Y		
112.90	1100	12	1163	12	76X		
112.95	1100	36	1037	30	76Y		
113.00	1101	12	1164	12	77X		

DME Channel - Frequency - Spacing Correlation

VORTAC Freq. MHz	AIRBORNE DME Freq. MHz	Spacing μsec	TACAN Freq. MHz	Spacing μsec	TACAN Channel	MLS Channel	GS Freq. MHz
113.05	1101	36	1038	30	77Y		
113.10	1102	12	1165	12	78X		
113.15	1102	36	1039	30	78Y		
113.20	1103	12	1166	12	79X		
113.25	1103	36	1040	30	79Y		
113.30	1104	12	1167	12	80X		
113.35	1104	36	1041	30	80Y		
113.40	1105	12	1168	12	81X		
113.45	1105	36	1042	30	81Y		
113.50	1106	12	1169	12	82X		
113.55	1106	36	1043	30	82Y		
113.60	1107	12	1170	12	83X		
113.65	1107	36	1044	30	83Y		
113.70	1108	12	1171	12	84X		
113.75	1108	36	1045	30	84Y		
113.80	1109	12	1172	12	85X		
113.85	1109	36	1046	30	85Y		
113.90	1110	12	1173	12	86X		
113.95	1110	36	1047	30	86Y		
114.00	1111	12	1174	12	87X		
114.05	1111	36	1048	30	87Y		
114.10	1112	12	1175	12	88X		
114.15	1112	36	1049	30	88Y		
114.20	1113	12	1176	12	89X		
115.10	1122	12	1185	12	98X		
115.15	1122	36	1059	30	98Y		
115.20	1123	12	1186	12	99X		
115.25	1123	36	1060	30	99Y		
115.30	1124	12	1187	12	100X		
115.35	1124	36	1061	30	100Y		
115.40	1125	12	1188	12	101X		
115.45	1125	36	1062	30	101Y		
115.50	1126	12	1189	12	102X		
115.55	1126	36	1063	30	102Y		
115.60	1127	12	1190	12	103X		
115.65	1127	36	1064	30	103Y		
115.70	1128	12	1191	12	104X		
115.75	1128	36	1065	30	104Y		
115.80	1129	12	1192	12	105X		
115.85	1129	36	1066	30	105Y		
115.90	1130	12	1193	12	106X		
115.95	1130	36	1067	30	106Y		
116.00	1131	12	1194	12	107X		
116.05	1131	36	1068	30	107Y		
116.10	1132	12	1195	12	108X		
116.15	1132	36	1069	30	108Y		
116.20	1133	12	1196	12	109X		
116.25	1133	36	1070	30	109Y		
116.30	1134	12	1197	12	110X		
116.35	1134	36	1071	30	110Y		

DME Channel - Frequency - Spacing Correlation

VORTAC Freq. MHz	AIRBORNE DME Freq. MHz	Spacing μsec	TACAN Freq. MHz	Spacing μsec	TACAN Channel	MLS Channel	GS Freq. MHz
116.40	1135	12	1198	12	111X		
116.45	1135	36	1072	30	111Y		
116.50	1136	12	1199	12	112X		
116.55	1136	36	1073	30	112Y		
116.60	1137	12	1200	12	113X		
116.65	1137	36	1074	30	113Y		
116.70	1138	12	1201	12	114X		
116.75	1138	36	1075	30	114Y		
116.80	1139	12	1202	12	115X		
116.85	1139	36	1076	30	115Y		
116.90	1140	12	1203	12	116X		
116.95	1140	36	1077	30	116Y		
117.00	1141	12	1204	12	117X		
117.05	1141	36	1078	30	117Y		
117.10	1142	12	1205	12	118X		
117.15	1142	36	1079	30	118Y		
117.20	1143	12	1206	12	119X		
117.25	1143	36	1080	30	119Y		
117.30	1144	12	1207	12	120X		
117.35	1144	36	1081	30	120Y		
117.40	1145	12	1208	12	121X		
117.45	1145	36	1082	30	121Y		
117.50	1146	12	1209	12	122X		
117.55	1146	36	1083	30	122Y		
117.60	1147	12	1210	12	123X		
117.65	1147	26	1084	30	123Y		
117.70	1148	12	1211	12	124X		
117.75	1148	36	1085	30	124Y		
117.80	1149	12	1212	12	125X		
117.85	1146	36	1056	30	125Y		
117.90	1150	12	1213	12	126X		
117.95	1150	36	1087	30	126Y		

Index

424

About the Author

For 45 years Professor Albert Helfrick has been a designer, consultant, teacher and author in the field of avionics. He currently is chairperson at Embry-Riddle Aeronautical University in the Electrical and Systems Engineering Department. He holds a BS degree in physics, MS in mathematics and Phd in applied science.

While Director of Engineering at Tel-Instrument, he designed avionics test equipment widely used to maintain General Aviation, airline and military aircraft. He is a consultant to FAA, NASA, Boeing and major avionics manufacturers, and is a regular participant at the annual Digital Avionics Systems Conference. In addition to teaching university courses, he presents numerous short courses in avionics.

Since the first edition of *Principles of Avionics* appeared in 2000, Prof. Helfrick has continuously

Prof. Albert Helfrick in a hybrid race car constructed by his mechanical and engineering students at Embry-Riddle Aeronautical University in Daytona Beach, Florida.

revised and updated the book to where it is now the world's most widely used text on avionics engineering for schools, engineers, government officials, corporate engineering staffs and military organizations.

426